Vanadium - Tool steel very hard, brittle — slow cooling process
Plain Carbon Tool Steel - Fast Quench
Molybdenum - Wear Resistance

CORROSION
1. Galvanic - Electrolytic Action (Salt water)
   Aluminum + Cu resists corrosion
2. Oxidizing
Prevention - alloying agent; Paint; plating; galvanizing
Case Hardening - Put hard case on surface metal
   by cyaniding; carburizing; nitriding

Eutectic - from liquid solution
Eutectoid - from solid solution
Iron Carbon Alloy - .03% C to 1.7% C
Steel up to 1.7% C
Malleable CI - special heat treatment (cementite & pearlite
   special white Cast Iron (into ferrite + free carbon
Cast Iron - graphitic carbon + free carbon
   several days annealing

ENGINEERING MATERIALS

ENGINEERING MATERIALS

BY

ALFRED H. WHITE

*Professor of Chemical Engineering and Chairman
of the Department of Chemical and Metallurgical
Engineering, University of Michigan*

First Edition
Sixth Impression

McGRAW-HILL BOOK COMPANY, Inc.
NEW YORK AND LONDON
1939

Copyright, 1939, by the
McGraw-Hill Book Company, Inc.

PRINTED IN THE UNITED STATES OF AMERICA

All rights reserved. This book, or parts thereof, may not be reproduced in any form without permission of the publishers.

THE MAPLE PRESS COMPANY, YORK, PA.

*This book
is dedicated to my wife
whose forbearance and helpfulness
have made it possible.*

PREFACE

The engineer of today is faced with a bewildering variety of materials which he must use in his work. The simple conception of steel held by a past generation has been complicated by considerations of grain size, hardenability, and heat-treatment, and the many varieties of alloy steels have multiplied the materials that are available. The plain portland cement of a few years ago has been split into several specialized varieties. The old white lead and linseed oil have been supplemented by new products that refuse to fall into older classifications. Light alloys and plastics have provided entirely new types of materials. The boiler plant seems to demand the ministrations of a dietitian rather than a brawny stoker.

These advances have been due to intensive research on the part of consumers and producers alike. The structure of our knowledge is still far from complete, but the foundations are sufficiently visible to permit a survey of properties as a function of internal structure.

The present book is intended primarily as a text for all engineering students who have had the usual course in freshman chemistry. It is hoped that practicing engineers may also be interested in a systematic presentation of recent advances in the field of materials. No knowledge of organic chemistry is assumed and the treatment of protective coatings and plastics therefore has had to be elementary and to be preceded by a very brief introduction to the chemistry of carbon compounds. The limitations of space imposed by the primary purpose of the book have prevented the inclusion of much desirable material.

An engineer does not need to memorize a multitude of facts, but he must be able to solve problems as they arise. The course in Engineering Materials as taught to all engineering students at the University of Michigan approaches the subject from that viewpoint. In all recitations and examinations, questions demand the interpretation of graphs and diagrams and a consideration of the specific materials that would be adapted to a given purpose. Students must spend a reasonable amount of time in preparation to make a good showing in a course conducted in this way, and experience has demonstrated that they acquire a much better understanding of the subject than through the older method when memorizing was demanded. This text has been used for two semesters in a preliminary edition and has been revised in the light of that experience.

The author is grateful for assistance from many sources. Members of the technical staffs of the International Nickel Company, Bethlehem Steel Company, Aluminum Company of America, Harbison Walker Manufacturing Company, and Sherwin-Williams Company have read portions of the manuscript and made valuable criticisms and suggestions. Permission to use tabular data and illustrations has been freely granted by numerous corporations, publishers, and societies to whom general acknowledgment is made here in addition to the specific references that occur throughout the book. The author's thanks are especially due to his colleagues who have furnished illustrative materials from their files and have reviewed the text with care as they have collaborated in teaching the course.

A. H. WHITE.

ANN ARBOR, MICH.,
August, 1939.

CONTENTS

	PAGE
PREFACE	vii

CHAPTER
- I. THEORETICAL INTRODUCTION 1
- II. IRON AND ITS ALLOYS WITH CARBON 31
- III. EFFECT OF HEAT-TREATMENT ON IRON-CARBON ALLOYS . . . 50
- IV. THE MANUFACTURE OF IRON AND IRON-CARBON ALLOYS FROM THE ORE 71
- V. EARLY METHODS OF PRODUCING WROUGHT IRON AND STEEL FROM PIG IRON 90
- VI. THE MANUFACTURE OF STEEL BY THE BESSEMER, OPEN-HEARTH AND ELECTRIC-FURNACE PROCESSES 99
- VII. INFLUENCE OF CHEMICAL COMPOSITION AND MILL-FINISHING OPERATIONS ON THE PROPERTIES OF PLAIN CARBON STEEL . . 112
- VIII. THE PROPERTIES OF PLAIN CARBON STEEL AS AFFECTED BY METHODS OF FABRICATION 134
- IX. CASTING PROCESSES 149
- X. GRAY CAST IRONS AND MALLEABLE CASTINGS 160
- XI. STEELS WITH ONE ALLOYING ELEMENT 182
- XII. STEELS WITH TWO OR MORE ALLOYING CONSTITUENTS AND STEELS FOR SPECIAL PURPOSES 203
- XIII. COPPER, NICKEL, ZINC, TIN, AND THEIR ALLOYS 225
- XIV. ALUMINUM, MAGNESIUM, AND THE LIGHT ALLOYS 256
- XV. LEAD AND ITS ALLOYS. SOLDERS AND BEARING METALS . . 276
- XVI. CORROSION OF METALS AND PROTECTION BY METALLIC COATINGS 290
- XVII. ROCKS AND THEIR DECOMPOSITION PRODUCTS. CLAY PRODUCTS 313
- XVIII. FUSED SILICATES. VITRIFIED CLAY PRODUCTS. GLASS, SLAGS, AND REFRACTORIES 336
- XIX. LIME, GYPSUM, AND MAGNESIUM OXYCHLORIDE PRODUCTS . . 367
- XX. THE SILICATE CEMENTS: POZZUOLANIC CEMENTS, HYDRAULIC LIMES, NATURAL CEMENTS, PORTLAND CEMENT 388

CONTENTS

Chapter		Page
XXI.	Fuels and Combustion	429
XXII.	Water and Its Industrial Utilization. Soaps	464
XXIII.	Organic Preservative Materials and Protective Coatings	497
XXIV.	Plastics and Related Products	516
Index		537

CHAPTER I

THEORETICAL INTRODUCTION

Introduction.—The engineers of the Pharaohs erected marvelous buildings three thousand years ago with no power except that of men and animals, and virtually no materials except stone, brick, and gypsum plaster. Steel and bronze were used for weapons but were too expensive for general use as tools. The situation had not changed much when Caesar invaded Britain, when Columbus discovered America, nor even when George Washington became the first president of the United States. The art of casting cannon had been developed during the centuries, wrought iron was more common, steel hatchets and other hand tools were of better quality and cheaper, but the only power which could be brought to a job was still that of animals. This extraordinarily slow progress had not been due to lack of mental ability on the part of engineers all through the centuries but to lack of materials with which to work. The idea of the steam engine had been in men's minds for centuries, and cumbrous steam-driven pumps were in use to raise water from British mines before the days of James Watt. His conception of the engine with a separate condenser was clearly outlined in his patent for which he made application in 1775. He was himself an instrument maker and soon secured the active support of one of the best machine builders of Great Britain, and yet it took him 25 years to produce an engine that would function satisfactorily. His inventive genius could design governors, linkages, and gears, but he could not obtain a true cylinder or a tight piston. When he did get a cylinder only $\frac{1}{8}$ in. larger in diameter at one end than the other, he hailed it as a triumph. There were no heavy rolling mills or power hammers in Watt's day, and the only sheets available for boiler plate were of wrought iron and so small and light that most of Watt's engines were made to use steam of substantially atmospheric pressure.

The whole development of steam power had to lag until large machine tools could be built, and large machine tools had to await the production of large ingots of steel, and large ingots of steel were unknown until Bessemer invented his steelmaking process in 1856. That invention struck off the fetters which had hampered engineering development through the centuries. When Bessemer discovered his process of making steel, the chemist had gained knowledge of methods of analysis and was commencing to trace the influence of chemical composition upon the physical properties of metals. The recent knowledge of the structure of the atom and of interatomic forces is now permitting us to outline the fundamental forces that influence the physical properties of the materials which the engineer uses. The picture is still lacking in detail, but it helps to clarify and systematize our knowledge.

Atomic Forces.—The materials that engineers use for structures are almost all solids in which the properties of strength and toughness are desired. To the physicist and the chemist, neither steel nor glass are solids in the sense that they consist of solid atoms packed so closely together that there are no empty spaces between them. An airplane is a strong and rigid structure in spite of the fact that it is largely an empty shell, because the forces that tend to cause its destruction are opposed at every point by an adequate resistance from the light members that make up the frame. According to the Bohr hypothesis, an atom consists of a nucleus whose mass is almost infinitesimally small but whose energy content is large, surrounded by a planetary system consisting of shells of electrons held in their positions by strong forces, but susceptible of distortion when stronger forces are applied. When two atoms approach each other, they may be repelled or attacted. If they are attracted, there is frequently an interchange or a fitting together of electrons in the outer shells with formation of a molecule. Sometimes the union of two atoms results in a stable configuration, and an inert gas like nitrogen (N_2) or carbon monoxide (CO) results. Sometimes a great number of atoms unite to form very large molecules as is the case with glass, most solid metals, and the hydrocarbons of lubricating oil.

Effect of Temperature on Properties of Materials.—When materials like metals or glass are heated, the energy absorbed increases the activity of the various atoms in the structure, loosening the bonds that hold the atoms together, thus making the material weaker as is illustrated in Fig. 1. When the temperature becomes high enough, the material will melt, and at still higher temperatures it will vaporize. Sometimes, like carbon, it sublimes or passes directly from the solid to the gaseous state, and sometimes if compounds are present, they decompose in the process. This is the case with the carbide of iron (Fe_3C) which decomposes into iron and carbon below its melting point.

Since almost all structural materials are molten during some stage of their manufacture, a study of the properties of materials may well start with the molten or fused state and a consideration of the changes that take place as the material cools. A molten liquid may contain only one species of atoms or particles as is the case with gold and other pure metals, or it may be a complex mixture of different molecules as is the case with slag and glass. In the case of glass, the molten liquid always consists of complex silicates, but their degree of mutual attraction decreases with the temperature, so that at high temperatures the liquid is quite fluid, and as the temperature drops the liquid becomes more viscous.

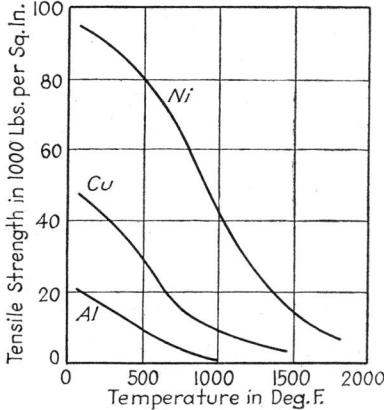

FIG. 1.—Change of tensile strength of metals with temperature. (*From S. Dushman. Proc. A.S.T.M.* 1929, II, p. 9.)

At the temperature that the glass blower uses when he is working the glass, it may be a question as to whether the glass should be called a "viscous liquid" or a "plastic solid." Pure metals have definite melting and solidifying points, but complex materials usually pass through an intermediate stage in which part of the material is solid and part is liquid.

Phases and Equilibrium.—The term "phase" is sometimes used with almost the same meaning as state. Water may exist simultaneously in the solid, liquid, and gaseous state, or phase. If ice is dropped into water in a thermos bottle, all three states, or phases, will be present. At first the ice and the water will be at different temperatures, and some of the ice will melt. If we assume that the amount of ice is sufficient, that the thermos bottle provides perfect heat insulation, that the barometric pressure does not change, and that the stopper of the bottle is perfectly tight so that the system within the bottle is completely isolated, then a condition of steady state, or equilibrium, will in time be reached where the three phases solid, liquid, and gaseous will all be present in unchanging amounts. One of the conditions that must be present, if equilibrium has actually been obtained, is the complete uniformity of each phase. Successive samples taken from various portions of a phase must show no differences in composition. This condition is rarely realized in practice, but it may be approached rather closely, and very many of our theoretical studies are based on systems which have reached equilibrium conditions so closely that we can assume they represent true equilibrium. The water in this thermos bottle consists of H_2O in various states of aggregation. The vapor phase consists of separate H_2O molecules. The liquid and solid phases consist mainly of aggregated molecules of $(H_2O)_3$ or $(H_2O)_4$.

If we should replace the thermos bottle by a closed crucible, also tight and thermally insulated, it would be possible to have in it a pure metal, such as lead, existing in the solid, liquid, and gaseous states. This condition of three coexistent phases is possible only under one particular environment. If, for example, the temperature should be lowered by a very small amount, the liquid phase would disappear and we would have in one case ice with a small amount of water in the vapor phase, and in the other solid lead with a very small amount of lead vapor.

The vapor state is characterized by great molecular mobility. The forces of convection and diffusion act freely, and uniformity of composition and equilibrium are attained rapidly. The liquid state shows less molecular activity. Diffusion is much slower, but convection currents are still active, and uniform composition and equilibrium conditions are obtained rather rapidly. In the solid state, molecular activity is greatly restricted, convection currents are absent, and diffusion is very slow. If we wish therefore to make an alloy from two metals, the common practice is to melt them together so that they may be incorporated in the liquid state. Sometimes, however, metal powders are mixed very intimately and forced into dies under high pressure to form an object which is then heated moderately until diffusion has taken place, at least on the boundaries of the original particles, and an alloy has formed whose melting point is low enough so that the particles become fritted together. Some magnets, bearings, and cutting tools are formed in this manner.

Formation of Crystals.—Both the gaseous and liquid phases are characterized by freedom of molecular motion. This freedom becomes less as the temperature is lowered, and ultimately the molecules commence to arrange themselves in definite crystal patterns, as solidification takes place. If the cooling of an absolutely pure substance should take place extraordinarily slowly, it is conceivable that the whole mass of material might solidify as a single crystal. Under actual conditions, crystallization usually starts at the surface of a crucible or mold where the cooling effect is greatest. The small crystals that are first formed grow in a branching or dendritic manner. This is frequently illustrated in the ice crystals on a window pane which represent the result of crystallization of a thin layer of liquid. With a large mass of liquid, the crystals would have continued to grow until they interlocked to form a solid mass in which the dendritic habit of growth could not be detected without special treatment. The slower the cooling, the larger will be the individual crystals.

Although most materials form crystals on solidification, glass and slags may frequently change on cooling from a rather thin liquid to one that is viscous and slowly grows stiffer until, without any definite transition point, it becomes solid. Ordinary window glass is sometimes referred to as a "supercooled liquid" because of the fact that it does not show any definite melting point or crystal structure. On long standing, especially if the temperature is rather high, crystals sometimes do form, and the glass is said to be "devitrified." This interferes with its transparency because of the distortion of a beam of light passing from one crystal to another.

Metals and alloys almost always assume the crystalline condition no matter how rapidly they are cooled. The crystals are usually too small to be seen with the naked eye but are sometimes large enough to be readily apparent. "Galvanized iron" which is made by dipping steel sheets into molten zinc shows crystals of zinc as large as a thumbnail. On the other hand, tin plate which is made by dipping steel sheets into molten tin shows a bright surface whose crystalline nature can only be shown after etching.

In order to show the crystalline structure of a metal or alloy, it is customary to grind and polish a small piece until it has a plane surface free from scratches. This surface appears like a mirror even under the microscope. If the specimen is immersed in a dilute acid or some other etching reagent, the surface is attacked unevenly. The boundaries between the crystals etch at a different rate than the main surface of the crystals, and if, after suitable etching, the surface is examined under a microscope, the crystal boundaries will appear as narrow lines between the crystals, as shown in Fig. 5. Ideal crystals are definite geometrical structures with planes of symmetry and flat faces intersecting at definite angles. The crystals of metals revealed under the microscope do not usually show this symmetry because their growth has been restricted by contact with neighboring growing crystals. The etched surface frequently shows rounded boundaries of the crystals, and these imperfectly formed crystals are often termed "grains." Commercial specifications frequently call for a definite grain size, since the size of the grain has a marked influence on the properties of the metal.

Structure of Crystals.—Although the outlines of the grains are frequently imperfect, the main body of the grain is truly crystalline, being made up of small building blocks all identical, and each a perfect unit crystal. The microscope is not powerful enough to show this internal structure, but X rays with their shorter wave length may be used to produce photographic patterns that permit a calculation of the system upon which the crystal is built. Each atom consists of a characteristic nucleus around which electrons vibrate in definite orbits, and the structure of the nucleus and its surrounding electrons determine the properties of each chemical element. The process of solidification of a pure element is accompanied by the association of groups of atoms to form crystals. We represent these as solid geometrical forms, but actually they are not rigid and not solid. Steel is not, in the last analysis, a solid. It is a network of atoms, each consisting of a minute nucleus surrounded by a planetary system of electrons. Metals and brick and stone are rigid because the powerful atomic forces hold each atom firmly in its place in the network. The distances of the atoms from each other and the forces holding them together are known with considerable accuracy. Figures for some of the commoner elements are given in

THEORETICAL INTRODUCTION

TABLE 1.—PHYSICAL CONSTANTS OF ELEMENTS*

Name of element	Symbol	Atomic number	Atomic volume[1]	Melting point, °F	Boiling point, °F	Electrical resistivity[2]	Modulus of elasticity[3]	Type of crystal lattice[4]	Lattice constants,[4] A° a₀	Lattice constants,[4] A° c₀	Closest approach of atoms, A°	Energy to isolate atoms[6]
Aluminum	Al	13	9.99	1215	3733	2.67	10.	F.C.C.	4.04		2.86	60
Carbon	C	6	5.41	....	....	3500.	1.2	Hex G.	2.46	6.79	1.42	150
Chromium	Cr	24	7.29	2822	4500	13.1	....	B.C.C.	2.88		2.49	83
Copper	Cu	29	7.11	1981	4703	1.68	16.	F.C.C.	3.61		2.55	76
Iron	Fe	26	7.1	2795	5430	9.8	30.	B.C.C.	2.86		2.48	108
Lead	Pb	82	18.3	621	2948	20.6	2.6	F.C.C.	4.94		3.49	41
Magnesium	Mg	12	14.0	1204	2007	4.5	6.2	Hex C.P.	3.20	5.20	3.19	63
Manganese	Mn	25	7.6	2273	3452	5.	....	Cubic	8.89		....	
Mercury	Hg	80	14.8	−38	674	95.8	....	....	....		....	
Nickel	Ni	28	6.64	2645	5252	10.9	30.	F.C.C.	3.52		2.49	101
Silicon	Si	14	11.7	2588	4712	85 × 10³	16.	Cub.D.	5.42		2.35	81
Silver	Ag	47	10.27	1761	3542	1.62	10.3	F.C.C.	4.08		2.82	64
Tin	Sn	50	16.23	449	4100	11.5	5.9–7.8	Tetr.	5.82	3.17	3.02	76
Tungsten	W	74	9.53	6098	10652	5.48	60.	B.C.C.	3.16		2.71	
Zinc	Zn	30	9.16	787	1661	6.0	12.4	Hex C.P.	2.66	4.93	2.66	32

* Selected from Metals Handbook—1939, pp. 78–82.
[1] In cubic centimeters per gram atom.
[2] In micro ohms per centimeter.
[3] In tension, psi × 10⁶.
[4] F.C.C. = face-centered cubic, B.C.C. = body-centered cubic, Hex C.P. = hexagonal close-packed, Hex G. = hexagonal graphite type, Cub. D. = cubic, diamond type, Tetr. = tetragonal. a_0, c_0 refer to axes.
[5] Expressed in Ångstroms = 10^{-8} cm.
[6] Energy to break down crystals into atoms in kilogram-calorie per gram atom, from Grimm and Wolf, Handbuch der Physik, Vol. 24, Part 2, p. 1073, 1934.

8   ENGINEERING MATERIALS

Table 1 for the purposes of showing the variation of the values. Some progress has been made in correlating the physical properties of the metals with these values, but they can at present be used only in a qualitative way.

If small spheres like shot are piled in layers as regularly and compactly as possible, it will be found that they are arranged so that their centers fall on the corners of a cube with one at the center of each face of the cube as shown in Fig. 2. This arrangement is called the "face-centered cubic system." Fifteen elements have their atoms arranged in this face-centered cubic manner. They are all metals and all ductile. Not all of them are of importance as engineering materials, but the group includes

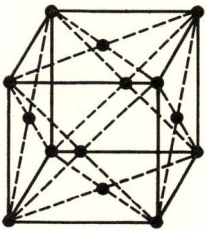 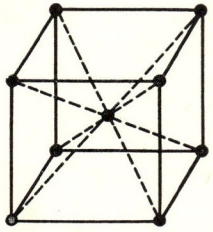

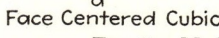

FIG. 2.—Models of crystal lattices.

aluminum, copper, lead, nickel, silver, and gamma iron, which is the crystalline form of iron at the forging temperature. The system in which magnesium and zinc crystallize is a division of the hexagonal system and permits equally close packing. The body-centered cubic system ranks next in compactness and includes chromium, molybdenum, tungsten, vanadium, and alpha iron, which is the crystalline state of iron at room temperature. Iron has been mentioned as crystallizing in one form at room temperature and at another at a higher temperature. This variation in crystal structure is called an "allotropic" change. It is a common phenomenon observed with many metals and nonmetals, and with compounds as well as elements.

Intercrystalline Material.—When a perfectly pure metal changes from the molten to the solid state, a process sometimes called "freezing," submicroscopic crystals form and grow until they come in contact with another crystal. The very last film of liquid between the two is sought by both crystals and is held by both crystals. It may be that this dividing film cannot form perfect crystal units because it is strained in two directions, and some have spoken of it as noncrystalline or amorphous. It might be expected that this film would be more rigid since it is held by the forces of two crystals and that therefore it would be stronger. This is known to be the case. When metal is ruptured in a testing machine at room temperature, the break usually takes place through the body of the crystal and not through the intercrystalline film. With rising temperature, the amorphous film between the crystals loses its cohesion faster than the crystal itself, and at some temperature roughly halfway to the melting point, the cohesion of the two becomes equal. Above that temperature, the intercrystalline films rupture more readily than the crystals. The phenomenon of "creep" in metals when exposed to moderate stresses for long periods of time at elevated temperatures, as in furnaces for cracking petroleum or in power plants using very high steam pressures, is associated with this change in the amorphous intercrystalline material.

The line of demarcation between the grains is accentuated if foreign substances are present, as is always the case in practice. If there is present even a small amount of material that dissolves in the liquid phase but is insoluble or less soluble in the solid phase, then this material rejected by the crystal will concentrate in the liquid that freezes last and will appear in concentrated form in the film between the crystals. Plain carbon steel is injured by even a few hundredths of one per cent of oxygen or phosphorus, because these materials form oxides and phosphides which concentrate at the grain boundaries and make the boundary film brittle. This concentration of foreign material hinders crystals from forming a complete physical union.

If two materials can exist dissolved in each other in the liquid state, but are incapable of remaining dissolved in the solid state, it is evident that two different types of crystals must form when the melt freezes. If one material is present in large amount, it will appear as large crystals and that present in small amount will be crowded into the intercrystalline spaces. There may be two or more types of crystals with different material between the grains.

Molecules and Atoms.—It is customary in discussing structures to speak of molecules and atoms. The atom has a definite structure, but the molecule does not have a definite meaning in the field of solid materials. In a pure metal, the atoms are linked together in definite patterns to form a unit crystal, but each atom is also linked to the atoms in the adjacent unit crystals, so that each final large crystal has sometimes been called a "molecule." In glass, the various atoms are bound together by uniform forces throughout large masses, and the term molecule loses its meaning. Since the forces binding atoms together are known fairly accurately, it should be possible to calculate the stress required to rupture a single crystal. These calculated values are far higher than anything that has been obtained in practice, and it is assumed in explanation that actual single crystals are never of an ideal uniform structure but are made up of a great many microscopic blocks that have cracks or other imperfections between them so as to form what has been called a "mosaic" pattern. The structure of a mass composed of a number of crystals must be much less homogeneous than a single crystal, and the strength of the material will be influenced by the nature and size of the crystals, the nature of the intercrystalline film, and the number and size of the cracks between or within the crystals.

Behavior of a Pure Metal on Heating and Cooling.—At the highest temperature to which metals are usually subjected in industrial practice, the metal is a fused liquid whose surface is constantly giving off a small amount of vapor. As the metal cools, its volume decreases and its viscosity increases somewhat until the freezing point is reached when the whole mass becomes solid with a considerable decrease in volume. The latent heat of fusion is evolved at the freezing point, and the temperature theoretically stays constant during the whole process of solidification. The process of cooling is represented graphically in Fig. 3. Curve A shows the theoretical curve for a pure metal with its freezing point at absolutely constant temperature. No curve obtained in actual practice shows such a sharp horizontal line, but otherwise the curve represents experimental conditions. The metal while molten cools rapidly as shown by the slope of the curve, the horizontal line indicates evolution of heat as the metal freezes at constant temperature, and the curve with diminishing slope shows that the solid metal is cooling at a diminishing rate as it comes closer to room temperature. Occasionally metals are found whose curves show more than one point of thermal change. The upper point always shows the temperature of freezing and since the metal is, by hypothesis, pure and already solid, the other thermal disturbances as shown in curve B can be due only to changes in position of the atoms in the solid metal, which are reflected in changes in the crystal structure and are accompanied by evolution of heat. Curve B illustrates a cooling curve for pure iron and shows the four allotropic forms

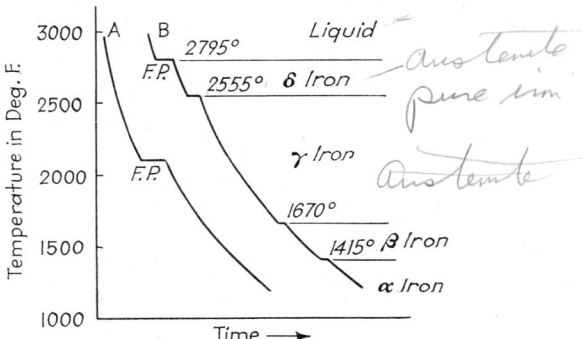

Fig. 3.—Cooling curves of pure metals. A, any metal not showing an allotropic change; B, pure iron.

alpha (α), the stable state at room temperature, which crystallizes on the body-centered cubic system; beta (β), which is a transition phase; gamma (γ), which represents the stable phase at the temperature at which metal is forged and which crystallizes on the face-centered cubic system; and delta (δ), which is stable just below the melting point and which crystallizes on the body-centered cubic system. The allotropic forms of a metal are identical in chemical composition, but the rearrangement of the atoms in the crystals imparts quite different physical properties to the metal.

When a piece of pure metal is placed in a hot furnace, it absorbs energy which loosens the interatomic bonds. Its density and strength become gradually less as the temperature rises, but there is no abrupt change until an allotropic transformation takes place or the melting point is reached. In either case, heat absorption continues but the temperature theoretically remains constant until all of the metal has been transformed to the new allotropic variety or until the metal is completely melted. The true equilibrium temperatures at which the allotropic changes take place and even those at which melting occurs are apt to be overrun in both the cooling and heating curves unless elaborate experimental precautions are taken. This lag or hysteresis becomes important in industrial operations.

Alloys.—If two metals are melted in separate vessels and then mixed, they will usually dissolve in each other to form a homogeneous solution. The atoms of both metals become dispersed uniformly throughout the liquid and will remain uniformly dispersed so long as the mixture is liquid. Under these conditions, the metals are said to have formed an "alloy." There are a few metals that do not behave in this way. If molten aluminum and lead are mixed and allowed to stand at a temperature not much above the melting point, two layers are formed with almost pure lead on the bottom and almost pure aluminum on the top. Such metals are said not to form alloys, although if the two layers were carefully examined, it would be found that the lead layer had actually dissolved a small amount of aluminum, and the aluminum layer a small amount of lead. If a cooling curve of this mechanical mixture of aluminum and lead should be made, it would be found that the aluminum and lead each froze at their regular temperatures without the other metal having exerted any perceptible influence. This would be true only if absolutely no lead dissolved in the molten aluminum and no aluminum in the molten lead. Two metals that do dissolve in each other in the molten state always influence each other's freezing points.

Alloys of Copper and Nickel as Illustrations of Solubility in the Solid State in All Proportions.—As the first illustration of two alloys with complete mutual solubility, the alloys of copper and nickel will be considered. They may be melted together to form a homogeneous liquid in all proportions. Cooling curves for selected compositions are shown in Fig. 4, where curve A represents pure copper freezing at 1981°F (1083°C), curves B to E represent alloys with the percentage of nickel increasing by increments of 20 per cent, and curve F represents the behavior of pure nickel freezing at 2645°F (1452°C). The curves of the various alloys do not show solidification at constant temperature as the pure metals do. They show instead solidification proceeding on a falling temperature, which necessarily means a constant change in composition of the liquid phase during the solidification. The composition of each layer which is added to a crystal is richer in copper than the preceding, because copper has the lower melting point, and the liquid is being continually enriched

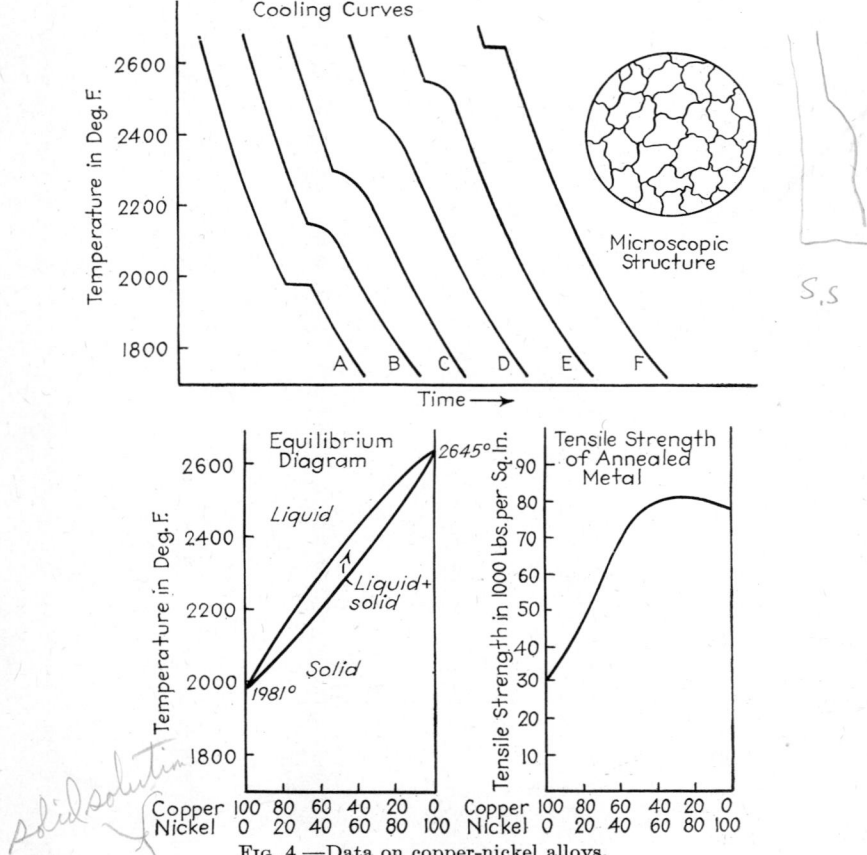

Fig. 4.—Data on copper-nickel alloys.

in copper as crystals richer in nickel separate. The crystals, if examined immediately after rather rapid solidification, will show a higher content of nickel in the center of each crystal and a decreasing quantity of nickel and a higher content of copper as the outer layers are approached. It is difficult to tell from the cooling curves the exact temperatures at which solidification begins and ends, but if the cooling has been slow, the point at which a change in the slope of the line occurs can be determined with approximate accuracy. In taking cooling curves, the rate of cooling should be so slow that equilibrium is substantially obtained at each temperature. Theoretically, the time would have to be infinite.

Equilibrium Diagrams.—If the cooling has been so slow as to approach equilibrium, it is proper to combine the data from the cooling curves showing temperatures of initial and final solidification into an equilibrium diagram in which temperatures are plotted against percentage composition as shown in Fig. 4. At all temperatures above the upper curve, the whole mass is liquid. The Latin name *liquidus* is sometimes used to denote this area, and the line forming its lower boundary is called the "liquidus line." Between the two curves, there is a mixture of liquid solution and solid crystals and at all temperatures below the lower curve the whole mass is solid. The Latin word *solidus* is applied to the solid area, and the line forming its upper boundary is termed the "solidus line."

The equilibrium diagram given in Fig. 4 is characteristic of all solid solutions in that there is no discontinuity or abrupt change of direction in the curves showing the progress of solidification. Some curves showing solid solution are more complicated than that for the nickel-copper system, but all are characterized by gentle curves without any horizontal lines or abrupt changes of direction.

Copper and nickel are very much alike in their crystal structure as may be seen from Table 1. Both crystallize on the face-centered cubic system, and their space lattices have almost the same dimensions (3.52 Å for nickel and 3.61 Å for copper). Their atomic volumes and the distance of closest approach of the atoms to each other will therefore also differ a little. These similarities permit the atoms of nickel and copper to enter the same crystal quite freely. It has been mentioned that the successive layers of the crystals became steadily richer in copper and that with rapid cooling a cored structure could be detected as a result of this. From thermodynamic reasoning, it is known that the most stable system is that in which the copper and nickel are uniformly distributed instead of existing in different layers.

The copper and nickel atoms diffuse fairly rapidly at elevated temperatures, and if the cooling rate has been sufficiently slow, no evidence of nonuniform composition can be detected with the microscope, or by any other available means, in the cooled metal. It is therefore believed that the theoretical condition of complete uniformity of composition may be actually attained in practice. The same idea may be expressed in other words as infinite dispersion of the atoms of one material in another. Since all nickel and copper alloys that have been very slowly cooled fulfill this condition, they are said to form solid solutions in all proportions. Nickel and copper form a homogeneous solution in all proportions in the liquid phase. During the period of solidification, there exists a mixture of solid crystals and liquid whose compositions change as the temperature falls. After solidification, provided sufficient time has been allowed, the alloy consists of a mass of crystals, each one identical with the others in internal structure and each consisting of an infinite dispersion of nickel and copper.

Microscopic Structure.—If these alloys are polished and etched to bring out the grain structure, there will be some differences noted in the size and shape of the individual grains but none in their surface appearance. Since the two metals are in solid solution, each grain of a particular alloy must have the same proportion of nickel and copper, with the atoms so uniformly dispersed that the microscope cannot detect the individual particles, which are by theory atomically dispersed.

The diagrammatic sketch of microscopic structure which forms part of Fig. 4 shows grains that vary somewhat in size but are otherwise indistinguishable. Such an appearance would be characteristic of any pure metal or any solid solution. Therefore this one sketch will serve to illustrate the microscopic structure of the whole series of copper nickel alloys. An actual photomicrograph of a complex solid solution is shown in Fig. 5 where each grain is magnified 100 times in diameter. The magnification is indicated by the term ×100.

Strength and Ductility of Solid Solutions.—The equilibrium diagram does not give direct evidence as to the physical properties of the alloys. It might perhaps be assumed that since there is a gradual change throughout the equilibrium diagram that there would also be a gradual change in physical properties with change of composition, and this assumption would be correct. The similarity of the crystal lattices of copper and nickel has already been mentioned. However their lattice constants are not quite the same, and there must be some distortion of the lattices to permit both types of atoms to exist in a single crystal. The effect of a slight distortion is apparently to increase the strength of the alloy. This is shown in the graph of tensile strengths presented in Fig. 4. Since nickel has more than twice the tensile strength of copper, it would be expected that the addition of nickel would increase the strength of copper. The unexpected effect is the

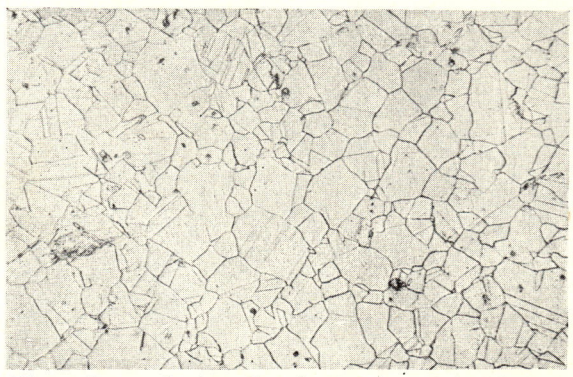

Fig. 5.—Photomicrograph of an alloy showing complete solid solution. ×100. The small black dots and other imperfections may be due to small fragments of slag or other inclusions in the metal or may have been produced accidentally in the polishing operation. (*Courtesy International Nickel Company.*)

strengthening of the nickel by the addition of the weaker copper. This strengthening effect when solid solutions are formed is so usual that the generalization has been made that the addition of a second metal will increase the strength and, frequently, the ductility of the resulting alloy so long as the alloying element forms a solid solution with the first metal.

Lead-tin Alloys As Instances of Limited Solubility in the Solid State.—There are many pairs of metals that form liquid solutions in all proportions but form solid solutions only within limited ranges of composition. It is theoretically possible to assume that one metal might be absolutely insoluble in another in the solid state, as was done in the earlier discussion of aluminum and lead, but in practice there is always some solubility even if to the extent of only a few hundredths of a per cent.

The alloys of lead and tin will be used to illustrate an alloy whose constituent metals have only limited solubility in each other in the solid state. Some data for selected alloys are given in Fig. 6. The first curve shows lead freezing at 621°F (327°C) and the next for 90 Pb-10 Sn shows a solid solution. The curve

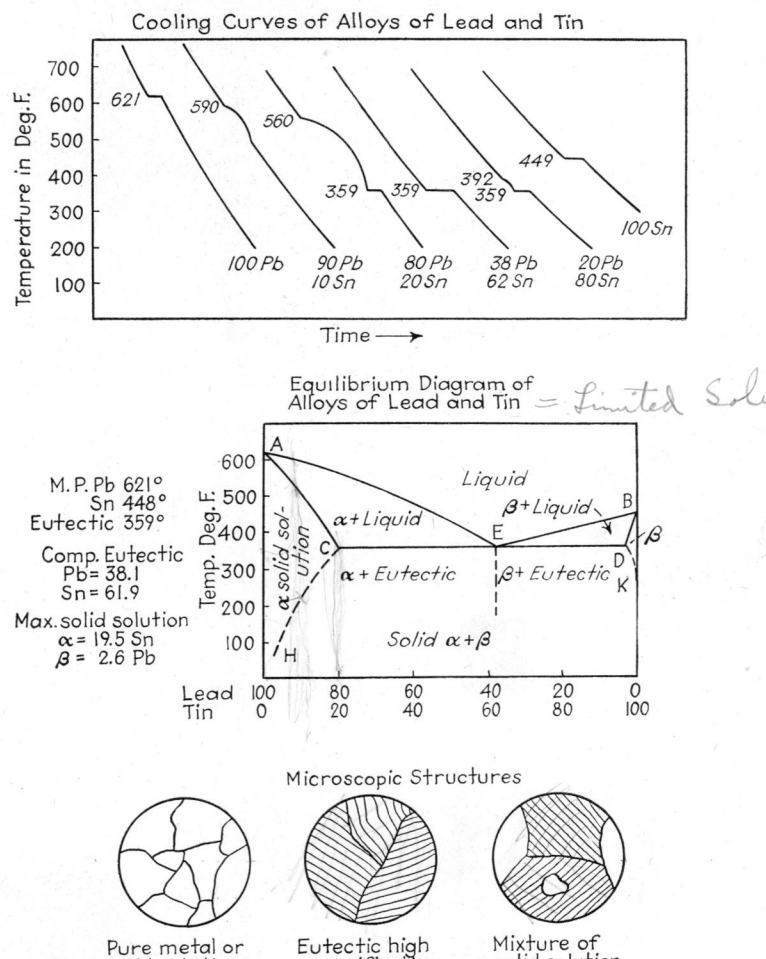

Fig. 6.—Data on lead-tin alloys.

for 80 Pb-20 Sn shows the reversal of the cooling curve over a considerable range characteristic of a solid solution but also shows at 359°F a horizontal line indicating that the balance of the liquid is freezing at a constant temperature. The composition 38.1 Pb-61.9 Sn freezes at a constant temperature of 359°F. The composition 20 Pb-80 Sn indicates a small amount of solid solution with a rather large proportion of the alloy solidifying at 359°, and the final curve shows pure tin freezing at 449°F (232°C). The new element in these cooling curves is the constancy of the temperature of final solidification (359°) of all of the alloys between the limits of 19.5 and 97.4 per cent of tin. The various alloys showing this phenomenon cover a wide range of composition, and the only explanation possible is that during the early stages of solidification a solid alloy separated from the cooling liquid to such an extent as to leave a residual fused liquid of constant composition that froze at a constant temperature, irrespective of the composition (within certain limits) of the original alloy. It is also to be noted that this composition freezes at a lower temperature than either of the pure metals. It is given a specific name "eutectic" derived from the Greek words meaning to melt easily. The formation of the eutectic may best be discussed with reference to the equilibrium diagram for the lead-tin series shown in Fig. 6.

The Eutectic.—The equilibrium diagram for the lead-tin alloys shows that as tin is added to lead in increasing amounts the initial freezing point is lowered, as shown by the line AE. As lead is added to tin, the initial freezing point is lowered as shown by the line BE. These two lines intersect at E, 359°F which must represent the lowest possible melting point and is called the "eutectic point." The composition of this alloy melting at 359° is 38.1 lead and 61.9 tin, and it is called the "eutectic alloy." A eutectic alloy in any system is the composition that solidifies (and also melts) at the lowest possible temperature. Just prior to solidification, the alloy is a homogeneous liquid. What happens during solidification? In the case of the nickel-copper system, no eutectic was formed because the two metals were completely soluble in each other in the solid state and the melting points changed gradually. In this lead-tin system, the two branches of the curve intersect and may, on supercooling, be conceived to cross. But if they crossed, there would be two supercooled liquids which, on equilibrium being reached, would have to come back to the eutectic composition, by each separating in solid form its excess constituent and liberating the latent heat of fusion. This would raise the tem-

THEORETICAL INTRODUCTION

perature slightly, and no more solid would separate until the temperature had dropped again. Thus during freezing of a eutectic solution, each side alternates in giving up its excess constituent as small crystals, and the liquid remains at constant temperature until it is all frozen as a finely divided mixture of the two solids. These solids frequently crystallize as alternate thin plates of the two constituents and are visible after proper etching under a high-power microscope as a pattern sometimes called the "thumbprint pattern" as sketched in Fig. 6. If the two metals lead and tin had been completely insoluble in each other in the solid state, the excess constituents deposited during the freezing of the eutectic would have been pure lead and tin. Since each of these metals dissolves a small percentage of the other, the excess constituent on the high lead side of the diagram will be a solid solution (α) of 81.5 lead and 19.5 tin. On the high tin side of the diagram, the excess constituent will be a solid solution (β) with 2.6 lead and 97.4 tin. The alloy with 38.1 lead and 61.9 tin will consist of a finely divided mechanical mixture of the α and β solid solutions. The proportions of these two constituents may be obtained by measurement from the diagram where the line CD represents 100 per cent of the eutectic, DE the proportional percentage of α, and CE of β. The microscopic structure of an alloy with 50 per cent tin may be shown by drawing a vertical line through the diagram from the 50 per cent point. This line will be on the high lead side of the eutectic. As the solution starts to freeze, the α solid solution will commence to form and will grow as dendritic crystals while the temperature drops, until at 359°F the liquid will have given up so much of the lead that it has reached the eutectic composition when all of the remaining liquid will solidify as the eutectic. This microscopic structure is illustrated in Fig. 7b, where the dark material represents α solid solution and the lighter constituent the eutectic, which will be identically the same as the eutectic shown in Fig. 7c. The proportions of α solid solution and eutectic can be calculated geometrically. At C, there is 100 per cent solid solution and at E, zero solid solution. The microscopic structure of an alloy with 35 per cent tin is shown in Fig. 7a. The constituents are the same as for the 50 per cent alloy, but the proportion of α solid solution is larger. The microscopic structure of an 85 per cent tin alloy is shown in Fig. 7d. This is on the high tin side of the eutectic, and the excess constituent is therefore β solid solution. The interstitial space is filled with eutectic of the identical composition as that in all of the other samples.

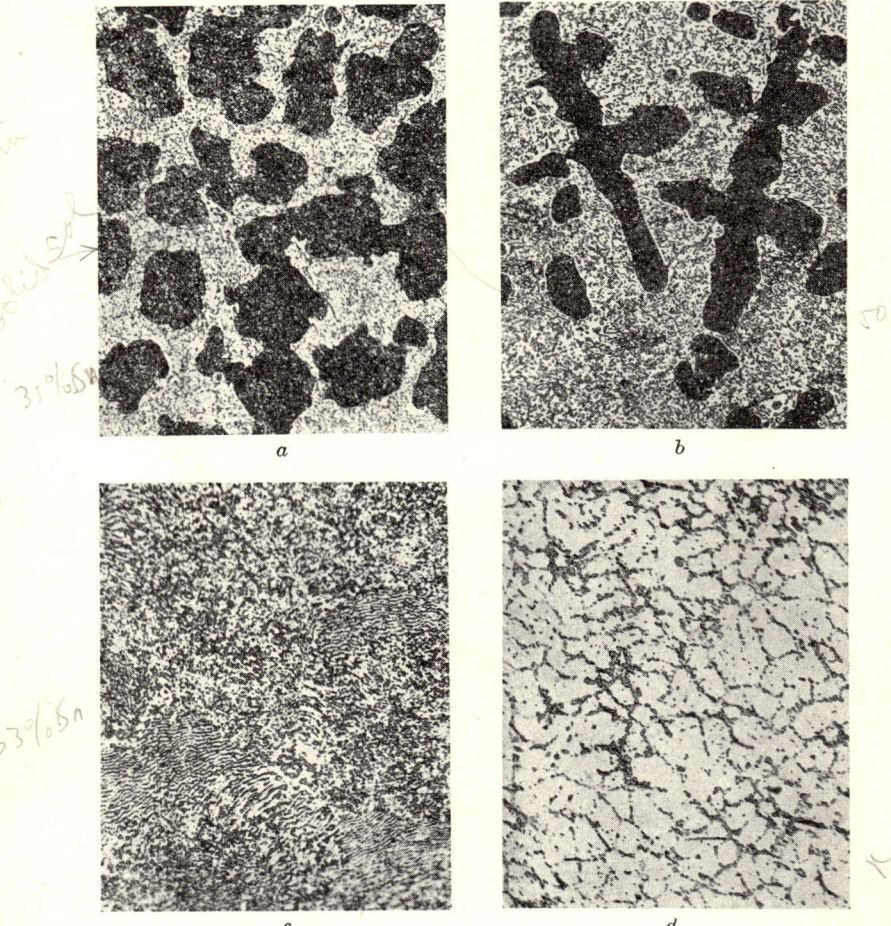

Fig. 7.—Microscopic structure of lead-tin alloys. *a*, (35 per cent tin) shows α solid solution (the dark constituent) and eutectic; *b*, (50 per cent tin) shows less α solid solution and more eutectic; *c*, (63 per cent tin) consists almost wholly of eutectic; *d*, (85 per cent tin) shows β solid solution and eutectic.

These photomicrographs are of metal cooled rather rapidly as they would be in commercial operation. The composition of the α solid solution is therefore approximately that shown on the equilibrium diagram (19.5 per cent tin), and the β solid solution is 97.4 per cent tin.

Both the α and β solid solutions reach their maximum richness at 359°F. As the temperature of the solid continues to fall, the solubility of tin in the α solution decreases and some tin diffuses out of the α solution at the grain boundaries. Diffusion in the solid state is slow, requiring days to obtain equilibrium, and the curve CH is dotted to show that its location is not definitely known. On the high tin side, the β solid solution behaves in a similar way, giving up lead as shown by the line DK

TABLE 2.—PHYSICAL PROPERTIES OF LEAD-TIN ALLOYS*

| Composition || Tensile strength, psi | Elongation, per cent in 4 in. | Brinell hardness |
Lead	Tin			
100	...	1780	39	4.1
70	30	5320	26	8.7
60	40	5500	35	11.3
50	50	5500	43	12.0
37	63	6700	32	13.9
	100	1880	55	4.6

* International Tin Council, *Bull.* 2, Solder, 1935.

and leaving a β solid solution so low in lead that some diagrams label it pure tin.

If these lead-tin alloys had been cooled extremely slowly all the way down to room temperature, the visible microscopic structure would not have changed much but the solid solutions would have changed in composition so that the α solution would have been almost pure lead and the β solution almost pure tin. The change in composition of the solid solution would also change the physical properties in a manner that will be made more clear by later illustrations.

Tin and lead are both soft and weak metals, each having a tensile strength of about 1800 pounds per square inch (psi) and a hardness of a little over 4 on the Brinell scale. As shown in Table 2, the addition of tin to lead increases both the strength and the hardness to more than three times that of either metal alone. The greatest strength and hardness come at the eutectic

22   ENGINEERING MATERIALS

composition where the two solid solutions reinforce each other to the maximum extent. The data of Table 2 do not give smooth curves when plotted owing in part to the difficulties of obtaining accurate figures when testing these soft and ductile metals, and in part to lack of constancy of properties of an alloy of given composition. The physical properties of an alloy will vary considerably with the rate of cooling.

Tin and lead are both soft and weak metals which are not ordinarily used in engineering structures. Their strength and

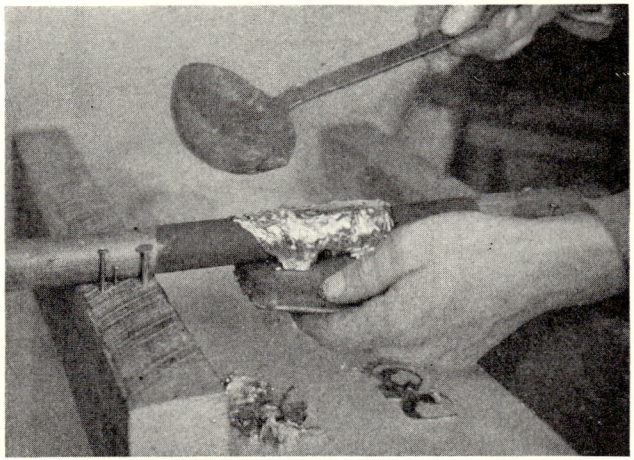

FIG. 8.—Wiping a joint on a lead cable. (*Courtesy International Tin Council.*)

hardness are however improved by forming alloys as indicated in Table 2.

One of the most common uses of the lead-tin alloys is to form a solder. Both lead and tin melt at relatively low temperatures and resist oxidation well. Some alloys melt at lower temperatures than either of the pure metals, and one with equal parts lead and tin is strong and especially useful where two lead pipes are to be joined together by wiping as shown in Fig. 8. The plumber scrapes the surface of the two pipes near their ends to get a clean metal surface. The two pieces of pipe are placed, preferably horizontally, on blocks raised so that the plumber can work around the whole circumference. The solder is melted in a ladle and allowed to cool until it has just commenced to solidify. It is then poured in a thin stream over the ends of the pipes and onto an asbestos pad held in the hand of the plumber. As the metal commences to solidify, it becomes increasingly pasty as the solid phase increases in amount and the liquid phase decreases. This pasty condition permits the plumber to shape the solder before the mass becomes entirely solid, so that a strong joint will result.

Plastic and Elastic Deformations.—If a force is applied to a material and, on the release of that force, the material returns to its original dimensions, the material has shown itself to be elastic. If successively greater forces are applied to this same material, there comes a time when it no longer returns to its original dimensions but suffers a permanent deformation. Its elastic limit has been passed. When a stress is applied within the elastic limit, the material is deformed slightly but resists further deformation no matter how long the same load may be applied. When a train passes over a bridge, all of the members of that bridge are slightly deformed. If the train stayed on the bridge all day, there would not be increasing deformation. It is a peculiar and valuable property of elastic materials that they yield slightly to any slight stress but stiffen and do not yield further to that same stress. The theory is that it requires very little energy to displace the unit crystal cells slightly, but progressively greater energy to displace them further. So long as only stresses that are safely below the elastic limit are applied, the material returns to its original state and is uninjured even if the stress is applied and released many million times. The crankshaft of an automobile engine is subject to alternate stresses and consequently to distortion at every revolution, but it returns to its original dimensions when the stress is released, and turns over many million times without injury.

A plastic material is one that does not stiffen when an initial stress is applied, so that a force which produces a small deformation will produce a progressively larger deformation with continuing application of the same force. A plastic material has many of the properties of a viscous liquid. A piece of petroleum pitch may appear hard and brittle, but if allowed to stand, even at room temperature, it will gradually flow to form a flattened mass. This makes pitch a valuable material for use in filling cracks in concrete pavements, but it prevents its use as a load-bearing material.

The forces acting between the unit cells of any slowly cooled crystal are in equilibrium. If the atoms are forced closer together, the forces of repulsion become stronger. If they are pulled apart, the forces of attraction increase. If the applied stress becomes too great, there must be a rupture of these interatomic forces which manifests itself in a permanent distortion of the material. A shaft may be said to have taken a "permanent set," a spring

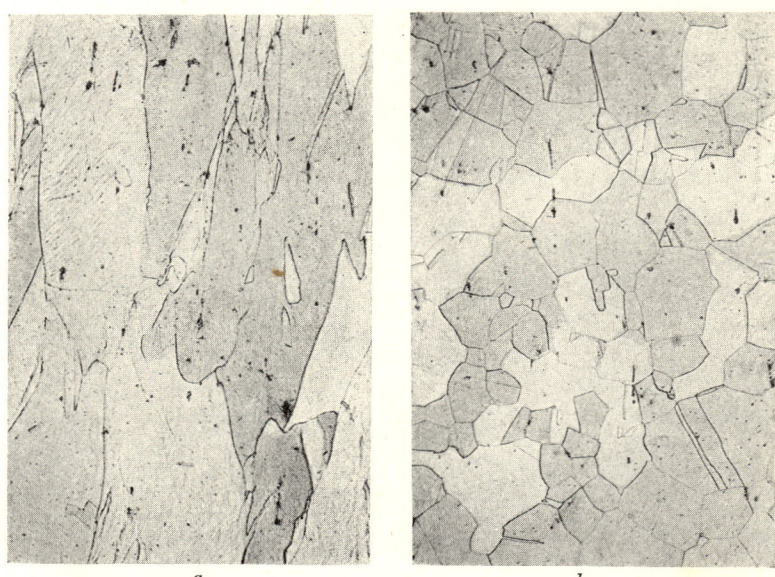

a   *b*

FIG. 9.—Effect of annealing in removing stresses due to cold work and in causing recrystallization. *a*, cold-drawn nickel alloy showing large distorted crystal- and faint slip bands, ×100; *b*, the same alloy after having been annealed 45 minutes at 1950°F. ×100. (*Courtesy International Nickel Co.*)

fails to return to its original length, and a plane surface becomes warped under these conditions of stress. The microscope is sometimes able to show that this permanent distortion has produced slipbands occurring on one of the planes of symmetry of the crystal, and hence parallel to one another. If the stresses are repeated, especially if they alternate in direction, the slipbands will increase in number and length, and become definite cracks running through several grains, ultimately causing rupture of the specimen. The effect of cold work on the same alloy whose microscopic structure was shown in Fig. 5 is illustrated in

Fig. 9. The left picture shows the elongated grains and the faint lines indicating slipbands. The right picture shows the cold-worked alloy after having been annealed. The large distorted crystals broke up on annealing into smaller crystals which grew as the annealing progressed. The picture of Fig. 5 shows the effect of annealing this cold-worked alloy for 30 min. at 1400°F. The grain size is smaller than in Fig. 9 which shows the structure obtained by annealing for 45 min. at 1950°F.

Cold Work and Recrystallization.—The first effect of this deformation of a crystal is to strengthen, harden, and embrittle the metal. The distorted crystals on the surface of the slip planes are apparently stronger than the original material. One theory is that the fragments become amorphous. The process of cold work is one of distortion of a metal beyond its elastic limit. The strength is increased but the ductility is always lessened by this process.

As the temperature at which the deformation takes place is raised, the cohesion becomes less and the metal deforms more readily as is shown in Fig. 1. The broken crystals strive to resume their normal structure, and at some temperature which is relatively a constant for each material, each fragment of a distorted crystal is able to reorient itself to form a new small crystal. The small crystals will grow by absorption of their neighbors, and so in time large crystals free from distortion or slipbands may be formed. This method of removing the strains due to cold work by heating the metal to a suitable temperature and holding it at that temperature for a time sufficient to permit recrystallization is termed "annealing" or "normalizing." The two terms are sometimes used almost interchangeably.

Physical Testing of Metals.—The simplest and commonest way of determining the strength of a metal is to measure the force required to pull a test piece apart, and thus determine its tensile strength. Metals are used frequently in compression, but the machines to test this property must be much stronger than those for tension, and compression tests are seldom made. In actual structures, pure tension and pure compression are rarely met. Shear stress is much more common, but its magnitude and direction vary so greatly that it is difficult to agree upon a standard method for testing metals in shear. In practice also, stresses are frequently applied rapidly, first in one direction and then in another, as in the case of the axle of an automobile that is traveling over a rough road. The analysis of stresses does not come within the province of this book, but consideration will be given to the effect of simple stresses on the metal.

When a metal is slowly deformed, the first effect visible to the microscope is the formation of slipbands showing that the metal has started to separate into blocks sliding somewhat as a pack of cards. When this condition has been reached, and even before slipbands have grown to visible size, the metal will no longer return to its original dimensions if the stress is relieved. The condition may be described in various ways: the metal has been cold-worked until it has acquired a permanent set, or has been stressed beyond the elastic limit. If a smaller stress had been applied and then released, the metal would have returned to its original dimensions. If this were not so, we could not have automobile springs that retain their properties unimpaired after millions of alternations.

The resistance of a metal to deformation will depend, to a minor extent, upon the rate at which the stress is applied. A load applied suddenly will rupture the fibers that first receive the impact before the other fibers have picked up their share of the load and so will break a piece which would easily carry that same load if it had been applied slowly. The rupture under sudden load is partly due to the fact that a metal can never be absolutely homogeneous. It always contains some foreign bodies, such as oxides or slag, as well as other materials which were in solution in the molten state but have been thrown out of solution on solidification and have become concentrated at the grain boundaries. Even if there were no foreign bodies, the changes in volume after solidification or during heat-treatment would have caused internal strains in the metal. Submicroscopic cracks resulting in a mosaic structure are believed to exist, no matter how carefully a metal is treated. The size of grains and the relative number of grains of metal in a cross section of the test piece certainly influence the results. All these considerations lead to the conclusion that if mechanical tests of metals are to be at all comparable, all of the conditions relating to the test piece and the method of testing must be carefully standardized. The American Society for Testing Materials issues standard specifications which are generally recognized as authoritative.

Other societies such as the Society of Automotive Engineers have formulated specifications for tests and materials that are peculiar to their own special field.

A recommended test piece for determining the tensile properties of steel consists of a cylindrical portion 0.505 in. in diameter and somewhat over 2 in. long with larger ends threaded or machined to fit the jaws of the testing machine. Before commencing the tests, two small marks are made with a punch 2 in. apart, as indicated in Fig. 10, to permit measurement of elongation. An extensometer clamped to the specimen provides a more accurate method of determining elongation. As soon as the stress is applied the metal begins to stretch, and while the metal behaves elastically the deformation or strain is proportional to the applied stress, and if the stress is released the test piece will in a short time return to its initial length. As the stress continues to be applied, slips commence to occur in the grains and the test piece will no longer return to its original length. The "elastic limit" has been passed. The extension of the test piece is also no longer proportional to the stress, and so the "proportional limit" has also been passed. If a recording extensometer is attached to the test piece, a graph similar to that in Fig. 10c will be obtained. The line ON is straight and commences to curve above N. It is very difficult to decide just when curvature begins, and it is easier to determine when the curvature reaches a slight amount, 0.1 to 0.2 per cent of the gaged length of the test piece. The load at this point indicates the "yield strength." In commercial testing of steel, where the load is applied more rapidly than in scientific work, the test piece yields suddenly and the pointer on the lever arm of the testing machine drops. This point is called the "yield point." It is evident that all of these four names indicate attempts to determine the true elastic limit

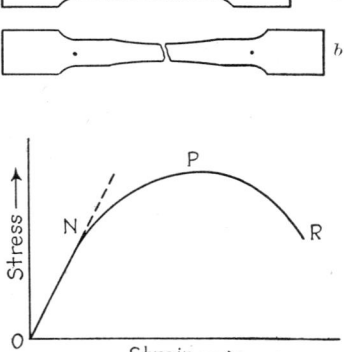

Fig. 10.—Results of tensile test. a, test bar before testing; b, test bar after it has been pulled apart; c, stress-strain diagram.

where strain ceases to be proportional to the applied stress. For the purposes of this elementary consideration of the properties of material, the terms elastic limit, proportional limit, and yield strength will be considered to be practically synonymous. The term yield point is less commonly used in modern practice and represents a stress slightly higher than that of the other three.

If the test piece is homogeneous in composition and uniform in cross section between the gage points, and the stress is applied parallel to the axis of the test piece, the greatest strain will be at the middle of the test piece and the first slipbands will occur in that region. The lengthening of the test specimen will be accompanied by a constriction or "necking down" in the middle region, and the more ductile the material, the greater will be the elongation before rupture finally occurs.

When the test piece has broken, the two parts are taken out and put together as shown in Fig. 10b. The distance between the gaged points is measured and the elongation determined and reported in percentage of the initial length. The area of the section at the break is measured as accurately as possible, and the diminution from the original cross section is recorded as reduction in area.

During the process of elongation, the specimen becomes severely cold-worked in the region where elongation is taking place. The amorphous metal or distorted grains on the slip planes resist further deformation, but the increasing load continues to produce more deformation. The embrittled grains finally give away suddenly. The graph of Fig. 10c shows that as the load was increased, elongation proceeded at an accelerating rate for each unit of stress applied beyond N, but that the total load which the test piece could support increased in a rather gentle curve to a maximum which reflected the strengthening effect of cold work even though the cross-sectional area of the test piece was diminishing constantly due to elongation. When the maximum point on the curve had been passed, the metal continued to stretch even at decreasing loads until rupture took place. The stress in pounds at P, the top of the curve, divided by the cross section of the original test piece in square inches is reported as the tensile strength in pounds per square inch, a term that is frequently abbreviated to psi. Some writers have referred to this value as the ultimate strength instead of the tensile strength.

Testing Hardness.—The earliest scale of hardness was that of Moh, a mineralogist who selected a series of minerals each of which would scratch the mineral ranking lower and be scratched by the one ranking higher. The width of a scratch produced on steel by a diamond point applied in a standard manner is one of the methods now in use for metals. The resistance to indentation forms the basis of the widely used Brinell test, in which a hardened steel ball is forced into the metal by a definite load. The diameter of the depression is measured, and the Brinell number is obtained by dividing the load by the area of the spherical depression in the metal. The Rockwell hardness test is also a penetration test. A simple test that is rapid and does not injure the piece being tested is provided by the scleroscope which measures the height to which a small weight will rebound when dropped from the machine upon the flat surface of the test piece. The behavior of the steel when filed gives a valuable indication of hardness. There is no absolute method of measuring hardness, and these various machines and methods measure somewhat different properties of the metal, although they are all grouped under the name hardness.

Electrical and Magnetic Properties.—Both electricity and magnetism are phenomena connected with electrons. When an electric current flows across a metal, it travels through the free electrons in a manner that has been compared with a wind, and the conductor does not undergo any permanent change. All of the good conductors are metals whose outer shells are not completely filled with electrons and permit rather free interchange of electrons. The best conductors copper, silver, and aluminum have only one electron in the outer shell. Each component of an alloy makes its own contribution to the resistance, and solid solutions cause an increase in resistance to the passage of an electric current. The conductivity of metals decreases as the temperature rises, with rather large changes at transition and melting points. The conductivity of fused metals is about one-fifth as great as that of the metals before melting. The conductivity of metals increases rapidly as the temperature is lowered, and in the neighborhood of the absolute zero, most pure metals become almost perfect conductors.

Solid substances that are not metals possess at least small conductivity for electricity, even if the conductivity is so low that they are classed as insulators. They differ from metals in that their conductivity becomes greater at high than at low temperatures. An electrolytic conductor is one in which the passage of an electric current causes definite changes in the conductor. All water solutions come in this category.

When a metal is magnetized, a change in temperature may be observed. There is also a change in shape which may cause the metal to swell, stretch, or twist. Magnetism is associated with the spinning motion of the electrons in the outer shells. Atoms with parallel spins will attract or repel each other differently from atoms with antiparallel spins. The rather small group of ferromagnetic materials that are spontaneously magnetized includes iron, cobalt, nickel, and some of their alloys. Materials that are attracted only feebly by a magnet are termed "paramagnetic." The magnetic susceptibility is affected by cold work and by temperature. When ferromagnetic metals are heated, they become paramagnetic at fairly definite temperatures known as the "Curie temperature."

References

JEFFRIES and ARCHER: The Science of Metals, McGraw-Hill Book Company, Inc., New York, 1924.

TAYLOR and TAYLOR: Elementary Physical Chemistry, D. Van Nostrand Company, Inc., New York, 1937.

MOTT and JONES: The Theory of the Properties of Metals and Alloys, Oxford University Press, New York, 1936.

BITTER, F.: Introduction to Ferromagnetism, McGraw-Hill Book Company, Inc., New York, 1937.

MOSING, G.: Handbuch der Metalphysik, Band 1, Erster Theil, Der Metallische Zustand der Materie, Akademische Verlagsgesellschaft Leipzig, 1935.

ROSENHAIN, W.: Introduction to the Study of Physical Metallurgy, revised by J. L. Haughton, Constable and Co., Ltd., London, 1935.

CHAPTER II

IRON AND ITS ALLOYS WITH CARBON

Pure Iron.—Iron is one of the most common metals, but as is the case with many other metals, it has never been obtained in a perfectly pure state. High-purity iron fused and slowly cooled in vacuum has the following physical properties, when tested at room temperature:

Tensile strength	35,000–40,000 psi
Yield strength	10,000–20,000 psi
Elongation	30–60 per cent
Reduction of area	70–90 per cent
Young's modulus	30,000,000 psi
Brinell hardness	60–70
Density at 20°C	7.87 g. per cc

Impurities that are present in even the best of the samples of iron prepared on the commercial scale influence its electrical and magnetic properties strongly. The resistivity of high-purity iron is 9.8 microhm-cm at 68°F (20°C). This resistance increases, with rise of temperature, to 105 at 1472°F (800°C) with a smaller rate of increase above that temperature. At temperatures approaching the absolute zero, its resistance is less than 2 per cent that at room temperature.

The melting point of iron is 2795°F (1535°C), and after solidification, three points of retardation in the cooling curve due to evolution of heat are noted, as shown in Fig. 3 of Chap. I. These points of arrest in the rate of cooling due to allotropic changes were first noted by Osmond in France who used the symbol A (*arrêt*) followed by subscripts commencing with 1 at the lowest transformation point noted. When iron is heated, absorption of heat occurs as the allotropic forms change. It was found that the temperatures for the points on the cooling and heating cycles did not agree, and the terms Ar (*refroidissement*) were used for the points on the cooling curves and Ac (*chauffage*) for points on the heating curve. More recent work has shown

31

that if the heating and cooling are performed extremely slowly there is almost no difference between the Ac and the Ar points, and the letter A without any following subscript letter is used to indicate the mean value. The first cooling curves were made on steel, and the lowest retardation was named Ar_1. This point is due to the separation of the solid solution of carbon and gamma iron into the eutectoid pearlite, as will be explained later, and therefore does not appear on the cooling curve for pure iron.

The curve of Fig. 3 shows that iron freezes at 2795°F (1535°C) to form delta iron which changes at Ar_4 2550°F (1400°C) to gamma iron, which undergoes a further transformation at Ar_3 1670°F (910°C) into beta iron, which in its turn becomes changed to alpha iron at Ar_2 1415°F (770°C). Some investigators have claimed to have found evidences of allotropic changes as cooling continues further, but the evidence has not been accepted as conclusive.

Delta iron is stable only at temperatures above those used in forging or rolling steel, and it possesses little practical importance for our purpose. Gamma iron, on the other hand, is the stable form at the forging and hot-rolling temperatures, and its properties are of great importance. It crystallizes on the face-centered cubic system, and its lattice has an edge length of 3.68 Å (1 Ångstrom unit is 10^{-8} cm). It is paramagnetic. Its strength is so low so that it is readily deformed, and it is plastic rather than elastic at the high temperatures at which it is stable in ordinary steels. At the next lower transformation point Ar_3, iron changes from the gamma to the beta form. Beta iron is a transition phase of little industrial importance since, as will be seen later, its range narrows as the carbon increases, and it disappears altogether when the carbon content of the steel reaches 0.6 per cent. Beta iron becomes transformed to alpha iron at 1415°F (770°C). Alpha iron crystallizes on the body-centered cubic system lattice whose edge length is 2.86 Å. It is ferromagnetic.

Following now the changes that iron undergoes as it is heated from room temperature, alpha iron persists up to the Ac_2 point which with very slow heating is almost identical with the Ar_2 point. At this temperature, the atoms retain their positions in the lattice, so the crystal is still body-centered cubic, but a change occurs in the grouping of the electrons which causes the iron to lose its ability to become readily magnetized (ferromagnetism) and to retain that property only in a slight degree (paramagnetism). On heating to the Ac_3 point, the lattice changes to a face-centered cubic structure with an edge length of 3.68 Å. This linear expansion of 25 per cent in the edge length of the lattice is compensated by the larger number of atoms and by the closer packing in the face-centered cubic system so that there is actually a slight decrease in volume and an increase in density during the transition from the alpha to the gamma form. The change in properties is very profound, and gamma iron is in many respects quite a different metal from alpha iron.

Recrystallization of Iron.—When iron cools from the molten state, the size of the crystals formed is to a large extent dependent on the rate of cooling. Steel ingots often weigh several tons and necessarily cool slowly with a resultant structure so coarse that it has been given the name of "ingotism." If iron is cold-worked, the crystals are deformed and embrittled. Annealing will cause recrystallization of the distorted fragments just as it will with other metals, and this effect may be produced very slowly at as low a temperature as 850°F. Pure iron is like all other metals in that large crystals may be broken up by heat-treatment only after prior mechanical deformation. On the other hand, when coarsely crystalline steel is heated until it has all become gamma iron, the great changes in the ultimate crystal structure of the iron-carbon alloy cause complete reorientation of the crystals. The large distorted crystals break down to fine crystals which may be prevented from growing by cooling soon after the steel has become converted to the gamma form. If held long above the transformation temperature, the fine crystals grow and again become coarse.

Carbon and Iron.—Carbon dissolves in molten iron to a limited extent, and on cooling a definite compound Fe_3C, cementite, containing 6.67 per cent of carbon is formed, which is the hardest constituent in ordinary steel and cast iron. If cementite is heated by itself, it decomposes rapidly at about 2000°F (1100°C) into iron and graphite. Its melting point, therefore, cannot be determined, and it cannot be made by direct fusion of iron and carbon. It may be isolated as a crystalline material by careful solution of annealed steel in dilute acid. When an alloy of iron and carbon is slowly cooled from the molten state to room temperature, a very small amount of carbon remains in solid solution but the balance of the carbon all enters into combination as cementite.

The decomposition of cementite at high temperatures to iron and graphite has led to arguments as to whether cementite is really the stable phase at lower temperatures or whether the transformation to graphite is merely so slow that cementite persists even during what we consider to be slow cooling. The evidence seems to be that graphite is really the stable phase and that if steel could be cooled so slowly that perhaps several hundred years would be consumed in the process, then the resultant material would be a mechanical mixture of iron and graphite, and not steel as we know it. For all practical purposes, cementite is the stable phase and is so considered in the discussion that follows.

Hardness of Cementite.—Since cementite cannot be obtained in any form except fine crystals, it is evidently not possible to determine its tensile strength. It is known to be brittle and hard. Boynton[1] has reported figures for the resistance due to abrasion by a rotating diamond drill so small and delicate that it could be placed under the objective of a microscope. The diamond point was set on the particular crystal whose hardness was to be measured, and the number of revolutions required to drill a hole of standard depth was determined. By this means, he obtained valuable information on the hardness of various materials. The values cannot be correlated with any of the figures for hardness obtained by commercial methods, since all of the latter depend upon the resistance of masses of crystals to deformation, whereas Boynton measured the resistance of single crystals. He found that it took only 460 revolutions to drill his standard hole in pure electrolytic iron, although it took 125,000 revolutions to drill the same depth of hole in cementite. This gives some quantitative measure of the hardness of cementite.

The Iron-carbon Equilibrium Diagram.—All equilibrium diagrams are constructed from experimental data, and therefore the diagrams constructed by different experimenters and writers will not be identical. The diagram given in Fig. 11 is taken from a compilation of the best sources of information, but is simplified somewhat to eliminate details that are not important for this elementary discussion.

[1] *Jour. Iron Steel Inst.*, 1906, II, 287 and 1908, II, 136–152.

A diagram of this sort is frequently termed the "iron-carbon diagram." An iron-carbon diagram should properly cover the whole range from zero to 100 per cent carbon, but the solubility of carbon in liquid iron at atmospheric pressure does not extend above 6 per cent, and the diagram is customarily shown as terminating at 6.67 per cent carbon which is the composition of cementite. The diagram in its lower temperature ranges may more properly be termed an "iron-iron carbide diagram," an "iron-cementite diagram," or even better a "ferrite-cementite diagram." The term "iron" is used so loosely that the term "ferrite" has been coined to indicate pure iron. Since cementite contains 6.67 per cent carbon, 1 per cent of carbon corresponds to almost exactly 15 per cent of cementite, and the diagram as given carries both sets of values.

The Diagram at Temperatures above 2000°F.—The upper half of this iron-carbon diagram is very similar in its outlines to that given for the lead-tin alloys in Fig. 6. The liquid freezes to a solid solution for all compositions up to a maximum of 1.7 per cent carbon, and with higher percentages of carbon a eutectic forms.

The melting point of pure iron is shown at A, and immediately adjacent to it there is a complicated series of transformations involving the formation and disappearance of delta iron. These have no important meaning for our purpose and will be neglected. The temperatures of beginning solidification are traced by the lines $ABCD$, and those of complete solidification, the small area around B being neglected, by the lines $BECF$. The areas between these two sets of lines contain both liquid and solid material.

The maximum amount of carbon that can exist in solid solution is 1.7 per cent at 2065°F (1130°C). For convenience of discussion, this solid solution has been given a specific name, austenite. When fused solutions with more than 1.7 per cent and less than 4.3 per cent of carbon solidify, the solid becomes a mixture of austenite and a eutectic consisting of a mixture of austenite and cementite. It has been previously stated that cementite decomposes rapidly at this temperature. The assumption is usually made that the liquid solution consists of carbon dissolved in molten iron and that the solid solution austenite just after solidifying consists of carbon dissolved in gamma iron, but that the eutectic consists of a mechanical mixture of austenite and cementite. There is no definite evidence as to the temperature at which this change from dissolved carbon to cementite takes place, and for that reason the right-hand side of the diagram is shown with the lines *CD* and *CF* dotted over part of their length. The uncertainty is only as to the temperature at which cementite

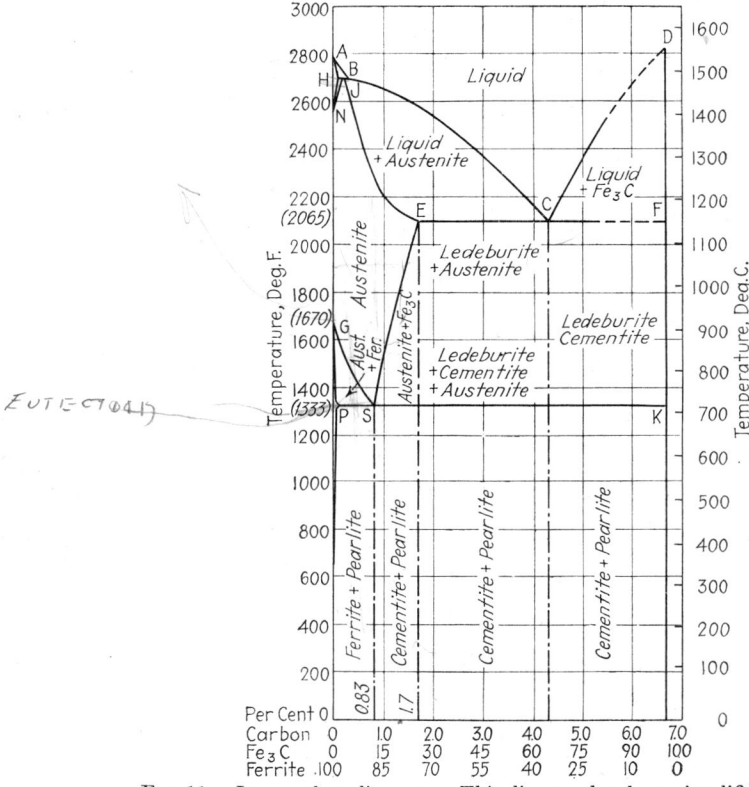

FIG. 11.—Iron-carbon diagram. This diagram has been simplified by omission of all reference to beta iron and the A_2 transformation, and to the A_0 transformation.

forms. There is no doubt of the existence of cementite at lower temperatures.

When solutions with exactly 4.3 per cent carbon solidify, the whole mass forms a eutectic mixture consisting of 47.7 parts of saturated austenite with 1.7 per cent carbon and 52.3 parts of cementite with 6.67 per cent carbon. For convenience of discussion, this solidified eutectic is often termed "ledeburite."

IRON AND ITS ALLOYS WITH CARBON

The region on the right-hand side of the eutectic is of little practical importance, since alloys are not made with such high percentages of carbon. If they could be made, the solid metal would consist of the eutectic ledeburite, plus free or massive cementite in amount increasing as the content of carbon increased above 4.3 per cent.

The diagram therefore shows that when molten solutions of carbon in iron are cooled slowly until they have just solidified,

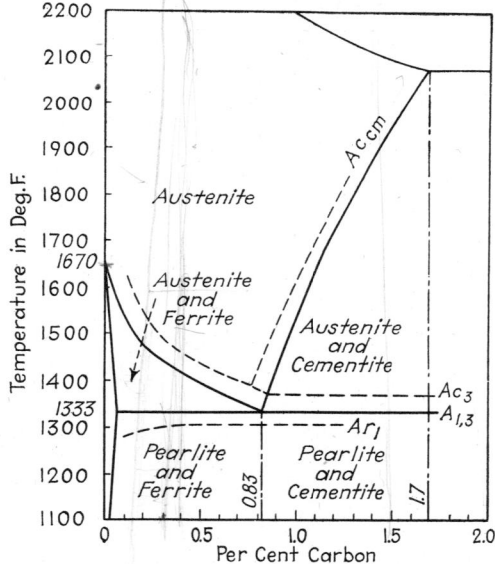

FIG. 11a.—Detail of iron-carbon diagram showing critical range.

any alloy up to 1.7 per cent carbon will consist of austenite, a solid solution of carbon in gamma iron. Any alloy with more than 1.7 per cent carbon will consist of a eutectic of austenite and cementite (ledeburite), plus excess austenite if the alloy contains less than 4.3 carbon and plus cementite if it contains more than 4.3 carbon. If the alloy contains exactly 4.3 carbon, it will consist wholly of the eutectic ledeburite. The diagram does not reveal anything about grain size, but since the metal has been slowly cooled, the grains of austenite separating along the line AE will be large. The eutectic separating at 2065° will be in smaller grains which, if the quantity is also small, will be found between the austenite grains.

The Iron-carbon Diagram below 2000°F.—It is convenient to divide the iron-carbon diagram for further study into an area containing less than 1.7 per cent carbon in which all of the commercial steels are found, and an area above 1.7 carbon in which white cast iron belongs. At 2000°F, all alloys with less than 1.7 per cent carbon consist of a solid solution of carbon in gamma iron (austenite). A solid solution possesses many of the properties of a viscous liquid solution. Diffusion is slow, but it does take place rather rapidly at 2000°F, more slowly at lower temperatures. The particles of carbon are able to migrate through the iron particles and to come together to form a definite compound of iron and carbon as soon as such a compound becomes stable thermodynamically. Cementite is known to be stable at 1333°F. It dissociates slowly at higher temperatures, and it is probable that austenite gradually changes from a solution of carbon in gamma iron to a solution of cementite in gamma iron as it cools from 2000 to 1333°, so that the austenite at intermediate temperatures contains a mixture of carbon and cementite in solid solution.

The diagram shows that the maximum amount of carbon that can exist in austenite decreases from 1.7 per cent at 2065°F to 0.83 per cent at 1333°F, as indicated by the line ES. As the temperature drops, cementite separates from the saturated solid solution and being now a foreign body is forced to the boundary of the austenite crystals in amounts that increase as the temperature falls, so that just above 1333° an alloy with 1.7 per cent carbon would have 0.83 carbon existing as solid solution in the austenite and 0.87 carbon existing as separate grains of free cementite between the shrunken crystals of austenite.

Let us consider next the alloys that contain less than 0.83 per cent carbon. There is no change in the left-hand margin of the austenite field until 1670°F (910°C) is reached where pure iron is changed from the gamma to the beta modification. Carbon and cementite are both almost completely insoluble in the body-centered alpha iron, and probably in the body-centered beta iron also. As soon therefore as any iron changes from the gamma state, it must be rejected by the solid solution and forced to the grain boundaries as alpha ferrite (with beta ferrite as a possible transitory phase). This change from gamma to alpha ferrite is shown by the line GS. As the temperature falls and the alpha ferrite is rejected by the austenite, the solid solution becomes enriched in carbon until at a temperature of 1333°F it reaches a content of 0.83 per cent carbon, which is identical with the residual solid solution which resulted when austenite with more than 0.83 per cent carbon was cooled slowly to the same temperature.

The Eutectoid Pearlite.—An inspection of the lower part of the austenitic area of the equilibrium diagram will show that we

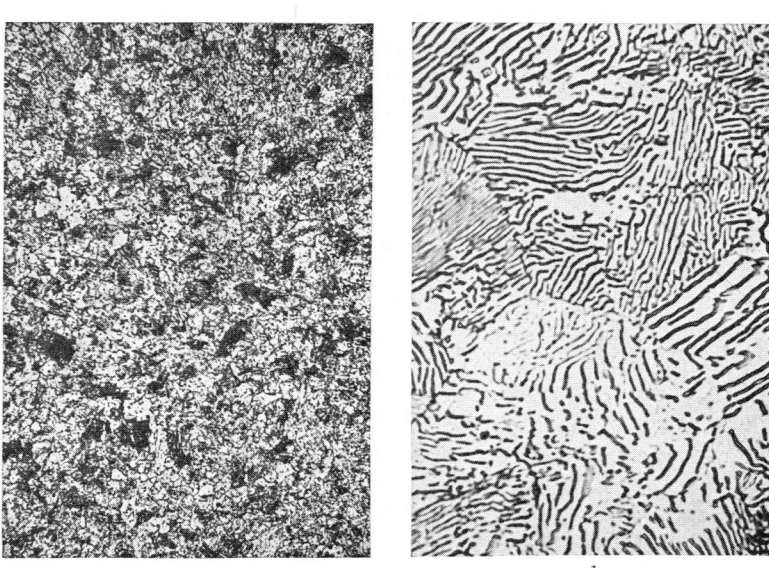

a   *b*
Fig. 12.—Microscopic structure of a steel of approximately eutectoid composition, 0.85 per cent carbon. Annealed one hour at 1500°F. The structure is wholly lamellar pearlite. *a*, ×100; *b*, ×1000.

have all of the conditions which point to the formation of a eutectic except that we are dealing with a solid instead of a liquid solution. Since however there is already a eutectic on the diagram, the second transformation, the decomposition of the solid solution at the lower temperature (1333°F), is called a "eutectoid," and the mixture resulting after the transformation is complete is called "pearlite." Any alloy of iron and carbon after slow cooling to below 1333°F will show a microscopic structure that contains pearlite as one of its constituents. The second constituent will be ferrite if the percentage of carbon is less than 0.83 per cent (hypoeutectoid) and cementite if the carbon is more than 0.83 per cent (hypereutectoid). If the composition is exactly 0.83 per cent (eutectoid), the microscope will show nothing but grains of pearlite. The microscopic appearance of this structure is shown in the photomicrographs of Fig. 12. The photograph taken with 100 diameters magnification does not show the details of the structure but that at 1000 magnification shows the alternate plates of cementite (black) and ferrite (white) in the typical thumbprint structure of lamellar pearlite. Only minor changes will take place in the crystal size or the microscopic structure below 1333° provided the alloy has been slowly cooled. The microscopic structure shown in Fig. 12 is all lamellar pearlite. If the steel had been annealed for a longer time at about 1300°F,. the long thin plates of cementite would have commenced to contract to globules, and the pearlite would have become "spheroidized." The appearance of partially spheroidized pearlite is shown in the photomicrograph D of Fig. 15.

An Iron-carbon Alloy with 0.03 Per Cent Carbon.—An alloy with only a few hundredths of a per cent of carbon does not become hard on quenching and is usually considered to be an iron rather than a steel although it is manufactured in the same way as steel. Ingot iron and Armco iron are illustrations of this type of material. An alloy with 0.03 per cent of carbon passes through several complicated changes just below its freezing point, but below 2600°F it consists wholly of austenite, a solid solution of carbon in gamma iron. If this alloy were only a little richer in carbon, there would be a separation of a small amount of the eutectoid pearlite at 1333°F. The more detailed diagram of Fig. 11a shows that about 0.06 per cent of carbon can be retained in solid solution in the alpha iron at 1333°. The diagram also shows that this solubility decreases as the temperature drops, but diffusion is extremely slow in steel at a low red heat, and an alloy cooled at any ordinary rate will retain 0.03 per cent carbon in solid solution at room temperature. The microscopic structure of annealed Armco iron as shown in Fig. 13 reveals nothing but ferrite, even at a magnification of 1000 diameters. The carbon is either present in true solid solution or in particles of submicroscopic size.

Steel with 0.15 Per Cent Carbon.—A steel with 0.15 per cent carbon will solidify about 2700°F to form austenite which will not undergo any change that is evident on the equilibrium diagram until about 1600°F. If there had been no carbon present, the gamma iron would all have changed to alpha (with beta as a transitory state) at 1670°. The carbon retards the change, but about 1600° gamma iron commences to change to alpha, and since the solubility of carbon in alpha iron is very small, grains of alpha ferrite start to separate, with the result that

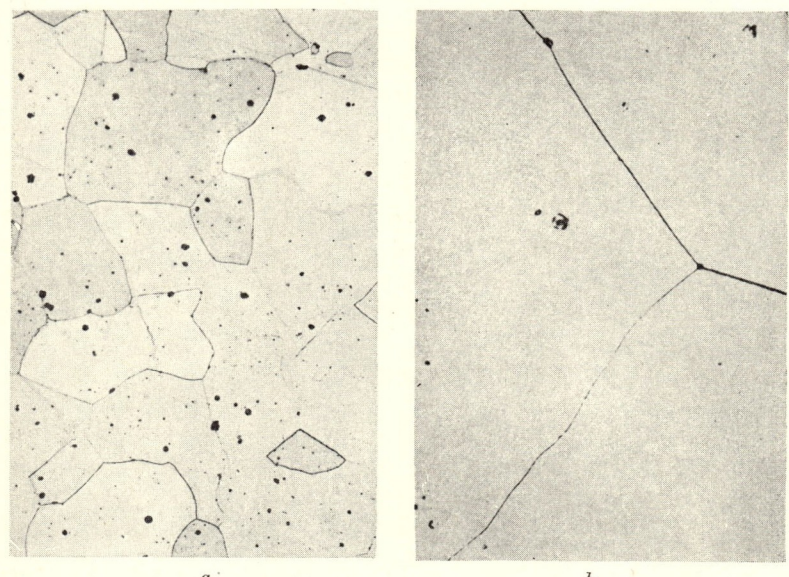

a   *b*

Fig. 13.—Microscopic structure of Armco iron containing only about 0.03 per cent carbon. Annealed one hour at 1700°F. *a*, ×100; *b*, ×1000. The structure shows nothing but ferrite. The black dots are either foreign inclusions in the metal or are due to imperfect polishing. (*Courtesy Dr. C. L. Clark.*)

the remaining austenite is enriched in carbon. The changing composition of the austenite, as alpha ferrite continues to separate, is shown by the line *GS* of the diagram. The grains of ferrite grow in number and size, and the residual austenite becomes less in quantity but richer in carbon. At 1333°, the austenite has reached its maximum content of 0.83 per cent carbon and separates as the eutectoid pearlite.

The structure of a commercial steel with 0.15 per cent carbon is shown in Fig. 14. It is labeled a 1015 steel following the nomenclature of the Society of Automotive Engineers which

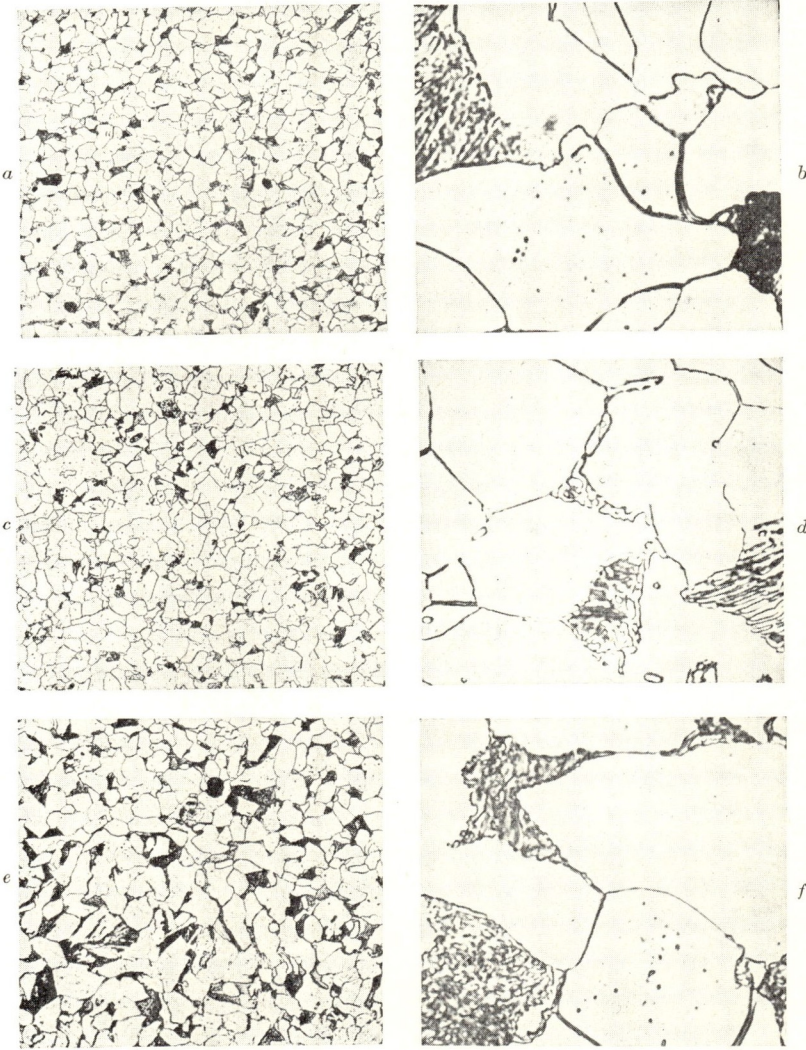

Fig. 14.—Microscopic structure of 1015 steel at ×100 (left) and ×1000 (right).

a and *b* as received from the rolling mill as a one-inch bar. The structure is ferrite, with pearlite which is not definitely laminated because of the rather rapid cooling. The grain is fine.

c and *d*, the same steel annealed at 1500°F for one hour and cooled in furnace. The grain is small and the pearlite is lamellar.

e and *f*, the same steel after normalizing for one hour at 1725°F and then holding for one hour at 1200°F. The grain has become coarser and the pearlite is partially spheroidized.

(*Courtesy Dr. C. L. Clark.*)

designates plain carbon steels by the number 10 followed by a number indicating the percentage of carbon in the steel. Commercial steels contain other elements in such small amount that they do not usually change the deductions to be drawn from the iron-carbon diagram.

The photomicrographs of Fig. 14 represent the structure of a steel that had been rolled to a bar 1 in. square according to the ordinary mill procedure and annealed later. These photomicrographs will be discussed more fully in the next chapter. At present, the important thing to be noted is that the structure consists of many granules of ferrite and relatively few of pearlite. The pearlite is identical with that shown in Fig. 12. The relative proportions of ferrite and pearlite can be calculated arithmetically or read graphically from the relative length of the line *PS* on either side of the intersection of the 0.15 carbon line, remembering that the point *S* corresponds to 100 per cent pearlite and the point *P* to zero pearlite.

Steel with 0.40 Per Cent Carbon.—The history of the solidification and the changes in the structure on cooling can be read from the iron-carbon diagram as was done for a steel with 0.15 per cent carbon. After the steel has cooled below 1333°F, the microscopic structure will again be ferrite and pearlite, but the proportion of pearlite will be larger than in the 1015 steel. The microscopic structure of an S.A.E. 1040 steel is shown in Fig. 15. This steel is not as uniform in its structure as was the 1015 steel, and the reasons for the stringers of ferrite will be discussed later. The magnification of 1000 diameters shows lamellar pearlite in the specimen annealed at 1550°, and spheroidized pearlite in the sample that was heated for 1000 hr at 1200°F.

Steel with 1.10 Per Cent Carbon.—The history of a steel with 1.10 per cent carbon may be read from the iron-carbon diagram just as for the steels with lower content of carbon. The liquid steel will start to freeze at approximately 2650°F and become a completely solid mass of austenite at 2175°. Gamma iron can hold 1.7 per cent of carbon in solid solution at 2065°F, but the amount it can retain in solid solution decreases as shown by the line *ES*. The diagram shows that the vertical line representing the 1.10 carbon composition would cut the line *ES* at about 1600°F. At this temperature, the austenite with 1.10 carbon becomes a saturated solid solution and the excess constituent,

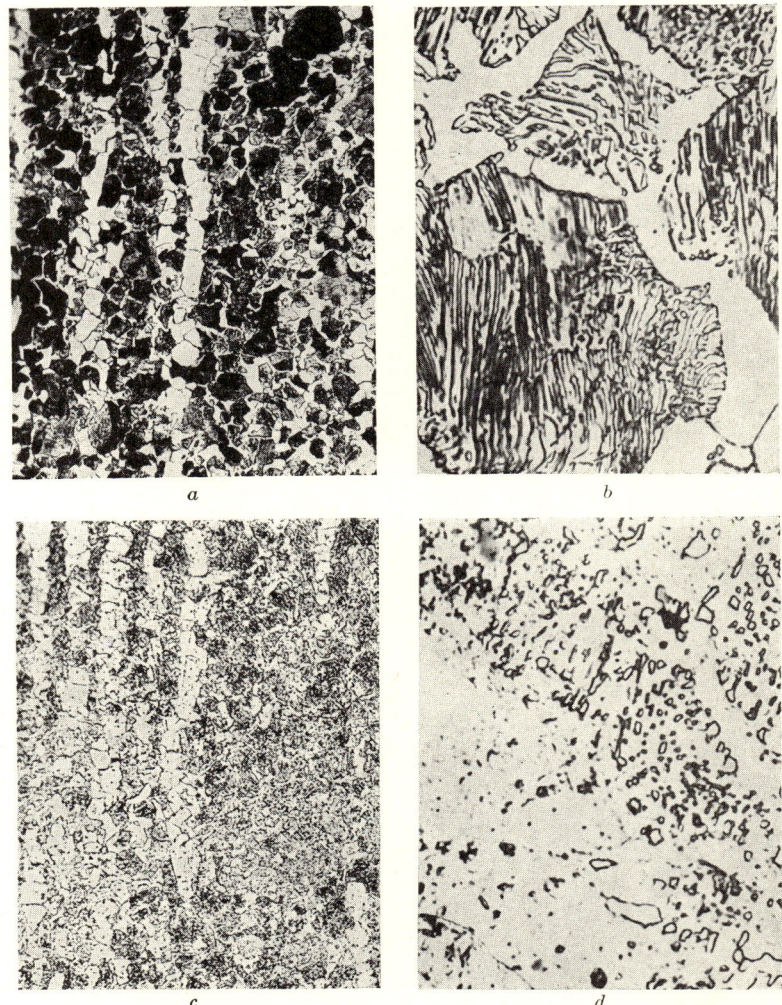

Fig. 15.—Microscopic structure of 1040 steel at ×100 (left) and ×1000 (right).

a and *b*, this is an open-hearth steel received as a one-inch hot-rolled bar which had been annealed one hour at 1550°F and cooled in the furnace. The structures consist of ferrite and pearlite. The white stringers of ferrite shown in *A* are due to the action of the rolling mill in drawing out crystals of ferrite which break into smaller grains during annealing.

c and *d*. This steel was then given a very long heat-treatment (1000 hours) at 1200°F. The pearlite has become unusually well spheroidized, but the ferrite streaks have persisted, since 1200° is below the critical range and diffusion is so extraordinarily slow at that temperature that even 1000 hours did not eliminate the coarse streaks.

(*Courtesy Dr. C. L. Clark.*)

carbon, must be discarded to the grain boundaries as the temperature falls. This elimination of carbon from the austenite results in the impoverishment of the solid solution, and when the temperature of 1333 is reached, the austenite has the eutectoid composition of 0.83 per cent carbon and breaks up into pearlite. Somewhere along the road, the discarded carbon has also changed

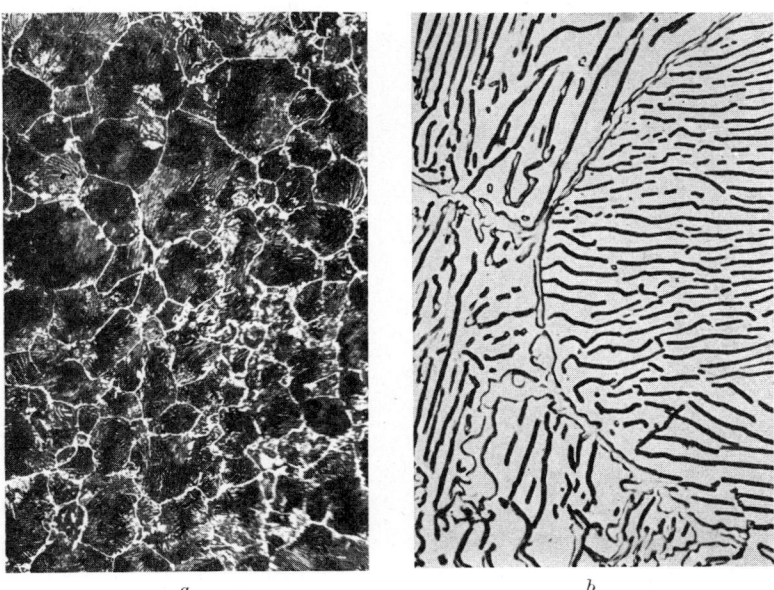

Fig. 16.—Steel with 1.10 per cent carbon. Annealed. Magnifications $a \times 100$, and $b \times 1000$. The structure at a magnification of 100 diameters shows coarse grains of pearlite (black) with cementite (white) at the grain boundaries. The structure at 1000 diameters shows lamellar pearlite with the cementite between the grains appearing as a narrow white band with black edges. (*Courtesy Dr. C. L. Clark.*)

to cementite. No way has yet been devised of telling at what temperature cementite becomes stable, but there is no doubt but that below the temperature of the eutectoid transformation the microscopic structure consists of grains of pearlite surrounded by a network of cementite. The structure of an annealed steel with 1.10 per cent carbon is shown in Fig. 16. The relative amounts of pearlite and cementite can be calculated arithmetically or read graphically from the line SK of the diagram, S corresponding to 100 per cent pearlite and K to 100 per cent cementite.

The Iron-carbon Diagram for Alloys with More Than 1.7 Per Cent Carbon.—The changes taking place during solidification have already been discussed. Below 2065°F (1130°C), all compositions are completely solid. We do not know the exact form in which the carbon is combined at a slightly lower temperature of, say, 2000°. Austenite has been defined as a solid solution of carbon in gamma iron with a maximum of 1.7 per cent carbon at 2065°F. If the alloy contains 3.0 per cent carbon, in what form is the other 1.3 per cent? It must be separated either as free carbon or cementite. It is customary to dodge the issue in a rather illogical manner and hold that austenite is composed of carbon in solid solution but that the material not in solid solution is cementite Fe_3C. The confusion exists only as to the mechanism of the transformations during the cooling process. There is no doubt as to what the situation is after the alloy has cooled below the eutectoid transformation.

Below 2065°F (1130°C), all compositions are completely solid and consist of grains of the eutectic ledeburite with excess austenite, if the carbon content is below 4.3 per cent, or excess cementite if the carbon is above 4.3 per cent. As cooling proceeds, the cementite already formed does not change, but the austenite which initially contained 1.7 per cent carbon separates cementite as indicated by the line ES until the residual austenite is resolved into pearlite at the eutectoid temperature of 1333°F. Below the eutectoid, therefore, all compositions will consist of pearlite and cementite. The original austenite with 1.7 carbon will have decomposed into cementite and pearlite. The ledeburite consisting at the higher temperature of austenite and cementite will have changed through decomposition of the austenite. The final structure will be pearlite and cementite, but the grain structure may be quite complicated.

This diagram may be further explained by tracing the changes in an alloy with 2.0 per cent carbon. Initial solidification commences at 2525°F. As the temperature drops, austenite separates as a solid, and the residual liquid becomes progressively richer in carbon until at 2065°F (1130°C) the liquid contains 4.3 per cent of carbon and solidifies as the eutectic mixture ledeburite containing 47.7 per cent saturated austenite and 52.3 per cent cementite. After solidification, some granules will consist wholly of austenite and some of ledeburite, and the relative proportion of the two may be obtained from the line *EC*. *E* represents 100 per cent austenite and *C* 100 per cent ledeburite. This alloy with 2.0 per cent of carbon will contain austenite in the ratio of 4.3 − 2.0 = 2.3 to ledeburite 2.0 − 1.7 = 0.3. This particular composition after solidification and before it has started to cool below 2000°F will contain 88 per cent of crystals of saturated austenite (with 1.7 per

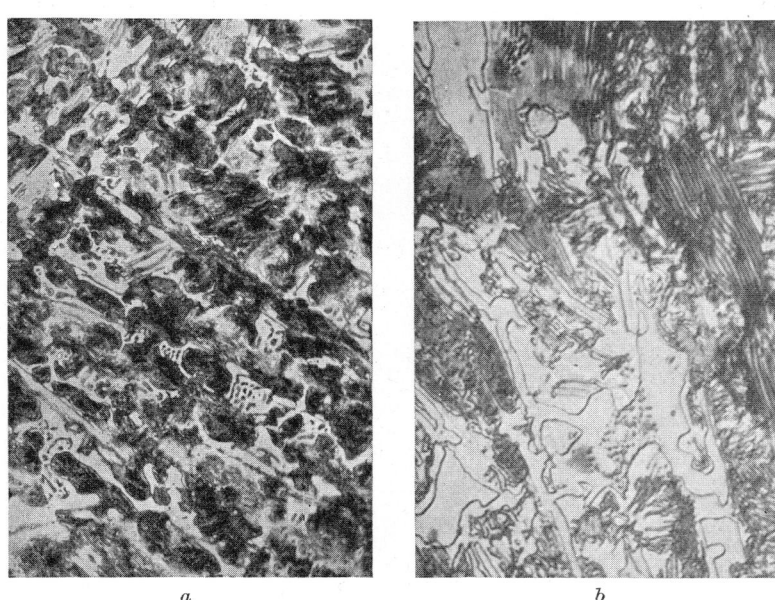

a *b*

Fig. 17.—Iron-carbon alloy with 2.0 per cent carbon. Cast in sand. Magnifications *a* ×100 and, *b* ×1000. In *a* the black elongated areas are pearlite formed by the decomposition of austenite dendrites separating from the liquid melt. The white areas represent the cementite which has coalesced into large masses during the decomposition of the ledeburite. In *b* the lamellar pearlite is clearly shown, intermingled with the white masses of cementite. (*Courtesy Dr. R. Schneidewind.*)

cent carbon) and 12 per cent of ledeburite composed of a finely divided mechanical mixture of saturated austenite plus cementite, the mixture containing 4.3 per cent carbon. On cooling below the eutectic temperature, the austenite starts at once to separate cementite, irrespective of whether the particular crystal was formed during initial solidification of the liquid or as part of the eutectic. At 1333°F (723°C), all of the residual austenite separates as pearlite, and the only constituents remaining will be cementite in separate granules, sometimes called "massive cementite," and pearlite which in itself is a mechanical mixture of cementite and ferrite. Because of the large amount of austenite decomposing after the initial crystals were formed, the microscopic structure will be very complicated. It is illustrated in Fig. 17.

Physical Properties.—The preceding review of iron and its compounds with carbon has been confined to their behavior when slowly cooled from the molten state. The changes that occur on rapid cooling will be discussed later. The discussion of physical properties which follows is restricted to alloys that have been slowly cooled from the melting point or reheated to a high temperature and slowly cooled, as in the process of annealing. The properties of relatively pure ferrite have already been given. Those for a slowly cooled commercial steel of 0.83 per cent carbon will approximate those for pearlite. The only figure available for

TABLE 3.—MECHANICAL PROPERTIES OF PEARLITE AND FERRITE

	Commercial steels*		
	0.1% carbon	0.83% carbon pearlite	Pure ferrite†
Brinell hardness................	120	245	60–70
Tensile strength, psi.............	48,000	135,000	35–40,000
Yield strength, psi...............	30,000	75,000	10–20,000
Reduction of area, per cent.......	72	15	70–90
Elongation in 2 in., per cent......	38	9	30–60

* These figures are taken from the compilation given by Sisco for hot-worked steels in The Alloys of Iron and Carbon, p. 85.
† These figures are from the summary by Cleaves and Thompson in The Metal Iron, p. 351.

cementite is that for its hardness already given. This whole series of slowly cooled alloys contain only the two constituents ferrite and cementite. Pearlite is such a definite complex that it is often considered as a third constituent although it is actually only a mechanical mixture of ferrite and cementite.

Since hypoeutectoid steels, when slowly cooled, are made up of mixtures of soft and ductile ferrite, with hard and brittle cementite, it is evident that the physical properties of the alloys will depend to a great extent upon the size of the crystals and the extent of dispersion of the two components. Pearlite consists of a fine-grained structure, frequently alternate plates of ferrite and cementite spaced only about one-ten thousandth of an inch apart. In this structure, the hard cementite reinforces the soft ferrite so that pearlite is stronger and harder, but less ductile than ferrite. Boynton investigated the hardness of pearlite and found that it required about 2000 revolutions of his drill to bore a hole in pearlite although 460 sufficed for pure iron and 125,000 were required for cementite.

Very little study has been given to the physical properties of pure iron-carbon alloys. Commercial steels have been studied, and a comparison between hot-rolled steels with 0.1 and 0.83 per cent carbon is given in Table 3. Figures for ferrite of exceptional purity are also given in the same table.

Sisco states:[1]

If all other conditions are equal there is probably a fairly straight-line relationship between carbon, from 0.05 to 0.60 per cent, and tensile strength and hardness, in which each 0.01 per cent carbon increases the tensile strength about 1000 lb. per sq. in. and the Brinell number by 2.

The properties of commercial steels will be discussed more fully in later chapters.

References

CLEAVES and THOMPSON: The Metal—Iron, Alloys of Iron Research, Monograph Series, McGraw-Hill Book Company, Inc., New York, 1935.

EPSTEIN, S.: The Alloys of Iron and Carbon, Vol. I, Constitution, Alloys of Iron Research, Monograph Series, McGraw-Hill Book Company, Inc., New York, 1936.

SISCO, F. T.: The Alloys of Iron and Carbon, Vol. II, Properties, Alloys of Iron Research, Monograph Series, McGraw-Hill Book Company, Inc., New York, 1937.

[1] Alloys of Iron and Carbon, vol. II, Properties, p. 91

CHAPTER III

EFFECT OF HEAT-TREATMENT ON IRON-CARBON ALLOYS

Long before it was known that carbon was the hardening agent, the name steel had been given to that form of iron which could be forged at a red heat and which became hard when plunged into water while still at a bright red heat. Plain carbon steel is essentially an alloy of iron and carbon, although it always contains small amounts of silicon, manganese, sulfur, phosphorus, and oxygen as compounds or in solid solution. These other materials exert an important influence upon the properties of the alloy. Sulfur, phosphorus, and oxygen are harmful and are usually restricted to a few hundredths of a per cent. Silicon and manganese are helpful but are restricted to a few tenths of a per cent. The influence of these elements will be discussed later, and in the present chapter carbon steel will be considered to be merely an alloy of iron and carbon. The new factor introduced will be the effect of heat-treatment.

Austenite.—The equilibrium diagram can be applied only when an alloy has been so slowly cooled that the austenite has completely changed to pearlite, with ferrite as the excess constituent with a hypoeutectoid steel, and cementite the excess constituent with a hypereutectoid steel. This decomposition of austenite requires an appreciable time. Austenite is by definition a solid solution of carbon in gamma iron. The equilibrium diagram shows that, for a steel of 0.83 per cent carbon, only austenite exists above 1333°F (723°C) and only pearlite exists below that temperature. The implication is that with this particular composition carbon changes to cementite, gamma to alpha iron, and the cementite and alpha ferrite arrange themselves in definite pearlite formation, all at constant temperature. This can hardly be the case, and there is some experimental evidence to show it, not enough however to warrant any changes in the diagram.

If austenite should be instantaneously cooled to room temperature, it would not have been given any opportunity to change and should therefore remain as a solid solution of carbon in gamma iron. No ordinary quenching of steel in water is rapid enough to retain much austenite, but Boynton was able by special technique to chill an alloy with 3.24 per cent carbon so that the microscope revealed nothing but austenite. The hardness of this steel by the diamond-drill method was 47,600, much softer than cementite whose hardness was 125,000. This corresponds to what might be expected from a solid solution. When small pieces of hypereutectoid steels are quenched in water, as much as 30 per cent of the carbon may be retained as austenite. In steel with 0.4 per cent carbon, it is possible to keep 10 per cent of the carbon as austenite.

Martensite, Troostite, Sorbite.—The metallographer with his microscope can detect various intermediate stages in the transition from austenite to pearlite. Three of them martensite, troostite, and sorbite have received general acceptance and are terms regularly used in metallurgical discussions. When steel is quenched rapidly, a small amount of austenite is preserved, as has been stated, but the major microscopic structure is martensite, the constituent that gives the greatest possible hardness to steel. X-ray examination shows that in martensite the gamma iron has changed to alpha and that the carbon is so completely dispersed that it is substantially in solid solution. Neither the X ray nor any other method of examination can state definitely whether the carbon is still in the free state or has combined to form Fe_3C, cementite. Since however Fe_3C is extremely hard, and martensite is also extremely hard, it will be assumed in the following discussions that martensite consists of cementite in solid solution, or at least in an extremely fine state of dispersion in alpha iron. Since martensite is a solid solution, it should exist in steel within the whole range of possible percentages of carbon. Boynton showed the hardness of martensite to vary with the carbon content from 17,900 for 0.20 per cent carbon to 120,300 for 1.52 per cent carbon. If the cooling is somewhat slower than that which will retain martensite, troostite appears as the major microscopic constituent. This consists of a mixture of cementite and alpha iron in which the particles of cementite have grown to a size visible under a high-powered microscope. With slightly slower cooling, the cementite arranges itself in a somewhat more definite pattern to form sorbite.

Martensite, troostite, and sorbite represent unstable configurations of cementite in alpha iron. The only stable configurations of the carbide are free cementite (in hypereutectoid steels) and pearlite. Ferrite is soft and ductile, rather like copper. The hard particles of cementite act as pegs to prevent slip in the

TABLE 4.—COMPARISON OF HARDNESS AND MICROSCOPIC STRUCTURE

Variations in the hardness and microscopic structure of a piece of steel with 0.58 per cent carbon which was heated, at one end only, to a white heat and then quenched in water, according to Boynton. This piece of steel was 2 in. long and ½ by ⅜ in. in cross section. The figures represent the hardness of the hardest constituent present at any point by Boynton's diamond-drill method.

Structure Commencing at Cold End and Proceeding Toward End That Had Been at White Heat.	Average Hardness of Hardest Constituent in Boynton's Hardness Numbers
Unheated end, pearlite and ferrite	2,050
Sorbitic pearlite, very little ferrite	2,500
Sorbite, little ferrite	7,310
Sorbite, trace ferrite	9,135
Sorbite, no ferrite	12,760
Sorbite, no ferrite	15,470
Small amount troostite, much sorbite	21,800
Troostite and sorbite	24,655
Martensite and troostite	40,564
Martensite only, at end heated to white heat	105,000

ferrite grains. If the hard particles are brought together in large masses, they are least effective as reinforcements, because large areas of soft ferrite are left without reinforcement. A steel is therefore in its softest state when cooled so slowly that the pearlite forms definite areas with large areas of free ferrite, if the steel is hypoeutectoid. A hypereutectoid steel is always relatively hard, but it is in its softest state when the pearlite is well spheroidized. A steel is in its hardest state when the ferrite grains are reinforced everywhere by fine particles of cementite as is the case in martensite. Boynton cites an interesting and simple experiment in which a bar of steel with 0.58 per cent carbon was heated, at one end only, to a white heat and then quenched in water. The other end of the bar had not been heated even to redness, and there had been a fairly uniform temperature gradient along the bar before quenching. The results of the microscopic examination at various points are given in Table 4. The cold end showed pearlite and ferrite with hardness of 2,000 for the pearlite, the heated end showed martensite only, with a hardness of 104,000, and intermediate points gave intermediate numbers with corresponding microscopic structures. This demonstrates that it is possible to secure graded hardness in steel by controlling the temperature to which the metal is heated (within the critical range) and then quenching the metal in cold water. This method is not practical and is rarely used.

The commercial method for hardening steel takes advantage of the fact that steel after quenching while in the austenitic state is not in equilibrium and that the carbides will attain apparent equilibrium at moderate temperatures if sufficient time is allowed. A steel cooled rapidly from the austenitic range will consist mainly of martensite with perhaps some austenite. Diffusion in steel at room temperature is almost nonexistent, and therefore the unstable condition is considered permanent. However Campbell[1] was able to show that the electrical resistance of quenched steel changed materially on immersion in boiling water, and other investigators have alluded to "age-hardening" as occurring in steel.

Age-hardening.—It will be observed from the iron-carbon diagram Fig. 11a that alpha iron at the eutectoid transformation temperature of 1333°F (723°C) is capable of holding about 0.06 per cent carbon in solid solution. This amount decreases as the temperature falls, until at room temperature it is probably not over 0.01 per cent. This dissociation of the dilute solid solution occurs very slowly, and steels cooled in air slowly enough to cause the pearlite to be well differentiated will still carry more carbon in solid solution than the diagram indicates they should, some of the carbon existing as supersaturated solid solution. Boynton noted that the hardness of electrolytic iron after fusion in vacuum was 460, whereas the ferrite present in a steel of 0.68 per cent carbon was 660. When the unstable solid solution separates to form a fine suspension of cementite in iron, the steel will become gradually harder. This slow decomposition of a solid solution at room temperature, or slightly higher temperatures, with separation of a hard constituent is termed "age-hardening."

[1] *Jour. Iron Steel Inst.*, **92**, 164–180 (1915).

It is of rather minor importance in steel because the amount of carbon in the solid solution is very small, but a much more important transformation of a similar nature will be discussed later in connection with Duraluminum.

Changes in Steel on Heating through the Critical Range.—The equilibrium diagram of Fig. 11a shows a portion of the iron-carbon diagram in greater detail. The solid lines showing equilibrium conditions are the same as those shown in Fig. 11. The lag in the transformations has been mentioned, and at any ordinary rate of cooling all of the transformation will occur 50 to 100°F below the true equilibrium temperatures. The dotted line marked Ar_1 indicates this retarded formation of pearlite.

When steel is heated at any ordinary rate, transformations into austenite are retarded so that they appear at temperatures higher than those which represent equilibrium. The Ac lines of Fig. 11a show the approximate temperatures at which the transformations may be completed.

On heating a piece of steel, an increasing brittleness appears in the range 400 to 600°F which has not been explained. When steel is heated in air at this temperature, it becomes covered with a blue film of oxide, and the "blue-working" of steel has long been considered harmful on the ground of practical experience, without any adequate scientific reason being yet available. If the steel has been cold-worked, the fragments separated by slipbands will readjust themselves in the temperature range above 600°F and the strains due to the cold work will be removed, but so slowly that it is not practicable commercially.

There are two branches to the Ac line for the hypereutectoid steels. It will be remembered that the microscopic structure of these steels, when cooled slowly, consists of grains of pearlite surrounded by a network of cementite. On reheating, the pearlite may be expected to be transformed to austenite when the Ac_3 line has been passed. The network of excess cementite cannot go completely into solution until the Ac_{cm} line has been passed, so that if complete conversion of the cementite into austenite is demanded, the temperature must be raised to the figures corresponding to the upper branch of the curve. As the transformation proceeds, cementite starts to diffuse through the adjacent bands of ferrite, alpha ferrite changes to gamma, cemen-

EFFECT OF HEAT-TREATMENT ON IRON-CARBON ALLOYS

tite dissociates into carbon and iron, and the carbon diffuses into adjacent crystals. It is not possible to state the exact order in which these changes occur. When they are completed, the structures present at room temperature have all been changed to austenite and the original crystal structure has been broken up. This region of transition is called the "critical range."

Critical Range.—The critical range may be determined from cooling curves and heating curves, and also by determining the

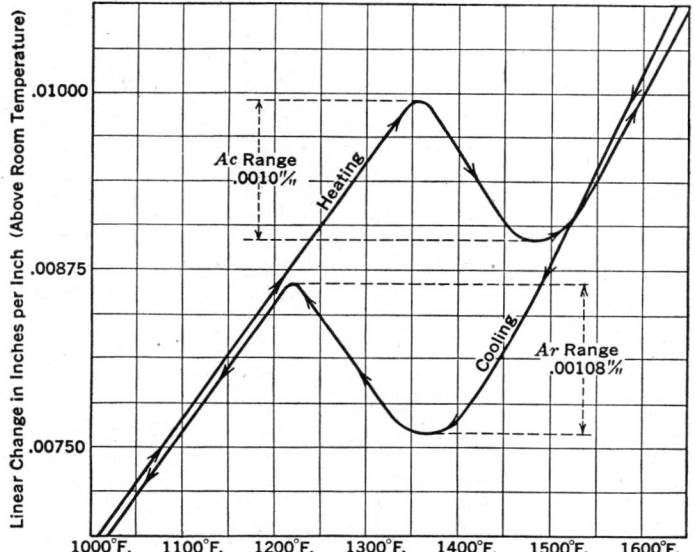

FIG. 18.—Dilatometer curves for 1045 steel. (*From Bethlehem Steel Co. Catalog 144.*)

volume changes that take place as a piece of steel is heated or cooled. The changes in length for a piece of 0.45 per cent carbon steel are shown in Fig. 18. The heating and cooling took place at the rate of about 7°F per minute, which is slow for industrial operations. During the heating cycle, the length of the test piece increased at a regular rate until 1350°F was reached. The temperature continued to rise, but the length started to decrease and continued to decrease until it had shrunk 0.001 in. per inch of length while the temperature rose 125°. At this point, the transformation to austenite had been completed and the volume then started to increase and was soon increasing at about the rate it had followed prior to its entry into the critical range. When this piece of metal was cooled, it contracted regularly until it reached 1375° and then expanded, although it was still cooling, until a temperature of 1225° was reached, which marked the completion of the transformations and the lower boundary of the critical range.

The critical range is defined by the American Society for Testing Materials by reference to the Ac points as shown in the curve of Fig. 19. When their specifications direct that a steel is to be heated through the critical range, it is to be heated through the $Ac_{3,2,1}$ points.

It should be emphasized that in commercial work the position of these lines will shift with the rate of heating and cooling. Where large numbers of parts are being treated as in the automobile plants, the best procedure for heat-treatment is determined by repeated experiments in the laboratory before the shop instructions are prepared.

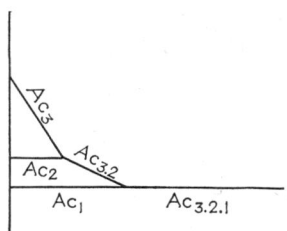

Fig. 19.—Critical range as defined by the American Society for Testing Materials. (*From A.S.T.M. Standards for 1936 Part I, p. 412.*)

Grain Refinement.—It has been stated previously that steel, in common with all other alloys, may have its grain refined by a suitable amount of cold work followed by a heat-treatment whose duration and temperature will vary for every alloy. If the duration of heating is too prolonged and especially if the temperature is too high, the fine grains formed during the rearrangement of the distorted crystals will grow again to coarse grains.

The alloys of iron and carbon are unique in that grain refinement is possible by heat-treatment only, without previous cold work. The changes in crystal structure of the iron and in the cementite while passing through the critical range are so profound that the old grains are broken up in the transition through the critical range.

Annealing and Normalizing Steel.—Annealing is an old process used to bring steel to a soft state for machining. It was usually accomplished by putting the pieces in a hot furnace and then drawing the fire and letting the pieces cool slowly. The American Society for Testing Materials, the Society for Automotive Engineers, and the American Society for Metals have agreed on somewhat more accurate definitions of annealing and some of the other fundamental operations in heat-treatment. The following definitions are copied directly from the official specifications.[1]

Full Annealing.—Heating iron base alloys above the critical temperature range, holding above that range for a proper period of time, followed by slow cooling through the range.

NOTE.—The annealing temperature is generally about 100 degrees Fahr. above the upper limit of the critical temperature range, and the time of holding is usually not less than one hour for each inch of section of the heaviest objects being treated. The objects being treated are ordinarily allowed to cool slowly in the furnace. They may, however, be removed from the furnace, and cooled in some medium that will prolong the time of cooling as compared to unrestricted cooling in the air.

It will be noted that the temperature of full annealing is stated to be about 100°F above the Ac_3 range and that the duration of heating is considerable. Steel expands as it gets hotter except while it passes through the critical range when it shrinks. It must be heated rather slowly so that there will not be too steep a temperature gradient between the surface and the center of a heavy piece. A piece with sections of different thickness will warp unless it is heated carefully. Time must be allowed for the diffusion of the cementite and its dissociation product, carbon, throughout the surrounding grains. The grain size does not increase much until the diffusion of the carbon has been almost completed, but as soon as that point has been reached it increases more rapidly.

If the temperature for a full anneal is high, the time is long, and the rate of cooling is slow, the annealed steel will have coarse grains. If on the other hand, the temperature of the furnace is kept only 100°F above the critical range and the cooling process is commenced as soon as the grain has been refined, then the grain size will be small. The result in any case will be to give, in hypoeutectoid steels, grains of soft ferrite with pearlite which is well differentiated. Pearlite in this form exerts a minimum reinforcing action, and the steel will be in a soft state suitable for machining.

[1] American Society for Testing Materials, A.S.T.M. Standards 1936, Vol. I, p. 413.

The tool steels which represent the commonest type of hypereutectoid steels are usually furnished by the manufacturer in the annealed state and with a rather fine grain consisting of pearlite within a network of cementite as shown in Fig. 16. The toolmaker should forge this steel at a rather low temperature so as to avoid giving the grain much opportunity to become coarser. If the steel is to be annealed before machining, the temperature in this process need only be raised above the Ac_3 line of Fig. 11a. This will not change the cementite network around the grains, but it will remove forging or cooling strains, bring the pearlite into solid solution as austenite, and permit it to separate again on cooling as well-segregated pearlite with a tendency towards the spheroidized form. Such a steel consisting of pearlite within a network of cementite can never be soft like a hypoeutectoid steel, but this treatment will make it as soft for machining as is possible. The shaded area of Fig. 20 shows the annealing range.

The definition for normalizing states the temperature to which the piece is to be heated in the exact words of the definition of annealing. The only real difference in the definitions is that in normalizing, the piece undergoing treatment is to be cooled fairly rapidly, such as by air cooling, to below the critical range, whereas in annealing the piece is to be cooled slowly. The process of normalizing has been developed more recently, since the advent of pyrometers for measuring temperature and the introduction of furnaces whose temperature may be controlled readily.

Grain refinement will occur more rapidly at temperatures 200°F above the critical range than it will at temperatures 100°F above that range. As soon as the grains have been refined, they will start to grow more rapidly and to much larger size than at the lower temperature. Consequently if the heat-treatment is to be carried out at temperatures 200° above the critical range, the time, as well as the temperature, must be watched closely, and the cooling must be done rather rapidly so as to prevent the grains from becoming coarser while they are cooling. Normalizing has therefore come to be used as a rapid method of securing grain refinement and machinability under controlled conditions. The areas of Fig. 20 which reflect commercial practice show that normalizing takes place at a higher temperature than annealing.

EFFECT OF HEAT-TREATMENT ON IRON-CARBON ALLOYS

In normalizing hypereutectoid steels, the temperature of heating is to be high enough to dissolve the cementite network surrounding each grain and bring all of the carbides into the austenitic form. The temperature required for this transformation is so high that coarse grains are apt to form unless the metal is forged or rolled while hot. Normalizing is therefore used

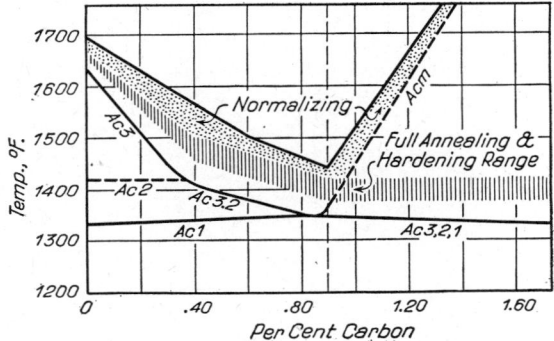

FIG. 20.—Heat treating diagram for carbon tool steels. (*From Gill, Tool Steels, p. 63.*)

rather infrequently as a method of heat-treatment of hypereutectoid steels.

Process Annealing [A.S.T.M. Definition].—Heating iron base alloys to a temperature below or close to the lower limit of the critical temperature range, followed by cooling as desired.

NOTE.—This heat treatment is commonly applied in the sheet and wire industries and the temperatures generally used are from 1020 to 1200 degrees Fahr.

It is apparent that process annealing is used to remove the effects of cold work. The duration of the heating and the rate of cooling are left to the judgment of the operator. Cold-drawn sheets and wires have been rendered stronger and more springlike but also more brittle by the cold-drawing process. These properties may be removed in varying degree by controlling the conditions of process annealing.

Normalizing [A.S.T.M. Definition].—Heating iron-base alloys to above the critical temperature range, followed by cooling fairly rapidly to below that range.

NOTE.—Normalizing is rarely practiced with hypereutectoid steels because of the coarsening of the grain and the tendency to crystallize cementite at grain boundaries or in needles. However, it may sometimes be necessary to normalize these steels by heating them above the Ac_{cm} line of the iron-carbon diagram (as shown in Fig. 11a).

Full annealing of hypoeutectoid steels produces segregated pearlite, but also produces coarse grains of ferrite which weaken the metal. Since the grain size is small at the close of the transformation of cementite into austenite, and grows rather rapidly after that change has been completed, it should be possible to retain a fine grain by careful attention to the time and temperature of heating and the rate of cooling. The temperature of the furnace and the duration of heating are the most important factors, and they must be determined experimentally. As soon as the pieces are taken out of the furnace and placed in still air, the temperature drops so rapidly that the grains do not have time to grow appreciably. Air cooling is usually slow enough so that pearlite forms quite completely, and the metal is not hardened appreciably during the cooling.

The treatment of high-carbon steels is always a difficult problem. In the A.S.T.M. directions for full annealing treatment, the temperature was kept so low that there was no change in the cementite network. If that is to be broken up the temperature must be carried above the line A_{cm} of Fig. 20, and time must be allowed for all of the cementite to become austenite. The diffusion of the carbon from the massive cementite takes time, and there is danger that before that process is completed the grains will have become coarse.

Patenting [A.S.T.M. Definition].—Heating iron base alloys above the critical temperature range, followed by cooling to below that range in air or in molten lead which is maintained at a temperature of about 700 degrees Fahr.

NOTE.—This treatment is usually applied in the wire industry as a finishing treatment or, especially, in the case of eutectoid steel, as a treatment previous to further wire drawing. Its purpose is to produce a sorbitic structure.

This is an instance of a single heat-treatment designed to refine the grain by heating above the critical range for a definite time, and then to toughen the metal by cooling it at such a rate that pearlite will not have time to form as a definite structure. The intermediate sorbite gives a stronger wire. Wire drawing is a continuous process, and the conditions of heating and cooling can be kept under close control.

Spheroidizing [A.S.T.M. Definition].—Prolonged heating of iron base alloys at a temperature in the neighborhood of, but generally slightly below, the critical temperature range, usually followed by relatively slow cooling.

NOTE.—(a) In the case of small objects of high-carbon steels, the spheroidizing result is achieved more rapidly by prolonged heating to temperatures alternately within and slightly below the critical temperature range.

(b) The object of this heat treatment is to produce a globular condition of the carbide.

When steels are cooled slowly from above the critical range, the pearlite is usually separated in the form of parallel plates. Its reinforcing action is less if, instead of parallel plates, the cementite can be brought into spherical shape, thus leaving larger areas of ferrite free from carbide. The microscopic structure has been illustrated in Fig. 15. This may be accomplished just below the critical range without dissociating the cementite or increasing the grain size. Low-carbon steels usually do not need this treatment because they machine quite easily without it. High-carbon steels are improved. A eutectoid steel after annealing may have a Brinell hardness number of 225 but after spheroidization have a Brinell number of only 165.[1] If the spheroidization is carried out below the critical range, the result is satisfactory but the time required is excessive. The time may be shortened by raising the temperature to just above the Ac line, whereby some austenite is formed and the rate of diffusion becomes more rapid. The temperature is then lowered just below the Ac point to make this austenite precipitate cementite again. This alternation of temperature just below and above the Ac point permits more rapid spheroidization.

Hardening and Tempering.—If a small piece of steel is heated through the critical range and then cooled rapidly as by quenching in cold water, the microscopic structure will be mainly martensite, and the steel will be as hard as it can be made. The temperature and nature of the quenching medium exert an important influence on the properties of the product. Experi-

[1] *Am. Soc. Steel Treating*, **14**, II, 535 (1928).

ments at the Bureau of Standards[1] have shown that water at 165°F is only about 25 per cent as effective as water at 78°F. Salt solutions may be 20 per cent more effective than water at the same temperature, and oils whether animal, vegetable, or mineral are only from 15 to 45 per cent as effective as cold water. The effect of temperature of the water is more pronounced than that of the oil, probably because in hot water a film of steam forms on the surface of the metal and cuts down the rate of heat

TABLE 5.—EFFECT OF QUENCHING MEDIUMS ON TENSILE STRENGTH*
Steel of 0.19 per cent carbon heated above the critical range and treated as indicated.

Quenching Medium	Tensile Strength, Psi
Iced brine	235,000
Cold water	215,000
Oil	175,000
Air	85,000
Furnace cooled	80,000

* From Am. Soc. Steel Treating, 14, 751, 1928.

transfer. Violent stirring of the cooling mediums increases the rate of cooling. The experiments at the Bureau of Standards cited above showed great differences in tensile strength of small pieces of steel with 0.19 per cent carbon dropped from a temperature above the critical range into different quenching mediums and tested without tempering. The figures are given in Table 5. With a large piece of steel, the center will cool more slowly than the surface and the hardness after quenching will not be uniform throughout the cross section. The steel should not be cooled more rapidly than is necessary in order to avoid shrinkage strains and possible cracks. Steel contracts as it is cooled, except during the transition from austenite to martensite, when an expansion takes place. If a steel plate is quenched, it sometimes splits into two plates, each warping away from the center plane, because each face had changed to martensite and was shrinking at the time when the center of the plate expanded due to the austenite-martensite change.

Steel cooled very slowly through the critical range and not cold-worked suffers no change on reheating to just below the critical range, except for minor magnetic changes and transitory brittleness in the blue-heat range. Even the pearlite will not change on reheating, because if the cooling was slow enough it

[1] *Trans. Am. Soc. Steel Treating*, **14**, II, 750 (1928).

EFFECT OF HEAT-TREATMENT ON IRON-CARBON ALLOYS 63

will be spheroidized already. This does not hold true however for steel that has been quenched from above or within the critical range. The cementite held in dispersed form as martensite in the alpha ferrite after quenching seeks to agglomerate into larger particles and will diffuse at a measurable rate if given the opportunity, resulting in a progressive softening of the steel. The only exception to progressive softening is in the case of small pieces of steel quenched so rapidly as to retain some austenite. Here the first effect of the reheating is to cause the austenite to change to martensite with an increase in hardness.

This process of changing the physical properties by gentle heating of steel which has been hardened by quenching from above the critical range is known as "tempering" or "drawing." The changes take place slowly enough to be susceptible of close control. The process of obtaining a desired hardness by quenching from above the critical range and then tempering by heating below the critical range is the usual method for heat-treating steel.

Blacksmiths and other workers who do not have pyrometers find a fairly good guide for tempering by watching the change in the colors of the iron oxide film that forms on the bright surface of steel when heated in the air. A very thin film of oxide appears yellow, and as the temperature rises and the film thickens, it changes to blue, to purple, and finally

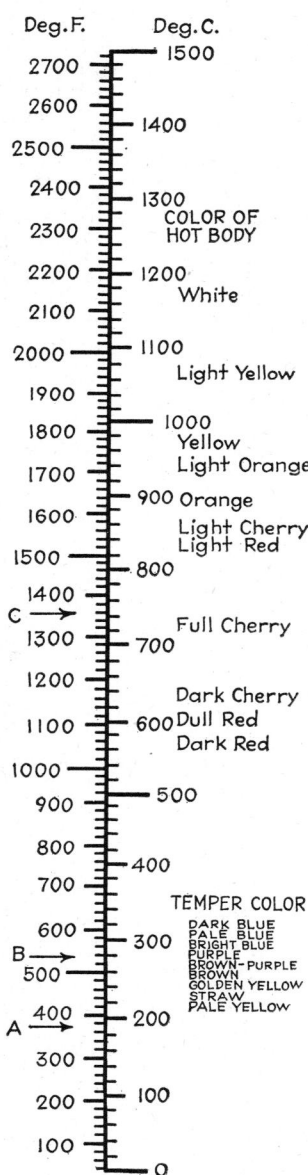

Fig. 21.—Column showing colors of steel at various temperatures. (*From Trans. Am. Soc. Steel Treating*, 1928.)

to a brown. The process of tempering proceeds as a function of both time and temperature, and since the formation of the film of scale is also a function of these two variables, an expert blacksmith can obtain good results. This use of film colors is wholly dependent on individual skill and is never used in mass production. The relation of temperature to the film colors and the colors that appear above a red heat is shown in Fig. 21.

TABLE 6.—CHANGE OF HARDNESS AND FILM COLORS IN TEMPERING STEEL OF 0.86 PER CENT CARBON*

Samples of a ½ in. round bar were quenched from 1562°F (850°C) in cold water and then held for ½ hr. at the temperature indicated.

Temperature of reheating		Boynton hardness number	Color of oxide
°F	°C		
Not reheated		110,560	No color
212	100	107,890	No color
302	150	105,515	No color
392	200	102,925	Light yellow
482	250	100,680	Yellowish brown
572	300	97,050	Light blue
662	350	93,790	Blue
752	400	81,940	Dark blue
842	450	64,170	Bluish film
932	500	9,205	Bluish film
1022	550	1,895	Bluish brown
1112	600	1,925	Brown
1202	650	1,961	Brown

* From BOYNTON, Hardness of the Constituents of Iron and Steel, *Jour. Iron Steel Inst.*, 1906, II, 316.

The correlation of hardness with color of film developed on tempering is shown for an 0.86 per cent carbon steel from Boynton's experiments. He used short pieces from a round bar ½ in. in diameter which he quenched in cold water from a temperature of 1562°F (850°C). He then polished the flat surface and reheated for a uniform time of ½ hr at each temperature. The results are shown in Table 6. The hardness decreases slowly from 110,000 Boynton drill numbers for the quenched specimen to 103,000 for the sample reheated to 392°F (200°C) when the first yellow oxide color is noted. As the temperature of reheating is raised by successive steps, the yellow color of the surface changes to light blue, then to dark blue, and then to a bluish film, which is reported as appearing at 842°F (450°C) with 64,170 as the Boynton hardness number. This temperature is high enough so that diffusion is becoming more rapid, and the next sample, as a result of reheating ½ hr at 932°F (500°C), shows a precipitous drop to a hardness of 9205 Boynton units while the color is still reported as a bluish film. The next step 1022°F (550°C) shows a hardness of 1895, and further steps at higher temperatures show the same result within the limit of experimental error because all of the carbides that were in the martensitic form in the quenched metal had opportunity to diffuse and form sorbite on reheating ½ hr to 1022°F. Further heat-treatment would produce little further change, although prolonged heating at somewhat higher temperatures would have produced spheroidized pearlite.

The blacksmith working mainly with tool steel which is to remain hard finds a fairly good guide in the yellow to light-blue oxide colors, which indicate that the structure is changing from martensite to troostite. The colors in the dark-blue range do not give accurate information as to the extent of formation of sorbite or pearlite. The color of the oxide films and of the color of the metal above a red heat are expressed in a temperature scale in Fig. 21.

Physical Properties of 1045 Steels.—Variations in the heat-treatment of steel affect not only its hardness but also its other physical properties. The Society of Automotive Engineers publishes much information in its S.A.E. Handbook, from which the curves of Fig. 22 are taken. The Society of Automotive Engineers has devised code numbers for steels to indicate their general composition. Plain carbon steels are all placed in the 1000 class, with the last two digits indicating the approximate percentage of carbon. Thus 1045 means a plain carbon steel with 0.45 per cent carbon and with low silicon, manganese, sulfur, and phosphorus.

The properties, uses, and heat-treatments for which this steel is recommended in the S.A.E. Handbook are indicated below.

S.A.E. 1045

This is a medium carbon steel intended for the larger sizes of plain carbon steel forgings used in automotive construction, such as crankshafts, starter ring gears, axle and spline shafts. Some hard-drawn wire for coiled springs is also made to this specification.

Caution should be used in water quenching this steel in parts of small diameter or thin sections.

Heat Treatment 1045-I
   (1) Heat to 1450 to 1550 deg. fahr.
   (2) Quench in oil or water depending upon section.
   (3) Temper to required hardness.

Heat Treatment 1045-II
   (1) Normalize at 1600 to 1700 deg. fahr.
   (2) Reheat to 1475 to 1525 deg. fahr.
   (3) Quench in oil or water depending upon section.
   (4) Temper to required hardness.

The physical properties are given in Fig. 22. Each steel was heated through the critical range for a sufficient time to give fairly fine grains, quenched either in water or oil, and then tempered (drawn) at temperatures ranging from 800 to 1300°F.

The charts do not give any values for the properties of the quenched steel before tempering because these steels are not ordinarily used in that relatively hard and brittle condition. There is some danger of cracks forming if small pieces are quenched in water, and oil quenching is recommended for such parts. The lowest drawing temperature included in the chart is 800°F, which will probably leave the microscopic structure as troostite or sorbite, depending on the length of time at which the metal is held at the drawing temperature, and also on whether the quenching was in oil or water. Quenching in water would have kept the steel martensitic. Quenching in oil might have given a troostitic steel at once. The oil-quenched steel will soften still more on tempering and with the same subsequent heat-treatment will always be weaker, softer, and more ductile than that quenched in water.

At the highest drawing temperatures of 1300°F, the effects of quenching have been largely removed and the tensile strength is little higher than that of the same metal as received from the rolling mill where it had been cooled in air to give a pearlitic structure with perhaps a trace of sorbite.

As the drawing temperatures increase from 800° to 1300°, there is a steady decrease in tensile strength, yield point, and hardness, with an increase in elongation and reduction of area.

EFFECT OF HEAT-TREATMENT ON IRON-CARBON ALLOYS

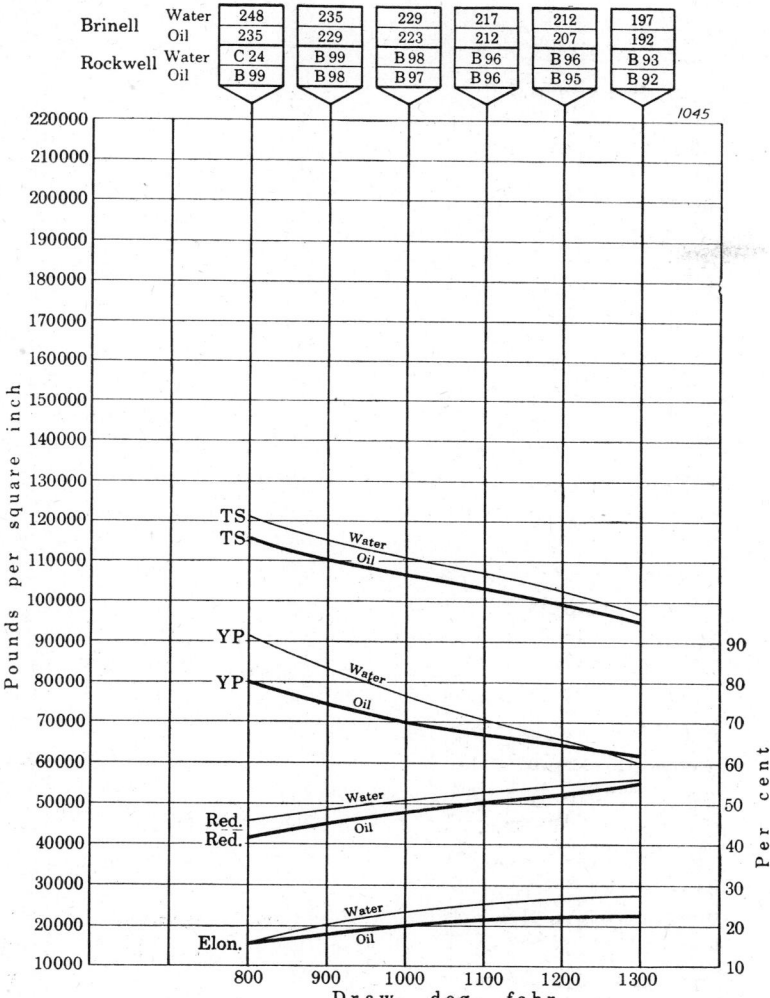

FIG. 22.—Physical property chart for 1045 steel when quenched in water or in oil.
TS = tensile strength.
YP = yield point.
Red. = reduction of area in per cent.
Elong. = elongation in per cent.
(From the S.A.E. Handbook.)

These differences in properties may all be explained from the theoretical considerations which have already been outlined.

The values for physical properties read from the curves of Fig. 22 may be expected to be shown by rolled bars of rather small cross section. If the pieces are larger than 1½ in. diameter or square, the rate of cooling or quenching becomes perceptibly slower than with small pieces, especially in the center of the piece. There will be some variation in hardness from the center to the surface in all cases, and the Society of Automotive Engineers recommends that the hardness be tested at a distance from the center of the bar equal to one-half of the radius.

Physical Properties of 1080 Steel.—The properties of steels with 0.80 per cent carbon are shown in Fig. 23 from the handbook of the Bethelehem Steel Company. At the left of the graph are shown the physical properties as rolled, as annealed and furnace-cooled, and as normalized and air-cooled. There is almost no difference between the properties of the steels as rolled and after being normalized. The annealed steel with its large crystals of ferrite and well-developed pearlite is softer, weaker, and more ductile. All samples of steel were heated to 1500°F and quenched in oil. This steel showed a maximum hardness of only 388 because of the slow quenching resulting from immersion in oil. Tempering was performed at various temperatures from 800 to 1300°F. Increasing temperature had the usual effect of decreasing tensile strength, yield point, and hardness, and increasing elongation and reduction of area. Although most of the effects of quenching were removed by drawing at 1300°F, the yield point, reduction of area, and elongation were all definitely superior to those of the normalized steel.

Effect of Grain Size on Physical Properties.—Grain size is so intimately affected by such factors as method of manufacture and composition that only a very brief discussion will be given here. Steel castings cool slowly, and there is no opportunity to break up the grains by hot work, but the grain of the casting may be rendered smaller by subsequent heat-treatment. Steels that have been rolled at a proper temperature have a fine grain, but if the rolling or forging has been finished at too high a temperature, the grain will have again become larger. The fine-grained steels have a better ductility as revealed by the reduction of area and elongation, but there is not much difference in the

EFFECT OF HEAT-TREATMENT ON IRON-CARBON ALLOYS

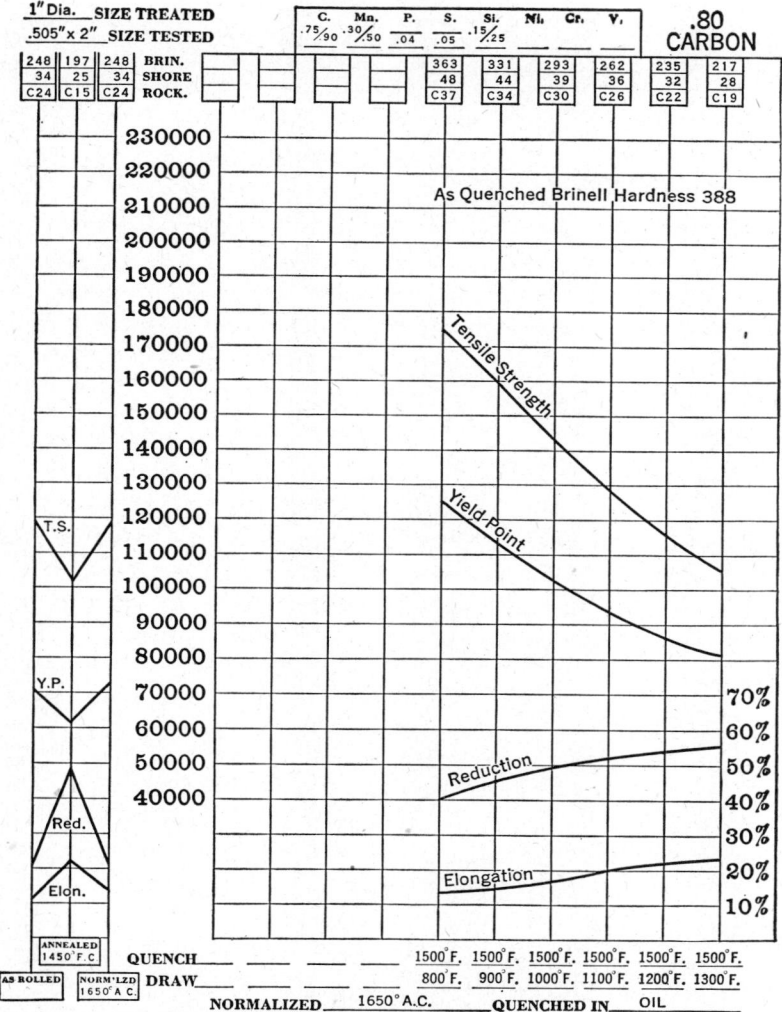

Fig. 23.—Physical properties chart for 0.80 carbon steel (av. values). (*From Bethlehem Steel Co. Catalog 144.*)

tensile strengths due to grain size. The impact resistance of the steel with fine grains is much superior to that which is found if the grains are coarse.

References

Sisco, P. T.: The Alloys of Iron and Carbon, Vol. II, Properties, Alloys of Iron Research, Monograph Series, McGraw-Hill Book Company, Inc., New York, 1937.

American Society for Testing Materials: A.S.T.M. Standards (issued triennially), 1936, Part 1, Metals.

Society of Automotive Engineers: S.A.E. Handbook (issued Annually), 1938 ed., New York.

American Society for Metals: Metals Handbook, 1939 ed., Cleveland.

The Metallurgical Staff of the Bureau of Standards: Principles of the Heat Treatment of Steel, *Trans. Am. Soc. Steel Treating*, **14**, 502, 744, 893 (1928).

CHAPTER IV

THE MANUFACTURE OF IRON AND IRON-CARBON ALLOYS FROM THE ORE

The various commercial classes of iron and steel consist of alloys of iron with other elements which have either been added intentionally to impart desirable properties or been acquired in the manufacturing process and are mostly regarded as necessary evils. The composition of the alloys is bound up so intimately with the process of manufacture that some knowledge of manufacturing methods is necessary to an understanding of commercial specifications.

Iron Ore.—Iron reacts readily with oxygen in presence of moisture to form a hydrated oxide, as may be noted in the rapid formation of rust on a steel surface. Iron is never found in the metallic state, except in occasional meteorites which are intruders and have not yet been corroded by the atmosphere of this planet. The core of our earth is probably metallic iron, and in some localities iron is found as iron pyrites (FeS_2) or as more complex sulfides mixed with other metals. These sulfides will all decompose, when exposed to the atmosphere, to give hydrated oxides and sulfuric acid which may later unite with constituents of the rocks such as $CaCO_3$ to form $CaSO_4$. The deposits of iron ore in the United States all consist of oxides, most of which were originally hydrated but which have become quite completely dehydrated by pressure and heat through geological periods. They all contain other products of the decomposition of rocks. Among the important ones are silica (SiO_2), alumina (Al_2O_3), lime (CaO usually in the form of $CaCO_3$), magnesia (MgO usually in the form of $MgCO_3$), manganese oxide (MnO), sulfates (SO_4), and phosphates (PO_4) in various combinations, the exact form of the combination being relatively unimportant for our purposes. The iron exists in the ore as an oxide which may be of a definite formula as magnetite (Fe_3O_4) with 72.5 per cent Fe or hematite (Fe_2O_3) with 70.0 per cent Fe.

A chemical analysis of iron ore does not attempt to enumerate the combinations but merely the amounts of the various elements grouped in a conventional way. It is desirable to have an iron ore with a high percentage of iron, but it is more important that it be low in the harmful impurities, of which sulfur and phosphorus are the most common. The United States is extremely fortunate in the quality, quantity, and commercial availability of its iron ores. In addition to the high-grade deposits, it has also very large deposits of lower grade ores which can be used at greater cost after the high-grade ores have been depleted. Some typical analyses of iron ores are given in Table 7.

TABLE 7.—COMPOSITION OF IRON ORES

Source	Alabama brown ore*	Alabama red ore*	Mesabi (Minn.) ore†
H_2O	13.98	3.88	12.53
SiO_2	14.10	7.74	4.76
Al_2O_3	5.70	4.83	1.81
Fe_2O_3	61.70	43.25	75.45
MnO	1.02	0.14	0.72
P_2O_5	1.56	0.21	0.15
CaO	0.22	20.91	0.50
MgO	0.22	0.90	0.15
K_2O	0.30	0.60	
Na_2O	0.30	0.50	
S	0.10	0.10	
CO_2	0.80	16.93	
	100.00	100.00	96.07

* U. S. Bur. Mines, Tech. Paper 391.
† U. S. Bur. Mines, Tech. Paper 442.

In order to obtain iron in the metallic form, it is necessary to remove the oxygen from the ore by bringing it into contact with some agent whose binding power for oxygen is greater than that of iron for oxygen. There are various materials that can accomplish this. Hydrogen is occasionally used in practice but carbon, either in the solid form or as CO, is almost universally employed.

Heats of Reaction.—The binding power of two elements is usually measured by the heat evolved by their combination, calculated as if they were to interact at room temperature. These values for binding power change with temperature, but the figures for different metals remain fairly comparable with each other, and so the tables compiled for room temperature form a guide to their behavior at higher temperatures. The heats liberated when some metals combine with oxygen to form oxides is given in Table 8. It will be seen that gold reacts with oxygen with an absorption of heat. The reverse reaction will evolve heat, hence gold oxide is not stable at room temperatures, and gold is found in the ore in the metallic state and not as an oxide. Copper oxide has such a low positive heat of formation

TABLE 8.—HEATS OF FORMATION OF METALLIC OXIDES IN KILOGRAM-CALORIES

Name	Formula	Per gram formula weight	Per gram formula weight of oxygen
Gold oxide	Au_2O_3	−12.3	−4.1
Silver oxide	Ag_2O	6.9	6.9
Copper oxide	CuO	34.9	34.9
Lead oxide	PbO	52.5	52.5
Tin oxide	SnO	69.8	69.8
Nickel oxide	NiO	57.9	57.9
Iron oxide (ferrous)	FeO	65.7	65.7
Zinc oxide	ZnO	85.0	85.0
Manganese oxide	MnO	90.8	90.8
Phosphorus pentoxide	P_2O_5	365.7	73.1
Magnesium oxide	MgO	143.9	143.9
Aluminum oxide	Al_2O_3	399.0	133.0
Calcium oxide	CaO	151.9	151.9
Chromium oxide	Cr_2O_3	267.8	89.3
Silicon oxide	SiO_2	210.4	100.7
Sulfur trioxide	SO_3	103.2	34.4

that copper is sometimes found as the free metal, and the oxide is readily reduced to the metal. Iron has a higher binding power for oxygen, and aluminum shows still higher values. The amount of energy required to dissociate these oxides is theoretically the same as that evolved in their formation. Carbon is of great value as a reducing agent because its binding power for oxygen is high and becomes higher with increase in temperature. It can take the oxygen away from copper at a low red heat and can take much of the oxygen from iron at the same temperature. If present in excess, it can take all of the oxygen from iron at a

74   ENGINEERING MATERIALS

higher temperature. The heats of formation of alumina and lime are so great that carbon cannot take oxygen from these materials at any temperature that can be reached by the combustion of carbon with air. Carbon can remove oxygen from both alumina and lime at the higher temperature attainable in the electric furnace.

Fig. 24.—Primitive iron smelting furnace in operation in India in 1832. [*From Jour. Asiatic Society of Bengal*, **1**, 121 (1832).]

Primitive Manufacture of Iron.—The manufacture of iron did not come as early in man's industrial development as that of copper because of the higher temperature required for the reduction of iron. Historically, the copper and bronze ages preceded that of steel. The knowledge of iron probably goes back 5000 years, and it is still manufactured by the primitive natives of Africa in much the same way as by their ancestors. Figure 24

THE MANUFACTURE OF IRON AND IRON-CARBON ALLOYS 75

illustrates a primitive iron furnace[1] operated in India 100 years ago according to the method "pursued from time immemorial." The smelter was 2 ft in diameter at the bottom, 6 ft high, and made of fire clay. The operator pushed small amounts of the mixture of damp charcoal and crushed ore from the trough into the furnace at frequent intervals so as to keep the smelter nearly full at all times. When a mass of softened iron had collected in the bottom of the furnace, it was dragged out by the tongs shown and beaten on the flat stone with the wooden mallet sketched leaning against a primitive ladder.

In a furnace of this type using an excess of charcoal, the temperature was not high enough to melt the iron, but it was hot enough to reduce the ore to metal in the form of red-hot plastic grains. The silica, alumina, and lime that were present as earthy impurities (called "gangue") in the ore were not reduced under these conditions. Fortunately, they united with each other and with iron oxide to form a glass or slag which was fusible at the temperature of the furnace, so that, as the operation proceeded, there was formed in the bottom of the furnace a pasty mass consisting of particles of nearly pure metallic iron surrounded by films of a fused but viscous slag. The films of slag kept the iron from oxidizing in the air when the mass was drawn out, and the clean particles of metal welded readily. Much of the slag was squeezed out as the bar was forged, and the resulting product was a bar of soft iron, called "malleable iron." It contained too much slag to be useable, and so it had to be reheated and reforged several times with loss of material in each operation. If the early ironmaker had been able to examine his product by modern scientific methods, he would have found it to consist of flattened grains or threads of nearly pure ferrite separated by thin films of a glassy slag composed largely of silicate of iron with some lime and alumina. Its structure would have been almost identical with our modern wrought iron as shown in Fig. 33. The method was very wasteful of time and fuel, but it provided primitive peoples with a metal not obtainable in any other way.

The metal produced by these primitive methods was not always soft iron. Homer, writing perhaps 850 years before the Christian era, speaks of the smith who "plunges the loud-hissing axe into cold water to temper it, for hence is the strength of

[1] *Jour. Asiatic Soc. Bengal,* **1**, 150 (1832).

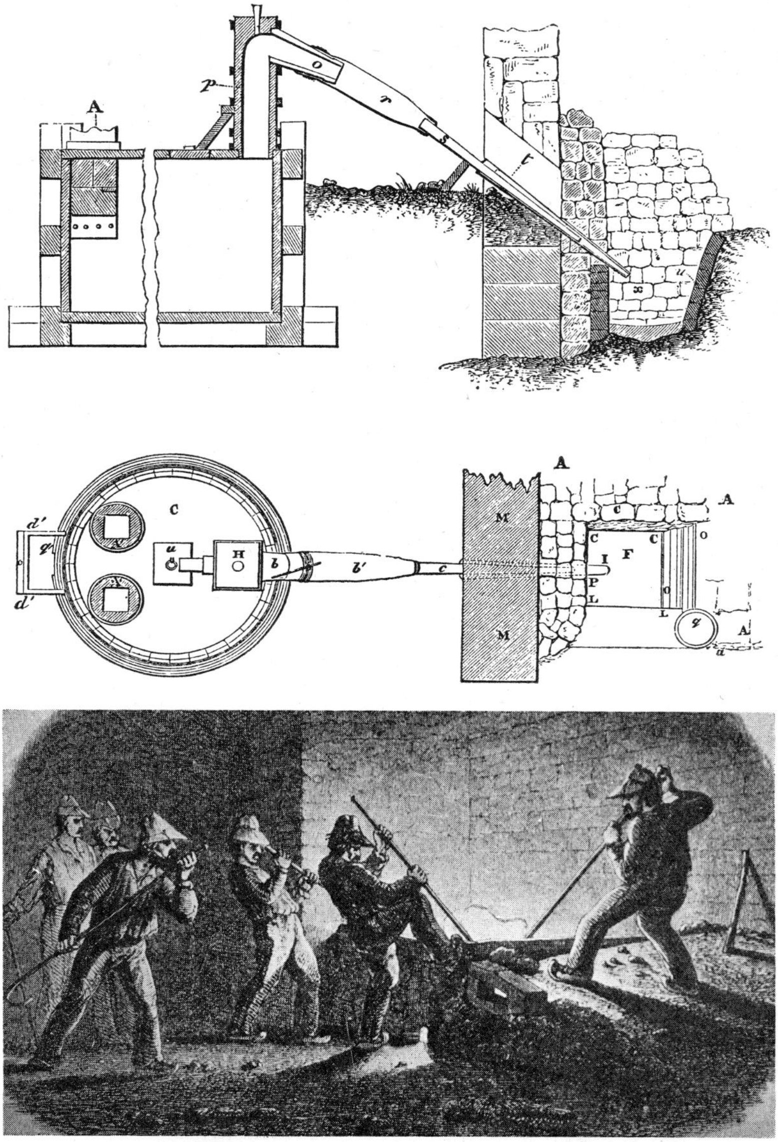

Fig. 25.—The Catalan forge for making malleable iron directly from the ore. (*From Percy, Metallurgy of Iron and Steel, published in* 1864.)

iron." It is easy with modern knowledge to say that if the early metalworker had left his lump of soft iron in the bottom of the furnace in contact with charcoal at a temperature above the critical range, carbon would have dissolved in the iron to form austenite, and steel would have resulted. If conditions in the bottom of the furnace were kept slightly oxidizing, the product would have been soft iron. It is no wonder that the ironmaker, who knew nothing of the chemistry of his process, relied much on incantations and produced a product whose properties could not be predicted in advance.

Four or five centuries ago the Catalan forge developed in France and Spain. The illustrations of Fig. 25 are from a description of an installation operating in France in 1840.[1] The working hearth was only a little over a foot square. Blast was supplied by a water aspirator discharging into a cistern, where the air separated from the water and passed through the nozzle into the fire. The hearth was kept heaped with a mixture of crushed ore and charcoal, and about once in 6 hr the mass of reduced iron and slag was pried out of the furnace, as shown in the cut, and dragged to a tilt hammer operated by water power. The weight of the mass pried out was sufficient to yield 350 lb of bar iron. The Catalan forge persisted with little modification until rather recent times. In the United States, it was modified somewhat and called the American bloomary, but the size of the plant was not increased much. The blooms weighed 300 to 400 lb each, and each furnace produced about 1 ton of billets in 24 hr. The last American bloomary did not discontinue operation until 1901.

The Blast Furnace.—The stacks of the furnaces of the Catalan-forge type were gradually made taller, probably to promote fuel economy, and kept filled to the top with a mixture of ore and charcoal. This procedure increased the time of contact of the ore and charcoal, and the more efficient use of water power permitted a stronger blast of air which increased the temperature, so that the amount of carbon in the iron increased and its melting temperature was lowered. At some date not known, but before 1500, it was found that molten metal could be tapped from such furnaces and could be used in making castings. The furnaces were small, and in 1740 the average output of pig iron from each

[1] PERCY, Metallurgy of Iron and Steel.

78   ENGINEERING MATERIALS

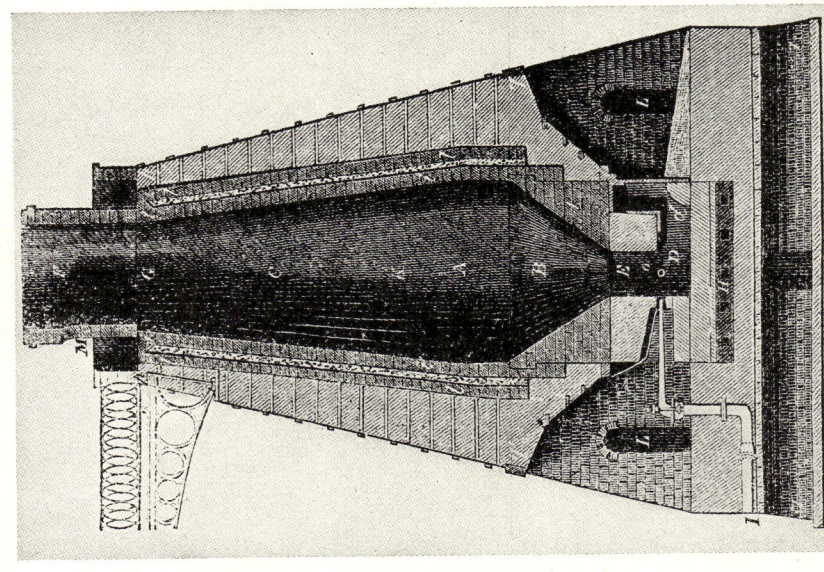

FIG. 26.—Views of blast furnaces as operated in England in 1854. (From Tomlinson, *Encyclopedia of Useful Arts*, Vol. II, published in 1854.)

THE MANUFACTURE OF IRON AND IRON-CARBON ALLOYS 79

furnace in Great Britain was less than 1 ton a day. One hundred years later, 1845, it was only 15 tons a day. The various illustrations of Fig. 26 show the appearance and construction of a furnace operating in England in 1854.[1] The iron was run from

Fig. 27.—Typical modern blast furnace. (*From Harbison-Walker, Modern Refractory Practice.*)

the furnace along a furrow made in sand and into side furrows from which smaller furrows branched as shown in the picture. The larger lengths of iron were termed "sows" and the smaller lengths "pigs." This method of casting has been superseded,

[1] TOMLINSON, Encyclopedia of Useful Arts, Vol. II, pp. 77, 80, 81, 1854.

but the name "pig iron" persists for the product made by the blast furnace.

The changes that have taken place in the blast furnace during the last hundred years have been to increase its size, temperature,

Fig. 28.—View of modern blast furnace showing elaborate superstructure. The cars containing the charge are hoisted on the inclined plane shown at the right. The gas offtakes are in the center. The dust separator is at the lower left. The stacks of the hot blast stoves are at the rear. (*Courtesy Republic Steel Corporation.*)

and capacity. The modern blast furnace is shown in Figs. 27 and 28. Its daily capacity is fifty times as great as it was 100 years ago, and the costs of manufacture have been greatly reduced, but the product is substantially the same.

The blast furnace consists of a steel shaft lined with firebrick which is kept full of a mixture of iron ore, coke, and a flux which is usually limestone. Coke made from coal commenced to replace charcoal made from wood about 200 years ago, but a few charcoal furnaces still survive in the United States. It was found that if lime or limestone was added to the charge it took the place of the more expensive iron oxide in the slag and yet gave a slag that was fusible at the temperatures attainable in the blast furnace. The function of the slag in the blast furnace is, as it was in the Catalan forge, to convert the gangue, or clay-like constituents of the ore, into a fusible form so that they may be separated from the iron. In order that the slag may be fusible, there must be a proper balance between the acidic constituents, silica and secondarily alumina, and the basic constituents, lime and secondarily magnesia. The slag contains roughly about 50 per cent of the basic and 50 per cent of the acid constituents, but it will be varied according to the quality of iron that the furnace is to produce, and also with the composition of the ore.

The air for combustion of the coke is blown into the furnace through 10 to 16 water-cooled nozzles called "tuyères." It has been preheated to about 1000°F by contact with hot firebrick in hot blast stoves in which the waste gases from the top of the furnace have been burned. Each furnace usually has four of these stoves, three of them in process of heating, and one in use heating the blast and itself thereby cooling off. There is a systematic alternation of the stoves so that the temperature of the blast is kept quite constant. When this hot air enters the furnace, its oxygen reacts extremely rapidly with the coke which is already at a white heat. The first product of the reaction is CO_2, but at the high temperature 2400 to 2800°F and in the presence of an excess of carbon, the CO_2 is reduced almost instantly to CO.

The iron ore, coke, and limestone are fed into the top of the stack through a double cone and bell trap which prevents the escape of much gas. The charge is heated by the hot gases rising in the stack and soon reaches a temperature of 700°F. It descends at the rate of about 15 ft per hour as the contents of the lower part of the furnace become melted and are drawn off.

Reactions in the Blast Furnace.—CO reacts with Fe_2O_3 with evolution of heat according to two possible equations

$$\text{Fe}_2\text{O}_3 + 3\text{CO} \rightarrow 2\text{Fe} + 3\text{CO}_2 + 11.7 \text{ kg-cal}$$
$$2\text{Fe}_2\text{O}_3 + 8\text{CO} \rightarrow 4\text{Fe} + 7\text{CO}_2 + \text{C} + 64.9 \text{ kg-cal}$$

These reactions are of course governed by the laws of chemical equilibrium and do not actually give complete reduction to metallic iron. The equation as written with only one arrow means that if the reaction did go to completion, then the amount of heat indicated would be evolved. These heats of reaction are calculated as if they took place at room temperatures, but

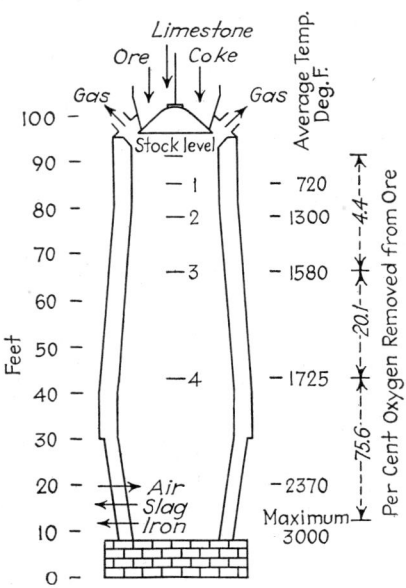

FIG. 29.—Diagram of modern blast furnace showing temperatures and extent of reduction at various levels. (*Adapted from Bur. of Mines, Tech. Paper* 442.)

they indicate qualitatively what takes place at the moderate temperatures prevailing in the upper part of the blast furnace. Both of these reactions will proceed spontaneously since they do evolve heat, and the second reaction evolving the greater amount of heat is the one that occurs to the larger extent. It is fortunate that this second reaction also liberates carbon, for the operation of the blast furnace would be much more difficult if it were not for this carbon. When a lump of iron ore enters the top of the furnace and is heated to 700°F, the CO gas diffusing into the lump commences reduction of the ore and also deposits a finely divided carbon black through the lump. The temperature of the lump increases as it descends the stack, and the rate of reduction becomes more rapid. After the charge has traveled two-thirds of the way down the stack, the temperature has risen to 1700°F, but only about 25 per cent of the oxygen has been removed from the ore as is shown in Fig. 29. The limestone has been dissociated into lime and carbon dioxide according to the equation

$$CaCO_3 \rightleftarrows CaO + CO_2$$

There has been little change in the coke except that it has become hotter.

The most important work of the furnace is accomplished as the charge descends through the lower third of the stack to the tuyères. The gas is richer in carbon monoxide and at a higher temperature, and therefore is a more effective reducing agent than in the upper part of the stack. It readily reduces all of the Fe_2O_3 to FeO and can reduce a considerable amount to the metallic state. It cannot however reduce the last of the oxide to the metal because of the reversing action of the carbon dioxide present. The reduction of the last portion is accomplished by the finely divided carbon that was deposited in the lumps of ore in the upper part of the furnace. The equation

$$C + FeO \rightarrow CO + Fe - 39.3 \text{ kg-cal}$$

shows a marked absorption of heat, and hence complete reduction can take place only at a high temperature.

The cross section of the furnace increases from the top to the middle so that the charge may settle more easily. There is sometimes a short cylindrical section, and below that point the cross section decreases, the bosh, because the charge has commenced to soften and flow more like a viscous liquid.

In the lower third of the furnace, the lime and magnesia commence to unite with the silica and alumina to form a fusible slag. The iron dissolves carbon from that deposited in the lumps of ore, and its melting point is therefore lowered. The coke has suffered little change. At the tuyères, the red-hot air blown in under pressure combines at once with the white-hot coke to give carbon dioxide which by further reaction with carbon changes almost instantly to carbon monoxide. The temperature in front of the tuyères rises to 3000°F with an average temperature, 2400° at that level, sufficient to melt both the iron-carbon alloy and the slag, which collect as two layers of liquid in the crucible (or hearth) of the furnace below the tuyères. The lower part of the furnace must be cooled by water circulating in hollow plates set in the brickwork to prevent melting of the firebrick lining. The force of the air blast is not sufficient to penetrate to the center of the furnace, and a central pillar composed of lumps of unburned coke extends up from the brickwork at the bottom of the hearth to support the load of the charge that fills the stack. The molten iron and slag therefore occupy only the empty spaces between the pieces of coke, and when the furnace is tapped there is not much settlement of the stock.

The hearth fills with molten iron and slag in 4 to 6 hr, and when enough has accumulated, the slag is drawn off from one opening (cinder notch) and then the iron is drawn off from the tap hole (iron notch) at the bottom of the furnace. Both the slag and the iron are usually run into large ladles which may hold 50 tons of molten material. The slag is often thrown away as a waste material, but it may be used for building roads or as a raw material for the manufacture of portland cement. The iron may be taken in the molten state to the steel mill, or it may be poured into metal molds on a conveyor which carries the scarcely solid metal through a tank or spray of water and dumps the cold "pigs" into a car for shipment. Data from the operation of a modern blast furnace are given in Table 9.

Composition of Pig Iron.—The percentage of carbon in the pig iron is fixed within rather narrow limits. It has been mentioned that the spongy iron dissolves deposited carbon as the charge descends the lower third of the stack, and that, as it lies in the crucible awaiting tapping, it is in contact with coke for several hours. This gives the iron opportunity to saturate itself with carbon. One proof that it does so is furnished by the fine particles of graphite that can be observed flying in the air when the molten metal is flowing from the furnace. As the molten metal cools, its power to dissolve carbon decreases, and the carbon thrown out of solution while the iron is still molten rises to the surface and is blown away by the rising currents of hot air above the metal. The percentage of carbon remaining in the cold pig-iron will be 3.50 to 4.25 per cent.

THE MANUFACTURE OF IRON AND IRON-CARBON ALLOYS 85

Phosphorus may be present as phosphate in the ore, limestone, and coke. It will be noted from Table 8 that the amount of energy required to separate one unit of oxygen from phosphorus

TABLE 9.—DATA ON ONE DAY'S OPERATION OF 700-TON BLAST FURNACE*
Material for each charge (139 charges in 24 hr)

Mixed iron ores	24,500 lb
Limestone	3,900
Coke	9,000
	37,400

Blast 50,000 cu. ft. of air per minute measured at 62°F and 29.9 in. of mercury pressure, equivalent to 4,000 lb per minute. Actually blown in at a pressure of 17.6 lb and a temperature of 1130°F.

Percentage composition of materials charged, calculated on a moisture-free basis

	Ore	Limestone	Coke Ash†	Coke	
Fe	49.6	0.24	0.65	Volatile	1.4
Mn	1.4			Fixed carbon	94.5
SiO_2	8.5	0.48	4.49	Ash	8.3
Al_2O_3	3.7	0.28	2.56	S	0.62
CaO	4.9	57.21	0.37		
MgO		0.90	0.20		
P	0.06		0.008		

Percentage composition of products

	Iron		Slag	
Si	0.75	SiO_2	39.0	⎫ 50.75 acids
S	0.038	Al_2O_3	11.75	⎭
P	0.182	CaO	42.65	⎫
Mn	1.67	MgO	2.85	⎬ 48.14 bases
C	Not stated	MnO	2.64	⎭
		S	0.95	

* From *U. S. Bur. Mines, Tech. Paper* 442.
† Expressed as percentage on weight of coke.

(73.1 kg-cal) is only slightly higher than that required to take the same unit of oxygen from iron (65.7). This difference is too small to permit the reduction of the iron without reducing the phosphate, and as a result all of the phosphorus in the various materials of the charge is reduced and dissolved in the molten iron. As the iron cools, a phosphide of iron is formed. The only way to secure pig iron low in phosphorus is to choose raw materials low in that element.

Sulfur may also be present in the raw materials as sulfate, rarely as sulfide. It is easy to reduce the sulfate to sulfide, but fortunately the tendency to form calcium sulfide, which passes into the slag, is stronger than that to form iron sulfide, which remains with the iron. In the illustrations of Table 9, the pig iron contained 0.038 per cent, or 0.85 lb, sulfur per long ton of pig iron whereas the 1076 lb of slag that accompanied the iron carried 0.95 per cent, or 10.2 lb, of sulfur. High temperatures and basic slag favor the transfer of sulfur from the iron to the slag.

Manganese binds oxygen more firmly than does iron in the proportion of 90.8 to 65.7 cal, but the larger part of the MnO of the charge is reduced and dissolved in the iron. In the illustration of Table 9, the pig iron contained 1.67 per cent, or 37.4 lb, of manganese per ton of iron. The slag contained 2.05 per cent of manganese (existing as MnO) or 22.0 lb Mn in the slag accompanying 1 ton of iron. Almost two-thirds of the total manganese was reduced and dissolved in the iron.

Silicon binds oxygen still more firmly than manganese (100.7 as against 90.8 kg-cal), and it is only at the highest temperature of the blast furnace that any considerable amount of silica is reduced to silicon. In the illustration, the pig iron contained only 0.75 per cent of Si while the slag contained 39.0 per cent of SiO_2. Only about 4 per cent of the total silicon was found in the iron. This is about as small a percentage of silicon as will be found in pig iron. The metallurgist, by controlling the temperature of the furnace and the composition of the slag, can easily produce pig iron with 3.0 per cent silicon and by special means can raise the percentage of silicon to 14.0 per cent.

Summary of the Methods of Reducing Iron Ore.—This chapter has described the primitive methods of producing soft and malleable iron directly from the ore in small furnaces. It has not been found possible to adapt this process to modern large-scale operation, and it is entirely obsolete among industrial nations. The modern blast furnace produces an alloy with only 92 to 96 per cent iron, the balance being carbon, silicon, manganese, sulfur, phosphorus, and other elements of less importance. One furnace will produce 700 or more tons per

THE MANUFACTURE OF IRON AND IRON-CARBON ALLOYS

day with low labor cost and high efficiency. It offers substantially the only method now in commercial use anywhere in the world for reducing iron from its ore. All modern methods for making steel or wrought iron start with pig iron.

TABLE 10.—STATISTICS OF PIG-IRON AND STEEL PRODUCTION IN THE UNITED STATES

Year	Pig-iron production, long tons*	Steel production, long tons†
1820	20,000	
1840	286,903	
1860	821,223	
1880	3,835,191	1,247,335
1900	13,789,242	10,188,329
1920	36,925,987	
1929	42,613,983	56,433,473
1930	31,752,169	40,699,483
1931	18,426,354	25,945,501
1932	8,871,453	13,681,162
1933	13,345,602	23,232,347
1934	16,138,573	26,468,177
1935	21,372,699	34,550,494

* Mineral Industry, 1935, p. 322.
† CAMPBELL, H. H., Manufacture and Properties of Iron and Steel, p. 444.

Statistics of Production of Pig Iron.—The industrial growth of the United States is reflected in the amount of pig iron produced. Statistics for every 20 years commencing with 1820 are given in Table 10. The increase in production between 1860 and 1880 was caused mainly by the introduction of the bessemer steel process, and the manufacture of steel has continued to absorb the greater part of the pig iron made since that time. In 1935, 84 per cent of the pig iron was used for the manufacture of steel, 7.7 for foundry castings, and 5.6 for malleable castings. A comparison of the figures for production of steel and pig iron shows that the United States has, in recent years, manufactured 50 per cent more steel than pig iron. This larger production of steel is due to the large amount of steel scrap that is remelted and refined into merchantable steel. The most important source of iron ore in the United States is the Lake Superior district of Minnesota and Michigan which furnished 80 per cent of the ore

88   ENGINEERING MATERIALS

mined in 1935. Alabama furnished 10 per cent and Pennsylvania 3 per cent. The cost of shipment of iron ore by boat through the Great Lakes is low, and important centers of pig-iron manufacture are located rather near lake ports. Furnaces in Ohio, Michigan, Indiana, and Illinois account for 50 per cent of the total production. Pennsylvania produces nearly 25 per cent, and most of

FIG. 30.—The world production of pig iron from 1913 to 1937. (*From The Mineral Industry during* 1937.)

the balance is produced in the states along the Atlantic Coast from New York to Alabama. Statistics of world production of pig iron are shown graphically in Fig. 30 for the years 1913 to 1937. The world-wide business depression that commenced in 1929 reached its lowest point in 1932 when the production of pig iron was only 40 per cent of the 1929 figure. During all of these years, the United States was the largest producer. The rise of Soviet Russia from a negligible production in 1924 to 15 million tons in 1937 is especially noteworthy.

References

PERCY, JOHN: Metallurgy of Iron and Steel, John Murray, London, 1864.
TOMLINSON, CHARLES: Encyclopedia of Useful Arts, Vol. II, George Virtue & Co., London and New York, 1854.
KINNEY, ROYSTER, and JOSEPH: Iron Blast Furnace Reactions, *U. S. Bur. Mines, Tech. Paper* 391, 1927.
KINNEY, S. P.: The Blast-furnace Stock Column, *U. S. Bur. Mines, Tech. Paper* 442, 1929.
CAMP and FRANCIS: The Making, Shaping and Treating of Steel, 4th ed., Carnegie Steel Co., Pittsburgh, 1925.

CHAPTER V

EARLY METHODS OF PRODUCING WROUGHT IRON AND STEEL FROM PIG IRON

It is not known when or how the early ironworkers learned to convert their brittle pig iron back into a malleable product. It seems to have been remelted in a furnace like the Catalan forge with the pigs piled on top of the fuel and the molten metal dripping down through the ascending gases. Joseph Cort in 1784 made a notable advance in making a furnace with an arched roof under which was a fire box and a separate saucer-shaped hearth on which the iron could be melted and worked without coming in contact with the fuel. He also was the first to use grooved rolls instead of a hammer to work the finished iron. Joseph Hall in 1830 made the lining of his hearth from iron oxide and slags rich in iron oxide, and thereby contributed greatly to the efficiency of the operation.

Wrought-iron Manufacture.—The puddling furnace as used in the manufacture of wrought iron almost up to the present day is illustrated in Fig. 31. This type of furnace is sometimes called "reverberatory" because the flames are deflected by the roof and swirl over the charge to be melted. It is also called an "open hearth" because of the shallow, flat hearth. The furnace hearth is an oval about 5 ft long and 4 ft wide. It is maintained at a temperature, which may reach 2600°F, by the coal fire on the grate alongside of the hearth. It is not possible with natural draft to obtain a temperature on the hearth that will melt pure iron (2795°F), but the charge of pig iron can be melted readily. The puddler and his assistant throw 500 to 600 lb of cold pig iron onto the hearth and stir the mixture occasionally until it becomes melted and hot, which takes about $\frac{1}{2}$ hr. The metal must now be stirred with an iron rabble almost continuously for 10 min to promote the oxidation of the silicon by the air passing over the charge. A few shovels full of iron ore or mill scale (Fe_3O_4) are then thrown into the furnace and mixed by

EARLY METHODS OF PRODUCING WROUGHT IRON

frequent stirring or rabbling of the molten mass. The carbon of the molten bath reacts with the iron oxide added and also with the oxide in the lining to form carbon monoxide which

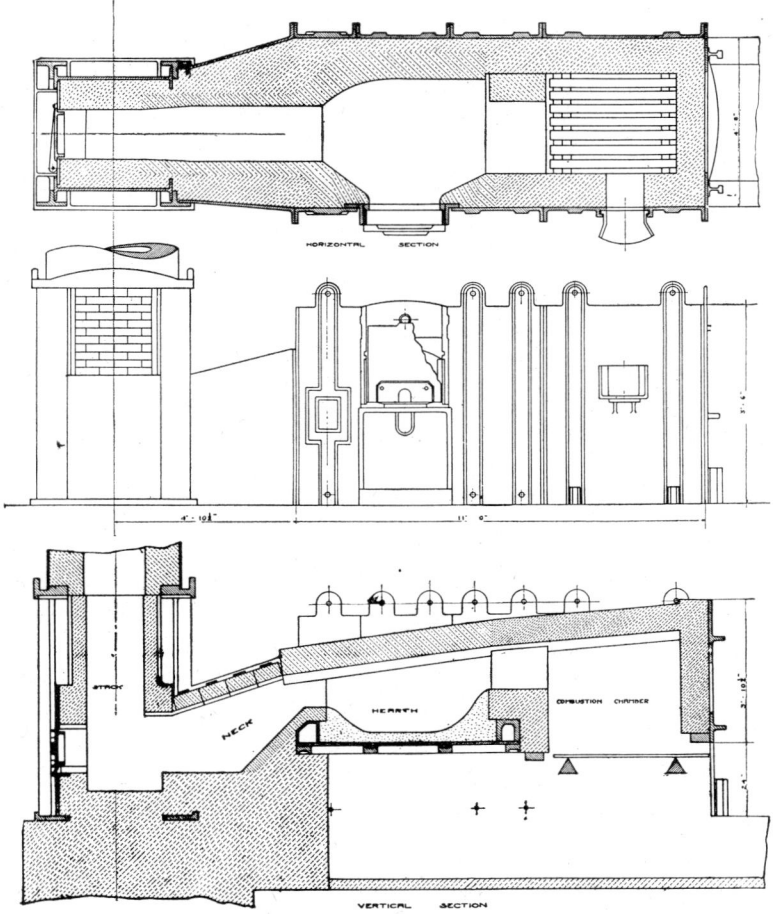

FIG. 31.—Drawings of a puddling furnace. (*From The Making, Shaping and Treating of Steel*, 4th ed., *Carnegie-Illinois Steel Corporation.*)

escapes as bubbles causing the bath to foam and boil. The melting point of the metal rises as the carbon is oxidized, and the mass would become solid in the furnace if it were not for a generous amount of slag, composed mainly of silicate of iron, which remains molten at the furnace temperature. This slag comes partly from the oxidation of the silicon and manganese of the pig iron, partly from corrosion of the lining, and partly from slag from a previous operation which is added at the judgment of the puddler. This second stage requires a half-hour of arduous work by the puddler, as shown in Fig. 32. At the end of the period, the carbon, silicon, manganese, and phosphorus of the pig iron have been oxidized and taken up by the slag. Part of the sulfur has also been oxidized and passed into the slag. The hearth contains

FIG. 32.—The operation of the puddling furnace. (*From The Story of Ancient Wrought Iron, A. M. Byers Co.*)

a stiff pasty glowing mass composed of grains of ferrite separated by films of molten slag. The puddler divides this mass and works it into three or four balls weighing 150 to 200 lb each. These are pulled from the furnace by tongs and taken to a squeezer where much of the slag is removed and the particles of iron welded together to form a rough bloom which is further worked into a rough muck bar in a rolling mill. The operation of the process is shown by the photograph of Fig. 32. Two men working together on a furnace can produce one heat which will yield about 500 lb of this muck bar in 1½ hr. The muck bar contains too much slag to be useable and is cut into lengths of 3 ft or less and reworked. The short pieces are made into piles of six or seven pieces which are wired together, placed in a reheating furnace, brought to a welding heat, and run through the rolls again, squeezing out more slag and yielding single refined iron. A second process of piling, heating, and rolling produces double-refined iron. Small pieces and scrap may be put back into the heating furnace in a box made of muck bars and welded together.

Wrought iron produced by the puddling process was much more expensive than steel, and there was a temptation to produce an inferior product at a lower cost. Steel turnings, borings, and other small bits of steel from miscellaneous sources were put into a "busheling" furnace with some slag, worked at a welding heat to mix the metal particles with the slag, and withdrawn as a dripping mass which when rolled had some of the physical properties of wrought iron. The metal particles however consisted of steel particles of diverse composition and not of pure ferrite.

The Aston Process for Manufacturing Wrought Iron.—Many attempts were made to introduce mechanical puddling furnaces to permit the production of wrought iron with less hand labor. All of them failed, and it was not until James Aston in 1925 developed an entirely new manufacturing process that wrought iron was produced in large units. The raw material of the Aston process is molten steel as it comes from the bessemer converter without being deoxidized. It is composed of iron that has absorbed rather large amounts of dissolved gases during the blowing process but may otherwise be considered as almost pure ferrite, with low percentages of carbon, silicon, manganese, sulfur, and phosphorus. A slag whose composition is approximately that obtained from the old puddling furnace and whose melting point is about 2100°F is artificially prepared in a separate open-hearth furnace. This slag is poured into a large ladle and cooled to a temperature well below the freezing point of the metal which is about 2730°F. The molten metal from the converter is poured slowly into the cooler molten slag. The metal freezes as it strikes the slag and gives up its dissolved gases. The effect is to produce a spongy mass consisting of spherical particles of hot solid metal separated from each other by molten slag, all at a temperature of 2500 to 2600°F. A mass of 3 or 4 tons can be produced in as many minutes. It is dumped from the ladle and conveyed through presses and modern rolling mills to produce a product that complies with the specifications for wrought iron. It is made in a large plant with scientific control and so is much more uniform in quality than the older product produced by the puddler. It is also possible to introduce alloying elements into the molten metal before it is poured into the slag.

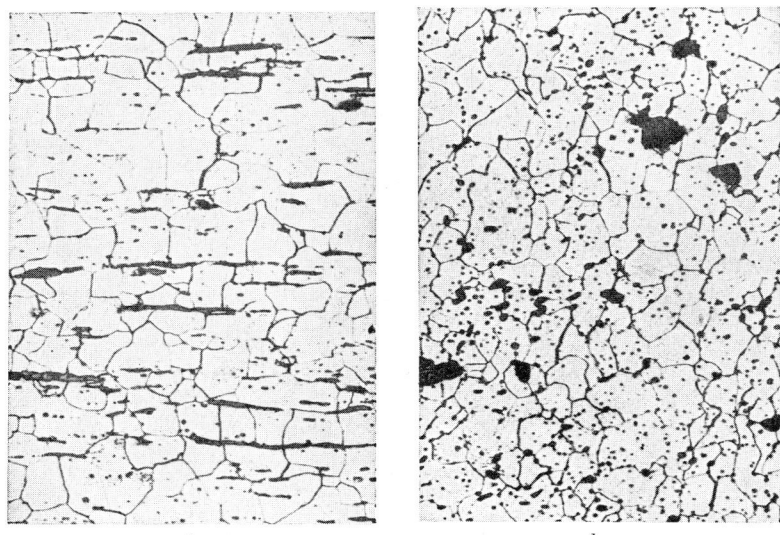

Fig. 33.—Microscopic structure of wrought iron. ×100. *a*, longitudinal section. *b*, transverse section. (*Courtesy A. M. Byers Co.*)

Properties of Wrought Iron.—Wrought iron is defined by the American Society for Testing Materials in the following words:

A ferrous material, aggregated from a solidifying mass of pasty particles of highly refined metallic iron, with which, without subsequent fusion, is incorporated a minutely and uniformly distributed quantity of slag.

This definition describes the product of the old puddling process and also that of the newer Aston process. The inclusion of the term "particles of highly refined metallic iron" excludes the use of miscellaneous iron and steel turnings in the busheling process. Specifications for some products carry clauses to further restrict the introduction of scrap and to specify the number of times the iron will have been piled and rerolled to ensure removal of slag and to promote uniformity.

The microscopic structure of wrought iron consists of filaments of almost pure ferrite separated by films of a slag which in its physical properties is a glass. This is illustrated in the photomicrographs of Fig. 33. Slag is brittle, and although in thin films it will stand more bending than in thicker masses, it cannot be considered as adding to the strength of the product. It does however contribute to the resistance to alternate bending stresses. When slipbands form in the ferrite, they may travel through a single filament but are stopped at its boundary, and do not spread to the neighboring filaments, which must initiate their own slipbands. The fracture of wrought iron broken in the testing machine or by alternate bending is therefore rough and fibrous, somewhat as if it had been made of strands like a wire rope.

The standard specifications for wrought-iron blooms (A.S.T.M. A 73-76) call for the following minimum requirements as to tensile properties:

Tensile strength, psi.......................... 45,000
Yield point, psi.............................. 0.5 tens. str.
Elongation in 4 in., %........................ 22
Reduction of area, %.......................... 30

The question as to whether the intermingled slag in wrought iron is a detriment or advantage has been debated ever since Bessemer invented his steelmaking process. The intermingled slag helps to prevent slipbands from spreading and also to stop corrosion. The function of slag in this latter respect may be roughly compared with that of the fused silicate enamel on steel cooking utensils and cast-iron bath tubs. It is only within recent years that the Aston process has permitted the production of wrought iron at a price comparable to that of steel.

The chemical analysis of wrought iron does not reveal the composition of the metal very clearly, since the analyst cannot easily differentiate between the composition of the slag films which form 2 to 4 per cent and the metallic filaments which comprise 96 to 98 per cent of the total. Swedish iron owed its high reputation for toughness and ductility to the low-phosphorus ore of Sweden. The analysis given in Table 11 shows that, even including the slag, the percentage of phosphorus was only 0.017 per cent. The tensile test showed a good elongation and an exceptional reduction of area, 77.6 per cent. The manufacturer of wrought iron had difficulty in increasing the tensile strength of his material, since the carbon was almost wholly oxidized in the process of manufacture and there was no way to put it back. Phosphorus causes brittleness, but it also raises the tensile strength by about 1000 lb for each 0.01 per cent present. Most of the phosphorus was removed by the slag in the puddling process, but by starting with high-phosphorus pig iron, a wrought iron high in phosphorus could be obtained. The sample reported in the third column of Table 11 contained 0.178 phosphorus of which two-thirds was probably in the metal. The tensile strength

TABLE 11.—COMPOSITION AND PROPERTIES OF WROUGHT IRON*

	Swedish iron	Double-refined hammered iron	Box-piled double-refined iron, high phosphorus
Chemical analysis:			
C	0.02	0.03	0.02
Mn	0.12	0.04	0.10
S	0.005	0.018	0.027
P	0.017	0.067	0.178
Si	0.051	0.11	0.17
Physical properties:			
Tensile strength, psi	41,280	45,700	52,920
Elastic limit, psi	30,310	30,960	37,390
Elongation in 8 in., per cent	33.5	33.1	25.8
Reduction of area, per cent	77.6	54.3	37.0

* From The Making, Shaping and Treating of Steel by Camp and Francis of Carnegie Steel Company, 4th ed., p. 231, 1925.

was 11,640 lb higher than that of the Swedish iron, but the reduction of area was 50 per cent less.

Cement or Blister Steel.—The cementation process of making steel was described by Réaumur as a well-developed industry in 1722, and survived with very little change in apparatus or method until quite recent times. Bars of wrought iron, usually about 3 in. wide and ¾ in. in thickness, were piled in a brick compartment of a furnace with charcoal between and around them. The furnace was heated to "glowing redness" and maintained at that temperature for 7 to 10 days, when the fire was allowed to go out and the bars to cool in the furnace. When taken out, each bar was broken to determine from the appearance of the fracture the amount of carbon absorbed.

It was necessary in this process to have the temperature of the furnace above the critical range. The iron bars absorbed carbon from the charcoal and also from the carbon monoxide gas formed by air leaking into the compartment. The amount of carbon absorbed depended on the time and temperature. The outer layers would contain about 1.0 per cent carbon, and the depth of penetration could be noted with the eye, and furnished a fair indication of the amount of carbon absorbed. The process was similar to that used at present for casehardening but was carried further. The bars of raw material placed in the carburizing furnace were wrought iron, and as the carbon dissolved in the metal and reacted with the iron oxide in the films of slag, bubbles of carbon monoxide gas were formed which puffed out the surface of the metal in blisters. Steel carburized by this process was known as "cement steel" or "blister steel." In the earliest days, the bars were made more homogeneous by repeatedly forging them out into thin bars which were then cut up and welded together. The result was a laminated structure of harder and softer steel filaments, which introduced a wavy pattern in the metal characteristic of the sword blades of Damascus and Toledo.

Crucible Steel.—The only way to make blister steel entirely homogeneous was to remelt it. The art of melting steel in crucibles is credited to Benjamin Huntsman of Sheffield, England, about 1770. His crucibles were made from fire clay and coke dust and held 30 to 50 lb of steel. They were placed in a furnace while empty and brought up to heat, before being charged with small pieces of blister steel. Melting took about an hour. At first there was evolution of gas caused by the reduction of the iron oxide of the intermingled slag. After a time, the steel became perfectly quiet and was said to be "killed." The slag on the surface was skimmed off and the molten steel poured in a mold. This process permitted the production of steel castings or ingots that were homogeneous and free from slag. The quality of steel was frequently excellent since it was made from wrought iron of good quality carburized by the cementation process. The long contact of the molten metal with the clay crucible reduced a little silicon from the clay, which improved the quality of the steel. The steelmaker by long experience was able to determine visually the carbon content of the bars of blister steel used as raw material and, by proper mixture from various bins, to secure a final product that had the properties he desired. Razors, knives, and other cutting tools made by this process were as good as any that can be made today from plain carbon steel.

The disadvantages of the crucible process were the large costs of fuel, crucibles, and labor. It was not possible to make ingots of more than 50 lb weight except with a large and well-trained staff. When the molten metal was poured into the mold, the process had to be continuous. Otherwise there was danger that the surface of the metal in the mold would freeze and not form a perfect union with the later metal. Workmen operating in relays, so that one was ready to pour the instant his predecessor had emptied his crucible, were able to build up large castings. At the British exposition of 1862, the Krupp works of Essen exhibited a casting weighing 21 tons made by the crucible process.

In later years, the raw materials for the crucible process were pieces of steel manufactured by the bessemer or open-hearth process, with pig iron or charcoal added as the carburizing agent. Steel melted in this manner did not necessarily have the high quality of the older product made from blister steel, because the steel scrap used in the charge might have been high in sulfur and phosphorus. Alloying elements could be incorporated in the crucible, and much alloy steel was made in that way in the early days. The electric furnace has superseded the crucible process, but the latter has not yet absolutely vanished, 642 tons of crucible steel being made in the United States in 1935.

References

TOMLINSON, C.: Cyclopedia of Useful Arts and Manufacture, Geo. Virtue & Co., London and New York, 1854.
BOYLSTON, H. M.: Iron and Steel, 2d ed., John Wiley & Sons, Inc., New York, 1936.
PERCY, JOHN: Metallurgy of Iron and Steel, John Murray, London, 1864.
SWANK, J. M.: History of the Manufacture of Iron in All Ages, published by the author, Philadelphia, 1884.
ASTON, JAMES: The Problem of Wrought Iron Manufacture and a New Process for Its Production, *Year book Am. Iron Steel Inst.*, 1925, p. 361.

CHAPTER VI

THE MANUFACTURE OF STEEL BY THE BESSEMER, OPEN-HEARTH AND ELECTRIC-FURNACE PROCESSES

Historical Development.—The era of modern steel manufacture commenced when Sir Henry Bessemer in 1856 announced the process that bears his name. The open-hearth process depends upon the gas producer and regenerative furnace first patented by Frederick Siemens in 1856. When this method of gas firing with regenerative heating of the fuel gas and air was applied to a puddling furnace, it permitted higher temperature to be obtained with less consumption of fuel. The same system of heating also permitted crucible steel to be melted more economically.

William Siemens, a brother of Frederick, announced in 1868 a process for making steel in what was essentially a puddling furnace, operating according to the methods of the puddling process, with the single but important exception that the temperature, thanks to the gas producer and the regenerative system of firing, was raised so high that the iron could be kept molten throughout the process. Instead of the mass being pasty and requiring laborious hand labor to work it during the later stages of the process, the bath remained fluid and was stirred by the evolution of carbon monoxide resulting from the additions of iron oxide. This permitted the hearth and the charge to be made much larger, and gave molten steel and molten slag as the products flowing from the furnace. An open hearth is any shallow hearth over which the gases of combustion sweep. The puddling process was carried out in an open-hearth furnace, and the name was carried over to the steelmaking process that Siemens developed.

The electric furnace for steelmaking has come into importance only in rather recent years. In 1909, it produced less than one-tenth of one per cent of the steel manufactured in the United States. The electric current is used solely as a heating medium, and the operation of the furnace is, in its broad essentials, the same as the open-hearth. The cost of electricity as a heating medium restricts the electric furnace mainly to the production of alloy and special steels, for which it possesses great advantages.

The Process of Steel Manufacture.—All of these processes for the manufacture of steel start with pig iron and refine it by oxidation. Scrap steel may be used as a part of the charge, but it requires little refining. Pig iron consists of an alloy of iron and carbon containing also silicon, manganese, sulfur, and phosphorus. It has been produced in a blast furnace and held molten in the hearth of the furnace in contact with coke where reducing conditions were very strong. Table 8 showed that much more energy was liberated when silicon and manganese united with oxygen than when iron united with oxygen, and that the union of carbon with oxygen to form carbon monoxide evolved more energy than when iron was oxidized. If molten pig iron is oxidized, the first constituents to change will be silicon and manganese, carbon following, and iron coming third. Phosphorus has a heat of oxidation somewhat higher than that of iron and should therefore take priority in oxidation, and it does so under certain conditions. However when carbon is oxidized, it disappears as a gas so that the reaction readily goes to completion. The phosphorus is oxidized to a phosphate which remains in contact with the iron and may undergo reduction again. In order that phosphorus may be removed effectively, it is not only necessary that oxidizing conditions be maintained, but that there be an abundance of a basic constituent in the slag (FeO, CaO, MgO) to hold the phosphate in combination and prevent it from being again reduced and seized by the metallic iron. If the slag is high in silica, which is an acid, the phosphorus stays persistently with the metal. The removal of sulfur from the metal is still more difficult, but is facilitated in the same way by oxidizing conditions and basic slag.

Acid and Basic Processes.—In the early history of both the bessemer and the open-hearth processes, the linings of the furnaces were of fire clay which is high in silica, and the slags were acidic so that there was no elimination of sulfur or phosphorus in the steelmaking process. Sulfur could be eliminated from the pig iron to a considerable degree in the blast furnace, but all of the phosphorus of the ore, coke, and limestone was carried through into the pig iron and then to the steel. The raw materials had to be specially selected, and ores, to be classed as bessemer, were required to have less than 0.05 or even 0.04 per cent phosphorus. Thomas and Gilchrist in 1878 developed the process for removal of phosphorus by adding lime to the slag to make it basic. This necessitated a lining for the furnace of basic material to prevent corrosion by the slag. Steelmaking processes are therefore classified into basic or acid according to the nature of the slag and of the lining. The processes most widely used in the United States are the acid bessemer and the basic open-hearth. The electric furnace operates sometimes on the acid but usually on the basic process and is frequently used only for a finishing process, taking molten metal that has already been refined in the basic open-hearth and giving it a final treatment which may include the incorporation of alloying materials.

The Bessemer Process.—Bessemer's first experiment on the manufacture of steel consisted in blowing air through a metal pipe into a crucible of molten pig iron as it stood in a hot furnace. He observed that the metal became much hotter as air was blown through it, and after further experiments, found that he could convert molten pig iron into steel by pouring it into a large ladle and blowing cold air through it without aiding the process by any external heat. He patented his process, which included a description of the tilting converter, on Dec. 7, 1855. It was adopted almost immediately and was greatly helped by the invention of Robert Mushet, who on Sept. 22, 1856, patented the addition of molten spiegeleisen to the blown metal after it has been poured from the converter. The process depends upon the large amount of heat that the silicon and manganese of the pig iron evolve when they are oxidized by the blast of air passing through the molten metal. There must be enough of these elements present in the pig iron to raise the temperature to the melting point of pure iron because the amount of heat liberated by the oxidation of the carbon is only sufficient to maintain that temperature and not raise it materially.

The bessemer converter is shown in cross section in Fig. 34. The converter may be made to hold as little as 1 ton, but with that small size the losses of heat by radiation are large and the pig iron must be very hot when introduced and quite high in silicon. Converters have been made to hold 25 tons at a charge, but an ordinary size for a steel mill is 10 to 15 tons. A 15-ton converter consists of a steel shell about 11 ft in diameter and 18 ft long with a lining of fire clay or other siliceous material.

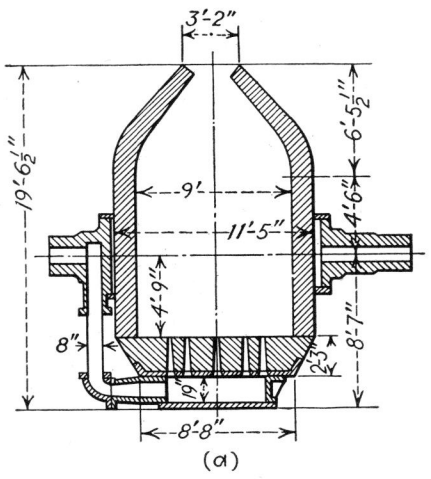

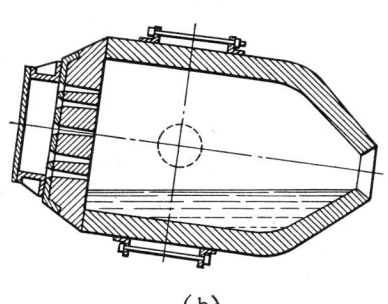

Fig. 34.—Drawings showing cross sections of bessemer converter. (*From H. H. Campbell, Manufacture and Properties of Iron and Steel.*)

The air enters through one of the trunnions and is distributed through a wind box to several tuyères made of fire clay. It is not feasible to provide stoppers for the outlet of the tuyères, and the only thing that prevents the metal from running down into the wind box is the opposing pressure of the air. When the converter is turned down for emptying or filling, there must be sufficient space in the body of the converter to hold the whole charge. For this reason and also because of the violence of the foaming during the blowing period, the charge is seldom greater than enough to fill the converter one-tenth full.

The converter should be kept in practically continuous operation because it must be hot when the metal is poured in. The molten pig iron is brought to the steel mill in the large ladles into which it was tapped at the blast furnace. It is usually stored in a mixer or reservoir made of steel lined with firebrick, which may hold 1000 tons of molten metal. The loss by radiation from this large vessel is small, and it serves to ensure a more uniform composition of metal for each heat in the converter. The whole charge of pig iron, at a temperature of 2200 to 2400°F, is poured into the hot converter while it is in a horizontal position. Air under 10 to 20 lb pressure is automatically turned on as the converter is raised to a vertical position, and a shower of sparks with smoke and flame follows at once. There is much brown smoke during the first 5 min of the "boil" as the manganese and silicon are oxidized. This smoke is replaced by a clear brilliant flame, which may be 30 ft long for the next 7 or 8 min, as the carbon is oxidized. This flame suddenly drops when the carbon has been burned out, and if the blast were continued the iron would be badly oxidized. The drop in the flame is the signal to turn down the converter, and the operation ends with the metal at a temperature of about 2900°F. The whole operation of converting 15 tons of pig iron takes only 15 min. If the pig iron is hot and high in silicon, it is possible and even necessary to throw some cold steel scrap into the converter, but the amount that can be used in this way is small.

The chemical changes that take place during a blow are shown in Table 12. It will be seen that the manganese disappears from the metal first, with the silicon a close second, and that the carbon has hardly started to be removed at the end of 3 min. After 9 min, the carbon has been reduced to 0.04 per cent and the blasting is then stopped. It is especially to be noted that the phosphorus (0.10 per cent) and the sulfur (0.06 per cent) remained almost constant throughout the blow. From 5 to 10 per cent of the weight of the pig iron is lost in the conversion by oxidation of the silicon, manganese, carbon, and some iron. The phosphorus is unchanged in total weight, but increases in percentage. Enough sulfur is volatilized so that the percentage of that element is the same in the steel as in the pig iron. The silicon and manganese of the pig iron formed a slag of manganese silicate as they were oxidized, and the small amount of iron that was oxidized also entered the slag.

TABLE 12.—CHANGES IN COMPOSITION OF METAL IN THE ACID BESSEMER PROCESS*

	Pig iron charged	\multicolumn{6}{c}{Time of blowing in minutes and seconds}
		2' 0''	3' 20''	6' 3''	8' 8''	9' 10''	After spiegeleisen
Carbon	2.98	2.94	2.71	1.72	0.53	0.04	0.45
Silicon	0.94	0.63	0.33	0.03	0.03	0.02	0.038
Manganese	0.43	0.09	0.04	0.03	0.01	0.01	1.15
Phosphorus	0.10	0.104	0.106	0.106	0.107	0.108	0.109
Sulfur	0.06	0.06	0.06	0.06	0.06	0.06	0.059

* CAMPBELL, H. H., Manufacture and Properties of Iron and Steel, 4th ed., p. 102, 1907.

Deoxidation and Recarburization.—Bessemer intended at first to interrupt the blowing when the carbon has been decreased to the amount desired in the finished steel. It was found impossible to determine the rate of removal of carbon with sufficient accuracy, and so within a few months the practice was changed, and the blow was stopped only after all of the carbon had been oxidized. This gave rise to other difficulties because the metal at this point contained enough dissolved oxides to make it brittle.

Mushet solved the difficulty by the addition of molten spiegeleisen to the metal as it ran from the converter. Spiegeleisen was the name given to a pig iron manufactured from ores high in manganese. It owes its name "mirror iron" to the large and brilliant crystals appearing on the fractured surface of the pigs. In Bessemer's day, this iron contained about 10 per cent manganese, about 4 per cent carbon, and 1 or 2 per cent silicon. The chemistry of the process was not well understood 80 years ago, and it is probable Mushet did not know the importance of manganese as a deoxidizer. At any rate, the process of adding spiegeleisen was called "recarburization" rather than deoxidation, and it still bears that name.

The steel, as it lies in the converter after the blow, will probably not contain over 0.15 per cent of oxygen in the form of dissolved oxides. That amount is however sufficient to spoil the steel. Since manganese and silicon can take oxygen away from iron oxide, they are both deoxidizers, but since the reactions are reversible, the deoxidizers must be added in slight excess to be effective. The molten spiegeleisen is added to the molten metal as it is poured from the converter into a large ladle. In modern practice, crushed solid ferromanganese with 80 per cent Mn, ferrosilicon with 50 per cent Si, and charcoal in paper bags are sometimes thrown into the ladle in amounts proportioned to

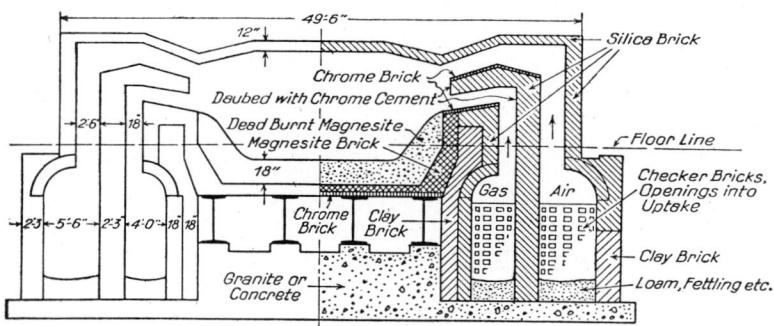

Fig. 35.—Cross section of a basic open-hearth furnace. (*From James P. Gill, Tool Steels.*)

give the composition of the steel that is desired. The molten metal is allowed to stand in the large ladle for a few minutes to permit the reaction to take place and the slag to rise to the surface, and then is taken in the ladle by a crane to the ingot molds into which the steel is "teemed" through a hole in the bottom of the ladle. In 1900, the acid bessemer process produced 65.5 per cent of the steel made in the United States. The exhaustion of the deposits of ore of bessemer grade and the necessity for reworking large amounts of scrap steel made the bessemer process less advantageous than the open-hearth, and in 1935 the proportion of bessemer steel had sunk to 8.2 per cent of the total.

The Basic Bessemer Process.—The operation of the bessemer converter with a basic lining, and with lime added to form a basic slag, permitted the elimination of much of the phosphorus from pig iron which was high in that impurity. American ores are, in general, too low in phosphorus to permit economical operation of the basic bessemer process, and no steel is manufactured in the United States by that method.

The Acid Open-hearth Process.—When Siemens introduced his open-hearth process in 1868, he followed the usual custom of metallurgists and used firebrick and fire clay for the lining of his furnace and a slag that would not corrode his acid lining badly, and was therefore itself siliceous. When it was discovered that, with a basic slag, phosphorus could be eliminated from the metal during the process, it was relatively simple to replace the firebrick by a basic material as a lining for the furnace, change the procedure rather slightly, and convert the furnace to one adapted to the basic process. The acid process suffered from the same handicap as the acid bessemer process in that it required low-phosphorus stock as its raw material. It could however use a large proportion of steel scrap in the charge. The acid open-hearth has never produced more than 8 per cent of the steel manufactured in this country, and its operation, which in general outline is similar to that of the basic open-hearth, will not be described more fully.

The Basic Open-hearth Process.—The basic open-hearth furnace, which is illustrated in Fig. 35 and is shown in greater detail in Fig. 152, may hold more than 200 tons of steel at a charge. Some furnaces are made with tilting instead of fixed hearths. The working hearth is made from burned magnesite (MgO) mixed with ground basic slag and fritted into place. The depth of metal is usually 24 to 30 in. The hearth is heated by gaseous fuel, and the air and also the gas, unless it is natural gas, are both preheated in regenerators placed below the furnace. The combustion processes will be further discussed in Chap. XXI and the linings and slags in Chap. XVIII. A temperature of 3000°F may be readily maintained in the furnace.

The raw materials are primarily pig iron, iron ore to oxidize the carbon and silicon of the pig iron, and limestone to provide a basic slag. When steel scrap commenced to become available in large amounts at low prices, it became an important constituent of the charge. The limestone, ore, and scrap steel are charged into the furnace first and are heated about 2 hr before the molten pig iron is added. The hot iron ore commences at once to react with the silicon, manganese, and some of the carbon of the molten pig iron. After a second 2-hr period, most of the silicon, manganese, and phosphorus have been oxidized and have passed into the slag which is high in lime and ferrous oxide. A small amount of the sulfur has also been oxidized and passed into the slag and some has been volatilized and gone out of the stack. On the other hand, some sulfur has been introduced with the ore and limestone, so that, on the whole, the sulfur remains unchanged. The charge boils and foams because of the carbon monoxide evolved, and some slag runs out of the taphole. More of the carbon is now oxidized by the occasional addition of iron ore, and the temperature of the furnace is raised so as to keep the metal fluid. When the carbon has been lowered to the proper amount and the temperature is right, the tapping hole is opened and the whole charge of metal run into a large ladle. The slag, which appears as the last of the metal runs out, is not allowed to flow into the ladle with the metal, because of its harmful action during deoxidation. The spiegeleisen or ferromanganese for deoxidation and recarburization are added in the ladle, as is the case with bessemer steel. The large mass of metal in the open-hearth ladle holds its heat longer and permits a longer time to be allowed for the thorough incorporation and reaction of the recarburizer. It is important that the slag be removed from the surface of the metal before the deoxidizer is added, since the phosphate in the slag is held there only so long as oxidizing conditions are maintained. When the ferromanganese is added, phosphorus is reduced from slag, which may still be held as fine globules in the molten metal or be floating on the surface, and passes into the metal. One advantage of the tilting open-hearth furnace is that the slag may be poured off, leaving a clean bath of metal so that deoxidation may be accomplished in the furnace itself and as long a time as may be necessary allowed for this important operation.

The open-hearth furnace requires about 10 hr to convert an initial charge of perhaps 100 tons of pig iron and scrap to finished steel. The bessemer converter will convert 15 tons in 15 min. The open-hearth construction is more expensive, and coal must be gasified and burned throughout the operation. There are three offsetting advantages that have caused the bessemer process to drop to a minor position as a producer of steel. The basic open-hearth furnace can start with stock of any percentage of phosphorus, whereas the bessemer converter is restricted to molten pig iron with less than 0.10 per cent phosphorus, it can use steel scrap in almost any quantity, and it permits more thorough deoxidation of the metal.

The ease with which silicon, manganese, and carbon can be eliminated in the bessemer converter permits large steel mills to effect economies by a duplex process which uses metal from the bessemer converter as an important part of the charge of the open-hearth furnace, and so cuts down the time required in the open-hearth.

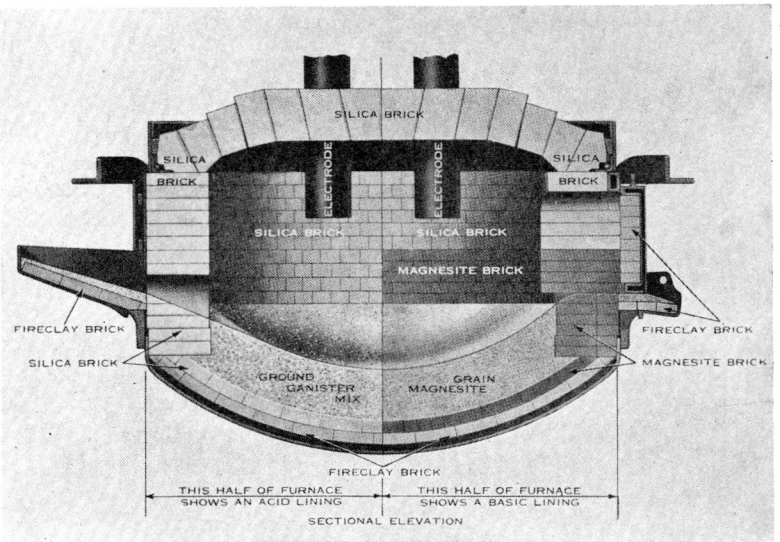

FIG. 36.—Cross section of a tilting electric furnace. (*From Harbison-Walker, Modern Refractory Practice.*)

Electric Furnace Steel.—The electric current is a convenient but expensive means of supplying heat to the steel furnace. The operations are usually those of the basic open-hearth with a finishing treatment that is possible because of the higher temperature and controlled atmosphere. In large steel mills, economy is effected by using molten steel from the basic open-hearth furnace as the charging stock for the electric furnace.

Electric furnaces may be either of the resistance, induction, or arc types, but the latter is by far the most common in the steel mills. The illustration of Fig. 36 shows a Heroult furnace. Each furnace is circular, about 16 ft in diameter, and rests on rockers. The electricity is supplied to three electrodes, each operating on its own phase, with a combined capacity of 3500 kw. About 20 tons of molten steel from the basic open-hearth furnace are poured onto the hot hearth of the electric furnace. The electrodes are adjusted so that they are slightly above the surface of the metal, and the current is turned on. An arc forms between the bottom of each electrode and the surface of the metal or of the slag that covers it. Most of the heat is generated by this arc, although the high resistance of the slag causes considerable heat to be evolved if the slag layer is thick. The resistance of the metal is small because of its large cross section. Since the molten metal from the open-hearth has no silicon to form a slag, the materials for the slag must be added. They consist of lime, with sometimes a little sand, and fluor spar (CaF_2) which promotes fluidity without performing any other function. If a duplex process is being used, the open-hearth furnace has already eliminated almost all of the silicon, manganese, carbon, and phosphorus, and the main function of the electric furnace is to deoxidize the charge thoroughly, eliminate some of the sulfur, and then permit the thorough incorporation of carbon and alloys as may be desired for the finished metal.

The electric furnace may be considered as a large, internally heated crucible. The atmosphere may be controlled at will to be reducing or oxidizing, and the charge can be held in the furnace as long as desired without the danger of oxidation which exists in the open-hearth furnace with its combustion gases sweeping over the metal continually. The first operation in the electric furnace charged with open-hearth steel is one of deoxidation, which is accomplished by powdered coke added with the materials for the slag. This first slag is poured off and materials for a second slag added consisting of lime and fluorspar with more coke dust if needed. This slag is still higher in lime, and the temperature of the furnace is pushed higher to keep it fluid. Under these conditions of high temperature and very basic slag, sulfur is taken out of the metal by the slag even though the bath is in a reducing condition. The equation is written

$$CaO + FeS + C \rightleftharpoons Fe + CO + CaS$$

At this point in the operation, alloying constituents, including alloy steel scrap, are added as may be desired, and also a high quality of pig iron, if needed to bring up the carbon content.

The molten steel is then allowed to lie quietly in the furnace until mixture has become complete and the proper pouring temperature has been reached, when it is run into a ladle and then teemed into ingot molds.

Relative Importance of the Various Methods of Producing Steel.—The quantities of steel made in the United States by the four major processes are shown in Table 13. In 1900, the

TABLE 13.—PRODUCTION OF STEEL INGOTS AND CASTINGS IN THE UNITED STATES*

Year	1900	1910	1920	1929	1935
Bessemer	6,684,770	9,412,772	8,883,087	7,122,509	2,835,031
Acid open-hearth	855,529	1,212,180	1,296,172	1,120,469	354,192
Basic open-hearth	2,547,023	15,292,329	31,375,723	47,232,419	34,550,494
Crucible and electric†	131,250	177,638	577,952	956,510	783,383

* From various volumes of The Mineral Industries.

† The tonnage of electric furnace steel was less than that of crucible steel until 1916. In 1920, the production of crucible steel was only 15 per cent of that made in the electric furnace, and the production of crucible steel is now negligible.

bessemer process produced somewhat less than 7 million tons of steel, and it did not average much more than that during the next 30 years. During that period, the total production of the United States increased more than fivefold so that the percentage of bessemer steel dropped from 65.4 to 12.6 per cent of the total manufactured in 1929. The acid open-hearth process in a similar way maintained its production at a little over a million tons, which in 1929 amounted to only 2.0 per cent of the total production. The crucible process starting with 1.3 per cent of the total tonnage disappeared almost completely and was replaced by the electric-furnace process whose production rose to 1.7 per cent of the total 1929 tonnage. The basic open-hearth process increased from 2,547,025 tons in 1900 to 47,232,419 in 1929 and in percentage from 25.0 to 83.7 of the total. The great business depression starting late in 1929 caused the production for that year to remain as the high point for the next 8 years. In 1935, the basic open-hearth and electric-furnace processes accounted for a somewhat larger proportion of the steel production than in 1929.

The basic open-hearth process has continually risen in importance in spite of the more expensive installation and fuel costs.

It can use pig iron too high in phosphorus to be adapted to the bessemer or the acid open-hearth process, it permits better control of composition and deoxidation than the bessemer process, and it permits large proportions of steel scrap to be remelted and reworked. This scrap can be charged into the furnace without regard for its content of carbon or phosphorus because those elements can be brought to the desired percentage in the routine operation of the furnace. Scrap high in sulfur would be objectionable, but fortunately the ores of the United States are low in sulfur, and very little steel high in sulfur is manufactured so that it does not need to be considered in purchasing scrap. Enough alloy steel comes on the market as scrap to make it necessary to consider its possible influence on the steel to be made from it. The extent to which scrap enters into the production of steel may be judged by a comparison of steel and pig-iron production given in Table 10. In 1900, the production of steel was 3,600,000 tons less than that of pig iron, the balance of the pig iron being used mainly for foundry castings. In 1929, the amount of steel manufactured was 13,800,000 tons *more* than the pig-iron production. By making a rough allowance for pig iron worked up into foundry castings and malleable castings, it is probable that over 18,000,000 tons of steel scrap were worked back into merchantable steel in the basic open-hearth furnaces. During the depression years, an even greater proportion of steel scrap was reworked, the total tonnage of steel being 162 per cent of the pig iron made as compared with 130 per cent in 1929.

References

CAMPBELL, H. H.: Manufacture of Iron and Steel, 4th ed., Hill Publishing Co., New York, 1907.

CAMP and FRANCIS: The Making, Shaping and Treating of Steel, 4th ed., Carnegie Steel Co., Pittsburgh, 1925.

BOYLSTON, H. M.: Introduction to the Metallurgy of Iron and Steel, 2d ed., John Wiley & Sons, Inc., New York,

Mineral Industry for 1937, McGraw-Hill Book Company, Inc., New York, 1938.

CHAPTER VII

INFLUENCE OF CHEMICAL COMPOSITION AND MILL-FINISHING OPERATIONS ON THE PROPERTIES OF PLAIN CARBON STEEL

The molten metal that has flowed from the steelmaking furnaces is poured from the ladles into metal ingot molds preparatory to rolling or into sand molds to produce steel castings. This latter operation will be treated in the chapter on cast metals. The rolling mill of the steel plant forms the hot metal into shapes that may go directly to the consumer in the form of railroad rails or structural steel beams or plates, or which may go as semifinished blooms to a plant that will forge and finish them to make the axle of an automobile or other specialized product. The modern steel mill usually carries its products continuously from the ingot to the finished rail or plate. It works rapidly and produces a rather small variety of standard products for which there is a large demand.

Dissolved Gases.—All steel whether molten or solid contains some dissolved gases, but the quantity that can exist in solid steel is much less than that which can dissolve in molten steel. The process of solidification is therefore accompanied by an evolution of gas which may be enough, if the steel has been poured at too high a temperature or has not been sufficiently deoxidized and is "wild," to cause much foaming, with loss of metal from the mold, and formation of a spongy ingot or casting. Steels that have been deoxidized thoroughly or "killed" and are poured at the proper temperature give much sounder ingots. The carbon of the steel aids in deoxidation, and the greatest trouble in preventing porous metal is experienced with the steels that are very low in carbon. A controlled amount of dissolved gases is retained in "rimmed" steel which will be discussed later.

Inclusions.—When the molten steel is run into the ingot molds, it is supposed to be free from drops of slag, particles of scale, or other foreign material which is not in solution in the molten metal. The longer the molten steel is held after recarburization, the better will be the opportunity for droplets of slag to rise to the surface, but it is not possible to remove all of them. The slag and other foreign matter which are retained are said to form inclusions in the finished steel. They are especially harmful as serving as centers from which fractures start under alternate bending stresses.

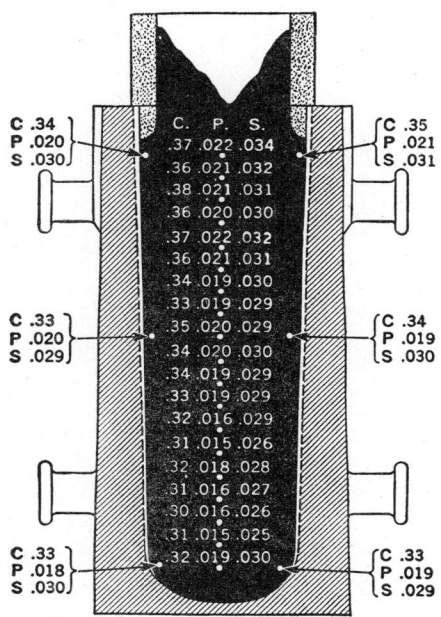

Fig. 37.—Cross section of ingot in mold with hot-top showing segregation and pipe. (*From Bethlehem Steel Co. Catalog* 144.)

Crystallization and Segregation.—The metal commences to solidify at the surface of the mold where columnar crystals start and grow towards the center. The first metal to strike the surface of a cold ingot mold will be chilled so fast that it will freeze without change in composition, whereas with somewhat slower cooling there is opportunity for selective crystallization. Even if the carbon is low enough so that it can all remain in solid solution as austenite, the rapid cooling will cause the surface crystals to be lower in carbon than those crystals formed from the liquid that solidifies in the later stages of the freezing process.

This lack of uniformity is termed "segregation." It is more pronounced with large ingots. Materials like oxides, sulfides, and phosphides have a low solubility in the solid metal and, if present in more than minimal amounts, concentrate or segregate at each grain boundary. There is also a tendency for them to concentrate at the center of the ingot in the metal that freezes last.

This lack of homogeneity in ingots and other castings is accentuated if the metal was not homogeneous when it was cast. The bessemer process is at a disadvantage because the metal

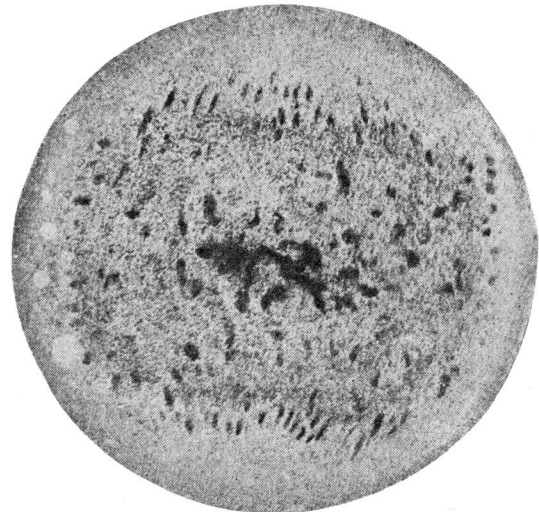

Fig. 38.—Segregation of sulfide in steel as shown by sulfide print on silver bromide paper. (*From Guillet and Portevin, Metallography and Macrography.*)

must be run into the molds only a few minutes after the recarburizer has been added, so that insufficient time has been allowed for reaction and mixing. The open-hearth process permits longer time after recarburization, and the electric furnace permits still greater uniformity to be obtained.

The amount of segregation in an ingot produced by the most approved methods is shown in Fig. 37. This ingot was split down the center, and drillings were taken at the points indicated. The samples taken from six points near the skin of the ingot show little difference in composition, although the two from the top are slightly higher in carbon, phosphorus, and sulfur. The

INFLUENCE OF CHEMICAL COMPOSITION 115

drillings taken along the center line where the metal solidified last show much greater divergence. The carbon varied from 0.30 to 0.37, the phosphorus from 0.015 to 0.022, and the sulfur from 0.025 to 0.034. Steels with higher percentages of sulfur

FIG. 39.—Pipes in older types of steel ingots cast with big end down. The steels are either "semi" killed or killed. (*From the Making, Shaping and Treating of Steel*, 4th ed., Carnegie-Illinois Steel Corporation.)

and phosphorus would show much greater segregation. Maitland[1] writing in 1887 cited an instance of a large ingot of gun steel whose percentage of carbon varied from 0.22 near the bottom to 0.78 near the top. The segregation of sulfur as occurring in the cross section of an ingot is shown in Fig. 38.

[1] *Minutes Inst. Civil Eng.*, **89**, 124 (1887).

a

b

FIG. 40.—Photograph of 4-inch billets etched with hot acid. *a*, showing rimmed steel; *b*, showing deoxidized steel. (*From Bethlehem Steel Co. Catalog* 144.)

INFLUENCE OF CHEMICAL COMPOSITION 117

It is evident that it is not safe to rely on drillings from any single point to determine the composition of an ingot or a billet. Several samples of the liquid metal are always taken as it runs from the ladle at the steel mill, and this "ladle analysis" gives a reliable figure for the average composition of the molten metal.

Pipes and Blow Holes.—There is considerable evolution of gas with consequent contraction in volume during the solidification of steel. The outer skin becomes rigid before the center freezes, and an irregular cavity or pipe forms in the top of the ingot. The

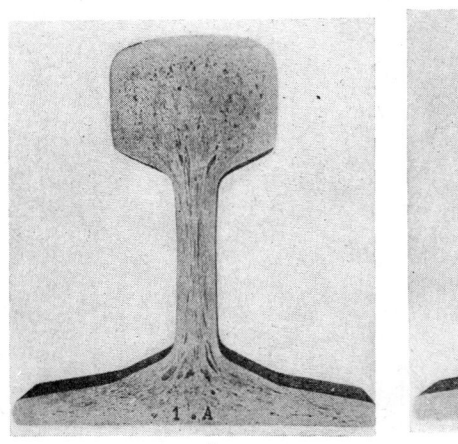 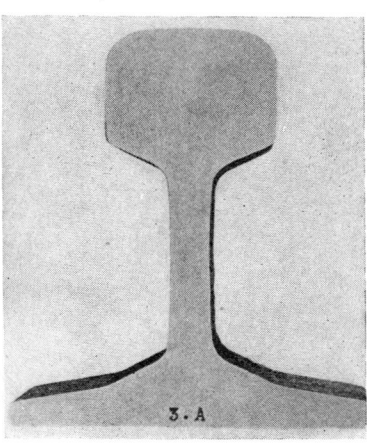

a   *b*

FIG. 41.—Segregation in steel rails as shown by etching with hot acid. *a*, rail from top of ingot; *b*, rail from bottom of ingot. These are old illustrations and not representative of modern practice. (*From Guillet and Portevin, Metallography and Macrography.*)

metal surface of this cavity will become oxidized through contact with the air and will not make a sound weld during the rolling process. A considerable part of the upper part of the ingot containing the pipe must be cut off and discarded, and so it is advisable to keep the pipe as small as possible. An additional cap or hot top of steel lined with fire clay is sometimes added to the ingot mold to hold a reservoir of metal which will be the last to freeze and so permit a greater proportion of the ingot to be acceptable in soundness. Such a hottop is shown in Fig. 37. Metal that tends to be wild may be quieted by throwing a few ounces of aluminum into the mold as it is filling. The high affinity of aluminum for oxygen makes it a much more powerful deoxidizer than manganese or silicon.

The appearance of ingots that have been cut open after cooling is shown in Fig. 39. The photographs do not show whether the metal just below the pipe is any different from that lower down in the ingot. The tendency to segregation is greater in the upper part of the ingot, and some railroads specify that rails for heavy duty shall be rolled only from the bottom half of the ingot.

Much information as to the growth of crystals and homogeneity of the metal can be gained by etching a smooth surface of the metal rather deeply with strong and hot acids and then examining the macrostructure, as distinct from the microstructure, with naked eyes. Two cross sections of 4-in. billets etched in this manner are shown in Fig. 40. The lower picture shows a steel that has been deoxidized well and has a uniform structure. The upper picture shows a small central pipe surrounded by a layer of bad segregation. The greater segregation in a steel rail from the top of an ingot as compared with one from the bottom is shown in Fig. 41.

Rimmed Steel.—The importance of complete deoxidation as an aid in producing sound ingots has been stressed. There are many purposes for which steel, low in carbon, is only partially deoxidized so that it will foam slightly in the ingot molds and almost eliminate the pipe. When this low-carbon steel is poured into the molds, the crystals forming next to the wall are almost pure ferrite and the evolution of gas seems to scour the crystals and keep them clean. The carbon concentrates somewhat in the center of the mold. The result is a rim of ferrite with very little carbon, surrounding a core of rather spongy metal higher in carbon. Some of the gas evolved is caught as fine bubbles as the center of the ingot cools, and produces a porous structure which eliminates the pipe almost completely. Rimmed steel is used for rolling into sheets that are to be used for automobile bodies because the surface takes an excellent finish and is ductile. It is also used for low-carbon wire, tacks, and other articles that are to be worked cold and where surface finish is more important than strength. The upper picture of Fig. 40 shows the results of deep etching the cross section of a billet rolled from an ingot of rimmed steel. The outer skin of nearly pure ferrite surrounding the core of more porous material is shown clearly. It seems peculiar that there should be such a sharp line of demarcation between the two types of metal. Some demarcation is evident in all ingots as shown in the lower picture of Fig. 40. The columnar, or dendritic, crystals starting at the surface of the ingot grow towards the center rapidly at first, and at a decreasing rate as the thickness of solid metal increases and as the ingot mold itself becomes heated

FIG. 42.—Removing an ingot from the soaking pit. (*Courtesy of Republic Steel Corporation.*)

so that it can absorb heat only as fast as it can dissipate it to the air. The rate of cooling and of crystal growth becomes much slower after one-third to one-half of the metal has solidified, with the result that the residual molten metal has almost a constant temperature throughout its mass and solidifies on nuclei scattered through the liquid as well as on the walls. The result is a change in structure after one-quarter to one-half of the metal has frozen, which is very marked in rimmed steel and is noticeable in all large ingots after appropriate etching.

Control of Grain Size by Aluminum.—The heat of formation of aluminum oxide is so high that aluminum acts as a much more powerful deoxidizing agent than either silicon or manganese. It also exerts a strong effect in preventing the formation of coarse

FIG. 43.—Ingot coming through first passes of rolling mill. (*From Bethlehem Steel Co. Catalog* 144.)

crystals when added to an already deoxidized steel in amounts of less than 2 lb per ton of steel. The addition is sometimes made in the ladle and sometimes as the metal is flowing into the ingot mold. It is not certain how this small amount of aluminum exerts such a powerful effect. One group of metallurgists believes that the submicroscopic particles of Al_2O_3 stimulate the formation of iron nuclei, and another group believes that its effect is in some way associated with the minute amount of aluminum that remains in solid solution. Aluminum is used in most kinds of steel except rimmed steel, and even there it is sometimes used in small amount.

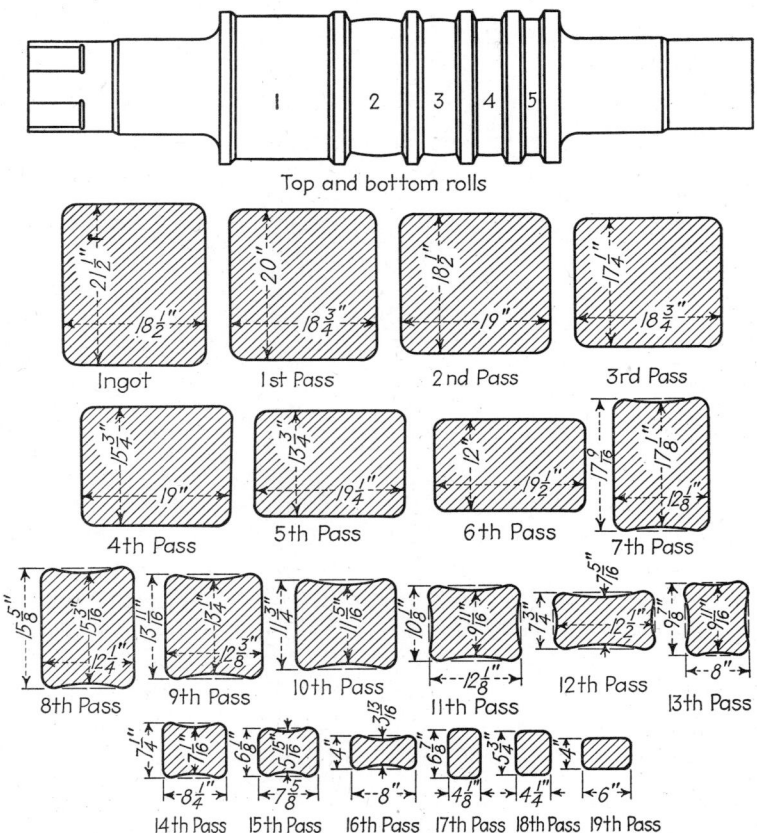

Fig. 44.—Drawing showing design of rolls and reduction in size of ingot 18½ by 21½ in. with successive passes to 4 by 6 in. bloom. The ingots are turned after passes 2, 6, 10, 12, 14, 16, 17 and 18. (*From the Making, Shaping and Treating of Steel. Carnegie-Illinois Steel Corporation.*)

Soaking and Cropping.—The ingot is stripped from its mold as soon as it has solidified and is sent to a soaking pit or reheating furnace before it is rolled, as is illustrated in Fig. 42. The soaking pits are brick chambers heated with gas and maintained at the proper temperature for rolling. The surface of the ingot is too cold and the center too hot, and so the ingot is allowed to "soak" until the temperature has become uniform. After a few passes through the rolls, it goes to the hot shears where it is "cropped." Enough of the head of the ingot is cut off to give sound metal in the remaining portion. Segregation is more pronounced in the upper portion, and in some cases nearly one-third of the ingot must be cut off.

Rolling-mill Operation.—In the modern rolling mill, an ingot as large as 20 in. square may be kept continuously in motion, passing through the rolls until it emerges as a steel rail, or as a sheet or strip with a thickness of less than $\frac{1}{8}$ in. The grain size of the metal of the ingot will always be large, and the grain size of the metal coming from the final pass of the rolls must conform to the purchaser's specification. The steel must not be worked after it has cooled below the critical range because of the danger of cracking and embrittling due to the growing rigidity of the metal. The steel cools continuously by radiation and also because water is sometimes sprayed upon it. It is heated by the mechanical work that the rolls put upon it. The initial temperature must therefore be such as to bring the metal out of the rolls at the temperature desired. The amount of reduction at each pass through the rolls is important as governing the grain size at the center of the ingot. Unless the work done by the rolls is severe, the crystals at the center will not be broken up. In any case, the action of the rolls is to draw the crystals into threads. A picture of an ingot coming through the first passes of the rolls may be found in Fig. 43. The changes in shape of an ingot as it goes through the various passes to form a billet are shown in Fig. 44.

INFLUENCE OF CHEMICAL COMPOSITION ON PROPERTIES

Carbon.—Carbon is the element that gives to steel its characteristic properties. Its influence on annealed and heat-treated steels has already been discussed. It will be considered further in connection with alloy steels and cast irons.

Silicon.—Silicon is almost completely removed from all classes of steel in the manufacturing process. It is added in the process of deoxidation because of its ability to take oxygen away from dissolved iron oxide, forming SiO_2, which is eliminated in the slag. Any small excess of silicon remains in solid solution in the steel, raising the strength and elastic limit without lowering ductility. It is added in amounts up to 0.35 per cent to spring steel to promote resilience. In high-carbon steels, it promotes the decomposition of cementite to form graphite, and so not more than 0.50 per cent is usually added to plain carbon steels. The effect of higher silicon will be referred to under alloy steels, and under cast-iron and malleable-iron castings.

Manganese.—Manganese, like silicon, is almost completely eliminated in the manufacturing process and is added during deoxidation, forming MnO which is insoluble in the molten steel and rises to the surface and forms part of the slag. It is added in slight excess to ensure better deoxidation and forms a solid solution with the iron, raising the tensile strength. Manganese above 1 per cent causes hardness and brittleness in mild steels, and a smaller quantity causes difficulties with high-carbon steels, so that in tool steels the manganese is frequently held below 0.25 per cent.

Manganese also acts indirectly to reduce the harmful effects of sulfur by forming MnS instead of FeS in the metal. The MnS is thrown out of solution as the metal solidifies and remains plastic at the temperatures at which metal is rolled.

Sulfur.—The sulfide of iron is thrown out of solution as the metal solidifies, and as its melting point is low it remains liquid and concentrates in those parts of the liquid which freeze last. It is found in the intercrystalline films and segregates rather badly. Its melting point is so low that it produces liquid intercrystalline films at the temperatures of rolling and forging. The metallic grains slip on these liquid films during hot working, and cracks form. The steel is said to be "red-short." Structural steel with as much as 0.1 per cent sulfur will probably not show any harmful effects from sulfur, if it is neutralized by 0.5 per cent manganese. American ores are so low in sulfur that there is little difficulty in keeping sulfur below 0.06 per cent.

Steel is manufactured with higher sulfur content to promote ease of machining. In automatic screwstock where good finish and ease of machining are more important than strength, the sulfur may run 0.15 to 0.30 per cent. The films of sulfide cause the chips to break off in small fragments rather than in long shavings, with the result that a cleaner cut may be obtained at a high machining rate.

Phosphorus.—Phosphorus is universally blamed for brittleness, or cold-shortness, in steel at room temperature. It unites with iron to form a hard and brittle phosphide which segregates at the grain boundaries and in larger amounts forms a eutectic of iron and iron phosphide to which the name "steadite" is given. It is especially harmful in steel that is subject to sudden impacts and shocks. On the other hand, when only 0.10 per cent of phosphorus is present, it strengthens and hardens steel to about the same extent as carbon. Present-day specifications usually limit the phosphorus to 0.05 per cent in structural steels and to lower amounts in tool steels.

Oxygen and Nitrogen.—The harmful effects of oxygen are universally recognized, but it is rarely mentioned in specifications because of the difficulty in determining how much and in what form it is present in steel. Bessemer steel, if cooled without deoxidation, would contain about 0.15 per cent of oxygen as dissolved oxides and would be so brittle as to be useless. The preference for electric-furnace and open-hearth steel is due, in considerable degree, to the better opportunity for deoxidation in those processes. It is stated that as little as 0.03 per cent of oxygen in the metal causes brittleness under shock. Oxygen present in films of slag does not exert the same harmful effect.

Chipman[1] has made analyses of commercial steels from the open-hearth and electric-furnace which contained from 0.002 to 0.011 per cent oxygen and from 0.010 to 0.030 per cent nitrogen. These figures are extremely small, but some idea of their possible importance may be gained by transferring the percentages by weight to volume. The higher figures given above for oxygen and nitrogen, if converted to volume at atmospheric pressure, would amount to a combined gas volume twice as great as that of the steel. The effect of the nitrogen is not well understood and is probably slight.

Specifications.—The American Society for Testing Materials publishes a volume of Standards triennially and one of Tentative Standards annually. The 1936 volume lists 93 specifications for different grades of steel. The Society of Automotive Engineers cooperates with the American Society for Testing Materials and in addition lists in its S.A.E. Handbook a number of specialized steels not listed by the American Society for Testing Materials.

[1] *The Michigan Technic*, October, 1934, p. 6.

These specifications are drawn up by committees representing both producers and consumers. After agreement has been reached by the committee, the proposed specification is submitted for ballot to the whole membership of the society. If approved by the membership, the specification is published as a tentative standard, and after a year it may be again submitted to vote for approval as a standard. The A.S.T.M. Standards therefore represent the mature judgment of those expert in the field, and may be used by the average engineer without hesitation. The S.A.E. Standards are in a similar way backed by the authority of the Society of Automotive Engineers.

The aim of a specification is to secure material of desirable quality with a minimum of restrictions on the producer. Almost all of the specifications state the methods of steel production that will be acceptable, and specify as few other items as will ensure a satisfactory result. Structural steel for buildings is subject mainly to static loads, and the specifications permit the use of either bessemer, open-hearth or electric-furnace steel, except that bessemer steel is not allowed for thick plates. There are no limits set for carbon, silicon, manganese, or sulfur. Phosphorus may be 0.10 per cent in bessemer steel but not over 0.06 in that made in the open-hearth or electric furnace. The tensile strength may be between 60,000 and 72,000 psi, and the yield point is to be at least half the tensile strength but in no case less than 33,000 psi. The elongation on a 2-in. piece is to be at least 22 per cent. This specification leaves the manufacturer free to adjust his carbon, manganese, and other constituents as he sees fit provided his physical tests are satisfactory.

Steel Rails.—Steel rails are subject to impacts and alternate bending stresses which become increasingly severe with heavier trains and higher speeds. Winter weather, with the greater brittleness of the metal at low temperature, increases the number of fractures in rails. The weight of rails has been steadily increased from 67 lb per yard for the first bessemer rails rolled in the United States to a maximum of 150 lb per yard in present practice. The percentage of carbon has also been increased to add stiffness. The 1936 A.S.T.M. standard specifications for heavy rails call for 0.69 to 0.82 per cent carbon, 0.70 to 1.00 manganese, 0.10 to 0.23 silicon, and a maximum of 0.04 phosphorus. None of the ordinary physical tests of the metal are specified, but acceptance is based on the behavior of lengths of full-size rails when placed on supports 3 or 4 ft apart and subjected to blows from a 2000-lb tup falling from a height that is 16 ft for light rails and increases to 22 ft for heavy rails.

The manufacturing problems have increased in complexity with the increase in weight of the rail and increasing service stresses. The usual T rail has a heavy head and a lighter web and flange. The metal in the head does not have its grain refined by the rolls as well as the metal in the thinner sections, and if the rolling is finished at too high a temperature, the grain in the head will increase in size. Rails are cut to length by saws working on the hot rails just after they emerge from the last rolls. The distance of the hot saws is set to allow for shrinkage on cooling, so that the inspector by applying a steel tape to the cooled rail can ascertain from its length whether it came through the rolls at too high a temperature. After being sawed, the rails are laid out on the hot beds on their sides, with the head of one in contact with the flange of its neighbor so as to equalize the rate of cooling and prevent uneven shrinkage strains.

The failure of rails in service has sometimes been traced to minor injuries such as a blow from a sledge in the hands of a workman while spiking a rail in place. The resulting slight cut on the head of the rail formed the starting point for a fissure which gradually spread under the alternate strains caused by traffic. Transverse cracks of this sort were usually detected by the track inspector before a break occurred. It has recently been shown that some transverse cracks have originated within the rail and could not be detected visually until the crack had made considerable progress, and perhaps had gone so far as to cause a broken rail. The cause of these hidden fissures has been traced to "shatter cracks" formed by uneven cooling of the metal through the temperature range just below a visible red heat (950°F).

The curves of Fig. 45 show the properties of 1045 steel when the test piece is heated during the test by a small electric furnace which surrounds it while the pulling takes place. The critical range for this steel on cooling commences about 1425°F, and at this temperature the steel is a plastic mass with no determinable yield point. Its tensile strength is only about 17,000 psi and its elongation 70 per cent. In the rolling mill or forge shop, hot work would stop at about this temperature because the metal stiffens rapidly, and at 1000°F when the metal is at a very dull red heat, the tensile strength is 55,000 lb and the elongation only 22 per cent. At 700°F, which is in the "blue heat" range, the tensile strength is even higher than at room temperature and the elongation is only half that which the metal possesses when cold. The scientific explanation of this blue-heat brittleness is not known, but there is no doubt about its existence.

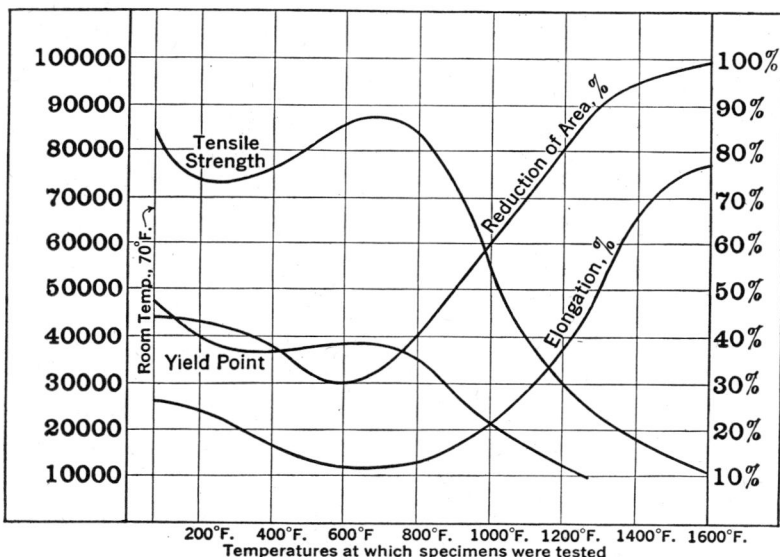

FIG. 45.—Effect of elevated temperatures on the physical properties of an S.A.E. 1045 steel as received from the mill as a 1-in. round bar. (*From Bethlehem Steel Co. Catalog 144.*)

When a billet leaves the rolls and cools rapidly in air, differential expansion and contraction take place as the various portions cool through the critical range. The metal is however plastic enough at these temperatures to readjust itself without injury. On further cooling, the outer portion will have dropped almost to room temperature while the center is passing through the brittle stage. The result is that internal cracks, sometimes called shatter cracks may form in the interior of the billet. These are shown in a cross section of a 4-in. billet in Fig. 46. If this billet were to be reheated and forged, these shatter cracks would weld together quite perfectly because they are too deep seated to have become oxidized. A steel rail however goes into service without treatment after it leaves the rolling mill, and the best practice is to cool it in such a way as to prevent these cracks from forming. One steel mill[1] permits the rails to cool in air until they are just below a visible redness (about 950°F) and then piles them in a tank that is covered and therefore permits only slow cooling.

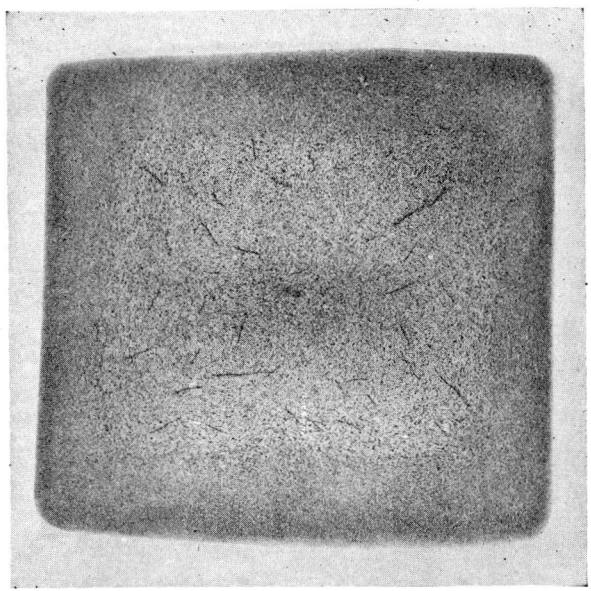

Fig. 46.—Photograph of cross section of a 4-in. billet showing internal cracks disclosed by etching with hot acid. (*From Bethlehem Steel Co. Catalog* 144.)

When the temperature in the tank has dropped to 400°F, the rails are removed and allowed to cool further in the open air. It is said that this process has eliminated shatter cracks and given a better rail in other ways.

Sheets and Strips.—The blooms are rolled into bars 8 to 16 in. wide, which are cut into lengths, reheated, and rolled again. When the sheets get as thin as $3/32$ in., they are run through the rolls in pairs. The temperature must not be hot enough to weld the sheets together. At some intermediate stage in the rolling, the sheets are pickled in dilute acid to remove scale, and there-

[1] Editorial report, *Metal Progress*, July, 1936, p. 41.

after the atmosphere of the reheating furnace must be kept as neutral as possible so as not to form a new scale on the sheets. These sheets are finished in packs of 4 to 8 and sometimes even 16 sheets. The sheets are trimmed and finished by cold-rolling to give a flat smooth sheet with the desired amount of springiness. If a ductile sheet is required as for the deep-drawing processes in the manufacture of automobile bodies, the cold-rolled sheets are annealed in boxes to prevent oxidation. It is difficult to carry the annealing temperature above 1000°F because of the tendency of the sheets to stick together. A perfectly flat sheet is obtained by clamping the ends of the sheets, one at a time, in a powerful machine that stretches each sheet slightly beyond its elastic limit and takes out all of the waves.

Tubing.—Tubes may be made from flat strips which are bent to shape and welded. Seamless tubes are made from a billet that is pierced while hot and rolled with a spiral motion which elongates it. This spiral working tends to equalize the effect of the regular rolling operation in drawing out the crystals into parallel fibers. The tubing may be brought to final size by cold-drawing.

EFFECT OF MILL OPERATIONS ON PHYSICAL PROPERTIES

The change in physical properties that a 1040 steel undergoes as it progresses from the ingot to seamless steel tubing has been summarized by Graham and Flaherty whose results are given in Table 14. The most striking changes are in the results for elongation which is only 2.0 per cent for the metal from the large ingot with its coarse crystals. After this 26-in. ingot has been rolled to a cylinder 6 in. in diameter, its elongation along a longitudinal section has been raised to 20.0 per cent, but in cross section the elongation is only 4.5 per cent. After it has been converted to a spiral hot-rolled tube, the ductility has been improved so that the elongation is 29.0 per cent for the longitudinal section and 10.0 per cent for the cross section.

The strength in the longitudinal direction was raised 23 per cent by the reduction from 26 to 6 in. in diameter, but in the cross section the tensile strength was increased only about 7 per cent. The spiral rolling in making a seamless tube eliminated much of the differences between the two directions and raised the tensile strength of both the longitudinal and cross sections somewhat higher than either had been in the 6-in. round. The yield point was not changed much by the hot work and was almost the same for the test pieces cut from the longitudinal and from the cross section. The Brinell hardness was raised from 143 in the ingot to 196 in the hot-rolled tube, with no difference between the two sections.

The low tensile strength and the very low elongation of the sample from the ingot is due to the coarse crystals of ferrite and the thick and unbroken envelopes of foreign materials that surround each grain and form a continuous brittle network. As

TABLE 14.—CHANGES IN PHYSICAL PROPERTIES OF 1040 STEEL DUE TO HOT AND COLD WORK*

	Brinell hardness No.	Tensile strength, psi	Yield point, psi	Elongation, per cent in 2 in.
Ingot, 26-in. round...............	143	74,000	56,000	2.0
After rolling to 6-in. round:				
Longitudinal section.............	187	91,300	59,900	20.0
Cross section....................	187	79,100	57,100	4.5
Hot-rolled seamless tube:				
Longitudinal section.............	196	95,500	55,700	29.0
Cross section....................	196	93,000	56,800	10.0
Cold-drawn (longitudinal section)...	228	103,400	79,600	22.0
Annealed at 1200°F (650°C).......	192	93,000	53,400	34.0
Normalized at 1550°F (843°C).....	196	95,100	64,000	32.0

* GRAHAM and FLAHERTY, *Am. Petroleum Inst.*, Nov. 13, 1935 (preprint).

these crystals are elongated to threads and the intercrystalline films become thinner, both the elongation and tensile strength increase for samples stressed in the direction of rolling, but are improved in much less degree for samples stressed across the direction of rolling. The elastic limit is passed when substantial slip occurs in the ferrite grains, and since the rate of cooling is in each case slow enough to permit the ferrite and pearlite to be well differentiated, the rolling operation does not affect the yield point to a large extent. The hardness is increased somewhat by the rolling because the pearlite reinforces the soft ferrite better with the small grains.

The operation of cold-drawing raised the elastic limit of a longitudinal section 24 per cent, the tensile strength less than

INFLUENCE OF CHEMICAL COMPOSITION

10 per cent, and the Brinell number from 196 to 228. These increases were accompanied by a decrease in elongation from 29 to 22 per cent. The curves of Fig. 47 show the effect of cold work as compared with hot work on three steels, and the photomicrographs of Fig. 48 show how the grain structure is affected by cold-drawing. When the hot-rolled tube was annealed at 1200°F which is below the critical range and constitutes process annealing, the yield point, tensile strength, and hardness changed

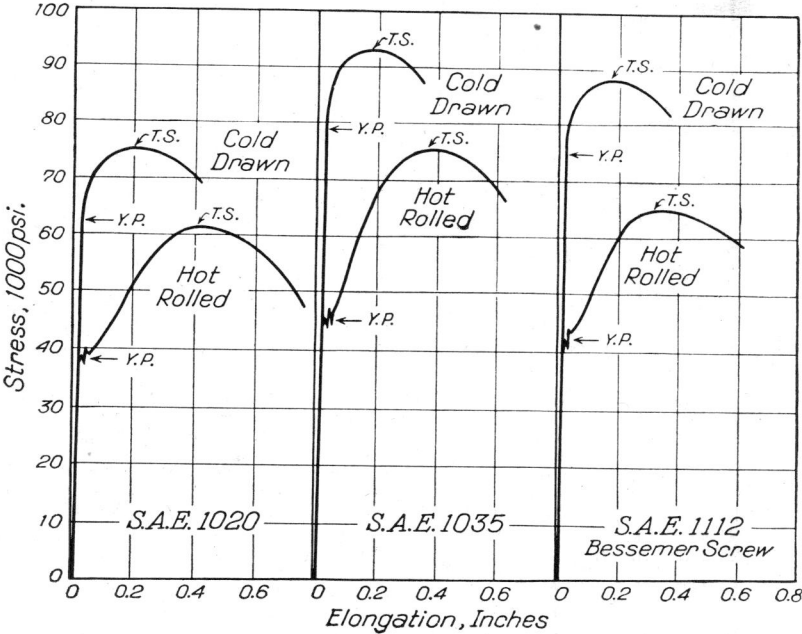

FIG. 47.—Typical stress-strain diagrams of hot-rolled and cold-drawn steels. [*From Trans. Am. Soc. for Metals*, **25**, 109 (1937).]

very little from the figures shown by the hot-rolled metal. The ductility as measured by the elongation became the highest attained, 34.0 per cent. This high value was probably due to the removal of strains left by the finishing rolling operation. The increase in the yield point after normalizing is probably due to a slight air hardening and a small amount of cold work caused by straightening after normalizing.

Aging.—The cooling of rails and beams in the steel mill is slow enough to permit a fairly good separation of the ferrite and pearlite. Nevertheless slow changes do occur in the metal after it has cooled. A committee of the American Society for Testing Materials has reported with regard to structural steel.

Aging reduces the yield point by a small amount, in these tests less than 5 per cent, and slightly increases the tensile strength of hot-rolled rods of low-carbon steel. Aging does effect a material increase in the ductility of such materials during the first month after rolling.

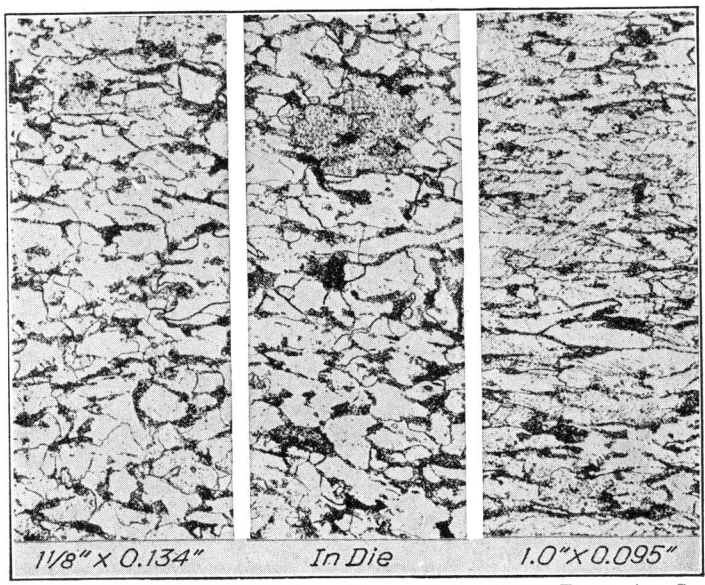

FIG. 48.—Effect of cold work in elongating crystals. [*From Trans. Am. Soc. for Metals*, **25**, 126 (1937).]

This effect is due to the slow agglomeration of some of the finely divided cementite into larger particles.

References

BOYLSTON, H. M.: Iron and Steel, 2d ed., John Wiley & Sons, Inc., New York, 1936.

BULLENS, D. K.: Steel and Its Heat Treatment, 3d ed., John Wiley & Sons, Inc., New York, 1935.

CAMPBELL, H. L.: The Working, Heat Treating and Welding of Steel, John Wiley & Sons, Inc., New York, 1935.

CAMPBELL, H. H.: Manufacture of Iron and Steel, 4th ed., Hill Publishing Co., New York, 1907.

CLARK and WHITE: Creep Characteristics of Metals, *Trans. Am. Soc. Metals*, **24**, 831–864 (1936).

DAWES, C. N.: The Steel Physical Properties Atlas, published by American Society for Metals, Cleveland, 1936.

GUILLET and PORTEVIN: Metallography and Macrography, George Bell & Sons, Ltd., London, 1922.

SHANNON, R. W.: Sheet Steel and Tin Plate, Reinhold Publishing Corporation, New York, 1930.

SOCIETY OF AUTOMOTIVE ENGINEERS: S.A.E. Handbook, New York, 1937.

STOUGHTON and BUTTS: Engineering Metallurgy, 3d ed., McGraw-Hill Book Company, Inc., New York, 1938.

HERTY, MCBRIDE, and HOLLENBACH: Which Grain Size?, *Trans. Am. Soc. Metals*, **25**, 297 (1937).

GRAVES, W. H.: What Steel Is Best for This or That Part?, *Metal Progress*, **29**, 36 (1936).

Improved Railroad Rails, editorial, *Metal Progress*, July, 1936, p. 41.

NEAD, J. H.: The Effect of Carbon on the Physical Properties of Heat Treated Carbon Steel, *Trans. Am. Inst. Min. Met. Eng.*, **53**, 218–257 (1915).

FRENCH, H. J.: Fatigue and the Hardening of Steels, *Trans. Am. Soc. Steel Treating*, **21**, 899 (1933).

WHITE, CLARK, and WILSON: Influence of Time on Creep of Steels, *Proc. Am. Soc. Testing Materials*, **35**, II, 167 (1935); **36**, II, 139 (1936).

CHAPTER VIII

THE PROPERTIES OF PLAIN CARBON STEEL AS AFFECTED BY METHODS OF FABRICATION

The preceding chapter dealt with the changes in properties of steel due to the operations that customarily take place in the steel mill. Much of the steel is shipped from the steel mill in a semifinished shape and must be reworked and fabricated before it reaches its finished form.

Reheating Steel for Forging.—In the steel mill, the ingots were brought to a definite temperature before rolling but were usually carried through the whole process of the rolling mill without reheating. When steel is to be reheated, as for forging, care is necessary to avoid injuring the metal. As has been stated, steel expands on heating, except when passing through the critical range. If the heating is too fast, cracks may be formed. The American Society for Metals committee states[1] that if steels contain less than 0.5 per cent carbon, a bar of 3 in. diameter may be heated to forging temperature in 15 min, or at the rate of 5 min for each inch of diameter. Larger bars and steel with higher carbon content must be heated more slowly. The proper forging temperature will be above the critical range, and the bar should be withdrawn from the furnace and forged as soon as the center has reached the proper temperature. If it is allowed to stay too long at the high temperature or to become overheated, the grain will become excessively coarse and more difficult to refine by hot work, as shown in Fig. 49. The atmosphere of the reheating furnace is usually oxidizing, no matter how the heat is applied, so that oxide scale forms on the surface and, especially in high carbon steels, carbon is removed from the surface skin. In extreme cases, the steel becomes "burned," a word used to convey the idea that it is no longer fit for forging. Burning is really only a condition of excessive heating in which some of the more fusible intergranular constituents of the steel have melted

[1] Metals Handbook, 1939 ed., p. 831.

THE PROPERTIES OF PLAIN CARBON STEEL 135

and may even have oozed out leaving a porous and oxidized structure. If the temperature has not been quite hot enough to cause the metal to run, there may still be enough of a molten film between the grains so that the grains will slip, and cracks will form when the piece is struck with a hammer. The danger of burning and of decarburization of the surface is greater with high-carbon steels.

a   *b*

FIG. 49.—Effect of overheating on crystal structure of S.A.E. 1045 steel. *a*, photograph of fracture of overheated steel in hardened condition, enlarged 3 times; *b*, micrograph of same steel at 100 diameters. (*From Bethlehem Steel Co. Catalog* 144.)

Forging.—The forging operation in modern industrial plants is usually performed with a steam hammer capable of giving powerful blows which will break up the grains even in the center of a fairly large billet. This process is called "hammer forging." For very large billets, a hydraulic forging press is desirable. It acts slowly but can produce deep-seated changes in the crystalline structure. Both the ram and the hammer of the forge frequently contain several recesses so that the metal is shaped with successive strokes in the various dies and assumes a definite form as is shown in Fig. 50. Such an operation is called "drop forging." The design of the dies must be such that the metal is distorted rather gradually so that it will flow, and not be torn and rewelded. The flow lines of good and bad forgings as revealed by etching with hot acid are shown in Fig. 51. These flow lines are an inheritance from the operation of the rolling mill which drew the large primary crystals of the ingot into long threads. Hyper-

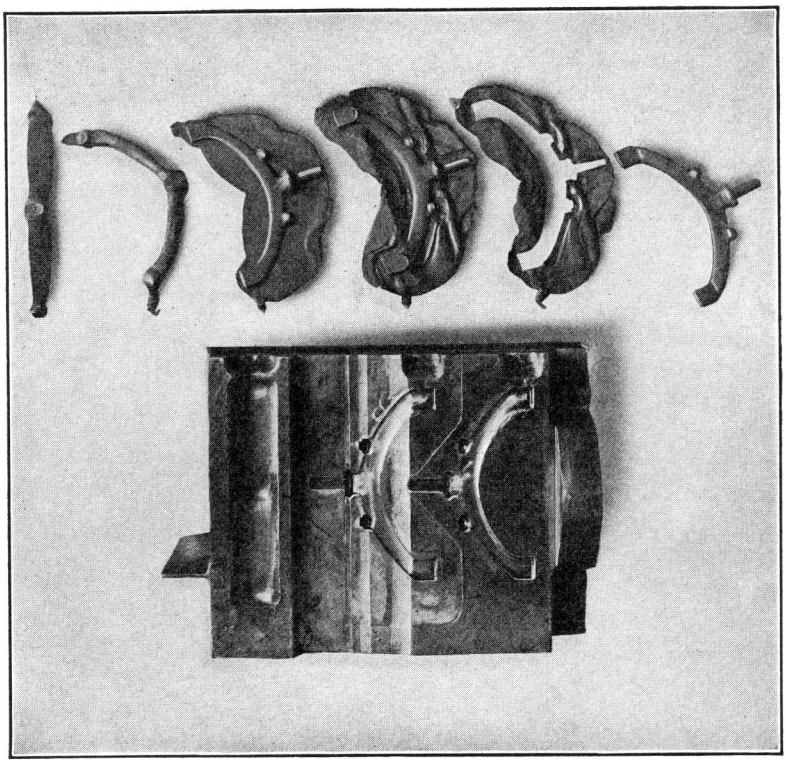

Fig. 50.—Photograph of drop forging die showing various operations and impressions. [*From Trans. Am. Soc. for Metals*, **25**, 13 (1937).]

eutectoid steels are especially brittle, and the temperature and rate of distortion require careful control.

Unless the forging operation is to be followed by a heat-treatment which will refine the grain, the temperature of the final forging operation must be watched closely. If it is too high, there will be grain growth after the forging has stopped and if too low, brittleness due to cold work.

THE PROPERTIES OF PLAIN CARBON STEEL 137

Machining.—The forged part is usually normalized before machining to be sure that there are no shrinkage strains or hard spots in the metal due to improper forging or to too rapid or uneven cooling after forging. The normalized steel will cut easily and will not undergo large volume changes due to aging after machining. During the cutting operation, the piece is often flooded with oil or other cutting fluid, partly to prevent a

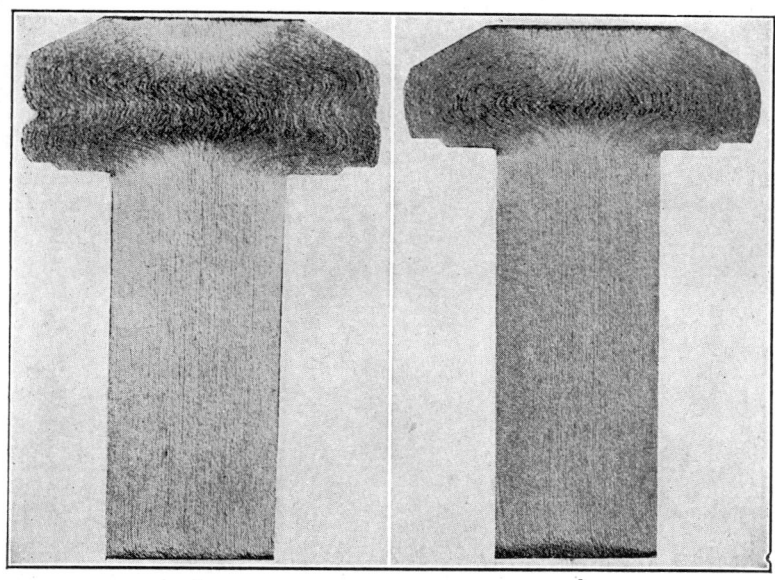

FIG. 51.—Results of good and poor die design on the flow of metal fibers. *a*, photograph of an upset in which improper die design has resulted in re-entering fibers in the head; *b*, photograph of an upset in which proper die design has resulted in proper fiber pattern in the head. [*From Trans. Am. Soc. for Metals,* **25**, 46 (1937).]

rise in temperature of the piece being machined, but more to cool the cutting edge of the tool so that it will not lose its hardness. If the cutting is very rapid, the surface of the metal may be raised to a high enough temperature to be hardened somewhat.

HEAT-TREATMENT AFTER MACHINING

Heating.—The metal part has frequently been machined to very accurate dimensions which must not be changed by subsequent heat-treatment. Heating in a furnace with an oxidizing atmosphere will cause scaling and decarburization of the surface. Both carbon dioxide and steam are oxidizing to steel at a red heat. Carbon monoxide and hydrogen will reduce iron oxide, and carbon monoxide will also impart carbon to the surface of the steel. A neutral atmosphere is one in which the influences of the oxidizing and reducing gases are balanced.

If the steel was normalized before machining, the grain is already fine and it is not necessary to heat the specimen so hot as would be required if grain refinement were necessary. The higher the temperature, the greater is the danger of warping and cracking on cooling. The piece must be heated through the critical range until the carbon is all in the form of austenite but should not be heated hotter. Automatic furnaces are frequently employed which carry the parts through a tunnel whose temperature is so adjusted to the speed of the conveyor that the pieces emerge as soon as they have reached the proper temperature. One difficulty with gears is that the tips of the teeth get hot before the body of the gear. A more refined method used for complicated parts, such as ring gears, calls for a separate heavy steel box for each gear. This box is almost like a forging die in that the lid contains projections that extend between the teeth of the gear. The top and bottom of the box fit so closely into the gear that all parts come up to temperature uniformly, and there are no currents of gases to cause oxidation or carburization of the surface. Each of the boxes carries a thermocouple connected to its own recording pyrometer placed close to the furnace where the heater can watch it. The pyrometer traces an even line showing temperatures steadily rising until the critical range is reached. Here heat is absorbed and the temperature rise is halted. As soon as the transformation to austenite is complete, the heating curve resumes its steady rate of rise, and the appearance of this "hump" in the curve is the signal to the heater to remove the gear, still in its box, for quenching.

Quenching.—The dangers of rapid quenching have already been explained. Oil is a preferable quenching medium to water if its quenching action is sufficient to give the requisite hardness. The quantity of heat to be abstracted from the metal is a function of its weight and temperature. The rate at which heat can be abstracted is a function of the surface. The surface of the metal cools very fast when immersed in the cooling liquid.

THE PROPERTIES OF PLAIN CARBON STEEL   139

The center will cool more slowly, and with heavy sections it is not possible to get the center hard as is shown in Fig. 52. A bar 1 in. in diameter showed maximum hardness only in the outer ⅛ in. The hardness decreased rapidly for another ⅛ in., and the balance of the cross section was very little harder than fine-grained pearlite. A bar 1⅝ in. in diameter showed about the same thickness of hard metal at the surface and a proportionately greater proportion of soft metal in the center. Fortunately, hardness is usually needed only at the surface. There is great

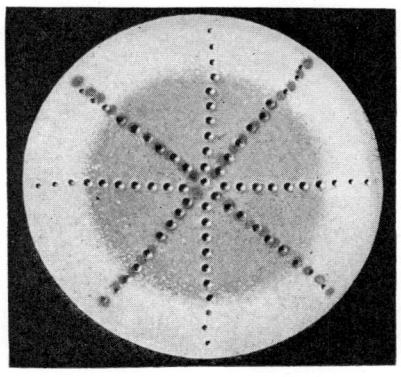 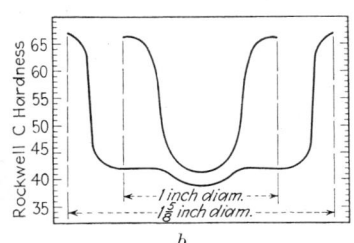

           a   *b*

Fig. 52.—Effect of size of specimen on distribution of hardness from surface of center. (*From Bain, Yearbook of American Iron and Steel Institute*, 1934, p. 97.)

a, Section of 1-in. round eutectoid carbon steel quenched in brine. Hardness determinations were made as shown on diameters of the specimen. Note change in penetration at circle representing the critical cooling rate; outside martensite, inside fine pearlite.

b, Average hardness distribution across diameters of two sections of the same carbon tool steel.

danger of minute cracks being formed during the quenching process, and these may have an important effect on the strength of the steel, especially as shown in its resistance to shock. The graph of Fig. 53 shows the great effect of these microscopic cracks on the impact strength. These steels were all quenched from a uniform temperature of 1400°F but had been given a previous heat-treatment at the temperatures indicated on the graph to give progressively larger grain sizes. The prevalence of quenching cracks increases with the grain size.

Tempering.—The piece after cooling is removed from the quenching bath and reheated to the temperature needed for the time required to soften the metal as much as may be desired. This softening process will naturally not affect the pearlite core of a large piece and will affect the martensite to a greater extent than the troostite or sorbite which may be present before tempering. All quenched metal contains shrinkage strains, and it is desirable to transfer the piece immediately from the quenching bath to the tempering furnace to prevent the formation of cracks.

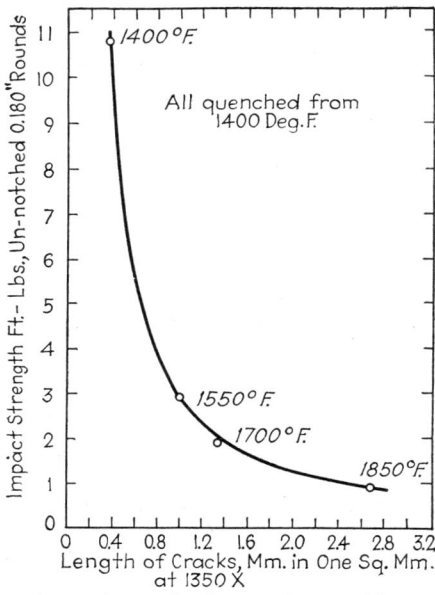

FIG. 53.—Effect of prevalence of microscopic quenching cracks upon impact strength of quenched and tempered steel. (*From Bain, Yearbook of American Iron and Steel Institute, 1934, p. 105.*)

It is preferable for the same reason to remove the piece from the quenching bath before it is entirely cold.

Casehardening.—The increased strength and hardness of high-carbon steel are obtained at a sacrifice of the softness and ductility that low-carbon steel possesses. Casehardening permits a part to be machined from soft low-carbon steel and then to be given a hard surface or case by carburizing or casehardening followed by heat-treatment. In the old process of manufacturing steel by the cementation process, bars of wrought iron were packed in crushed charcoal and heated above the critical range until sufficient carbon had been absorbed. The difference between this process and the modern casehardening is one of better scientific control.

When a hypoeutectoid steel is heated in an atmosphere of CO at a temperature above the critical range, some of the CO reacts with the skin of iron to form $FeO + C$. The latter is absorbed in the form of austenite, and the FeO is reduced by a fresh supply of CO. It is an equilibrium reaction, and if the concentration of the CO_2 is kept low, the film of oxide formed will always be very thin and the net result will be a continuous increase in the quantity of carbon dissolved in the steel up to a maximum of about 1.0 per cent carbon. When steel is packed in charcoal and heated above the critical range, the oxygen present in the porous mass forms CO_2 which is reduced to CO by reaction with the carbon of the charcoal, so that the concentration of CO_2 is always low at the temperature of carburization. If steel were packed in carbon in a vacuum, so that there would be no CO to act as the active carburizing agent, there would still be carburization where a particle of carbon was in direct physical contact with the surface of the steel. This process would however be slow.

The modern commercial solid carburizing compounds are made from charcoal or other form of soft carbon that has been activated. Barium carbonate ($BaCO_3$) decomposes at the temperature of the carburizing process to yield BaO and CO_2. The CO_2 drives out the inert nitrogen of the air originally present and reacts with the carbon to give an atmosphere much richer in CO than if the nitrogen of the air were still present. After the used carburizing compound has been cooled and exposed to the air, the BaO reacts with the CO_2 of the air, thus regenerating the $BaCO_3$. $CaCO_3$ and Na_2CO_3 are often used in admixture with $BaCO_3$. The duration of the casehardening process will be one or more hours depending upon the depth of case desired, the temperature, and the activity of the carburizing powder. Gas carburizing possesses many advantages for a large plant since the pieces may be placed on racks where each part receives the same treatment, and the temperature may be controlled more closely. The pieces after casehardening are usually allowed to cool slowly.

Cyanides and other nitrogenous compounds may form a part of the carburizing compounds, but since nitrogen plays a part in their action, they will be discussed separately.

Sometimes it is desirable to harden a portion of a surface, such as the wearing parts of a gear, and leave the balance of the surface unhardened. This selective carburization can be carried out only by protecting part of the surface from the action of CO gas. A plating of copper is effective, and a paste of clay and sodium silicate is easy to apply but less satisfactory.

Heat-treatment of Carburized Steel.—If steel has not been heated much above the critical range during the carburizing process, the grains of the core will not have become very coarse and a special heat-treatment to refine the grains of the core will not be necessary. If however the steel has become coarse grained in the carburizing process, then it will be corrected by the heat-treatment shown below, which is taken from the S.A.E. Handbook.

Heat-treatment 1020—IV
1. Carburize at 1650 to 1700°F.
2. Cool slowly or in box.
3. Reheat to 1650 to 1700°F.
4. Quench in oil or water.
5. Reheat to 1400 to 1450°F.
6. Quench.
7. Temper to 250 to 325°F.

The treatment of the third step consists in reheating to practically the same temperature as in the carburizing process. In reheating through the critical range, the coarse grain will be refined, and the piece should be quenched as soon as the 1020 core has been heated long enough to give the grain size that is desired. The critical range of the 1020 core is however much higher than that of the case, whose maximum carbon is somewhat over 0.83 per cent. The grain of the case will therefore have become coarse in operation 3, and operation 5 is to refine the grain of the case, without affecting the grain of the core because the temperature 1400 to 1450°F is not up to the Ac_3 range for a 1020 steel. When the piece is quenched from 1450, the case will be hardened, but not the core for the same reason. The last operation is to temper the case to the desired degree. The final result will be a fine-grained pearlitic core and a fine-grained case whose hardness will depend on the final tempering operation.

Cyaniding Steel.—Sodium cyanide (NaCN) fuses at temperatures below those used in casehardening, and metal pieces plunged in a cyanide bath maintained at a temperature above the critical range absorb both carbon and nitrogen. If only a very thin case is desired, powdered cyanide may be sprinkled on the hot steel. The temperature for cyaniding is usually just above the critical range for the steel to be treated, and the steel is quenched as soon as it is withdrawn from the bath. A 1020 steel immersed in cyanide for 1 hr at 1550°F will have a case 0.010 in. in thickness with a carbon content of 0.62 per cent. The time in the cyanide bath is usually sufficient to refine the grain but not to allow it to become coarse, so the piece after quenching will have a hard case and a fine-grained core. The outer zone of the case will be martensitic, and beneath that will be a zone of lower carbon content with a troostitic or sorbitic structure. The hardness of the case is greater than can be attributed to carbon, and a microscopic examination shows crystals of nitride intermingled with the carbide.

Cyanides are sometimes added as activators to the solid carburizing powders, and the carbon of these compounds was formerly derived from charred leather, bones, or other animal products that contain nitrogen. These materials give slightly greater activity, but are not considered so important a part of the mixtures as they were before the great importance of CO as a carburizing agent was known.

Nitriding Steels.—If the steel is heated in a current of dry ammonia gas at temperature of 900 to 1200°F, the NH_3 is decomposed on the metal surface and nitrogen is absorbed by the steel to form a hard nitride. Unfortunately the nitride of iron is unstable, and the process is not applicable to plain carbon steels. The nitride of aluminum is more stable, and most steels for nitriding carry from 0.9 to 1.5 per cent of aluminum. Small percentages of chromium, molybdenum, and vanadium seem to be helpful from the nitriding standpoint, as well as making their specific contribution to the strength of the steel, as discussed under Alloy Steel.

The machined piece should be heat-treated to have a fine grain and a sorbitic structure, and be free from strains before nitriding. The surface must not be decarburized. A case that is 50 per cent harder than that produced by carburizing may be obtained by nitriding. About 48 hr are required to produce a case 0.02 in. deep at 1000°F. The piece is cooled in the furnace to avoid scaling, but may be removed when a temperature of 700°F has been reached. It is ready for use as soon as it is withdrawn from the nitriding furnace and has cooled. If it is necessary to soften the steel, it can be accomplished by heating to 1500°F at which temperature the nitrides are decomposed and the nitrogen driven off. The hardness and wear-resistance produced by nitriding are greater than those obtained by any other steel-treating process, but the surface is also brittle.

Welding. *Pressure Processes.*—When two pieces of steel are heated well above the critical range and forced into close contact, they will unite if the surfaces were clean. This is the operation of forge welding as practiced by the blacksmith. Wrought iron welds more easily than mild steel because the intermingled slag acts as a flux to dissolve the oxide of iron that forms on the surface of the metal during heating. Borax (sodium borate) may be sprinkled on the surfaces before welding to form a fusible slag. The hammering process refines the grain of the metal which may have become coarse during the heating. The adjacent parts that had been heated and not forged will still have a coarse grain and will therefore be weaker. It is not uncommon, when a hammer-welded piece is broken, to have the break occur adjacent to the weld where the metal had not been hammered.

In factory operations such as the manufacture of steel pipe, a steel strip, bent to the proper curvature, is run continuously through a machine that applies a heavy electric current to the edges just when they are pressed together so that the heating and welding of a single small area are completed in a fraction of a second. In spot welding of sheets, heat and pressure are applied in localized areas for a time varying from a fraction of a second to a minute.

Fusion Processes.—In fusion welding, the two edges of the materials to be welded are heated until they are themselves fused momentarily. The thermit process produces a crucible full of superheated steel by the reaction of aluminum powder and iron oxide, with alloying materials added if desired. A form of fire clay, sand, or other refractory material is built around the parts to be welded so as to direct and confine the molten metal that is allowed to flow around and between the parts to be welded. The volume of superheated metal must be adjusted so that the surface to be welded will be brought to the proper temperature. After the weld has cooled, the surplus metal is ground away. The process is especially adapted to repairing large machine parts whose cross section is too great to be handled easily by the other methods.

In most welding operations, the heating agent is either an oxyacetylene gas flame or the electric current. The oxyacetylene torch with its tanks of gas is quite portable and used largely for cutting as well as welding metal. The flame may be adjusted so that it is either oxidizing, neutral, or reducing. A welding rod is frequently held in the flame and fused to build up the welded joint. The electric arc is also used as a source of heat with or without fluxes and welding rods. Welding has only recently been recognized as safe in important structures. The American Society of Mechanical Engineers in its Boiler Code permits boiler drums and shells to be fabricated by fusion welding even for the highest pressures. The welded joints are to be examined throughout their entire length by X-ray photographic methods to determine that the weld is sound and not porous. All pressure parts must have the strains relieved by heating uniformly and slowly to 1100°F and preferably to 1200°F. Steels with more than 0.35 per cent carbon are not advised for use in welds for pressure vessels. The specifications for steel for carbon-steel pressure vessels whose plate thickness is between 2 and 4 in. provide that the steel shall be made by the open-hearth or electric-furnace process with a maximum carbon content of 0.35 per cent. Sulfur and phosphorus must not be over 0.04 per cent. All plates before being fabricated shall be uniformly heat-treated to produce grain refinement.

Riveted Joints.—Plates are prepared for riveting by punching or drilling holes of the proper diameter at the exact points required. The holes in thin sheets and unimportant work may be punched at room temperature, but the process of punching entails severe cold work on the metal adjacent to the hole as is illustrated in Fig. 54 from Guillet and Portevin. The A.S.M.E. Boiler Code permits holes to be punched in plates less than 5/8 in. in thickness. Thicker plates must be drilled. The rivets come on the job with one head already formed. They are heated in a portable furnace to a forging heat and passed quickly to the riveter who inserts the rivet in the hole and, with the help of an assistant, upsets the cylindrical end of the rivet to form the other head and draw the two plates closely together. The process of upsetting should preferably be done by an air hammer to ensure proper working of the metal. The hot rivet cools very fast when it is inserted into the hole in the plates, and there is danger that it may be made brittle by working at a blue heat. Rivets are always made from steel with very low carbon so that they will be as ductile as possible. Where it is feasible to use

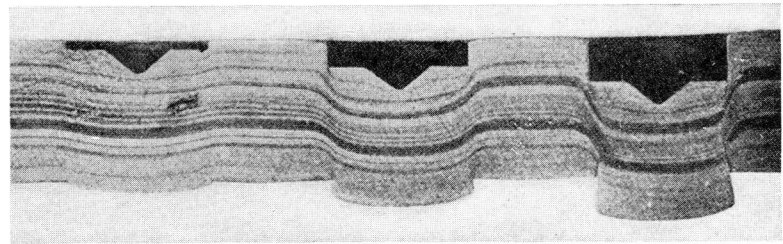

Fig. 54.—Deformation caused by punching a bar of wrought iron as shown by etching in hot acid. (*From Guillet and Portevin, Metallography and Macrography.*)

hydraulic pressure, it is sometimes considered better to head up the rivets at room temperature.

Cold-rolling and -drawing.—The shrinkage which steel undergoes and the scale which forms on the surface of metal while cooling from the hot-rolling temperature make it difficult to fabricate objects of exact dimension by the hot-rolling process. Cold work requires the expenditure of more mechanical energy, but it yields products with more exact dimensions and a smooth surface. The yield point increases more rapidly than the tensile strength, and the elongation decreases more rapidly than the reduction of area, as shown in Fig. 55. The effect of the cold work is to embrittle the metal, and in drawing wire, for example,

THE PROPERTIES OF PLAIN CARBON STEEL   147

the metal must be heated at intervals to remove the effects of the cold work and permit further drawing operations. Music wire (piano wire) is a cold-drawn wire containing 0.80 to 0.90 per cent carbon which may be coiled into springs without any further

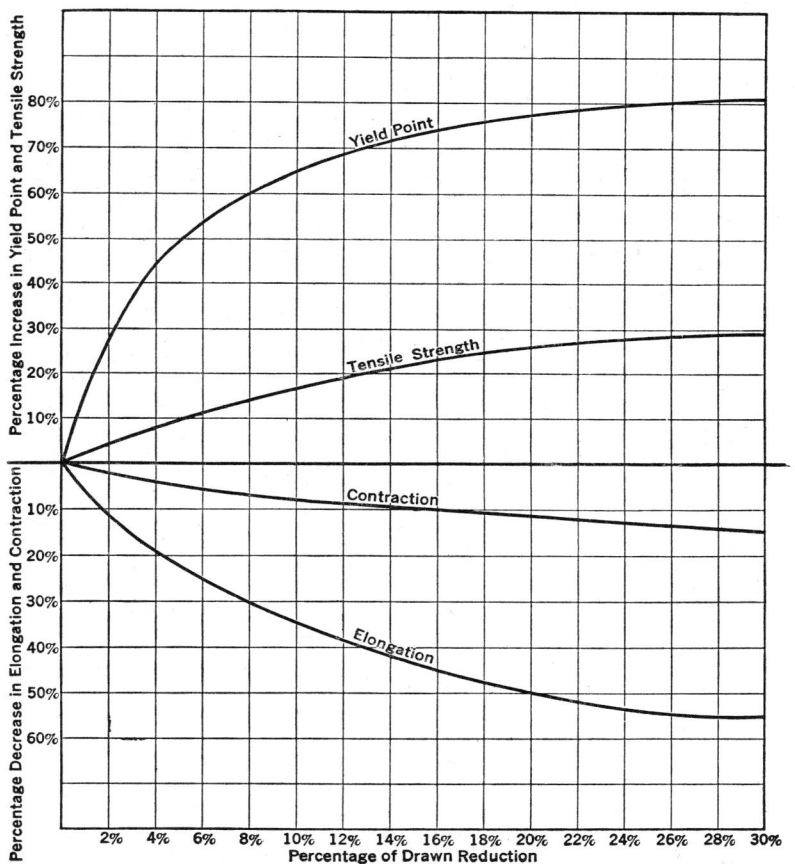

FIG. 55.—Effect of cold-drawing on the physical properties of carbon steel. (*From Bethlehem Steel Co. Catalog* 144.)

heat-treatment. Tubing for bicycle frames is cold-drawn to obtain higher elastic limit and accurate dimensions. Shafts of less than 2 in. in diameter are frequently cold-rolled. Sheet for tin plate and the strips used for forming automobile bodies are finished by cold-rolling. A view of a modern mill for strip up to

96 in. in width is shown in Fig. 56. If the cold-drawn metal is heated to 500 to 600°F, the tensile strength and yield point are raised somewhat without injury to the ductility or finish.[1]

FIG. 56.—Mill for cold-rolling steel strip. This mill will roll strip 98 in. wide continuously to extremely close tolerances. (*Courtesy of Republic Steel Corporation.*)

References

SISCO, F. T.: The Alloys of Iron and Carbon, Vol. II, Properties, McGraw-Hill Book Company, Inc., New York, 1937.
AMERICAN SOCIETY FOR TESTING MATERIALS: A.S.T.M. Standards and Tentative Standards, Philadelphia, 1936.
SOCIETY OF AUTOMOTIVE ENGINEERS: S.A.E. Handbook, 1938.
CAMP and FRANCIS: The Making, Shaping, and Treating of Steel, 4th ed., The Carnegie Steel Co., Pittsburgh, 1925.
AMERICAN SOCIETY FOR METALS: Metals Handbook, 1936.
BETHELEM STEEL CO.: Carbon Steel Bars and Special Sections, Catalog 144, 1937.
Symposium on Welding, American Society for Testing Materials, 1931.

[1] Metals Handbook, 1936 ed., p. 661.

CHAPTER IX

CASTING PROCESSES

The Cooling of Cast Metal.—Whenever molten metal is poured into a container where it solidifies, a casting results. In this sense, an ingot is a casting, but the term "casting" is usually restricted to a mass of solidified metal whose shape is not to be modified later by forging or rolling. In the discussion of solidification of steel ingots, it was noted that gases were evolved, and that there was considerable shrinkage in volume both during and after solidification. The ingot was cast into a simple cast-iron mold made slightly conical so that it could be easily removed and used over again. The gases escaped from the open top of the ingot mold. The shrinkage was concentrated in the top, where a reservoir of molten metal was provided which flowed into the center of the ingot to replace the shrinkage caused by solidification. After the whole mass became solid and the outer surface was no longer plastic, shrinkage strains did develop in the ingot and frequently became high enough to cause small cracks in the interior. Visible cracks did not start at the surface because when the surface chilled the center and top were still liquid, and so the surface metal could shrink freely. It was only after the outer skin became rigid and the metal was all frozen that large shrinkage strains developed in the metal. The unsound metal in the top in the ingot was removed by cropping, and the cracks in the center of the ingot were welded together in a satisfactory manner in the rolling mill, since their surfaces were not oxidized. If the cross section of the billet coming from the rolling mill was small, or if the cooling of pieces with large sections was slow, the rolled product would be free from large internal stresses, and hence free from visible cracks.

If a molten metal is to be cast into a complicated shape, provision must be made for elimination of gases and shrinkage strains. Metal molds are desirable because they can be used many times. They are used advantageously with castings of simple shapes and alloys of low melting point. Complicated shapes must be cast in a mold that is rigid enough to hold the molten metal when it is poured, but which will be weak enough to permit the metal to crush it during the shrinking process without injury to the metal.

Sand Molds and Cores.—Sand molds have been known to the iron founders since early times, and they are used now without any great change in the general procedure. The improvements have been in details and have come rapidly in recent years

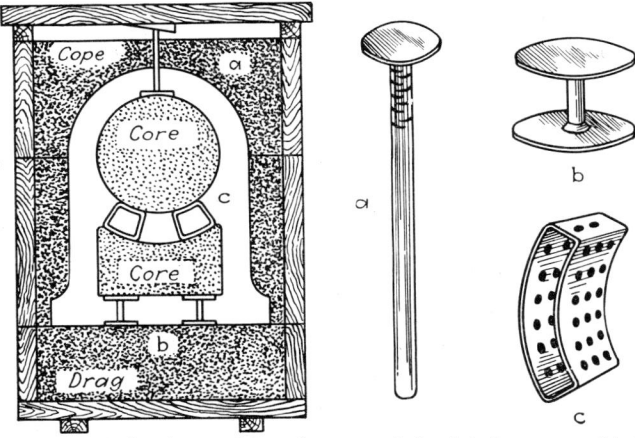

FIG. 57.—Sketch showing position of cores and chaplets in an assembled mold. (*From Foundry Work, by Stimpson, Gray and Grennan. Courtesy of American Technical Society.*)

because of the applications of scientific research. Clean sand such as is found on the seashore may be formed into definite shape while damp, the bond being provided by the thin films of water surrounding each grain. When the sand becomes dry, the bond has gone, and the definite shape collapses to a loose mass of grains of sand. Iron founders discovered, by experience, that there were foundry sands which could be formed into definite shape while damp and which retained the form even after the moisture had almost all disappeared by evaporation. DeWitt and Brown[1] showed that these foundry sands were coated with a thin film of clay containing some colloidal iron hydroxide, and that it was entirely possible to produce good foundry sands by

[1] *Trans. Am. Foundrymen's Assn.*, 1928, pp. 247–276.

coating clean sand with these materials. A mold of sand used without drying is called a "green-sand mold," and if it is baked before using, it becomes a dry-sand mold. If a hollow article such as a water pipe is to be cast, it is necessary to have a solid core placed in the mold and carefully centered so that the molten metal will flow only into the empty spaces between the core and the outer wall of the mold. This core must be accurate in dimensions and strong enough to stand handling. It must also break down to loose sand after the casting has been made, so that the hollow center may be emptied of the sand through a rather small opening. Cores are formed from sand mixed with binders which may contain starch, molasses, and a wide variety of other adhesives that are soluble in water. Linseed oil which forms a tough film on oxidation in the air is also used as a binder. These cores are formed in boxes and baked in an oven before use. The use of cores and methods of supporting them by thin shapes of steel called "chaplets" is shown in Fig. 57. The gates and risers are not shown in this sectional view. The core maintains its shape while the hot metal flows around it but collapses as the heat carbonizes and destroys the binder. The gases escape through vents which are properly spaced in the mold.

Patterns.—A pattern is an exact replica of the finished casting, except that it is made slightly larger to provide for shrinkage of the casting. Patterns are usually made of wood painted or waxed to give a smooth surface, but if a pattern is to be used many times it may be made of aluminum, brass, or cast iron so as to be more durable. Patterns that are to be used over and over are usually split. The two halves are fastened in exact position on opposite sides of a metal plate to facilitate the work of the molder.

Making a Sand Mold.—In the older foundry practice and in jobbing foundries that are only making a few castings from any pattern, the pattern is an exact replica of the article to be cast and is set by hand at the proper height in the sand. The flask is then filled completely with damp foundry sand uniformly rammed, and the surface is struck off with a straightedge. The pattern is then withdrawn carefully, leaving in the sand an imprint of the lower part of the pattern. Another flask containing the imprint of the upper part of the pattern is prepared in a similar way. The tamped green sand is strong enough so that the top flask may be carefully inverted over the lower flask, leaving a hollow space which, when filled with metal, will form the finished casting. Some means must be provided for pouring the metal into the hollow space, and for this purpose one or more passages called "gates" are provided in the sand of the top flask so that when the two flasks are put together there will be at least one funnel-shaped hole into which the metal may be poured. Other openings extending to the upper surface permit the gases to escape, and allow surplus metal to rise to the surface and form "risers" which act as reservoirs of molten metal to flow into the casting as it

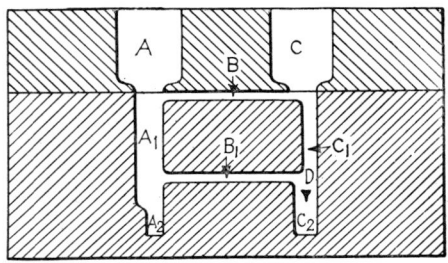

FIG. 58.—Sketch of arrangements to ensure proper flow of metal in making a casting. The risers are shown but not the gate. This drawing indicated the manner in which the location of sections in relation to others influences the ultimate soundness of a casting. The casting is represented by sections A_1-A_2. B-B_1, C_1-C_2 and risers A and C. In cooling A_2 is fed by A_1, which in turn received metal from riser A. Sections B and B_1 due to their lightness will cool almost instantaneously and will require little feeding. Such metal as is needed, is supplied by the adjacent sections. The location of heavy section C_2 below the lighter section C_1 effectively shuts off its supply of liquid metal because sections C_1 and B_1 solidify before C_2 is solid, leaving a shrink hole as at D. Design of these sections as at A_1 and A_2 would prevent this possibility of a shrink. (*From Cast Metals Handbook*.)

solidifies and shrinks. The assembly ready for pouring is shown in cross section in Fig. 58. When the foundryman pours the metal into the gate, the air that is contained in the mold escapes through the porous sand walls and the risers so that the metal fills the mold completely and rises in the gate and the risers until it is level with the top of the flask. The cross-sectional area of the riser should be so large that the metal in it remains liquid until all of the casting proper has solidified. Thus the riser serves as a source of molten metal to provide for the shrinkage of the solidifying casting. The skill needed in designing the pattern and providing for the gates and risers necessary to provide for a proper flow of the hot metal is illustrated in Fig. 59.

In modern foundry practice where a complicated casting such as the cylinder block of an engine may be made by the thousand, molding machines are employed which facilitate accurate work and decrease the hand labor. The principles of the operation are however the same as they were in the older days.

Solidification of a Casting.—The surface of the molten metal is chilled rapidly on contact with the sand, and the metal does not flow into the pores of the sand in the mold. The shrinkage of a steel casting is about $\frac{1}{4}$ in. on a foot. If the valve body of Fig. 59 is to be 12 in. long, then the pattern must be $12\frac{1}{4}$ in. in length and the newly solidified casting will be the same length. If the casting is restrained from shrinking, it will crack, and therefore the material of the mold must be friable enough to crush under a rather slight load. The heat of the metal drives off the combined water from the bond in the sand, thus decreasing the strength and permitting the casting to shrink without injury. The casting of Fig. 58 presents difficulty because the cross bars B and $B1$ are both of small cross sections and will solidify more quickly than the vertical bars $A1$ and $C1$.

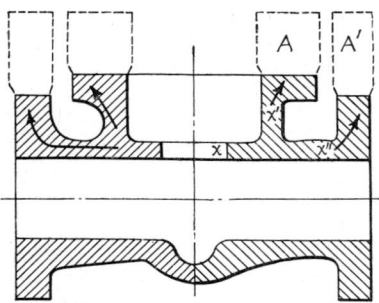

Fig. 59.—Sketch of modifications in design to ensure proper flow of metal in casting a steel valve body. Progressive solidification as applied to a cast-steel valve body. The right half represents an original valve design. The left half represents a design modified to permit progressive solidification. Since solidification will begin at the thinner sections, points x, x' and x'' will solidify first and solidification will proceed from these points. It is evident that the cross-hatched area included within x, x' and x'' will not be fed adequately by risers A and A'. In the design at the left, the section has been modified to permit controlled progressive solidification as indicated by the arrows. Solidification proceeds from the thinner sections, through the heavier sections to the head or riser. (*From Cast Metals Handbook.*)

B and $B1$ in shrinking may tear away from the vertical units which have hardly solidified. If that does not happen, B and $B1$ may not have enough strength to crush the sand between the two verticals and permit the casting to shrink properly. It is advisable to loosen the sand around the casting as soon as solidification is complete so as to decrease the resistance to shrinkage.

Finishing Sand Castings.—When the casting is shaken from the sand, the gates and risers are still adherent to it, and the surface is usually covered with adherent grains of sand. The gates and risers are cut off with a saw or an oxyacetylene torch, or knocked off if the metal is cast iron, and the surface is cleaned with a wire brush or a blast of air carrying suspended sand, known as a "sand blast." Small castings may be tumbled in rotating barrels to clean them. The cooling of a large casting will have usually been slow enough so that the grain is coarse, and if the design is at all complicated there will be shrinkage strains in the metal. Normalizing will remove the shrinkage strains and give a fine-grained structure.

MELTING METALS FOR CASTING

The Cupola.—The foundries making gray-iron castings usually melt pig iron and scrap iron in a cupola which is illustrated in Fig. 60. It bears some resemblance to a small blast furnace in that it consists of a stack lined with firebrick and kept full of a charge which consists of coke, limestone, and in this case, pig iron and solid scrap, instead of the ore charged into the blast furnace. Air, which is usually not preheated, is blown in near the bottom, and slag and molten iron are drawn off through separate spouts. The blast furnace is primarily a mechanism for reducing ore to iron, and the cupola is primarily a remelting furnace.

The blast furnace has an extremely high temperature and strongly reducing conditions. The cupola is not so strongly reducing because its temperature is not so high, and enough air is blown in at the bottom to give more CO_2 in the stack gases. The atmosphere is actually slightly oxidizing, and some silicon, manganese, and iron are oxidized and form a slag with the lime added. The cupola has a removable bottom, and it is customary to dump it at the close of a day's work. The cupola has good fuel economy, is simple in construction, permits the use of a large proportion of cast iron and steel scrap, may be made in a variety of sizes, and is widely used for melting pig and scrap iron to make foundry castings.

The Air Furnace.—In the process of making malleable-iron castings which will be described in the next chapter, the composition of the metal is usually modified during the melting operation by oxidation of part of the silicon. The cupola does not permit controlled oxidation, and much of the metal for malleable castings is melted in a type of reverberatory furnace which is frequently called an "air furnace." A modern furnace of this

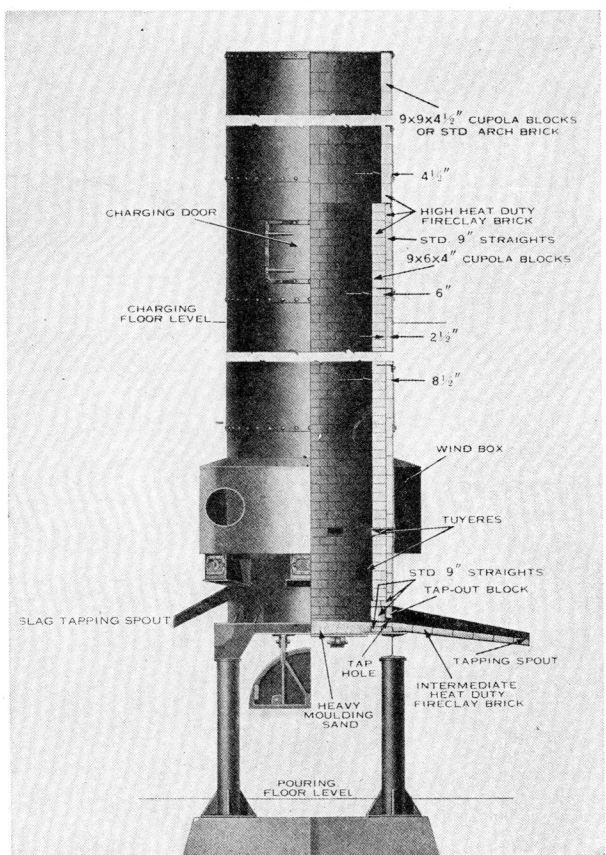

FIG. 60.—Construction of cupola for melting cast iron. (*From Harbison-Walker Co., Modern Refractory Practice.*)

type fired with powdered coal is shown in Fig. 61. It consists of a long and rather narrow hearth where the pig iron and scrap are melted. The atmosphere may be made oxidizing or reducing, and so the silicon and carbon can both be oxidized rather slowly if desired. The composition of the finished metal and the final pouring temperature are both under the control of the operator.

Melting Nonferrous Alloys.—Alloys of copper, zinc, aluminum, and other nonferrous metals are usually melted without any intentional change in composition other than that involved in mixing. Their price per pound is always higher than pig iron or steel, and therefore it may be economical to devote greater expense and care to the melting process. Crucibles are still

FIG. 61.—An air furnace fired with powdered coal. (*Courtesy of Whiting Corporation.*)

used, and if the melting point is low as in the lead alloys, iron pots give good results. Hearth furnaces fired with oil or gas are often found in the larger sizes, and electricity is frequently used as a heating agent.

Steel Castings.—Bessemer converters (side blown) may be made to hold only 1 ton of steel at a charge, and open-hearth furnaces of as little as 10 tons capacity are practical. Electric furnaces may be made of any size desired. The melting point of low-carbon steels is especially high, and the sand used for molds must be selected to stand the high temperature and the cutting action of the hot metal as it is poured into the gate.

The specifications for steel castings for railroad use as published by the American Society for Testing Materials[1] state the steel may be made by the converter, open-hearth, electric-furnace, or crucible process. The casting will in all cases be normalized or annealed, and this may be followed by heat-treatment. Phosphorus must be below 0.06, sulfur below 0.05, and manganese below 0.85 per cent. The percentage of carbon is left to the manufacturer who must produce a metal of the desired physical properties. For important castings such as locomotive frames, "coupons" must be cast attached at specified points of the frame. These coupons are cut off after the metal has been normalized or annealed, and the specimens for tensile test are machined from the coupons. The minimum physical properties of the steel for a purpose such as a locomotive frame are specified to be: tensile strength 70,000 and yield point 38,000 psi, with elongation 24 per cent and reduction of area 36 per cent on a standard 2-in. test piece.

Castings of plain carbon steel are not usually made with a carbon content of over 0.60 per cent. The high-carbon steels are sensitive to heat-treatment and are brittle unless skillfully handled. There is also danger of separation of graphite unless the tendency of the silicon to cause free graphite is counterbalanced by other alloying elements. Alloying elements are frequently incorporated in the steel for castings, and their influence will be considered in the chapter on Alloy Steels.

Permanent Metal Molds.—Where large numbers of parts of identical shape are to be cast, there are many advantages in metal molds which may be used over and over. Such molds are widely used in casting alloys of aluminum, magnesium, copper, and zinc, whose melting point is low. Cast iron with its higher melting point is more destructive to the mold, and steel castings are not often made in permanent molds because of the difficulty of finding a metal to withstand the high temperatures and the strains resulting from heating and cooling. It is sometimes difficult to provide for venting metal molds to permit the escape of gases. The metal cast into permanent molds chills rapidly because the metal is a better conductor of heat than is the porous sand.

[1] A.S.T.M. Standards, 1936 ed., p. 247.

158   ENGINEERING MATERIALS

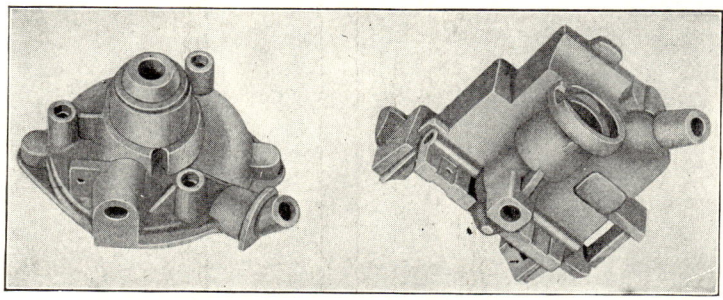

a

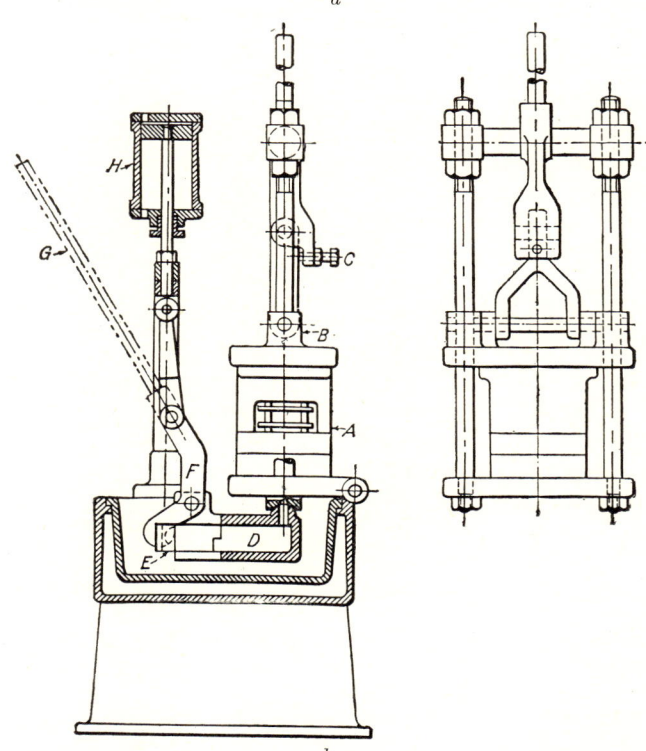

b

Fig. 62.—Die castings and die-casting machine. *a*, intricate speedometer and odometer die castings; *b*, Doehler plunger die-casting machine. (*From Stern, Die-Casting Practice.*)

Die Castings.—In die casting, the molten metal is forced into the metal mold under pressure. Such castings are smooth and clean and require little finishing treatment except to remove the surplus metal at the stem of the casting.

Stern[1] gives a description and cut of a simple type of die-casting machine which is widely used. As shown in Fig. 62, it consists of a pot of molten metal in which is the pressure chamber D and the plunger E. When the plunger is drawn back, the metal flows into the pressure chamber. When the plunger is advanced, the metal is forced upward into the die A which may be rapidly opened and closed by the mechanism partially shown at B and C. The illustrations that form a part of Fig. 62 show the intricate shapes which may be produced. The linotype and monotype machines used in preparing the printing plates for newspapers are specialized die-casting machines.

Centrifugal Castings.—Castings of simple shape such as cast-iron water mains are often produced by pouring the molten iron into a rotating metal mold. The Watertown Arsenal of the United States Army has developed the centrifugal casting of cannon with bore as large as 155 mm diameter.[2]

Recently the Ford Motor Company has developed centrifugal castings to a point where it is casting transmission gears and ring gears of a quality superior to those produced by forging. The mold is made of cast low-carbon steel and has only two parts—the removable top, and the base which is anchored to a revolving shaft. The castings are annealed, machined, and heat-treated as described in Chap. XII.

References

AMERICAN FOUNDRYMAN'S ASSOCIATION: Cast Metals Handbook, Chicago, 1935.

AMERICAN SOCIETY FOR METALS: Metals Handbook, Cleveland, 1939.

CAMPBELL, H. L.: Metal Castings. John Wiley & Sons, Inc., New York, 1936.

STERN, MARC: Die-casting Practice, McGraw-Hill Book Company, Inc., New York, 1930.

AMERICAN SOCIETY FOR TESTING MATERIALS: A.S.T.M. Standards, 1936.

STIMPSON, GRAY, and GRENNAN: Foundry Work, American Technical Society, Chicago, 1939.

[1] STERN, MARC, Die-casting Practice. McGraw-Hill Book Company, Inc., 1930, p. 169.

[2] DICKSON, T. C., Casting Guns by the Centrifugal Process, *Trans. Am. Soc. Steel Testing*, **18**, 212 (1930).

CHAPTER X

GRAY CAST IRONS AND MALLEABLE CASTINGS

The Different Types of Cast Iron.—Little attention has been paid so far in this text to the irons containing over 1.7 per cent carbon. In accordance with the iron-carbon diagram, their microscopic structure when slowly cooled consists of cementite

a *b*

Fig. 63.—Microscopic structure of white cast iron. *a*, the black is pearlite and the white portion is cementite, ×100; *b*, the same structure, ×1000.

and pearlite, and the metal is inherently hard and brittle. A small amount of material with this composition and these properties is produced under the name of "white cast iron." It is so hard that it cannot be machined with ordinary tools and is usually cast into simple shapes and finished by grinding for such purposes as brake shoes, plowshares, and other parts where resistance to abrasion is important. Most of the white-iron castings on the market are produced by quick cooling, and very few would remain white after annealing. The microscopic structure of such a chilled iron is shown in Fig. 63 to contain large amounts of hard cementite.

The gray cast iron of which most of our usual castings are manufactured has the same carbon content, 3.0 to 3.5 per cent, as the white iron. However the carbon, instead of existing in the form of cementite, has been transformed almost completely into graphite during solidification and subsequent cooling, so that the microscopic structure of the slowly cooled metal consists of granules of pearlite, with sometimes a little ferrite, which are separated by large flakes of graphite, as shown in the three pictures of Fig. 64. It is the graphite that gives iron its gray appearance. This metal is easily machined, because the ferrite grains are soft and the graphite flakes cause the chips to break off and clear the point of the tool. The graphite flakes also cut down the strength and ductility of the metal. This difference in properties between gray and white cast iron is due primarily to the influence of a third element, silicon.

There exists still another important class of castings with almost the same carbon content called "malleable castings." These are made from metal that, on very slow cooling, would yield gray castings. The castings are however of such small cross section that they cool so quickly that the cementite does not have opportunity to decompose. The castings are therefore white iron and are hard and brittle. If these castings are annealed under proper conditions, the cementite breaks down to graphite and the resultant structure changes to grains of ferrite with a little pearlite, mixed with graphite in a fine powdery form frequently called "temper carbon" or "secondary graphite." The structure is shown in G of Fig. 67. This finely divided graphite does not interfere with the tensile strength like the large flakes of graphite formed while the metal was solidifying, so that malleable castings are more like mild steel than like white or gray cast iron.

The percentages of carbon, manganese, sulfur, and phosphorus may be the same in each of these three types of irons. The controlling variable is silicon.

Influence of Silicon.—Silicon forms solid solutions with iron in all amounts up to about 15 per cent. When both carbon and

162   *ENGINEERING MATERIALS*

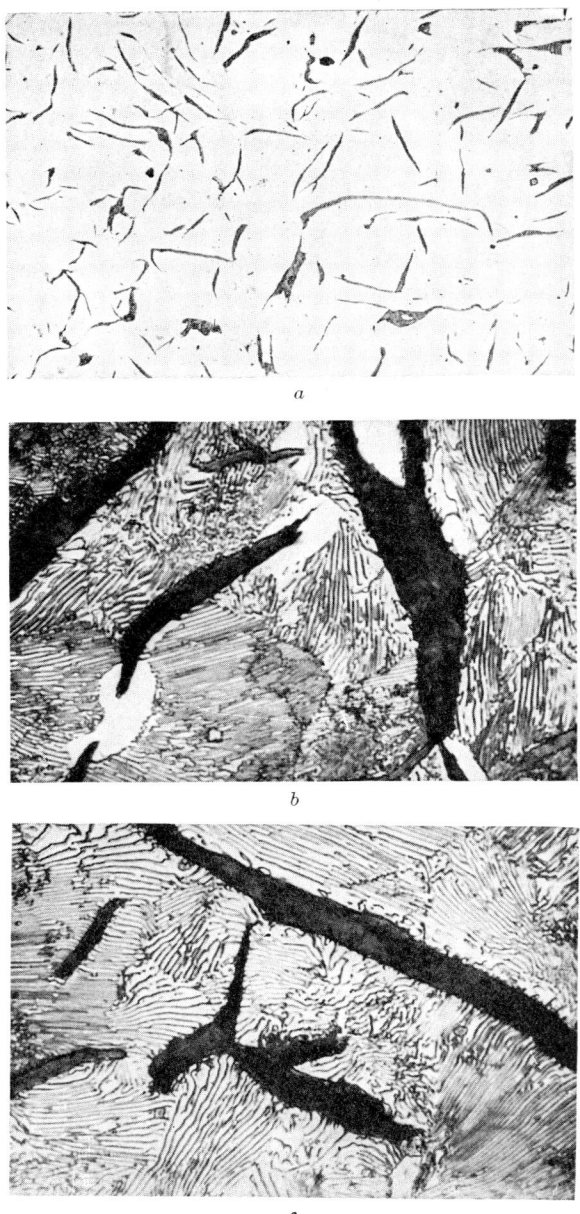

a

b

c

Fig. 64.—For caption see opposite page.

silicon are present, a complex system is formed that can be shown only by a ternary diagram which has not been worked out at all completely. Silicon apparently forms a solid solution, not only with ferrite but also with cementite, and decreases the stability of Fe_3C, forcing it to form graphite. Silicon also decreases the solubility of cementite in gamma iron so that the maximum amount of carbon in austenite becomes less with increasing amounts of silicon.

Greiner, Marsh, and Stoughton have compiled an equilibrium diagram indicating that, with 2.0 per cent silicon, the temperature of the eutectoid transformation has been raised to about 1425°F and the percentage of carbon in the austenite has been lowered from 0.83 to about 0.6 per cent. With 3.8 per cent silicon, the corresponding figures are 1525°F and 0.4 per cent carbon. The upper part of the equilibrium diagram is quite similar to the standard iron-carbon diagram, with the important exception that the eutectic consists of austenite and graphite instead of austenite and cementite. The graphite separates partly while the iron is still in the liquid state. The flakes of graphite rise to the surface of the molten metal as it is running from the blast furnace and are whirled away by the ascending currents of hot air, to fall again as fine black flakes like snow. The graphite that separates after solidification has commenced is forced into the intergranular spaces where it forms large flakes, if the freezing process proceeds slowly. The final solidification takes place somewhat above the plain iron-carbon eutectic temperature 2065°F (1130°C), and the eutectic contains 3.6 per cent carbon when the alloy contains 1.9 per cent silicon. The eutectic will consist of an intimate mixture of graphite and austenite with about 1.6 per cent carbon. As the alloy cools after solidification, the austenite will decompose as the temperature falls, with graphite separating and the austenite becoming impoverished,

FIG. 64.—Microscopic structure of gray cast irons. (*Courtesy of Dr. Richard Schneidewind.*)

a, Composition C 3.03, Si 2.01, Mn 0.76 per cent. Superheated to 2800°F and poured at 2540°F. Cast in sand as 2 in. bar. ×100. Not etched. The structure shows metal granules and flakes of graphite.

b, Same metal. ×1000. Etched. The structure shows pearlite and graphite with small areas of ferrite.

c, composition C 3.37, Si 1.64, Mn 0.65 per cent. Superheated to 2800°F and poured at 2520°F. Cast in sand as 1.2 in. bar. ×1000. Etched. The lesser amount of silicon has not produced any separation of ferrite so that the structure consists of pearlite and graphite.

until at a temperature of 1380°F (750°C) for the hypereutectoid alloys the remaining austenite, now containing about 0.5 per cent carbon, decomposes into alpha iron plus cementite, with a pearlitic structure.

The cementite that still exists at the eutectoid temperature breaks down on very slow cooling below the critical range to alpha iron and graphite so that the final product on cooling very slowly to room temperature will consist only of alpha ferrite and graphite. Hansen showed that an iron with 2.82 per cent carbon and only 0.39 per cent silicon could have all of its carbon changed to graphite by a cooling process so slow that 6 days were consumed in lowering the temperature from 2000 to 1175°F. This effect of small percentages of silicon on the decomposition of cementite explains some of the care necessary in forging or otherwise treating tool steel at a red heat.

Influence of Manganese and Sulfur.—Manganese and sulfur oppose each other in many ways. Sulfur has a marked effect in stabilizing cementite, and it has been stated that 0.1 per cent of sulfur, unless combined with manganese, can counteract the graphitizing effect of 1.0 per cent silicon. However, manganese forms manganese sulfide which is insoluble in the metal and exists as spherical inclusions, and the sulfur in this form is not harmful. There seems to be general agreement that if the sulfur is not over 0.10 per cent it will be quite adequately cared for by the 0.40 to 0.80 per cent of manganese that is usually present.

Influence of Phosphorus.—Phosphorus has its usual effect on the metallic granules in making them harder and more brittle under shock. It has little influence on the formation of the graphite. It promotes the fluidity of the metal as it is poured, and is helpful in casting thin sections. The A.S.T.M. Standard Specification for Cast Iron Locomotive Cylinders permits 0.90 per cent phosphorus, and the iron used for casting the thin sections of soil pipe and radiators may contain over 1.0 per cent phosphorus.

Grades of Foundry Pig Irons.—It has been shown that the blast furnace must produce iron almost or quite saturated with carbon. The quantity held in solution will depend on the temperature of the furnace and the degree of saturation, but will vary from 2.50 to 4.00 per cent. The silicon will be the chief variable and may vary from 1.0 to 3.0 per cent. In the old days before chemical control was customary and when pig iron was cast into sand beds, the pig iron was bought by the foundrymen on the basis of the appearance of the freshly fractured surface of a broken pig. If the grain was coarse and bright, it was graded as number 1 foundry and if small and dull as number 3 gray iron. At the bottom of the list were mottled and white irons. The assumption was that all sand-cast pigs cooled at about the same rate, and that a pig which showed a coarse fracture and large crystals of graphite would give the same fracture and type of metal if it was remelted and made into a casting that would cool at about the same rate as the pig did. When the practice of casting pigs into sand was abandoned for the process of machine casting into metal molds which cooled the iron quickly, the method of grading by appearance of the fractures had to be abandoned. Grading by chemical analysis was substituted, and the present classification is based on the silicon content. Number 1 foundry iron contains 2.50 to 3.00 per cent, number 2 carries 2.00 to 2.50, and number 3 has 1.50 to 2.00 per cent of silicon.

Iron with less than 1.5 per cent silicon keeps much of its carbon in the combined form (cementite) at any ordinary rate of cooling and so produces castings that are hard and brittle. Iron with 3.0 per cent silicon gives castings that contain very little cementite, almost all of the carbon being in the form of graphite with a little in the form of pearlite. If the silicon is increased much beyond 3.0 per cent, it commences to harden the ferrite through its direct alloying effect and to cause the flakes of graphite to be small, giving the iron a silvery appearance. These irons are hard and brittle but are known to the foundrymen as "softeners." If the pig iron that the foundryman has at hand is too low in silicon and will give too hard a casting, then the addition of a "softener" high in silicon to the charge going into the melting furnace will give the proper amount of silicon, and hence a softer iron.

The Effect of Graphite on Physical Properties.—The physical properties of cast iron are determined largely by the quantity and size of the flakes of graphite. The latter is a soft, almost greasy material whose density is only 2.25 whereas that of iron is 7.86. The part of the graphite that is liberated before the metal has started to freeze rises to the surface of the molten metal and blows away. That which is liberated after the metal has started

166 ENGINEERING MATERIALS

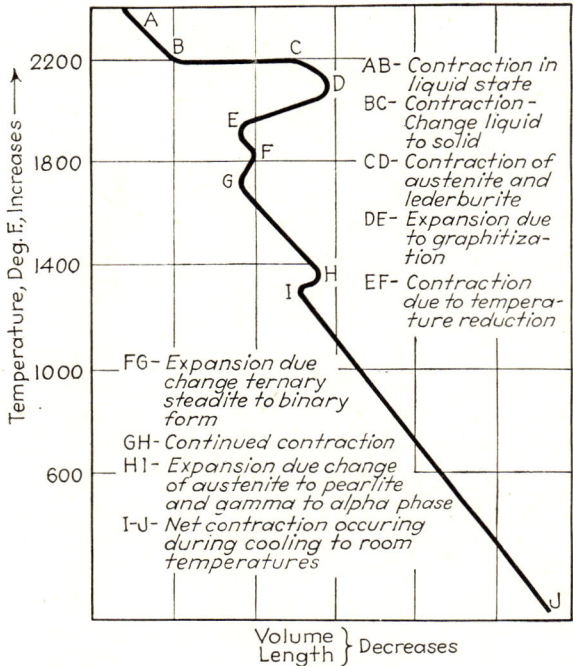

FIG. 65.—Diagrammatic representation of expansion and contraction effects in cast iron. (*From Bolton, Gray Cast Iron.*)

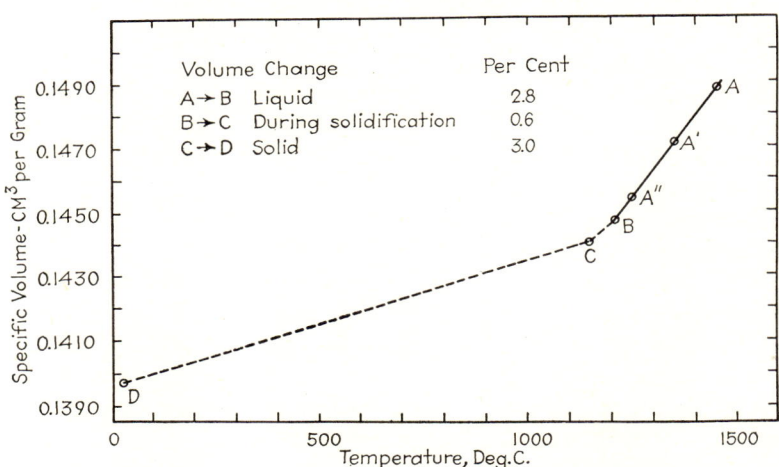

FIG. 66.—Volume changes on cooling a gray cast iron. [*From Ash and Saeger, Trans. Am. Foundrymen's Assn.*, **40**, 189 (1932).]

to freeze remains trapped in the pasty metal and is forced to the grain boundaries where, with slow cooling, it forms large flakes. The volume of the graphite is more than three times that of the same weight of carbon as cementite, and hence the decomposition of the cementite will be accompanied by an increase in volume of the casting. The gray iron will shrink after solidification, but only $\frac{1}{8}$ in. per foot need be allowed for shrinkage as compared with $\frac{1}{4}$ in. per foot for steel castings. It is evident that large flakes of graphite will constitute planes of weakness which will be especially harmful to tensile strength. The volume changes during solidification and cooling are shown diagrammatically for a gray cast iron in Fig. 65. Curves showing the actual shrinkage of a gray iron are shown in Fig. 66.

Effect of Rate of Cooling on Graphite Formation.—If molten cast iron should be quenched extremely rapidly, the carbon should theoretically remain in solid solution as austenite. If the rate of quenching should be slightly slower, very little of the carbon would have opportunity to separate as graphite, and the larger part of it would remain as cementite in the form of free cementite or of pearlite, troostite, or even martensite, giving a hard brittle iron. If the cooling was considerably slower and there was 3.0 per cent of silicon present, almost all of the carbon would appear as graphite, and with only 1.0 per cent silicon and the same rate of cooling, much of the carbon would stay as cementite. Castings of identical composition may therefore vary in properties, depending on the rate of cooling, from a hard, brittle white iron to a soft, gray iron which can be machined easily. None of the cast irons will show much ductility after being cooled from the molten state. If the carbon is in the form of cementite, the iron will be brittle, and if it is in the form of graphite there will be so few points of continuity of the metallic granules that rupture in tension will take place soon after the elongation commences. The effect of silicon on the proportion of graphite and the tensile strength is shown in Table 15.

Physical Properties of Gray-iron Castings.—It is evident from what has preceded that the physical properties of cast iron are very dependent upon the two variables of rate of cooling and chemical composition. The American Society for Testing Materials in its Standard Specifications for Gray Iron Castings[1]

[1] A.S.T.M. Standards, 1936. Specification A 48-36, p. 457.

classifies irons according to tensile strength, with the provision that the test piece shall be machined from a bar of a diameter to be agreed on, which is to be cast separately from the main casting. Cast irons are divided into six classes, 20, 25, 30, 35, 40, and 50, each of the classes corresponding to the number of thousands pounds tensile strength that the metal shows. The tensile strength of the usual foundry irons comprising classes 20, 25, and 30 will be not less than 20,000, 25,000, and 30,000 psi, respectively. The compressive strength for ordinary foundry irons is almost four times the tensile strength. Cast iron is so brittle that its elongation is not specified.

TABLE 15.—EFFECT OF VARIATION IN PERCENTAGE OF SILICON ON PROPERTIES OF CAST-IRON BARS

Bars 1 by 3/8 in. cross section were cast in sand at the same temperature. In each case, the Mn was not over 0.20, S not over 0.05, and P not over 0.05.*

| Percentage composition ||| Tensile strength, psi | Appearance of fracture |
Silicon	Graphite	Combined carbon		
1.10	Trace	3.0	32,000	White
1.68	0.65	2.3	22,800	Mottled
1.80	2.6	0.55	21,400	Gray
2.50	2.85	0.48	18,120	Gray

* From Hadfield's data.

A transverse test of a bar requires less equipment than a tensile test and is frequently made. The bar most commonly used is 1.20 in. in diameter and 21 in. long. It is tested just as it was drawn from the sand by placing it on knife-edges 18 in. apart and breaking with a load applied slowly midway between the supports. The bar will deflect from 0.16 to 0.40 in. and will support a load of 1800 to 3400 lb before breaking.

The effect of rate of cooling on tensile strength is exemplified in Table 16 for relative tensile strength of bars of different diameters cast from the same heat of metal. The larger the diameter of the bar, the slower will be the rate of cooling and the greater will be the proportion of graphite to cementite in the finished casting.

TABLE 16.—RELATIVE TENSILE STRENGTH OF BARS OF CAST IRON OF DIFFERENT DIAMETER*

Class of iron	Diameter of bar, in.			
	0.75	1.1	1.6	2.0
20	100	79	60	53
25	100	81	73	72
30	100	78	71	67
35	100	83	68	66
40	100	85	80	67
50	100	90	79	72

* From Symposium on Cast Iron published jointly by the American Society for Testing Materials and the American Foundrymen's Association, p. 77, 1933.

High-strength Cast Iron or Semisteel.—If a portion of steel scrap is added to the charge of pig-iron and cast-iron scrap going into the melting furnace, it may not make much change in the percentage of manganese, sulfur, and phosphorus, but it is certain to cut down the percentage of carbon and silicon. On cooling, the amount of carbon separating as graphite will be reduced by the dilution, and the resulting cast iron will therefore be stronger. Cast irons in the 40 to 60 class are generally produced by addition of steel to the mixture. The name "semisteel" was formerly applied to this material, but the term has become obsolete. The term "high-strength cast iron" which replaced the designation of semisteel is now itself being replaced by the more accurate designation of the class number corresponding to the tensile strength.

Chilled Castings.—It is sometimes desirable to produce a casting with a hard surface to resist wear and a tougher and softer core which may be easily machined. Wheels for freight cars are usually cast to produce a chilled rim and a center that is somewhat graphitic. The wheels are cast in sand molds except for the rims, where the mold consists of a heavy steel ring that chills the iron enough to produce white iron to the depth of about ½ in. At greater depths, the iron becomes mottled, and still further towards the center it shows a fine-grained gray structure. The physical properties of the surface and core are shown in Table 17. Sample II with its lower carbon content, and hence lower graphite, shows a tensile strength approximately 10,000 lb greater than Sample I. The change in microscopic structure from white cast iron at the face to a gray cast iron in the interior is shown in the pictures of Figs. 63 and 64.

TABLE 17.—PHYSICAL PROPERTIES OF CHILLED CAST IRONS*

	I	II
Total carbon, per cent	3.50	2.75
Silicon, per cent	0.75	0.75
Hardness of chilled surface, Brinell number	500	400
Tensile strength, psi:		
Chilled section	35,000 to 40,000	48,000 to 53,000
Gray core	16,000 to 25,000	22,000 to 39,000

* From Symposium on Cast Iron, American Society for Testing Materials and American Foundrymen's Association, p. 137, 1933.

Effect of Temperature of Molten Metal.—Pig iron and gray cast iron both consist of a mechanical mixture of graphite, whose melting point is about 6300°F, and metallic grains which are approximately a low-carbon steel with a melting point of perhaps 2700°F. The molten liquid resulting from complete solution of this mixture will commence to freeze at about 2300°, and if the mixture of metals charged into the melting furnace should be held for a long enough time at 2300°, there would be gradual diffusion and fusion at that temperature. In order to get rapid fusion, the furnace is heated to 2700 to 2800°F, and even at that temperature the complete solution of the graphite flakes requires time.

If a metal is poured into a sand mold while unusually hot, 2800 to 2900°F, it will be fluid, flow rapidly into the mold, and give a strong casting. If the metal is poured cold, 2300 to 2400°F, it will flow sluggishly and may give an imperfect casting or a weaker casting. Bolton cites experiments showing that the average tensile strength of a particular iron poured hot, 2570°F, was 37,880 psi whereas the same iron poured cold, 2339°F, gave bars apparently sound but only showing a tensile strength of 32,090 lb.

Annealing Gray-iron Castings.—Shrinkage strains in cast iron, like those in steel, may be relieved by heating below the critical range. A temperature of 800 to 900°F for a duration from 30 min to 5 hr will relieve strains but have little effect on the cementite or graphite, and so will not change the hardness or strength materially. Car wheels, like steel rails, are sometimes cooled from 1400 to 650°F in covered pits at such a rate that it requires two days to cool through this range. If it is desired to soften the iron to promote machinability, annealing may be conducted at 1400 to 1500°F. This treatment will change some of the cementite to graphite, as is explained more fully in the paragraphs on Malleable Castings.

Welding Castings.—Cast iron may be welded by fusion methods. If the piece to be welded is small enough so that the whole casting may be heated to a red heat, the welding may be performed with a cast-iron welding rod, and the whole casting allowed to cool slowly. If an attempt is made to weld together two cold pieces of cast iron, the rapid cooling will prevent the separation of graphite, and a hard spot and perhaps a crack may result. Sometimes bronze whose melting point is below that of cast iron is used as a filling agent. It alloys with the surface of cast iron and gives a joint sometimes equal in strength to the original metal.

Malleable Castings.—It is evident from the preceding sections that a casting made from iron with a silicon content of about 1.0 per cent will be a soft gray iron if it is cooled very slowly and a hard white iron if it is cooled quickly. Since equilibrium conditions call for the conversion of almost all of the carbon to graphite, it is also evident that the casting in which the carbon has remained as cementite, owing to rapid cooling, may be brought back to equilibrium by heating above the critical range for a sufficient time and then cooling slowly. Two castings poured from the same ladle will differ widely in the percentages of cementite and graphite, depending on the rate of cooling, but if the casting that was quickly cooled is annealed properly, the proportions of graphite and cementite may become identical with that in the casting that was slowly cooled. That does not mean that the two castings will have identical properties, because the form and distribution of the graphite will be very different. The casting that cooled slowly from the molten state will have large flakes of graphite and therefore be weak. The casting that was chilled will have its cementite decomposing at temperatures well below the melting point of the iron. The carbon will therefore be set free at innumerable centers, and although there is some migration of the carbon, it forms bushy clumps which do not interfere much with the continuity of the metal granules. Therefore this heat-treated casting may have a tensile strength and ductility almost as great as that of mild steel and is called a "malleable" casting.

The first description of malleable castings was made by Reaumur in France in 1722. He packed castings, presumably of white iron, in iron oxide and heated them for many hours to a red heat. In this process, the reverse of cementation occurred. The cementite did break down to carbon, but the carbon diffused out of the steel into the atmosphere high in CO_2 which surrounded the piece. A thin piece of metal would thus become almost completely decarburized and become known as a "white-heart" casting. The first manufacture of malleable iron in the United States was undertaken by Seth Boyden in 1826. He made some observations to indicate he knew the importance of graphitization, and there gradually grew up the industry of making "black-heart" malleable castings in which no attempt is made to remove the carbon from the metal but merely to convert cementite into the finely divided graphite to which the name "temper carbon" was given.

The Manufacture of Malleable Castings.—It is doubtful if any malleable foundry in the United States operated under chemical control before 1900, and it was only after some years of experimentation that the underlying chemical principles were established. The older iron founders therefore had to work entirely by experience, and as is not infrequently the case, the methods they evolved worked quite well. The pig iron preferred for malleable iron was that made in the small charcoal blast furnaces, which was low in sulfur and also in silicon because of the low temperatures at which the charcoal furnaces operated. When coke iron commenced to be used, the pigs showing a mottled fracture, which as we now know were low in silicon, were selected. The selected iron was melted in an air furnace, and from time to time test bars about 1 in. in diameter were cast in sand. As soon as they were cold, they were broken and the fractured face examined. If it showed any graphite, the heating was continued with air blowing from the tuyère over the molten iron. This oxidized silicon and also a small amount of carbon rather slowly, and after a few hours of this operation a sample bar was obtained which showed no graphite but only white iron.

If this metal were to be poured into a sand mold, the resultant casting would be white, provided its cross section was not over 1 in., and on annealing this casting, the cementite would decompose to graphite (temper carbon), and a malleable casting would result.

The temperature of annealing was usually so high that the castings softened somewhat and tended to warp, and so they were packed in large cast-iron boxes or pots with a filling material that consisted in large part of iron ore, although later ground bricks or similar inert material was used. The pots when full were wheeled into a cold furnace, and when a furnace was filled, the door was closed and heating started. Moldenke[1] writing in 1911 recommended a temperature of 1350°F for 60 hr. This called for a furnace cycle of 6 days, allowing time for heating and cooling the furnace and its contents.

The Cast Metals Handbook of the American Foundrymen's Association recommends that the furnace containing the pots filled with castings be heated to 1560 to 1600°F as quickly as possible. This temperature is to be maintained for 40 to 60 hr and then is to be lowered not more than 8 to 10 deg. per hour until it reaches about 1275°F. At this temperature, the pots may be removed and allowed to cool in the air.

Effect of Percentage of Carbon.—Cast irons may be malleabilized irrespective of their percentage of carbon. The relative properties of carbon, silicon, manganese, and sulfur must be balanced so that the casting when removed from the mold will have all its carbon in the form of cementite, and after proper heat-treatment will have substantially all of its carbon in the form of temper carbon. Temper carbon is the least objectionable form in which graphite may appear, but it is not in itself desirable and the lower the total carbon is in the casting, the better will be the result. If the carbon should be decreased into the steel range, a steel casting and not one of malleable iron would result. The A.F.A. Cast Metals Handbook gives data on relation of physical properties to chemical composition, and Table 18 is taken from their data. It will be observed that it is not recommended that total carbon be over 2.70 per cent and that it may be as low as 1.75 per cent. The A.S.T.M. specification (A 47-33) designates two classes of malleable-iron castings, 35018 with a

[1] The Production of Malleable Castings.

yield point of 35,000 psi and an elongation of 18 per cent in 2 in., and 32510 with a yield point of 32,500 lb and an elongation of 10 per cent. The tensile strengths 53,000 and 50,000 psi, respectively, do not differ much from each other.

The A.S.T.M. specification permits the metal to be melted only in the air furnace, open-hearth or electric furnace, all of which permit manipulation to control the percentage of carbon and silicon. The cupola furnace is more economical in operation than the others, but it does not permit such a close control in

TABLE 18.—DATA ON COMPOSITION AND PROPERTIES OF MALLEABLE CAST IRON*

These data pertain to irons intended to meet the A.S.T.M. specifications.

35018 denotes iron with a yield point of 35,000 psi and an elongation of 18 per cent in 2 in.

32510 denotes iron with a yield point if 32,500 lb and an elongation of 10 per cent.

	Class 35018	Class 32510
Chemical composition of:		
White iron		
Carbon	1.75–2.30	2.25–2.7
Silicon	0.85–1.20	0.80–1.10
Manganese less than	0.40	0.40
Phosphorus less than	0.20	0.20
Sulfur less than	0.12	0.07–0.15
Finished product, temper carbon less than	1.80	2.20
Mechanical properties:		
Tensile, psi	52,000–60,000	50,000–52,000
Yield point, psi	35,000–40,000	32,500–35,000
Elongation, per cent, in 2 in	18–25	10–18
Brinell hardness number	110–145	110–135
Fatigue endurance limit, psi	25,000–26,500	25,000–26,500

* From American Foundrymen's Association, Cast Metals Handbook, 1935 ed., p. 190.

chemical composition. Considerable malleable iron is produced from cupola metal by large producers of a standard product such as pipe fittings, but the practice is not recommended for manufacturers of miscellaneous parts.

Influence of Silicon, Manganese, Sulfur, and Phosphorus.— The influence of these elements in cast iron has already been

GRAY CAST IRONS AND MALLEABLE CASTINGS

discussed, and little more elaboration is needed here. The A.S.T.M. specification does not mention any of these elements, and the manufacturer is permitted to use any percentages he wishes, provided he obtains a final product with the physical properties specified. The A.F.A. Handbook suggests (Table 18) that the phosphorus be kept under 0.20 per cent, the sulfur under 0.12 or possibly 0.15, and the manganese under 0.40. The sulfur will act as a stabilizer of cementite, but its influence is lessened by manganese and by silicon. The three elements must be balanced by the metallurgist to give a satisfactory composition.

Rate of Malleabilization.—Much of the material in this paragraph is taken from the research papers of A. E. White and Richard Schneidewind who have made important contributions

TABLE 19.*—CHANGES IN COMPOSITION OF A WHITE CAST IRON

With 1.25 per cent silicon and 1.75 per cent carbon when subjected to heat-treatment as indicated below. A group of bars were heated in a gas-fired muffle with a neutral atmosphere. The bars came up to the full temperature in about 15 min. Individual bars were removed from the furnace for examination and cooled in air as indicated

Sample	Temp., °F	Duration at full temp.	Graphite	Austenite or pearlite	Cementite	Total combined carbon
A	1700	0 min	0.0	0.83	0.92	1.75
B	1700	2 min	0.08	0.83	0.85	1.68
C	1700	10 min	0.14	0.83	0.76	1.59
D	1700	30 min	0.60	0.83	0.35	1.18
E	1700	3 hr	0.92	0.83	0.0	0.82

After 3 hr at 1700°F, the specimens were slowly cooled to 1400°F at such a rate that the cementite decomposed as fast as it was formed.

| F | 1400 | ...... | 1.13 | 0.62 | 0.0 | 0.62 |

After temperature had been slowly lowered to 1325°F and held there.

| G | 1325 | 15 hr | 1.48 | 0.27 | 0.0 | 0.27 |
| H | 1325 | 20 hr | 1.67 | 0.08 | 0.0 | 0.08 |

* From WHITE and SCHNEIDEWIND, *Trans. Am. Foundrymen's Assn.*, Vol. 40, 1932.

to our understanding of this process. In the experiments that are now to be described, a number of small test bars were placed in a muffle in a gas-fired furnace with a neutral atmosphere. Individual bars were removed from the furnace, cooled in air, and examined microscopically and chemically. The progressive changes in the distribution of the carbon as shown by chemical analysis is given in Table 19. The structure of a white iron with 1.75 per cent carbon and 1.25 per cent silicon is shown in *A* and *B* of Fig. 67 to be composed of massive cementite and pearlite. The next photomicrograph shows that after being heated for only 10 min at 1700°F the pearlite has become diffused and small particles of graphitic temper carbon have already started to form. The cementite continued to disappear and the graphite to increase with more prolonged heating, until after 3 hr at 1700°, an equilibrium had been reached with the massive cementite all changed to graphite and some free ferrite appearing. This ended the first stage of graphitization, and further heating at 1700° would not affect further change. If the pieces had all been taken out of the furnace and cooled at this point, the product would have been almost as hard as an annealed steel with 0.83 per cent carbon. The solubility of carbon in austenite decreases as the temperature is lowered, and because of the silicon, the cementite separated will not be stable but will break down to graphite. The furnace was therefore slowly cooled from 1700 to 1400°F at such a rate that the cementite decomposed as fast as it was separated. This second stage required 1 hr, and when it was finished, there remained 0.62 per cent of carbon as austenite, which after cooling became pearlite, and 1.13 per cent of carbon in the form of graphite, as shown in picture *E* of Fig. 67.

The eutectoid transformation for this composition takes place a little below 1400°F, and when the gamma iron changes to alpha, the balance of the austenite will be decomposed liberating cementite which would form stable pearlite if it were not for the silicon present. The silicon however still renders the cementite unstable and decomposes it slowly. The ferrite has also the possibility of still holding about 0.05 per cent carbon in solid solution, and so carbon can still diffuse through the ferrite at a slow rate. The samples were therefore cooled very slowly through the eutectoid transformation range and to 1325°F. After 15 hr at 1325°F, there was still 0.27 per cent of carbon existing in the form

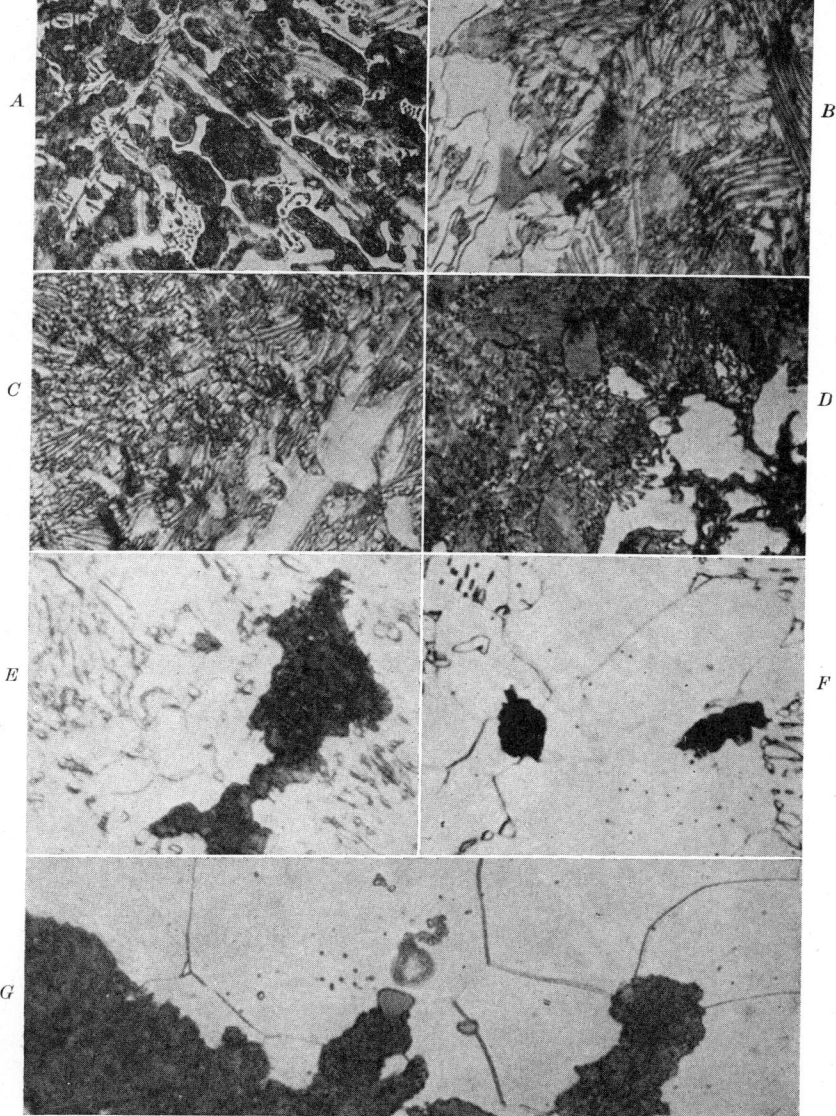

Fig. 67.—Changes in microscopic structure during malleabilization. Composition, C 1.75, Si 1.25 per cent. [*From White and Schneidewind, Trans. Am. Foundrymen's Assn.* **40**, (1932).]

A, as cast. ×100. Cementite and pearlite.

For remainder of caption see page 178.

of pearlite as shown in *F* of Fig. 67, but after 20 hr all but 0.08 per cent of carbon was in the form of graphite. This represents equilibrium and is shown in *G* of Fig. 67.

The series of photomicrographs shows the gradual change from a hard and brittle substance composed of cementite and pearlite to a soft and ductile ferrite whose grains are almost continuous, with patches of spongy graphite which have threads of ferrite running through them.

Short-cycle Malleabilization.—The speed at which cementite is decomposed at any temperature depends primarily on the amount of silicon present. The investigations by White and Schneidewind showed that with 1.0 per cent silicon 59.5 hr was the minimum time for complete malleabilization, with 1.5 per cent silicon, the time was only 17.5 hr, and with 2.0 per cent silicon, it was 5.4 hr. This would indicate the advisability of always using the higher content of silicon, but it must be remembered that the casting must be white iron when it goes to the annealing furnace, and that it is only castings with a thin section which will cool fast enough to retain the carbon in the combined form when 2.0 silicon is present.

Incomplete Malleabilization.—It is evident from the photomicrographs that it is possible to halt the malleabilization and leave a proportion of the carbon in the form of pearlite. This is sometimes called "pearlitic malleable iron." It is frequently heat-treated.

Heat-treatment.—There are two different methods by which heat-treatment may be accomplished. If a fully annealed malleable casting is heated above the critical range, the graphite will slowly start to diffuse back into the ferrite, and if it is then quenched, there will be areas of martensite or troostite in the zone

---

B, as cast. ×1000.

C, Heated 10 minutes at 1700°F. ×1000. Cementite and pearlite with occasional patches of graphitic temper carbon.

D, heated to equilibrium at 1700°F. ×1000. The cementite has disappeared and the white areas are ferrite. The graphitic temper carbon in small particles darkens the whole picture.

E, heated to equilibrium at 1700°F and cooled so slowly as to maintain equilibrium to 1400°F. ×1000. The graphitic temper carbon has collected in large clumps leaving areas of ferrite with some spheroidized pearlite.

F, heated to equilibrium at all temperatures above the critical temperature. Heated 15 hr at 1325°F. A small amount of pearlite still remains. ×1000.

G, complete malleabilization. Heated to equilibrium at all temperatures above the critical. Heated 20 hr at 1325°F. The structure is wholly ferrite and graphitic temper carbon. ×1000.

around each carbon nucleus. If the malleabilization is conducted in a gas-fired furnace from which the individual pieces can be readily removed, the pieces may be quenched after incomplete malleabilization.

The following data are from the work of Schneidewind and White[1] who treated bars cast at a commercial foundry in a manner shown more in detail in Table 20. The iron when com-

TABLE 20.—EFFECT OF VARIOUS DEGREES OF MALLEABILIZATION AND HEAT-TREATMENT*

Composition of iron
     Carbon... 2.35
     Silicon... 1.42
     Manganese....................................... 0.23
     Sulfur... 0.06
     Phosphorus....................................... 0.05

		Yield point, psi	Tensile strength, psi	Elongation, per cent in 2 in.	Brinell hardness
A	1700°F for 15 hr 1700 to 1525°, 2 hr Quench from 1525 in oil Temper 1325°, 2 hr	66,620	82,660	5.6	231
B	1700°F for 15 hr 1700 to 1525°, 2 hr Quench from 1525 in oil Temper 1325° for 4 hr	52,730	68,842	6.7	225
C	Completely malleabilized 1700°F for 15 hr 1700 to 1325 3 hr 1325°, 20 hr	38,200	57,300	9.9	160

* From SCHNEIDEWIND and WHITE, Trans. Am. Foundrymen's Assn., 45, 1–27 (1937).

pletely malleabilized in 38 hr showed satisfactory strength and elongation. When the malleabilization was interrupted after 17 hr and the specimens were oil quenched immediately after they were taken from the furnace at 1525° and then tempered, the strength, elastic limit, and hardness were all increased and the elongation decreased as would have been expected. It is note-

[1] Trans. Am. Foundrymen's Assn, 14, 1–27 (1937).

worthy that a malleabilized product with a yield point of 66,620 psi and an elongation of 5.6 per cent in 2 in. may be obtained in 19 hr. The microscopic structure of these heat-treated malleable castings is shown in Fig. 68.

Alloy Castings.—Alloying elements may be incorporated into the molten metal before casting. The influence of these elements will be discussed in the following chapters.

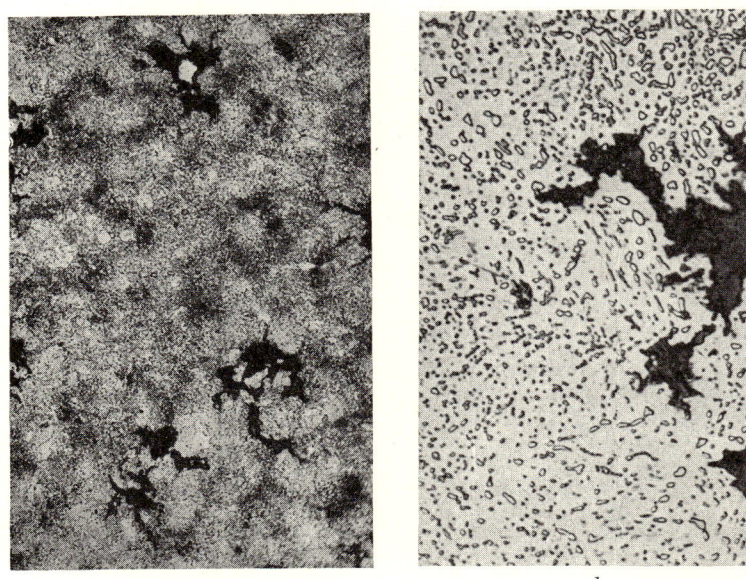

a *b*

Fig. 68.—Microscopic structure of malleable cast iron heated to 1525°F, then quenched, and drawn for 4 hr at 1325°F. *a*, ×100; *b*, ×1000. [*From Schneidewind and White, Trans. Am. Foundrymen's Assn.*, **45**, 69 (1937).]

References

AMERICAN FOUNDRYMEN'S ASSOCIATION: Cast Metals Handbook, 1935 ed., Chicago.

BOLTON, J. W.: Gray Cast Iron, Penton Publishing Co., Cleveland, 1937.

MOLDENKE, RICHARD: Principles of Iron Founding, McGraw-Hill Book Company, Inc., New York, 1930.

CAMPBELL, H. L.: Metal Castings, John Wiley & Sons, Inc., New York, 1936.

AMERICAN SOCIETY FOR TESTING MATERIALS: A.S.T.M. Standards (issued triennially), 1936, Part I, Metals, Philadelphia.

AMERICAN SOCIETY FOR TESTING MATERIALS: A.S.T.M. Tentative Standards, 1937, Philadelphia.

Symposium on Steel Castings, American Foundrymen's Association and American Society for Testing Materials, 1932, *Proc. Am. Soc. Testing Materials,* **32,** II, 43–292 (1932).

SAEGER and ASH: Properties of Gray Cast Iron As Affected by Casting Conditions, *Trans. Am. Foundrymen's Assn,* **41,** 449–468, 1933.

SAEGER and ASH: Volume Changes of Cast Iron during Casting, *Trans. Am. Foundrymen's Assn,* **40,** 182–187 (1932).

Symposium on Cast Iron, American Foundrymen's Association and American Society for Testing Materials, published by American Society for Testing Materials, Philadelphia, 1933.

VANICK, J. S.: Hardening Cast Iron by Heat Treatment, *Metal Progress,* January, **29,** 40 (1936).

DEWITT and BROWN: The Influence of Ferric Hydrogel in the Bond of Natural Molding Sands, *Trans. Am. Foundrymen's Assn,* 1928, pp. 247–276.

MOLDENKE, RICHARD: The Production of Malleable Castings, Penton Publishing Co., Cleveland, 1911.

SCHWARTZ, H. A.: American Malleable Cast Iron, Penton Publishing Co., Cleveland, 1922.

Symposium on Malleable Iron Castings, American Foundrymen's Association and American Society for Testing Materials, 1931.

WHITE and SCHNEIDEWIND: The Metallurgy of Malleabilization, *Trans. Am. Foundrymen's Assn,* **40,** 88–124 (1932).

SCHNEIDEWIND and WHITE: Properties of Fully Annealed and Heat Treated Malleable Castings, *Trans. Am. Foundrymen's Assn,* **40,** 1–28 (1937).

STERN, MARC: Die-casting Practice, McGraw-Hill Book Company, Inc., New York, 1930.

GREINER, MARSH, and STOUGHTON: The Alloys of Iron and Silicon, McGraw-Hill Book Company, Inc., New York, 1933.

FORBES, D. P.: New Cast Irons, Heat-treated, Rolled, *Metal Progress,* February, 1938, p. 137.

CHAPTER XI

STEELS WITH ONE ALLOYING ELEMENT

The steels previously discussed have been plain carbon steels carrying minor percentages of silicon, manganese, sulfur, and phosphorus. This chapter considers those alloys which, in addition to iron and carbon, contain a third alloying constituent of importance and are therefore often called "ternary" steels. Steels with more than one important alloying constituent will be considered in the next chapter.

The alloying constituents may be grouped into two main classes:

1. Alloys that form solid solutions in, and so strengthen, the ferrite include silicon, copper, manganese, and nickel.

2. Alloys that form hard carbides and increase resistance to deformation at high temperatures include chromium, tungsten, molybdenum, and vanadium, with manganese exerting a minor effect in this direction.

Silicon.—Silicon has been discussed as a deoxidizer and as an element promoting the decomposition of cementite to form graphite. Silicon forms a solid solution with alpha ferrite in all proportions up to 14 per cent Si. When added in small percentages to pure iron, it increases both the tensile strength and elongation, as is customary in solid solutions. It also raises the critical range so that steels with 1.25 to 1.50 silicon and 0.10 to 0.25 per cent carbon can be heated over 1600°F without suffering enlargement of the grains. Steels for leaf and coil springs are frequently made from an alloy with 0.5 per cent carbon, 0.7 per cent manganese, and 2.0 per cent silicon. Here the higher manganese prevents the silicon from breaking down the cementite to form graphite. The steel responds to the usual heat-treatment. When more than 2.0 per cent silicon is added, the ductility decreases rapidly, and with more than 4.0 per cent silicon, the tensile strength also falls off. The reason for these changes is not known.

In electrical machinery for alternating current, the flux in the core must change with minimum delay and loss of energy. Thin plates, of as pure iron as may be obtained commercially, are used in the manufacture of generators, motors, and transformers. The incorporation of 1 to 4 per cent silicon into the iron decreases the core and hysteresis losses, perhaps by converting the carbon to graphite, though less than 0.10 total carbon is allowed, and specifications sometimes call for its limitation to 0.05 per cent.

Castings that are very resistant to the action of acids are made from an alloy composed mainly of Fe_3Si_2 which contains 14.5 per cent silicon. The usual alloys contain 13.5 to 14.5 per cent silicon and 0.8 to 1.0 per cent carbon. Other alloying elements are added occasionally. These alloys are sold under a variety of trade names, of which the oldest is Duriron.

Silicon is also used as an alloying constituent in connection with chromium, manganese, and vanadium, and its uses will be discussed when the more complex combinations are being considered.

Copper.—Copper forms a solid solution in gamma iron with a maximum of 8.0 to 8.5 per cent at 2000°F. This solid solution separates copper on cooling and undergoes a eutectoid transformation about 1500°F, the resultant products being almost pure copper and alpha ferrite. Above 1500°F, the ferrite holds about 3.0 per cent of copper, but at room temperature only about 0.3 per cent can remain in solid solution. The microscopic structure of steels containing a small amount of copper does not differ much from that of plain carbon steel. Copper up to 2 per cent increases the yield point, tensile strength, and hardness and decreases the elongation and reduction of area rather slightly for all carbon contents up to 0.8 per cent, both in the normalized and quenched condition. Copper increases the resistance of steel to atmospheric corrosion, and its alloys appear on the market under the name of "copper-bearing steels" and various trade names. One such alloy carries 0.15 to 0.30 per cent carbon and a minimum of 0.20 per cent copper. Sheets of this composition are frequently used for the outside sheathing of steel mills and other manufacturing plants and for the fabrication of open freight cars. Copper-bearing steels corrode erratically when immersed in water or buried in soil, and the reasons for the lack of uniformity in the protective action of copper under these conditions has not been fully determined.

Manganese.—Manganese is added in the manufacture of plain carbon steel primarily to deoxidize the molten metal and to neutralize the bad effects of sulfur by forming MnS. Manganese forms solid solutions in iron only to the extent of about 1.0 to 1.6 per cent. It depresses the transformation points and makes the

Table 21.—Physical Properties of Steels 1040 and X 1340*
Bars 1 in. in diameter taken for heat-treatment.

	1040	X 1340
Chemical composition:		
C	0.35–0.045	0.35–0.45
Mn	0.60–0.90	1.35–1.65
P	0.045	0.045
S	0.055	0.075–0.150
Quenched from 1550°F in oil		
Brinell hardness as quenched	241	
Drawn at 1000°F:		
Tensile strength	105,000	138,000
Yield point	74,000	112,000
Elongation, per cent	22	18
Reduction of area	56	48

* From Bethlehem Steel Company Catalogue 144, pp. 165, 177.

change from austenite to pearlite so sluggish that the beginning and the end of the transformation range are sometimes 150°F apart. Manganese also forms a carbide Mn_3C similar in properties to Fe_3C but harder and more stable at high temperatures. Steels with medium carbon and manganese below 2.0 per cent show a microscopic structure of pearlite and alpha ferrite on slow cooling. They respond to heat-treatment and casehardening operations like a carbon steel, although they are more liable to crack on quenching and are usually quenched in oil. They machine well and sometimes have sulfur added to increase machinability. The S.A.E. Handbook states that 1040 steel may be used for forgings, including both front and rear axles. Steel X 1340 differs from 1040 in composition in that it has higher manganese and sulfur. It has improved machining properties, deeper hardening, and higher strength and elastic limit. The composition and mechanical properties are shown in Table 21. In spite of sulfur which may be as high as 0.15 per cent, the higher manganese, 1.35 to 1.65 per cent, prevents red-shortness. After quenching in oil from 1550°F and tempering at 1000°F, steel X 1340 showed a yield point of 138,000 psi and an elongation of 18 per cent as compared with 105,000 lb and 22 per cent for steel 1040.

Nickel, chromium, molybdenum, and vanadium are sometimes used as the alloying elements in these pearlitic manganese steels.

Manganese Austenitic Steels.—If manganese is increased to much over 2 per cent, the change from gamma to alpha iron proceeds so slowly that the pearlitic structure does not develop on cooling in the air. Instead, a martensitic structure appears on

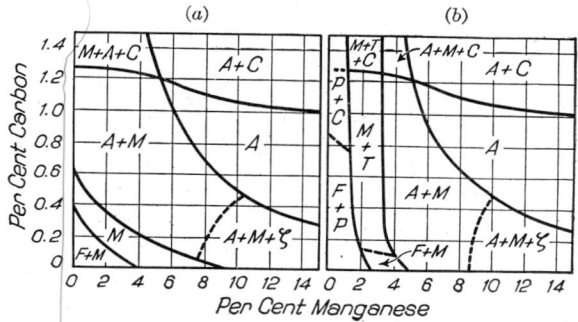

FIG. 69.—Effect of varying percentages of carbon and manganese upon the microscopic structure of steels. (a), quenched from 1740°F, (b), air-cooled from 1740°F. A, austenite, C, cementite, F, ferrite, M, martensite, P, pearlite, X, unknown. (From Metals Handbook, 1939 ed., p. 561.)

air-cooling which is hard, brittle, and of no commercial value. This condition is shown in the diagram of Fig. 69 taken from the work of Bain, Davenport, and Waring. If the manganese is increased to above 10 per cent, the transition points are depressed and the change retarded so that after air-cooling of alloys with more than 10 per cent manganese and less than 0.4 per cent carbon the structure is a mixture of austenite and martensite and is hard and brittle. If steel with more than 0.5 per cent of carbon and 10 per cent of manganese is either air-cooled or quenched from above the critical range, as the same figure shows, the structure remains as austenite which is strong but extremely ductile. The American Society for Testing Materials in its Standard Specification for Austenitic Manganese-steel Castings (A 128 − 33) specifies the following chemical composition by percentage:

186   ENGINEERING MATERIALS

	Per Cent
Carbon	1.00–1.40
Manganese minimum	10.
Phosphorus maximum	0.10
Sulfur maximum	0.05

It is directed that the castings shall be heated to 1832°F until the temperature is uniform throughout, and then be quenched in water. The official specifications do not demand physical tests but permit an optional bend test in which a cast bar ½ by ¾-in. cross section and 12 in. long is, after quenching, to be bent cold without breaking around a pin 1 in. in diameter to an angle of 150 deg. Hall[1] states that manganese steel hardens under cold work to an extraordinary degree, the Brinell hardness rising to 450 to 550. For this reason, the steel is difficult to machine and

TABLE 22.—PROPERTIES OF AUSTENITIC MANGANESE STEEL AFTER QUENCHING IN WATER FROM ABOVE THE CRITICAL RANGE*

	Rolled or hammered	Cast
Tensile strength, psi	130,000–160,000	118,000
Proportional limit, psi	40,000–60,000	42,900
Elongation per cent in 2 in	60–70	44.1
Reduction of area, per cent	40–60	39.0
Brinell hardness	230	180

* Metals Handbook, 1939 ed.

is usually cast and ground, although simple shapes may be rolled. The stresses produced by quenching are high, and it is not possible to relieve them by heat-treatment without changing the ductile austenite in part to brittle martensite. The metal can therefore not be cast in complicated sections but is restricted to simple shapes.

The effect of manganese in the heat-treated pearlitic steel of Table 21 was to raise the yield point to 80 per cent of the tensile strength. The effect of the higher manganese in the water-quenched austenitic steel as shown in Table 22 is to give a tensile strength about the same as for steel X 1340, but a yield point roughly half as great and an elongation twice as great. The elongation is as large as the reduction of area, a characteristic of

[1] Metals Handbook, 1939 ed., p. 569.

STEELS WITH ONE ALLOYING ELEMENT 187

austenitic steels. The austenitic manganese steels are largely used for railway crossings and switches, rock crushers, teeth for the dippers of steam shovels, conveyor chains, and other parts that must stand rough treatment and abrasion. Single castings may be made up to 30,000 lb in weight.

Nickel.—The metallurgy and properties of nickel and its alloys with metals other than iron will be discussed more fully in the chapter on nonferrous metals. It is a metal that in itself is strong, does not oxidize readily, and may be incorporated in molten steel without difficulty. Iron and nickel form solid solutions in all proportions. Iron in the gamma form crystallizes

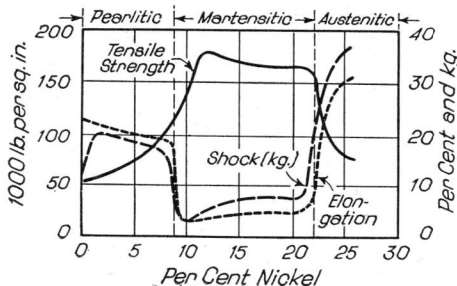

Fig. 70.—Changes in physical properties and microscopic structure of air-cooled steels with 0.25 per cent carbon as the percentage of nickel is increased. (*From Metals Handbook*, 1939 ed., after Bullens.)

on the face-centered cubic system with a lattice parameter of 3.63 Å. Nickel crystallizes at all temperatures on the face-centered cubic system with a lattice parameter of 3.52 Å. It is apparent therefore that nickel and gamma iron will readily form solid solutions. On cooling, the nickel exerts a restraining effect and lowers the temperature at which the gamma to alpha transformation takes place on cooling. Alloys with less than 15 per cent nickel, if cooled slowly, will be composed of the alpha modification with a lattice parameter closely that of alpha iron. Alloys with more than 34 per cent of nickel always appear in the gamma modification. Intermediate compositions may be mixtures of alpha and gamma.

The effect of nickel is to raise the yield strength and increase the ductility of the ferrite in which it is dissolved up to about the limit of the alpha range. The mixture of alpha and gamma phases shows some of the properties of martensite, especially when carbon is present. Above 34 per cent of nickel where the gamma iron is stable, the metal again becomes ductile, and if carbon is present, austenite is stable. The effect of increasing percentages of nickel on the physical properties of a cast steel with 0.25 per cent carbon is shown in Fig. 70 taken from Bullens.

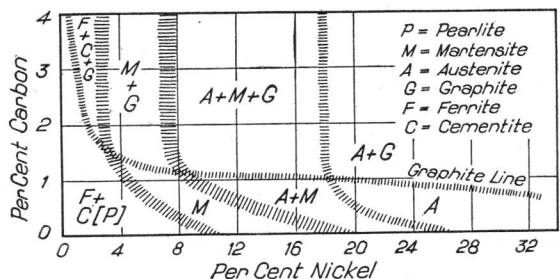

FIG. 71.—Changes in microscopic structure of steels with varying carbon and nickel content. (*From Metals Handbook*, 1939 ed.)

The elongation drops off rapidly if the nickel is increased beyond 7 per cent which marks the limit of the range in which the air-cooled metal is composed wholly of pearlite plus a solid solution of nickel in alpha ferrite. The figure shows that, with higher nickel, alloys are all brittle until 22 per cent of nickel has been added, when the gamma form of the solid solution becomes dominant and a ductile austenitic steel results.

Nickel also acts to decompose cementite and give graphite, behaving in this respect like silicon, though not being so powerful. The combination of the two effects of nickel on carbon steel is illustrated in Fig. 71 by Wickenden. One useful range of compositions contains less than 4.0 per cent nickel and 1.0 per cent carbon in which ferrite and pearlite are the stable constituents. The separation of martensite and graphite spoils the properties of the higher nickel alloys until more than 24 per cent of nickel is present, when with low carbon, a ductile austenitic steel results. If more than about 0.7 per cent carbon is present with these high percentages of nickel, graphite is set free.

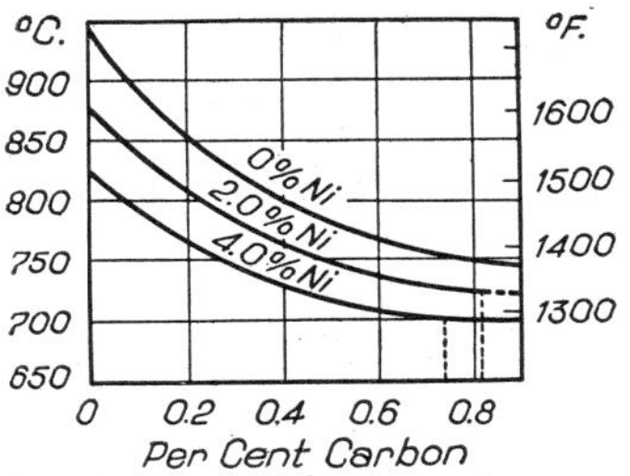

FIG. 72.—Effect of varying percentages of nickel and carbon on the Ac critical range. (*From Metals Handbook*, 1939 ed.)

Nickel depresses the critical range of carbon steel as shown in Fig. 72. A steel with 0.5 per cent carbon needs to be heated to 1430°F to pass the Ac_3 transformation if it has no nickel, whereas with 4.0 per cent of nickel, the Ac_3 transformation occurs 100° lower. The nickel steels may therefore be quenched from lower temperatures and thus have smaller shrinkage strains than plain carbon steels with the same carbon content.

Nickel Structural Steels.—The effect of increasing percentages of nickel within the pearlitic range is shown for annealed steels in Table 23. The effect of the nickel in solid solution is to increase

TABLE 23.—EFFECT OF INCREASING PERCENTAGES OF NICKEL ON ANNEALED STEEL*

Carbon, per cent	Nickel, per cent	Tensile strength, psi	Yield point, psi	Elongation, per cent in 2 in.	Reduction of area, per cent	Brinell hardness
0.30	0	70,000	40,000	26.0	50.0	145
0.30	3.50	90,000	60,000	27.0	55.0	175
0.30	5.00	95,000	65,000	28.0	56.0	185

* From Metals Handbook, 1936 ed., p. 412.

both the strength and ductility. The effect of successive additions becomes less marked, and the S.A.E. Handbook does not list structural steels with over 5 per cent of nickel. The S.A.E. Handbook codes the nickel steels in the 2000 group with the second digit giving the percentage of nickel. It recommends steels 2340 and 2345

... for structural purposes where greater strength and toughness are required such as propeller shafts, spline shafts, axle shafts and similar applications. S.A.E. 2345 has been used successfully as a gear steel. These steels are sensitive to heat treatment, hence water quenching is not recommended.

The physical properties of S.A.E. steel 2340 after heat various heat-treatments are shown in Fig. 73. If this steel is tempered to give 20 per cent elongation, its yield point will be 130,000 lb, whereas a plain carbon steel with the same carbon content heat-treated to give the same elongation will have a yield point of only 90,000 lb.

190   ENGINEERING MATERIALS

Austenitic Nickel Steels.—The curves of Fig. 70 show that in the range from 8 to 22 per cent nickel a slowly cooled steel is

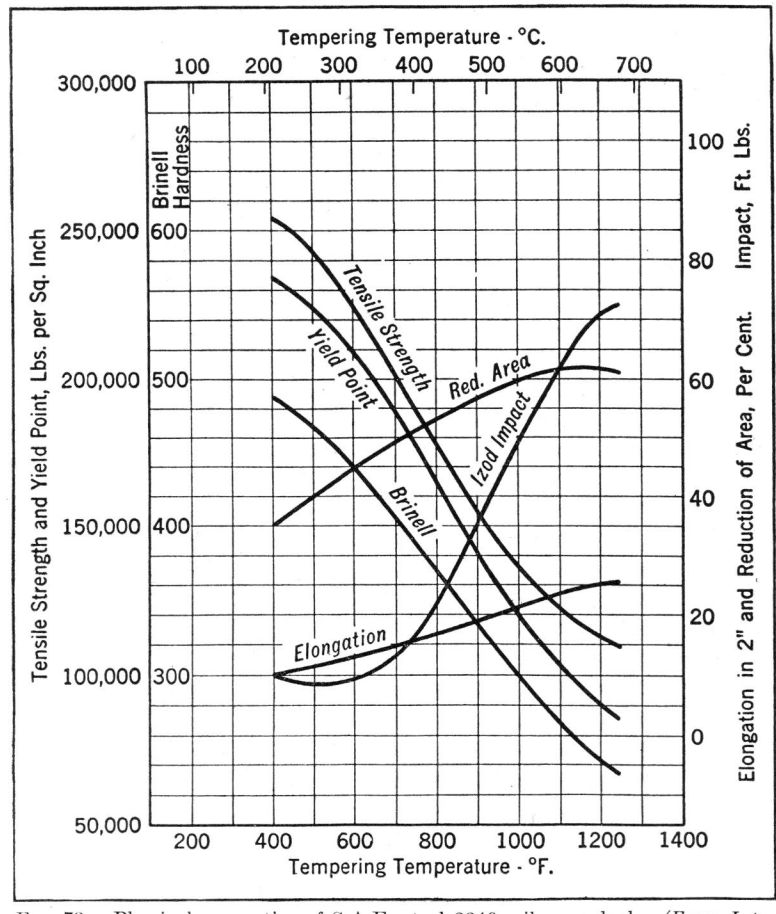

FIG. 73.—Physical properties of S.A.E. steel 2340, oil quenched. (*From International Nickel Co.'s Nickel Alloy Steel Data Book.*)

	Composition, per cent	Approx. critical range	Heat treatment
Carbon	0.35–0.45	Ac₁ 1290°F	Quenched from 1400°–1450°F
Manganese	0.50–0.80		Quenched into oil
Phosphorus	0.04 max.	Ac₂ ⎫ 1340°F	
Sulfur	0.05 max.	Ac₃ ⎭	Tempered as indicated
Nickel	3.25–3.75		

martensitic—strong and hard but brittle. These alloys do not find commercial use, except as their properties may be modified by other alloying elements. When the nickel is raised above 22 per cent, the austenitic form persists on cooling in air, with the iron in the gamma form and the carbon in solid solution. The alloy is paramagnetic. If alloys with 20 to 30 per cent nickel are cooled in liquid air, the gamma iron changes to alpha and the alloy becomes ferromagnetic. Alloys with more than 30 per cent nickel are in the gamma modification at all temperatures. The austenitic alloys are not used widely for structural purposes but are extremely valuable for scientific uses, because of their resistance to oxidation at high temperatures. They are also resistant to corrosion and have found some use in valves for gas engines, for

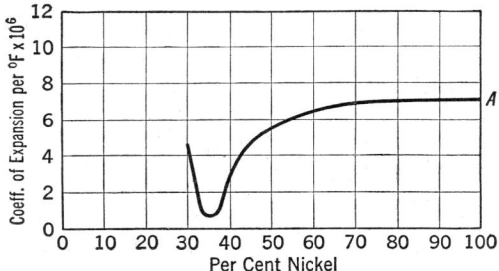

Fig. 74.—Coefficients of expansion of iron-nickel alloys at 68°F. (*From International Nickel Co.'s Nickel Alloy Steel Data Book.*)

boiler tubes, and for valve stems on pumps working in sea water. The coefficient of thermal expansion at ordinary temperatures changes abruptly within the compositions 30 to 40 per cent nickel as is shown in Fig. 74. The alloy with 36 per cent of nickel possesses such a low coefficient of expansion at room temperature that it has been called "Invar." It is much used for surveyors' tapes and other scientific instruments whose dimensions should not change at ordinary temperatures. The coefficient of expansion for Invar rises rapidly above 200°F, and at 500°F becomes greater than that of ordinary steel. The alloy with 40 per cent nickel has about the same coefficient of expansion as glass and is used for the lead-in wires passing through the glass of electric light bulbs. These nickel alloys find application in thermostats in which two metallic strips of quite different expansivity are welded together. When the compound element is subjected to heating or cooling, the differential expansion of the two metals causes the strip to be distorted and, for example, close an electric circuit. Alloys with 32 to 34 per cent nickel are used as struts in aluminum pistons in airplane engines. The aluminum piston expands so much more rapidly than the cast-iron cylinder block that Invar struts are cast in the piston to restrain the expansion.

The austenitic alloys are also used as structural materials where ductility is necessary at extremely low temperatures. Ordinary carbon steels are distinctly more brittle in winter weather than in summer, but an alloy containing 55 to 60 per cent nickel, 1 to 3 per cent manganese, and 0.2 to 0.4 per cent carbon when tested at −310°F showed a tensile strength of

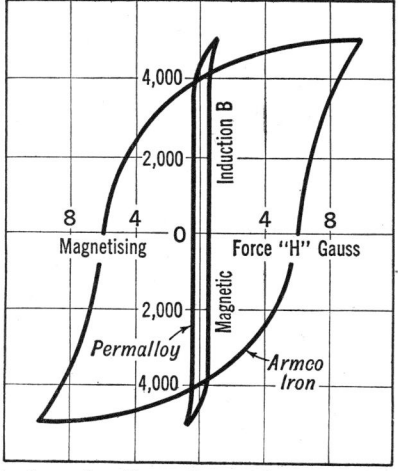

Fig. 75.—Hysteresis loop for Permalloy and annealed Armco iron. (*From International Nickel Co.'s Nickel Alloy Steel Data Book.*)

114,000 psi with an elongation of 40 per cent. It is valuable for parts of machinery used in commercial liquid-air plants, such as valves for expansion engines.

Magnetic Iron-nickel Alloys.—Nickel and iron are themselves both ferromagnetic, but as has been mentioned, the alloys in the neighborhood of 30 per cent nickel are paramagnetic because the gamma-iron phase is stable at room temperatures. The alloys with more than 35 per cent nickel become ferromagnetic but, in the annealed state, are not superior to iron with 4 per cent of silicon, or even to the commercial grades of low-carbon sheet steel. Heat-treatment improves the magnetic properties, and an alloy named Permalloy with **78** per cent nickel, **22** per cent iron, and a minimum amount of carbon and sulfur possesses remarkable magnetic properties after it has been air quenched. In telephone circuits, the electrical impulses must be short and sharp so that succeeding impulses will not become superimposed, with a resultant jumbling of the sound waves that come out of the receiver. A long transmission line has a capacity effect that produces this jumbling, and in modern practice inductance is added at intervals to counteract this effect. Permalloy has been especially valuable for the construction of the loading coils spaced at intervals along the land lines. It is used as a thin tape wrapped around the conductors of submarine cables. This alloy responds exceptionally quickly to a magnetizing force and shows very little hysteresis (lag). This is illustrated in Fig. 75 in which Permalloy is compared with Armco iron which is nearly pure ferrite.

Nickel in Steel Castings.—Nickel when added to steel castings in amounts not greater than 5 per cent produces similar results to those mentioned in the paragraph on structural steels, in that it forms a solid solution in and strengthens the ferrite. The property of producing a fine grain is especially helpful since in a casting the grain size is not refined by mechanical work. Since nickel lowers the critical range, it also permits quenching to be carried out at lower temperatures. An illustration of a large and important casting is given in Fig. 76 which shows an assembled butterfly valve 168 in. in diameter to control the water supply to the turbine operating under 300 lb hydraulic pressure and actuating one of the 82,500-kva generators at Boulder Dam. The casting for the valve leaf weighed 92,000 lb, and the body, cast in two pieces, weighed 150,000 lb. The total weight of the assembled valve was 400,000 lb. The castings were made from steel with 0.25 to 0.35 per cent carbon and 1.00 to 1.50 per cent nickel. The large bolts holding the two halves of the shell together were made from steel with 3.5 nickel and 0.40 carbon (S.A.E. 2340).

Nickel in Cast Iron.—Nickel improves the strength of the metallic grains of cast iron as it does in cast steel, but its most important influence is on the graphite. Nickel acts like silicon in promoting the formation of graphite and increasing machinability. It might seem that since silicon is cheaper than nickel there would be no commercial advantage in substituting nickel.

However the addition of 1.0 to 2.0 per cent nickel as a supplement to rather low silicon has been found to yield a stronger casting which is fine grained and yet may be machined without difficulty.

FIG. 76.—Photograph of valve assembly to control flow of water to one of the turbines at Boulder Dam. (*Courtesy of the Erie Forge Co., the Hardie-Lynes Manufacturing Co., and the International Nickel Co.*)

Nickel with Other Alloying Elements.—Other alloying elements are frequently used with nickel, and they will be discussed in the following chapters.

Chromium.—Chromium is found in nature as an oxide associated with iron ore. The principal mines are in South Africa, Turkey in Asia Minor, and Russia. Cuba is the only producer of importance in the Western Hemisphere. The binding power of chromium for oxygen is so strong that reduction in the iron blast furnace is very incomplete, and much of the chromium is lost in the slag. The ores are usually reduced in an electric furnace and marketed as a ferrochrome alloy containing 65 to 72 per cent of chromium with carbon varying from 0.06 to 4.50 per cent. Pure chromium may be deposited electrolytically and is extensively used for plating purposes. In steel manufacture, the chromium is usually added in the form of a ferroalloy during the finishing process in the open-hearth or electric furnace. Pure chromium

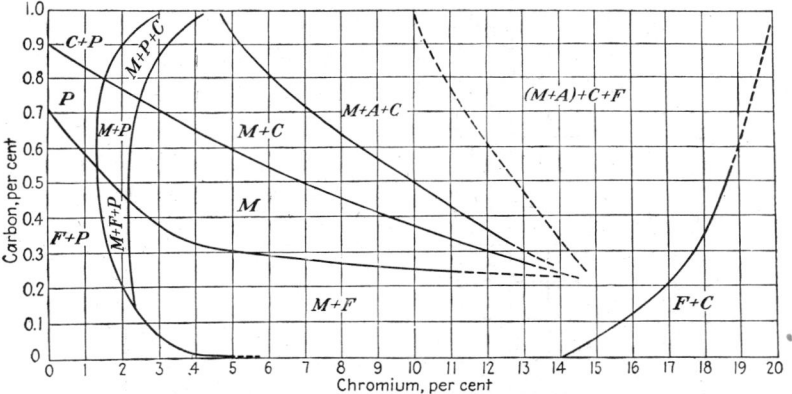

Fig. 77.—Structural diagram of iron-chromium-carbon alloys as shown by bars of 1-in. section cooled in air. (*From Kinzel and Crafts, The Alloys of Iron and Chromium.*)

has a melting point of 3326°F (1830°C). When cast, it has a Brinell hardness of 130 but in the plated form a Brinell number of 570 to 1250. It resists atmospheric corrosion remarkably well, and its hardness and corrosion resistance make it much used for plating automobile bumpers, fenders, and headlights, as well as machine and engine parts and printing plates.

Chromium and Iron and Carbon.—Chromium dissolves in iron and remains in solid solution on cooling in all proportions up to 30 per cent Cr. Chromium unites with carbon to form several carbides which are harder than the carbide of iron and also stable at higher temperatures. Chromium raises the temperature of the critical range of carbon steels on heating and increases the sluggishness of the transition on cooling. Steels with low chromium and low carbon may be heat-treated like a carbon steel with proper allowance for the difference in the critical range and the rate of cooling. The structural diagram of chromium steels for bars of 1-in. section cooled in air is shown in Fig. 77. It will be noted that if the carbon is only a few hundredths of 1

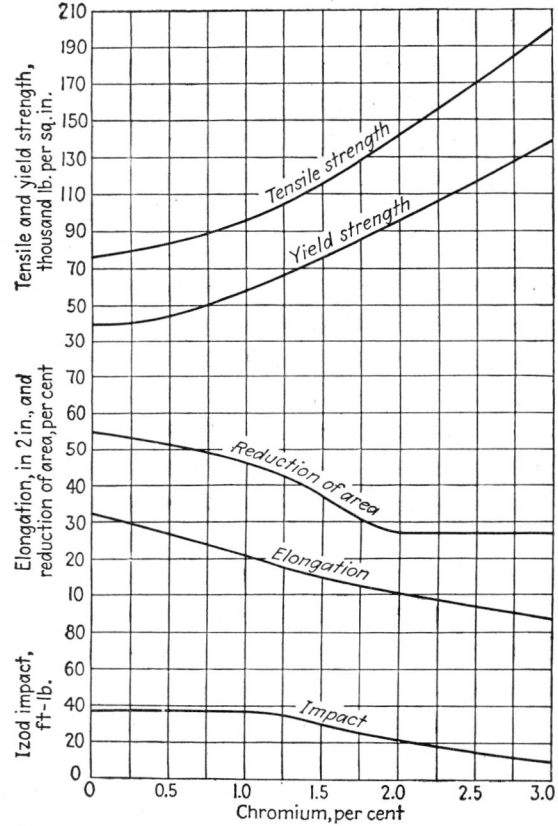

FIG. 78.—Effect of chromium on the mechanical properties of steel containing 0.30 per cent carbon and 0.30 to 0.60 per cent manganese. (*From Kinzel and Crafts, The Alloys of Iron and Chromium.*)

per cent, the chromium may run up to 3.5 per cent and still give a structure of ferrite and pearlite on cooling in air. If the carbon is 0.2 per cent, the chromium must be below 2.0 per cent to give a pearlitic structure on air cooling. When the percentage of chromium rises, the carbides remain in the martensitic form, which means that the steel is permanently hard and brittle, unless special precautions are taken to cool it very slowly through its critical range. Steels with less than 3.5 chromium and very low carbon are therefore susceptible to heat-treatment in much the same manner as a carbon steel, and even steels with 5.0 chromium respond to careful treatment.

Structural Steels with Low Chromium.—The effect of the increase of chromium on the properties of a normalized steel with 0.30 per cent carbon is shown in Fig. 78. This steel was normalized in bars ¾ to 1 in. in diameter and probably shows some air hardening. The tensile strength and yield strength increase regularly, and the decrease in elongation follows a smooth curve. The sharp breaks in the reduction of area and of the impact test may be due to the air-hardening effect which becomes more pronounced with high chromium.

The Society of Automotive Engineers lists three regular grades of chromium steel with 0.20, 0.40, and 0.50 per cent carbon and 0.60 to 1.10 per cent chromium. Steel 5140 is chosen as an example. It is recommended for heat-treated forgings requiring greater strength and toughness than are obtainable in plain carbon steel. The physical properties of this steel with various drawing temperatures are shown in Fig. 79. If this steel is compared with a plain carbon steel of the same carbon content, when both steels have been heat-treated to give an elongation of 20 per cent, the yield point of the 5140 steel will be found to be 112,000 psi and that of the 1040 steel will be only 78,000 lb.

The highest percentages of chromium and carbon usually included in this class of structural steel are exemplified in S.A.E. 52100 which contains 0.95 to 1.10 per cent carbon and 1.20 to 1.50 per cent chromium. This steel is used for ball and roller bearings and is drawn into tubing for the races of ball bearings. The transformation point is retarded to such an extent that hardening extends deeper than is the case with plain carbon steels.

Chromium is frequently used in connection with nickel, molybdenum, vanadium, and tungsten. These more complex steels will be discussed later.

Low-chromium Cast Iron.—Chromium hardens cast iron and increases its wear resistance due to the formation of the harder chromium carbides. It produces smaller flakes of graphite and

198   ENGINEERING MATERIALS

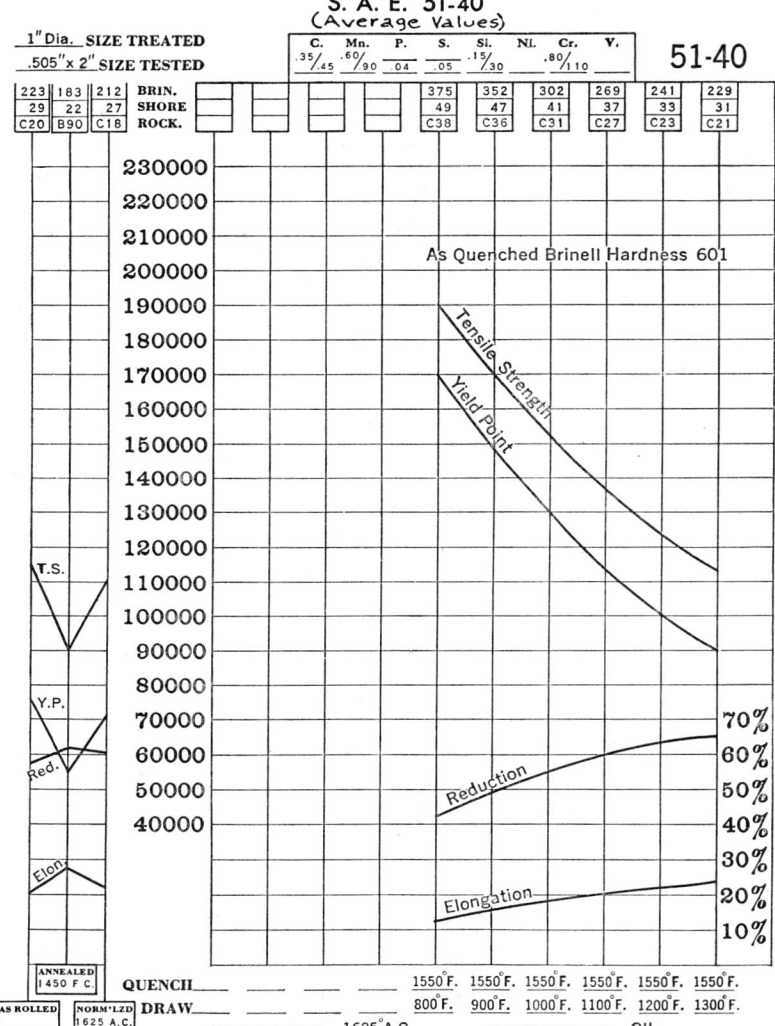

Fig. 79.—Physical properties chart of a chromium steel. S.A.E. 5140. (*From Bethlehem Steel Co. Catalog* 107.)

eliminates large patches of ferrite. It makes the iron less machinable. The influence of silicon is antagonistic to chromium in that silicon tends to form large flakes of graphite. If more than 1.0 per cent of chromium is present in castings of medium cross section, machining becomes difficult. Chromium prevents slow volume changes in cast-iron parts that are exposed for a long time to high temperatures, and this will be discussed later under Creep. Chromium may be added to the molten metal in the ladle in the form of finely crushed ferrochromium, and thus is available for treating only a part of the metal flowing from the cupola.

Chrome-magnet Steels.—It has been already noted that iron free from carbon loses its magnetism very quickly and is therefore valuable for the cores of transformers and electrical generators. Permanent magnets are made from high-carbon steels and are improved by the addition of chromium. A suitable steel for magnets may have 0.95 per cent carbon, 0.45 per cent manganese, and 2.25 per cent chromium. It should be hardened by quenching from about 1525°F into oil and is not usually heat-treated unless to give it an artificial aging treatment by immersion in boiling water. Permanent magnets often contain tungsten as well as chromium.

Medium-chromium Steels.—These steels with 4 to 10 per cent of chromium usually contain less than 0.20 per cent carbon. The chromium carbides harden the metal, and the chromium in solid solution increases the resistance to corrosion. High temperatures are required for normalizing and tempering, and on this account the metal is well adapted to resist moderately high temperatures. Steels of this type are used extensively in petroleum refineries when hot oil is to be treated under pressure. The diagram of Fig. 80 shows that a martensitic structure results if the carbon is raised over 0.2 per cent even with low chromium. This causes the steels to air harden. Thum[1] states that a steel with 0.10 per cent carbon and 5.20 per cent chromium showed a yield point of 108,860 psi and a Brinell hardness of 361 when air-cooled from 1600°F, but a yield point of 27,300 and a Brinell hardness of 136 when cooled in the furnace from the same temperature. In the latter case, the rate of cooling was slow enough to permit the complete decomposition of the martensite.

[1] The Book of Stainless Steel, p. 236.

Chromium Stainless Steels with Low-carbon, Chromium Ferrites.

—The stainless steels contain more than 10 per cent chromium. They also are frequently alloyed with nickel, and that composition will be discussed in the next chapter. The stainless steels are further divided sharply into two groups in accordance with their percentage of carbon.

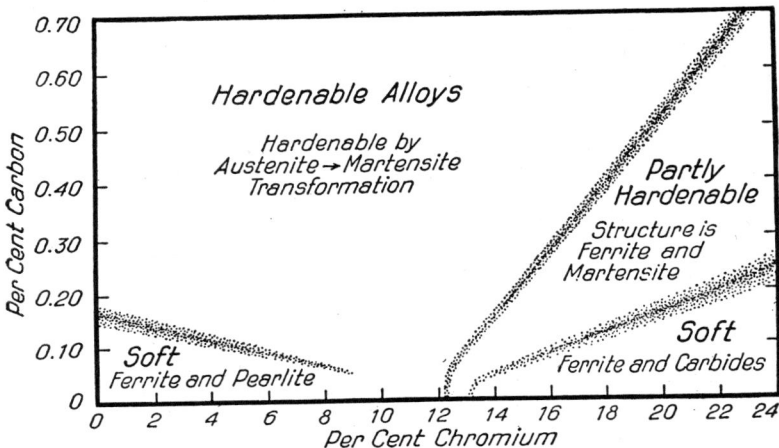

FIG. 80.—Effects of chromium and carbon on hardenability of alloys. (*From Thum, the Book of Stainless Steels.*)

The low-carbon stainless steels contain 12.0 to 14.0 and even 16.0 per cent of chromium and less than 0.12 per cent of carbon. They can be heat-treated and give fair resistance to corrosion whether annealed or heat-treated. The U. S. Navy specifies this grade of steel for heat-treated turbine parts and lists the following typical physical properties:[1]

	Yield point, psi	Elongation, % in 2 in.	Brinell hardness
Oil quenched from 1825°F and tempered:			
To 700°F....................	160,000	17.5	395
To 1200°F...................	100,000	22.5	240
Annealed 1600°F.............	58,000	33.0	165

[1] Quoted from Metals Handbook, 1936 ed., p. 374.

If the chromium content is raised to 16 to 20 per cent, with the carbon still below 0.12 per cent, the alloy loses its property of responding to heat-treatment because the ferrite remains in the alpha form and does not change to the gamma form on heating. These alloys are therefore sometimes called "chromium irons" or "chromium ferrites" rather than chromium steels. The metal does harden slightly on quenching in oil, but is usually considered to be permanently soft. It is very ductile, does not harden much with cold work, resists corrosion and oxidation well, and is much used for sheets and plates where resistance to corrosion is more important than strength. There is difficulty with grain growth in the chromium ferrites with more than 16 per cent chromium. The carbon is so low that the grain can be refined only after cold work, and so great care is necessary in the heat-treatment of these steels.

If the chromium is increased to 25 to 30 per cent with the carbon still kept low, the noncorrosive properties become still better. The alloys are also resistant to hot combustion gases even when containing large amounts of sulfur gases at temperatures almost up to the melting point of the metal.

Cutlery Steels.—The original stainless cutlery steel contained 12.0 to 15.0 per cent chromium and 0.30 to 0.40 per cent carbon. The diagram of Fig. 80 shows that this composition may be either austenite or martensite according to the heat-treatment. In order to bring out its maximum resistance to corrosion, it must be quenched, tempered, and thoroughly polished. If any scale pits are left in the metal, they become foci of corrosion. Some explanation of these phenomena will be given in the chapter on Corrosion. This steel is reasonably hard but does not hold a cutting edge as well as a good high-carbon steel. If the percentage of carbon is increased to 0.55 to 0.70 and the chromium to 15.0 to 18.0 per cent, a harder steel is obtained.

More Complex Alloys.—Chromium steels are frequently alloyed with nickel, molybdenum, vanadium, tungsten, and other metals. These alloys will be discussed in the following chapter.

Vanadium.—Vanadium is a powerful deoxidizer but is too expensive to be used for that purpose. It is added to the molten steel in the form of ferrovanadium after the deoxidation has been effected by manganese and silicon, but even then some vanadium is used up as a deoxidizer. It produces a very small grain size in steel and forms hard carbides which are resistant to high temperatures. When added in amounts of only 0.15 to 0.18 per cent, it increases both strength and ductility and promotes good machining qualities. It is added to the metal for large castings and also for forgings. It accentuates the benefits to be derived from other alloying elements such as manganese and chromium. The hard carbides make it an important constituent of alloy tool steels and of steels intended to resist high temperatures. Its use in the more complicated alloy systems will be discussed later.

Tungsten.—Tungsten forms hard carbides like chromium. It is usually employed with chromium and frequently also with vanadium for tool steels that are expected to work at high temperatures. Its advantages will be considered further when tool steels and steels to withstand high temperatures are discussed.

Molybdenum.—Molybdenum forms solid solutions with iron up to 7 per cent at room temperature. It also forms hard carbides like tungsten. It lessens grain growth and makes the thermal transformations sluggish. It lowers the critical point on cooling, and so increases the depth of hardening. It also increases toughness and strength at high temperatures. Molybdenum is largely used in connection with chromium and manganese, and its further use will be considered in the following chapter.

References

AMERICAN SOCIETY FOR METALS: Metals Handbook, 1939 ed., Cleveland.
Symposium on High-strength Constructional Metals, American Society for Testing Materials, 1936.
GREGG and DANILOFF: The Alloys of Iron and Copper, McGraw-Hill Book Company, Inc., New York, 1934.
GREINER, MARSH, and STOUGHTON: The Alloys of Iron and Silicon, McGraw-Hill Book Company, Inc., New York, 1933.
KINZEL and CRAFTS: The Alloys of Iron and Chromium, Vol. I, Low Chromium Alloys, McGraw-Hill Book Company, Inc., New York, 1937.
GREGG, J. L.: The Alloys of Iron and Molybdenum, McGraw-Hill Book Company, Inc., New York, 1932.
GREGG, J. L.: Alloys of Iron and Tungsten, McGraw-Hill Book Company, Inc., New York, 1934.
Alloys of Nickel and Iron, International Nickel Company, Bulletins.
Bethlehem Steel Company: Bethlehem Alloy Steels, Catalog 107, 1936.
GREAVES, R. H.: Chromium Steels, His Majesty's Stationery Office, London, 1935.

CHAPTER XII

STEELS WITH TWO OR MORE ALLOYING CONSTITUENTS AND STEELS FOR SPECIAL PURPOSES

Steels that consist of iron, carbon, and two important alloying constituents are known as "quaternary" steels. The systems are so complex that the equilibrium relations are worked out only imperfectly, and it is difficult to predict what alterations in properties will result from changes in chemical composition. Many of our finest steels for special purposes belong in this complex group. The preceding chapter classified the alloying constituents as forming solid solutions in the ferrite, or as forming hard carbides. The alloying elements continue to perform similar functions in the more complicated systems and are used where they can reinforce each other to the best advantage.

Chrome-nickel Structural Steels.—Since nickel stays in solid solution in the ferrite and chromium forms a hard carbide, it is logical to combine both of these elements in an alloy steel. If the steel is to be pearlitic on ordinary slow cooling and respond to the usual heat-treatments, both the nickel and the chromium must be kept rather low. The S.A.E. steels vary within the limits of 3115, which contains 1.00 to 1.50 nickel, 0.45 to 0.75 chromium, and 0.10 to 0.20 carbon, to 3450 with 2.75 to 3.25 nickel, 0.60 to 0.95 chromium and 0.45 to 0.55 carbon. These may all be normalized, machined, quenched, and tempered. Those with the lower percentage of nickel are extensively used in automobile construction for heat-treated parts such as crankshafts and axle shafts and for casehardened parts such as ring gears and transmission gears.

The mechanical properties of steel 3140 with 0.60 per cent chromium, 1.25 nickel, and 0.40 carbon are shown graphically in Fig. 81. They may be compared with Fig. 22 for the plain 1045 carbon steel and Fig. 73 for the 2340 steel with 3.5 per cent of nickel. When these steels are quenched in oil and tempered to have an elongation of 20 per cent in 2 in., the yield point of the

1040 steel will be about 70,000, that for the 3140 will be 100,000, and that for the 2340 will be 130,000 psi. The question of which

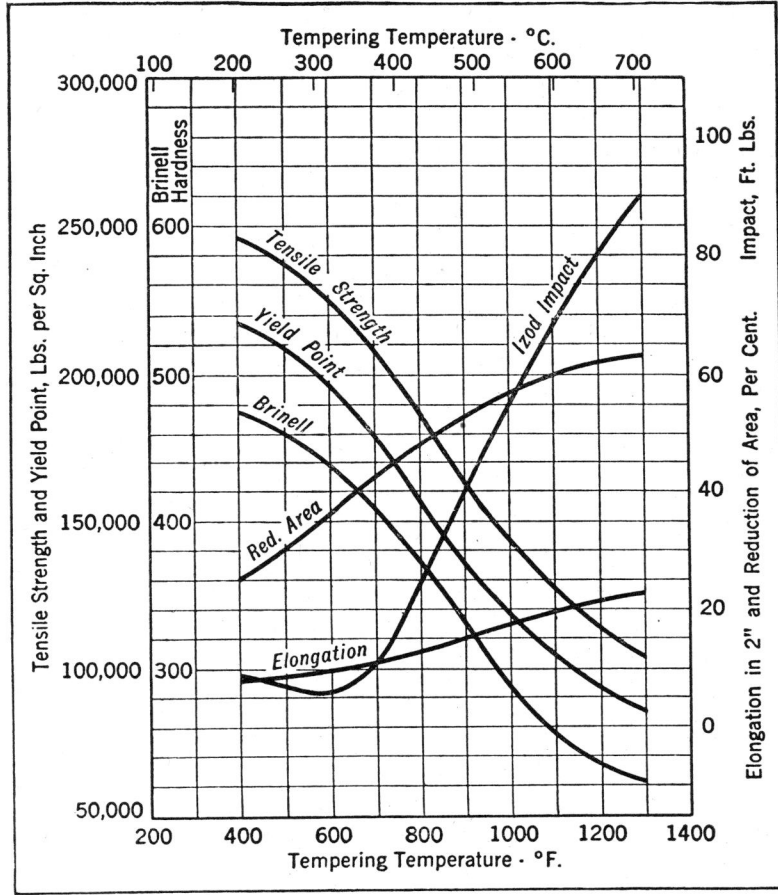

FIG. 81.—Physical properties chart for chrome-nickel steel S.A.E. 3140. (*From International Nickel Co.'s Data Book.*)

	Composition, per cent	Approx. critical range	Heat treatment
Carbon	0.35–0.45	Ac_1 1355°F	Quenched from 1475°–1525°F
Manganese	0.50–0.80		
Phosphorus	0.04 max.	Ac_2 1380°F	Quenched into oil
Sulfur	0.05 max.		
Nickel	1.00–1.50		
Chromium	0.45–0.75	Ac_3 1395°F	Tempered as indicated

steel to use for a given purpose can be answered only after a careful study of the relative dimensions and costs of the finished parts which will give satisfactory service.

STEELS WITH TWO OR MORE ALLOYING CONSTITUENTS

Chrome-molybdenum-nickel Structural Steels.—These steels provide a combination of very high strength, ductility, and resistance to shock. They permit a wide variation in properties with heat-treatment. Steel 4340 with 1.50 to 2.00 per cent nickel, 0.50 to 0.80 per cent chromium, 0.30 to 0.40 per cent molybdenum, and 0.35 to 0.45 per cent carbon, after oil quenching and tempering to show an elongation of 15 per cent, will have a yield point of 170,000 psi.

Chrome-vanadium Steels.—These steels contain only 0.15 to 0.18 per cent vanadium, 0.80 to 1.10 chromium, and carbon varying all the way from 0.10 to 1.05 per cent. The alloys with carbon up to 0.25 are used for carburized parts. The medium grades with 0.45 to 0.55 per cent carbon are sometimes used for leaf and small coil springs. The grades with higher carbon are used for balls and ball bearings and tool steels.

Chrome-nickel Stainless Steels.—In the discussion of the influence of nickel, attention was called to its ability to impart resistance to corrosion, and in the discussion of chromium, the stainless steels with low carbon and chromium above 12 per cent were treated. It should therefore not occasion surprise that a combination of nickel and chromium should give a very resistant steel. They all contain low carbon, less than 0.25 per cent, with chromium ranging from 7.0 to 25.0 and nickel from 8.0 to 25.0 per cent. They are all austenitic and do not harden with heat-treatment. They are tough and harden with cold work and are rendered ductile by cooling rapidly from a high temperature.

One of the most popular of these steels, usually spoken of as the 18 and 8 steel, has a chemical composition varying within the following limits according to the Metals Handbook:

	Per Cent
C	0.08– 0.20
Si	– 0.75
Mn	– 0.60
Cr	17.0 –19.0
Ni	7.0 – 9.0

The physical properties of this steel as influenced by cold work is shown in Fig. 82. These steels are not only resistant to atmospheric corrosion but also to many chemicals and find wide use in the food industries, in petroleum refineries, and in chemical plants. The combination of strength, ductility, and ability to be hardened by cold work together with their resistance to corrosion has caused this steel to be used largely in the construction of the streamlined lightweight railway trains. The addition of small quantities of other alloying materials improves their suitability for specific purposes. The steels may be cast or forged, but are too tough to machine rapidly. A free-machining type is produced by increasing the phosphorus to 0.125 and adding 0.250 per cent of selenium.

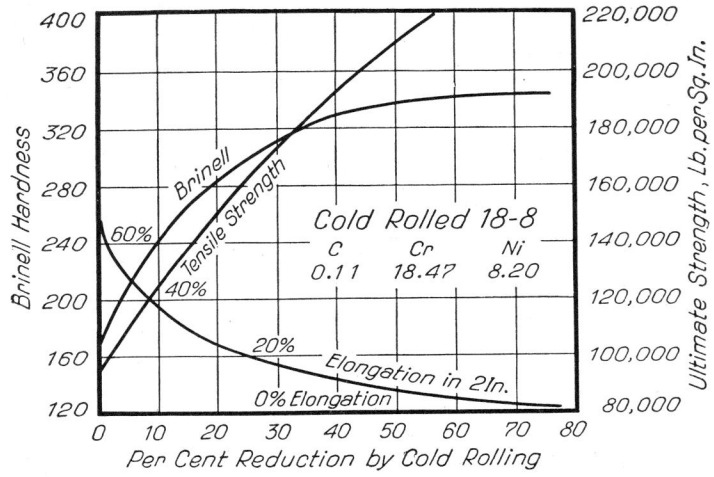

FIG. 82.—Physical properties of stainless chrome-nickel steel (18-8) as affected by cold-rolling. (*From Thum, The Book of Stainless Steels.*)

Endurance and Fatigue Failures at Room Temperatures. Endurance Limit.—It was stated in the earlier chapters of this book that a metal stressed within the elastic limit would return to its original dimensions after the stress was removed, provided sufficient time was allowed. The inference was that a metal might be repeatedly stressed within the elastic limit without harm. This may be true if sufficient time is allowed for complete recovery between the application of stresses. It does not hold true if the stresses are repeated rapidly. A common type of machine to test endurance, while also studying the effect of various atmospheres, is shown in section and as a photograph in Fig. 83. The test piece *B* is supported at one end only and is rotated rapidly. The unsupported end of the test piece has a weight hanging from it which causes definite and rapidly alter-

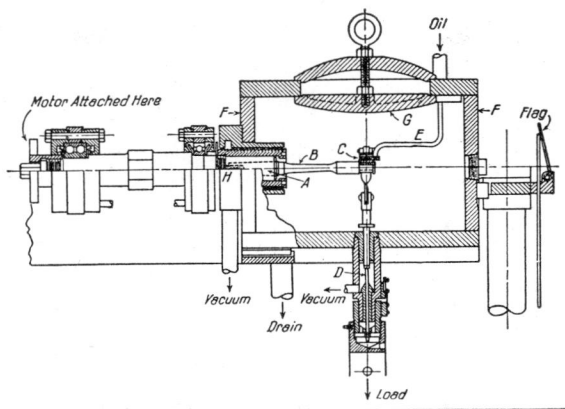

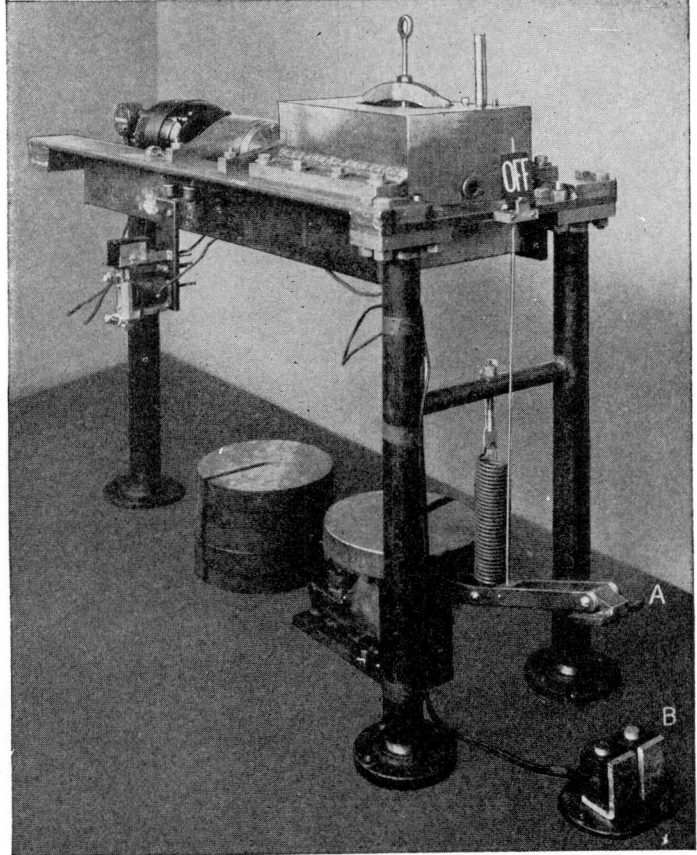

Fig. 83.—Apparatus for determining corrosion fatigue limits. (*From Thum, The Book of Stainless Steels.*)

nating strains to be set up. Devices are attached for counting the number of revolutions and automatically stopping the machine when the test piece breaks. The endurance or fatigue limit is

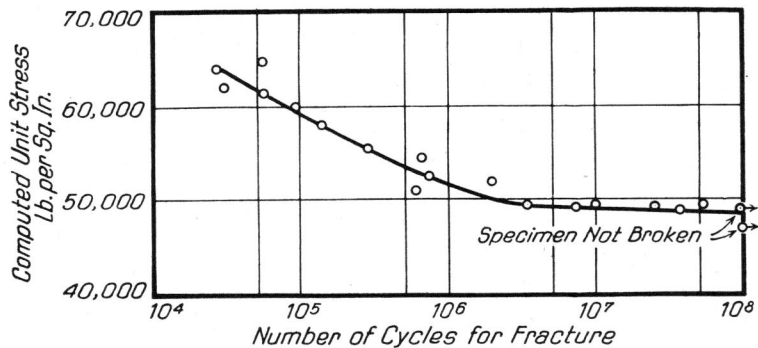

Fig. 84.—Graph showing relation between magnitude of unit stress and number of cycles of application to cause failure. (*From Thum, The Book of Stainless Steels.*)

defined as the maximum stress to which material may be subjected an indefinitely large number of times without causing failure. For purposes of testing, the term "indefinitely large" is frequently taken as 10 million. A number of test bars must be

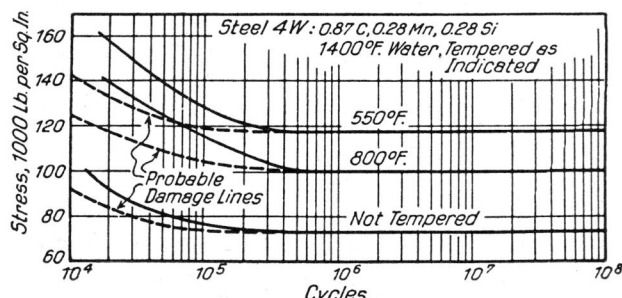

Fig. 85.—Graphs showing effect of tempering on resistance to fatigue. [*From French, Trans. Am. Soc. for Steel Treating,* **21**, 910 (1933).]

prepared and tested for each metal, and an illustration of the results as they appear after plotting is shown in Fig. 84. The graph shows that this particular alloy could withstand 60,000 lb unit stress for less than 100,000 cycles but could withstand 48,000 lb for 100,000,000 cycles and presumably indefinitely.

STEELS WITH TWO OR MORE ALLOYING CONSTITUENTS 209

The effect of heat-treating a quenched steel with 0.87 per cent of carbon is shown in Fig. 85 as determined by French. The endurance limit is increased over 50 per cent by proper heat-treatment after quenching.

Steel for Springs.—Steel that is to be made into springs is especially subject to fatigue failure, and both the design of the spring and the composition of the metal must be chosen care-

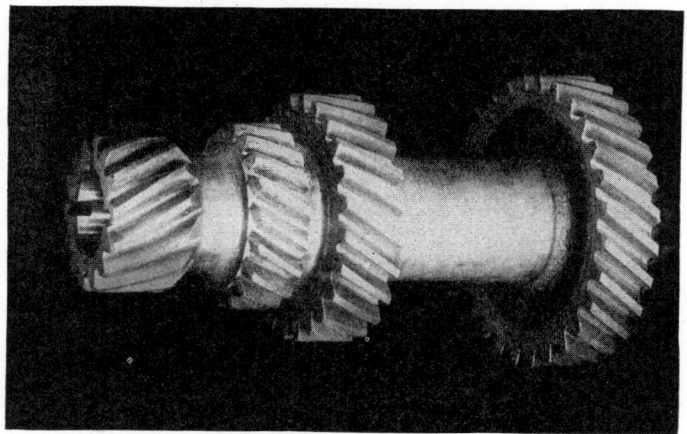

Fig. 86.—Photograph of finished cluster gear machined from centrifugal casting. (*Courtesy of Ford Motor Company.*)

fully. The surface of the spring must be free of seams, cuts, or areas of localized segregation, for these act as starting points for fatigue failure. Small coiled springs may be made from cold-drawn wire or from wire that has been tempered prior to coiling. They may also be made from annealed wire which is heat-treated after coiling. Small flat springs may be made from similar types of metal. A brief annealing treatment at temperatures of 450 to 850°F may be given the cold-worked springs to relieve forming strains. Alloy steels may contain approximately 1.0 per cent of chromium and 0.15 vanadium. A group of silicon-manganese steels with 1.80 to 2.20 per cent silicon, 0.60 to 0.90 manganese, and 0.50 to 0.65 carbon are also used. The behavior of springs at elevated temperatures is discussed under Creep.

Centrifugally Cast Gears for Automobiles.—R. H. McCarroll[1] advises that the Ford Motor Company is introducing centrifugal

[1] Personal communication.

210   ENGINEERING MATERIALS

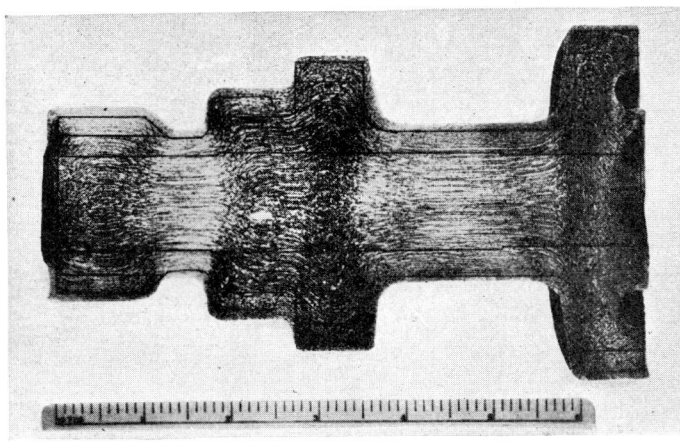

Fig. 87.—Cross section of forging (a) and of centrifugal casting (b) for cluster gear. Etched with hot acid. The lines drawn in ink show the dimensions of the finished gear. The central portion of both the forging and casting will be drilled out to receive the shaft so that the pipe in the casting will be eliminated in the machine process. (*Courtesy of Ford Motor Company.*)

STEELS WITH TWO OR MORE ALLOYING CONSTITUENTS 211

castings for its transmission gears and ring gears. The metal has the following composition:

	Per Cent
Carbon	0.35–0.40
Manganese	0.65–0.80
Silicon	0.20–0.40
Chromium	0.90–1.10
Copper	1.00–1.25
Phosphorus	–0.05
Sulfur	–0.05

The molten metal is poured at a temperature of 2860 to 2900°F into a low-carbon cast-steel mold revolving at 400 rpm

FIG. 88.—Photograph of finished ring gear. (*Courtesy of Ford Motor Company.*)

for the transmission gears and 350 rpm for the ring gears. Before machining, they are heated for 1 hr at 1800°F and air-cooled. This treatment gives a Brinell hardness of 170 to 196. After machining, the gears are casehardened in a gas carburizing furnace and quenched in oil. They are then heated to 360 to 400°F to relieve strains.

A photograph of the cluster gear is shown in Fig. 86, and cross sections of the forging and centrifugal casting used in making these gears is shown in Fig. 87. Ink lines have been drawn on

212   ENGINEERING MATERIALS

the photographs to show the dimensions of the finished gear. The whole central core of both the forging and casting must be bored out to receive the drive shaft so that the pipe of the ingot is eliminated in the machining process. The flow lines of the

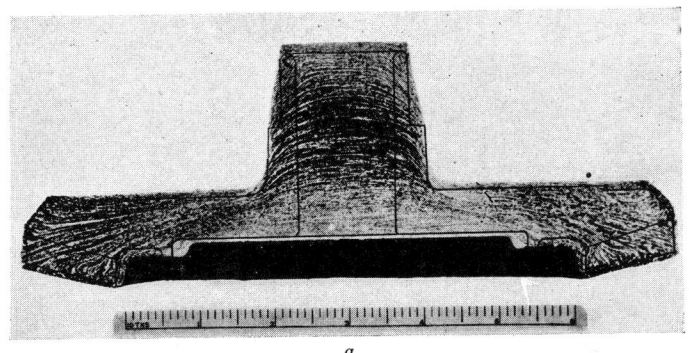

a

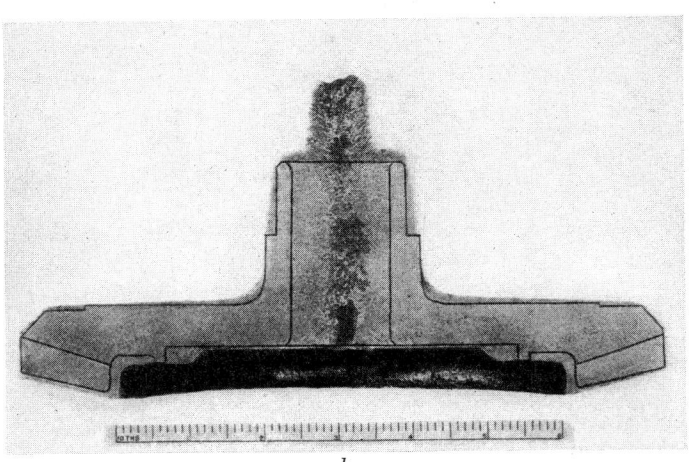

b

Fig. 89.—Cross section of forging (*a*) and of centrifugal casting (*b*) for ring gear. Etched with hot acid. The lines drawn in ink show the dimensions of the finished gear. The central portion of both the forging and casting will be drilled out to receive the shaft so that the pipe in the casting will be eliminated in the machining process. (*Courtesy of Ford Motor Company.*)

forging and the crystal structure of the casting have been shown in the cross sections by deep etching with hot acid.

A photograph of the ring gear is shown in Fig. 88 and one of the cross sections of the forging and of the casting from which they are made is shown in Fig. 89.

These cast gears are not only considerably less expensive than the forged gears but are also superior in quality.

Cast Crankshafts for Automobiles.—R. H. McCarroll and J. H. McCloud[1] report that the crankshafts of the Ford automobile have been machined from castings instead of forgings since 1933. The steel is melted in electric furnaces and has the following composition:

	Per Cent
Carbon	1.35–1.60
Manganese	0.60–0.80
Silicon	0.85–1.10
Chromium	0.40–0.50
Copper	1.50–2.00

After machining, the crankshafts are given the following heat-treatment in gas-fired furnaces:

Heat to 1650°F, and hold for 20 min.
Air quench to minimum of 1200°F.
Reheat to 1400°F, and hold 1 hr.
Cool in furnace to 1000°F another hour.

Tension tests on 0.505 round bars show:

Tensile strength	107,500 psi
Elastic limit	92,000 psi
Elongation in 2 in	2.75 per cent
Reduction of area	2.25 per cent
Brinell hardness	269

The microscopic structure of the alloy as cast is shown in Fig. 90 to be composed of grains of pearlite in a network of cementite. There is no primary graphite. It is annealed at 1650°F for 20 min., air quenched to 1200°F to remove shrinkage strains, and then heated to 1400°F and held for an hour before it is slowly cooled to 1000°F. This heat-treatment changes about 0.90 per cent carbon to secondary graphite. The remaining 0.6 to 0.7 per cent carbon remains as spheroidized pearlite as shown in the same figure. The copper is added to the alloy to increase the fluidity of the metal and reduce shrinkage, thereby reducing warpage. Silicon controls the solubility of copper, and about half as much silicon as copper is required. Chromium is added to improve the wearing properties, and the amount is limited by the increasing resistance to machining.

[1] Ford Alloy Castings, *Metal Prog.*, **30**, 33 (1936).

214   ENGINEERING MATERIALS

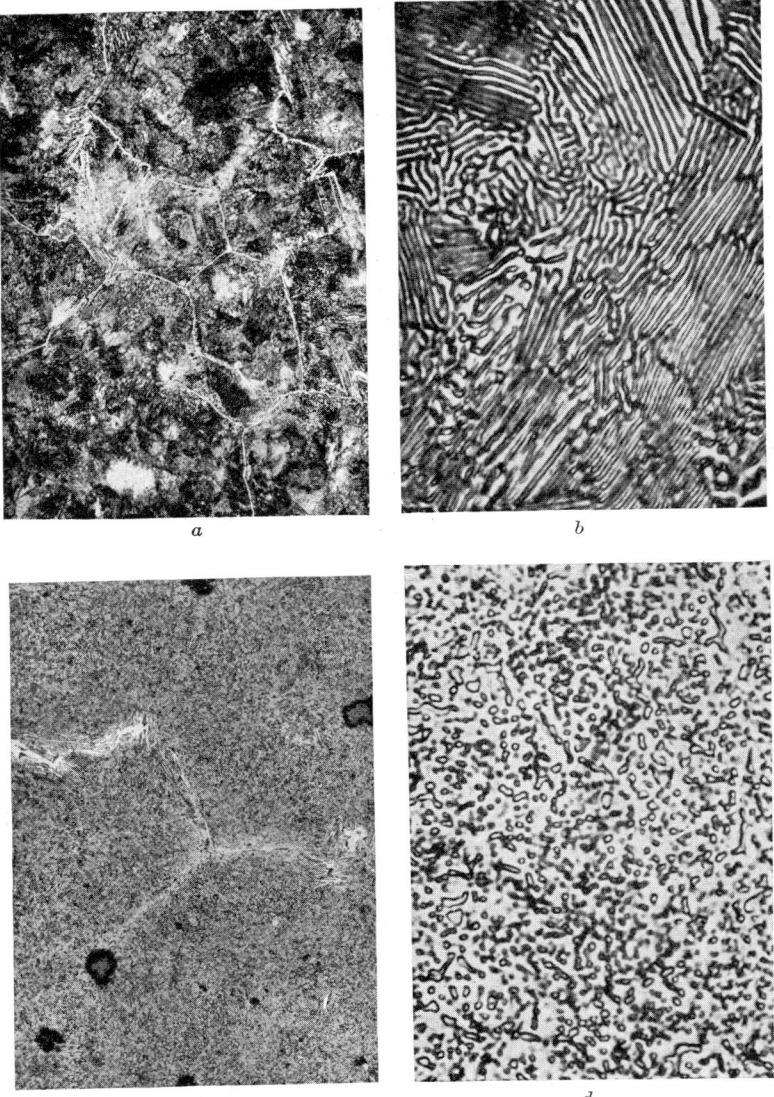

FIG. 90.—Microscopic structure of cast copper-silicon steel as used in Ford crankshaft. (*Courtesy of Ford Motor Company.*)

a, as cast, ×100, showing pearlite grains surrounded by a network of cementite.

b, the same, ×1000.

c, after heat treatment, ×100, showing grains of spheroidized pearlite with spots of secondary graphite.

d, the same, ×1000, showing spheroidized pearlite.

These cast crankshafts give better service than those formerly made from forged steel. In addition to the smaller number of fabricating operations, only 9 lb of metal need to be removed in the machining operations as compared with 24 lb, and the finished crankshaft weighs 10 lb less than that produced by the forging process.

Slow Deformation at High Temperatures. Creep.—It has already been stated that metals deform slightly when even the smallest load is applied. If the load does not surpass the elastic limit, the deformation soon becomes constant and remains so as long as the load is not changed. Such a state is characteristic of an elastic as distinguished from a plastic material, and is probably due to the work hardening produced by the load applied. As the temperature is raised, the forces holding the atoms together become weaker. The force required to deform the individual crystals decreases, and the fractured crystals produced by the deformation commence to reorient themselves, and thus slip occurs between the grains as well as within the grains. At and above this equicohesive temperature, a force that is capable of producing an initial deformation will also produce a continuing deformation so long as the force is applied. The metal behaves as a plastic rather than an elastic body. This slow deformation under a constant load at elevated temperature is called "creep." It has become of great importance in recent years in the petroleum industry where cracking operations are often carried out at temperatures of 1000°F and pressures of 800 psi. Some of the modern steam power plants are operating at pressures of 1400 psi in the boiler and temperatures of 925°F in the superheaters, and some chemical plants require pressure vessels to withstand pressures of 10,000 psi at 1000°F.

The specimen to be tested for creep is placed under a constant stress while held in a furnace whose temperature can be kept constant for months at a time. Provision is made for observing the slow stretching of this test piece as it remains under constant load at constant temperature. The behavior of a steel with 0.15 per cent carbon is shown in Fig. 91 taken from the work of A. E. White, C. L. Clark, and R. L. Wilson.[1]

---

[1] Influence of Time at 1000°F on the Characteristics of Carbon Steel, *Trans. Am. Soc. Testing Materials*, **36**, II, 139 (1936).

The tensile strength of this steel when tested at room temperature in the annealed condition was 62,500 lb, its elongation in 2 in. was 36 per cent, and its reduction of area 67.5 per cent. When tested at the ordinary rate used for testing at room temperature but with the test piece heated to 1000°F while it was being pulled, the tensile strength was only 36,500 lb but the elongation in 2 in. was 42.5 per cent. The behavior of several test specimens each kept at a constant temperature of 1000°F and under constant load is shown in Fig. 91. The specimen

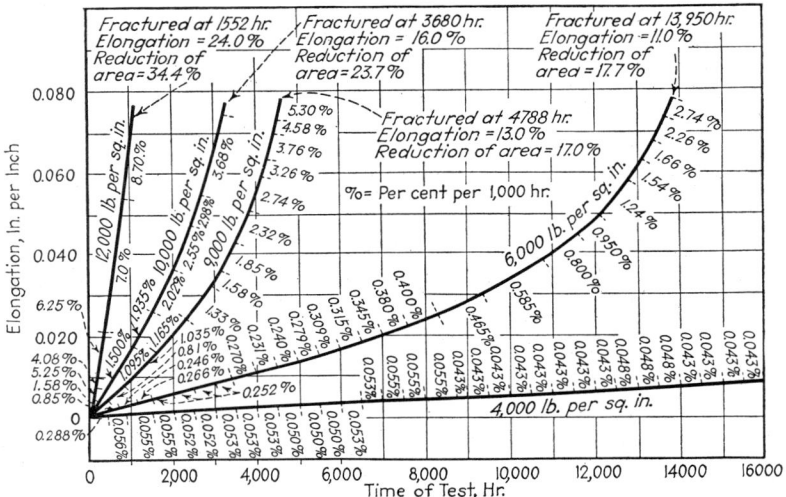

FIG. 91.—Graph showing creep of steel with 0.15 per cent carbon, annealed at 1550°F and then stressed as shown at 1000°F. [*From paper of A. E. White, Clark and Wilson, Proc. Am. Soc. for Testing Materials* **36**, II, 139 (1936).]

stressed to 12,000 psi stretched at an almost constant rate and broke after 1552 hr with an elongation of 24.0 per cent. Other specimens loaded with 10,000, 9,000 and 6,000 psi stretched at slower rates and broke after longer periods. The specimen stressed to 6,000 psi required 19 months to break after an elongation of 11.0 per cent had been reached. A specimen stressed to 4,000 psi had stretched only 0.043 per cent after 22 months. This last specimen was still in good condition and would have continued to support this load for many years. It is evident that where plain carbon steel is to be subjected to continuous stresses at these higher temperatures the safe load that the metal can carry is very much below the figures which may be used at ordinary temperatures. The addition of alloying elements that form hard and resistant carbides, such as chromium, molybdenum, tungsten, and vanadium produce superior steel for high-temperature uses.

Tool Steels.—The original tool steels were plain high-carbon steel, and this metal is still widely used. It takes a good cutting edge and possesses adequate hardness for cutting wood and the softer metals, including mild steel. A steel for this type of work may have 0.60 to 1.40 per cent carbon, 0.10 to 0.35 manganese, and 0.15 to 0.50 silicon with very low sulfur and phosphorus. It may be hardened by quenching in water and tempering in accordance with the principles laid down for the other grades of carbon steel.

More care must be used when working with the hypereutectoid steels, and the heat-treating diagram as given in Fig. 20 shows two critical ranges, one for annealing and hardening and one for normalizing. Tool steel is usually furnished by the manufacturer in an annealed condition soft enough to be machined, but without coarse grains. If such steel is heated to 1375 to 1425°F and held only long enough for the heat to penetrate fully to the center of the piece, the grain size will not be changed, but enough carbides will be brought into the austenitic form to permit adequate hardening on quenching. If the temperature is too high or the time is too long, the cementite will migrate to form large conglomerates which will not yield maximum attainable hardness. If it is necessary to anneal high-carbon steels, the pieces should be protected from oxidation, preferably by packing in carbon in closed containers. If the carbides are already segregated in large particles or if the grain is too coarse, the steel may be normalized by heating above the Acm range and cooling in air.

High-carbon steel is necessarily more brittle than the hypoeutectoid steels, and the brittleness is a disadvantage. The Carpenter torsion impact testing machine measures the footpounds of energy required to break a test piece with a torsional impact blow. The results of various drawing temperatures on the toughness of a rod of ¼ in. cross section containing 1.10 carbon after being quenched and drawn for 1 hr at several temperatures is shown in Fig. 92. The extraordinary peak in the toughness at 350°F represents a fivefold resistance to torsional impact. This is accompanied by only a small decrease in hardness from 66.8 to 64.0 as measured on the Rockwell C hardness tester. The curve shows a secondary rise in toughness at higher drawing temperatures, but it is accompanied by more rapid decrease in hardness, and at 800°F the Rockwell C hardness is only 46.0. It is evident that for this steel a drawing temperature of 350°F would be the best for almost all purposes. When this steel is quenched in sections larger than about ½ in., it is only the outside that will have the hardness indicated. The core will cool slowly enough to become rather soft but tough. If the cross

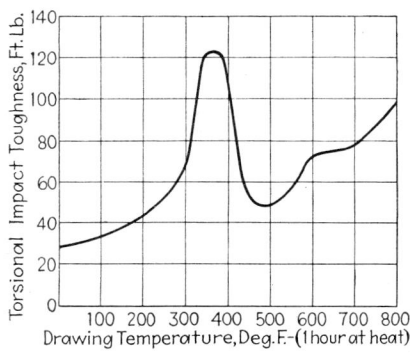

FIG. 92.—Effect of drawing temperature on toughness, when tested on Carpenter torsion impact testing machine.
These figures are only applicable to bars of less than ½ in. cross section which will harden completely to the center on quenching. (*From Carpenter Steel Co.'s booklet on Matched Tool Steels.*)

section of the tool is small, it should be quenched in oil instead of water.

Shallow- and Deep-hardening Steel.—The depth to which the hardness penetrates on quenching is in part a function of the temperature and size of the piece and the nature and extent of agitation of the quenching medium. The carbon is supposed to be all in the austenitic state before quenching, and if the metal is to be hardened, the carbides must all remain in a state of extremely fine dispersion when the cooling operation is completed. In plain carbon steels, a coarse grain gives a somewhat greater depth of hardening, probably because the transformation of austenite is slower than in fine-grained steels. Some alloys are very effective in promoting deep hardenability, notably manganese, silicon, and chromium, because they lower the critical range or make the reaction more sluggish, and so retard the change of austenite to pearlite and extend the temperature range where martensite is formed. The influence of chromium and nickel on deep hardenability is shown in Fig. 93 from Bain's work.

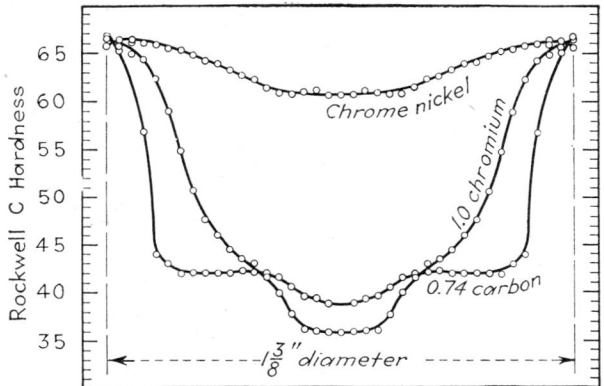

Fig. 93.—Deeper hardenability as influenced by chromium and nickel. (*From Bain, Yearbook of Am. Iron and Steel Institute, 1934, p. 98.*)

Low-alloy Tool Steels.—Chromium, vanadium, manganese, and tungsten are all elements that form hard carbides and are used singly or together with medium- or high-carbon steels. The process of hardening and tempering these steels is similar to that of the plain carbon steels, after allowance has been made for the change in the critical range and the sluggishness of transformation caused by some of the alloys. Gill[1] has divided tool steels into 14 classes whose compositions are given in Table 24. Attention may be called to numbers 6 and 7 of this table as illustrations of the effect of alloying elements. Steel 6 called "tungsten alloy chisel steel" has medium carbon 0.45 to 0.60, 1.0 to 2.0 tungsten, 1.0 to 1.5 chromium, and 0.15 to 0.30 vanadium. Gill says that these steels are frequently used for punches, chisels, shear blades, and battering tools of miscellaneous type and that their life for these purposes may often be three times as great as that of carbon tool steels. The tungsten finishing steels of class 7 are characterized by high carbon, 1.10 to 1.40 per cent, and higher tungsten, 3.0 to 5.0 per cent. These steels are characterized by intense hardness and keenness of cutting edge and

[1] Tool Steels, lectures before the American Society of Metals, 1934.

TABLE 24.—CLASSIFICATION OF TOOL STEELS*

No.	Type	C	Si	Mn	W	Cr	V	Mo	Co
1	Carbon tool steel	Variable							
2	Carbon vanadium	Variable					0.15–0.40		
3	Cr-V or low Cr†	Variable				0.30– 0.90			
4	High C—Low W	1.00–1.30			1.00– 2.00	0.50– 1.50	0.15–0.30		
5	Mn oil hardening‡	0.80–1.00		1.00–1.75	0.40– 0.60	0.40– 0.60			
6	W alloy chisel	0.45–0.60			1.00– 2.00	1.00– 1.50	0.15–0.30		
7	Finishing	1.10–1.40			3.00– 5.00				
8	Cr hot work	0.80–1.00				3.00– 4.00			
9	W hot work	0.25–0.45			8.00–15.00	2.50– 3.50			
10	Cr-W hot work	0.25–0.50			3.00– 7.00	3.00– 7.00			
11	Silicon manganese	0.50–0.65	1.50–2.50	0.75–1.00					
12	High C—High Cr	1.50–2.25				10.00–15.00			
13	High-speed steel	0.50–0.80			14.00–20.00	3.00– 4.50	0.75–2.25		
14	Cobalt high speed	0.60–0.80			14.00–20.00	3.00– 4.50	0.75–2.25		2.50–12.00

* From Gill, J. P., Tool Steels, p. 18.
† May or may not contain 0.15 to 0.25 per cent V.
‡ With Mn on high side may not contain other alloys.

STEELS WITH TWO OR MORE ALLOYING CONSTITUENTS

are used for thin finishing cuts. They do not stand up especially well at a red heat.

Steels for Hot Work.—These steels contain higher chromium and tungsten, with the carbon sometimes rather low. The tungsten carbides resist continuous heat better than the chromium carbides, and type 9 of Table 24, with 8 to 15 per cent tungsten, can be used for dies in drop-forging operations where the dies operate at almost a visible red heat. The percentage of tungsten in the upper ranges of these steels is high enough so that it imparts air-hardening properties.

High-speed Steels.—Steels with rather high percentages of tungsten were known for many years, but it was not until Taylor and White of the Bethlehem Steel Company announced the results of their long studies in 1906 that the desirable properties of tungsten were utilized to advantage. Their steels revolutionized the art of cutting steel by providing a tool that would not lose its temper even when working at such a speed that the point of the tool was heated almost to redness. The composition and the methods of heat-treatment that they advocated are still used, although modifications of composition have also been introduced as shown in Table 24. Taylor and White recommended that their steel should be heated to 2300°F, quenched, and then reheated to 1100°. The composition was as follows:

	Per Cent
Carbon	0.65–0.70
Tungsten	18.0
Chromium	4.0
Vanadium	1.0

The steel is sensitive to rapid heating and must be brought slowly up to 1650°F, when the steel should have become completely austenitic. It may then be heated rapidly to 2350°, removed from the furnace as soon as it has reached that temperature, and quenched. The transformations are so sluggish that a quick quench is not necessary, and a stream of compressed air often provides adequate cooling. For small parts, even cooling in still air is sufficient, and these steels are sometimes called "air-hardening" or "self-hardening" on that account. Steels quenched quickly must be tempered, with slow reheating up to 1100°F as a maximum. Harder and Grove[1] report that the

[1] *Am. Inst. Min. Met. Eng.*, 1933.

hardness of these steels when tested at 1100°F, which is a visible red heat, was 435 to 465 on the Brinell scale. This may be compared with the hardness of 380 obtained by quenching a 1080 steel in oil and measuring its hardness at room temperature. The

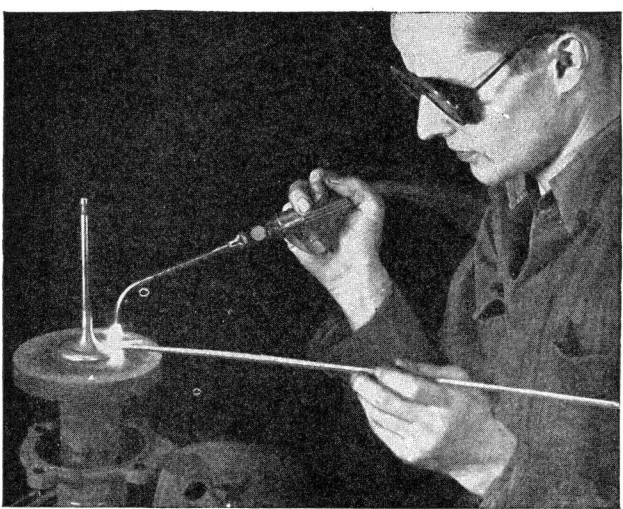

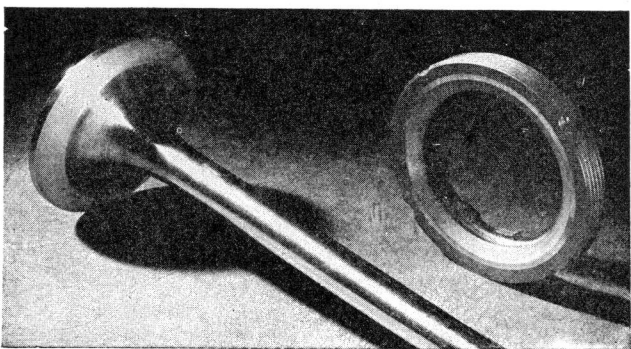

Fig. 94.—Application of Stellite to automobile valves and valve seats. (*Courtesy of Haynes Stellite Co.*)

addition of cobalt to these steels increases the "red hardness" to 500 to 555 Brinell at 1100°F.

High-cobalt Alloys. *Stellite.*—The high-cobalt alloys were first developed by Elwood Haynes who coined the word Stellite for an extremely hard alloy of 50 to 65 per cent of cobalt, 30 per cent of chromium, and 4 to 15 per cent of tungsten, with carbon in varying amounts, but very little iron. The structure is very complicated and not very well known. The alloy cannot be forged or rolled but must be cast and ground to shape. When cold, it is no harder than hard steel, but it retains its hardness practically unimpaired at the high surface heats developed by friction, even at a red heat. It is supplied by the manufacturers already fabricated into tool bits and milling cutter blades.

The alloy may also be applied as droplets of molten alloy with an oxyacetylene torch to provide a thin coating of a wear-resistant alloy to a steel part. The preparation and appearance of an exhaust valve and valve-seat insert for a large motor truck is shown in Fig. 94. These parts are said to run for 100,000 miles without any maintenance.

Tungsten Carbide Tools.—Tungsten carbide (WC) is one of the hardest substances known. When carbide powder is mixed with about 10 per cent of powdered cobalt and pressed cold in a hydraulic press, it yields a fragile product which, when sintered at a high white heat, forms a tool of extraordinary hardness which is capable of machining even glass or porcelain. Jeffries[1] reports that in turning commutators the mica separators between the copper bars made it necessary to regrind an ordinary tool after 100 commutators had been machined. When this tool was replaced by one of sintered tungsten carbide, it machined 15,000 units with one grinding.

References

THUM, E. E.: The Book of Stainless Steel, 2d ed., published by American Society for Metals, Cleveland, 1935.

MOORE and KOMMERS: The Fatigue of Metals, reference from Metals Handbook, 1936 ed., p. 569.

FULLER, T. S.: Endurance Tests of Steel in Thum's Book of Stainless Steels, p. 569 1935.

MOORE, H. F.: Textbook of the Materials of Engineering, 5th ed., McGraw-Hill Book Company, Inc., New York, 1936.

MCCARROLL and MCCLOUD: Ford Alloy Castings, *Metal Progress*, August, 1936, p. 33.

Symposium on Effect of Temperature on Metals, American Society for Testing Materials, 1931.

WHITE, CLARK, and WILSON: Influence of Time on Creep of Steels, *Proc. Am. Soc. Testing Materials*, **35**, II, 167 (1935); **36**, II, 139 (1936).

[1] *Metals and Alloys*, **1**, 223 (1929).

CLARK and WHITE: Creep Characteristics of Metals, *Trans. Am. Soc. Metals,* **24,** 831–869 (1936).

GROSSMAN and BAIN: High Speed Steel, John Wiley & Sons, Inc., New York, 1931.

GILL, J. P.: Tool Steels, reprints from *Trans. Am. Soc. Metals,* 1934.

HARDER and GROVE: Hot Hardness of High Speed Steel and Related Alloys, *Am. Inst. Min. Met. Eng.,* **105,** 88 (1933).

PALMER, F. R.: Tool Steel Simplified, The Carpenter Steel Co., Reading, Pa., 1937.

Vanadium Steels and Irons, published by Vanadium Corporation of America, New York, 1937.

Modern Materials of Construction, A group of papers in *Chem. Met. Eng.,* vol. 43, October, 1936.

CHAPTER XIII

COPPER, NICKEL, ZINC, TIN, AND THEIR ALLOYS

Copper ranks as the world's most important engineering material next to steel. The pure metal is indispensable in the electrical industries and has important uses as a structural material. When alloyed with zinc or tin, it finds extensive applications under the trade names of brass and bronze. Zinc and tin are used largely as protective metallic coatings for steel and are also used in alloys.

Occurrence of Copper and Its Extraction from the Ore.— Copper was one of the earliest metals to be known to primitive man. It is sometimes found in nature in the metallic state especially in the state of Michigan along the shore of Lake Superior where large masses are occasionally encountered. The mines were known to the American Indians in prehistoric times and provided material for weapons and ornaments. The art of reducing copper from its ores was practiced in the days of King Solomon.

Copper is usually found in nature as a sulfide mixed with sulfides of iron, lead, zinc, and other metals, and a gangue which is ordinarily siliceous. Gold and silver also occur in some copper ores. In extracting copper, the first step is usually to roast the raw ore by heating in a furnace to dull redness in presence of air. Most of the sulfur is oxidized to SO_2 and is subsequently recovered as sulfuric acid. The roasted ore which still contains a small percentage of sulfur is charged into a reverberatory furnace or a blast furnace together with coke and limestone to flux the siliceous gangue. It will be recalled by reference to Table 8 that much less energy is required to remove the oxygen from copper and lead than from iron, and that lime and silica part with their oxygen with still greater difficulty. The iron associated with copper ores rates as an undesirable impurity, and the furnace is operated at a rather low temperature so that the iron will not be reduced in any large amount but will pass into the slag. It will be recalled also that the sulfur associated with the iron ores remained in part as sulfide in the pig iron in spite of the efforts, by high temperature and a rather basic slag, to drive it into the slag. It will therefore not be surprising that, in the copper furnace, the sulfur remains for the most part associated with the metal as a sulfide (matte). The early development of the metallurgy of copper in America occurred in Mexico and what is now the southwestern United States at a time when Spain ruled those countries. A good many Spanish terms have been retained in our metallurgical vocabulary and among them is the term "matte" (dull) for the mixed sulfides coming from the reverberatory or the blast furnace. The products of the blast or reverberatory furnace will be slag, matte, and sometimes metal, although the amount of sulfur is usually large enough to cause almost all of the metal to be present as matte.

The matte separated from the molten slag by gravity will contain almost all of the copper and lead and part of the iron and zinc that may be in the ore. The matte may now be oxidized either by fusion in an open-hearth or in a modified bessemer converter, which is more common. The iron and zinc will be oxidized before the copper, and pass into a slag formed by reaction with sand added to the converter. The copper discharged at the close of the bessemerizing process known as "blister" copper may contain 99.3 per cent of copper with a few hundredths per cent of sulfur and iron and a few thousandths of arsenic, antimony, and lead. These may be removed by further cautious oxidation by air on a hearth furnace which results in overoxidation of the metal. After the slag has been skimmed off, the cuprous oxide in solution is reduced by an operation known as "poling." This formerly consisted of stirring the metal with a wooden pole which became charred during the process, evolving gases which kept the metal stirred and yielding charcoal which reduced the cuprous oxide. The process is now conducted partly by the addition of charcoal, but logs of wood are still kept with their ends submerged in the molten bath. The product from this poling process is commercial copper of satisfactory purity.

Electrolytic Refining of Copper.—It has been mentioned that the ores of copper sometimes carry gold and silver. These precious metals remain with the copper through the blast furnace and bessemerizing operation and may be removed from the blister copper only by electrolytic refining. For the electrolytic refining, the blister copper is cast into rectangular plates to serve as anodes. These have an area of 8 to 10 sq ft and a thickness of more than an inch. The cathode sheets are made from pure copper about $\frac{1}{16}$ in. thick which is sheared into sheets the same size as the anodes. The anodes and cathodes are placed alternately in the electrolyzing vat with an electrolyte of slightly acidulated copper sulfate. The voltage between each pair of electrodes is only 0.3 to 0.35 volts, and the current density is 15 to 20 amp per square foot of cathode area. An ampere efficiency of 90 per cent may be expected. The main reaction which takes place is that the SO_4 in discharging at the anode reacts and causes an ion of copper to go into solution. At the same time, a copper ion discharges at the cathode depleting the solution by one ion. The solution therefore stays of constant composition, and the only work that is theoretically done in this main reaction is to transfer the metallic copper horizontally about 2 in. A side reaction involving the electrolysis of water occurs to a small extent and wastes the electric current. The small amount of iron present in the anode copper goes into solution and accumulates as $FeSO_4$ in the solution, which must be removed periodically for chemical treatment. Gold, silver, and some of the objectionable impurities do not go into solution but settle in the tank as slimes which are subsequently removed and treated for the recovery of the values they contain. The cathodes build up to a thickness of nearly an inch and consist of copper of high purity, except that they contain enough hydrogen to make them brittle. They are therefore remelted in a hearth furnace which causes some oxidation, and the excess oxide is reduced by poling. The product is then cast into pigs or bars for the market.

Lake copper from the metallic deposits on the shores of Lake Superior needs to be only melted, and then finished by the poling operation. It sometimes carries a small amount of silver, too small to be commercially recoverable, which has so nearly the same electrical conductivity as copper that it is counted as copper when it is sold. The chemical composition of Lake copper and of electrolytic copper as furnished in the form of bars for fabrication into wire is shown in Table 25.

Properties and Uses of Copper.—Copper melts at 1981°F (1083°C) which is somewhat lower than the melting point of cast iron. It is a soft and ductile metal which may be rolled and worked both hot and cold. Its properties are affected by even small amounts of impurities, and one of the most powerful of these is oxygen which is present as Cu_2O. Commercial tough-pitch copper usually contains 0.03 to 0.04 per cent oxygen in the form of Cu_2O, and this has been held necessary for its toughness.

TABLE 25.—CHEMICAL COMPOSITION AND PHYSICAL PROPERTIES OF COMMERCIAL COPPER*

Element	Electrolytic wire bar, per cent	Lake high conductivity, per cent
Silver (Ag)	0.0001	0.03
Oxygen (O)	0.0350	0.0420
Sulfur (S)	0.0021	0.0015
Iron (Fe)	0.0026	0.0025

Standard Specifications for Copper Wire, A.S.T.M. Standards, 1936

Condition of wire, diameter, in.	Tensile strength, psi	Elongation, per cent in 10 in.
Annealed or soft:		
0.460–0.290	36,000	35
0.289–0.103	37,000	30
0.102–0.021	38,500	25
Hard drawn:		
0.460	49,000	3.75
0.289	56,100	2.17
0.102	64,900	1.00

* Chemical Composition from Metals Handbook, 1939 ed., p. 1389.

Recent work[1] has however shown that if the copper is deoxidized carefully its tensile strength and ductility will both be somewhat better than the usual tough-pitch copper.

Copper hardens with cold work and may be annealed like other metals. It cannot be hardened by heat-treatment, and the copper tools and weapons used by the American Indians were

[1] WEBSTER, CHRISTIE, and PRATT: Comparative Properties of Oxygen-free High-conductivity, Phosphorized and Tough-pitch Coppers, *Trans. Am. Inst. Met. Eng., Inst. Metals Div.*, **104**, 166 (1933).

COPPER, NICKEL, ZINC, TIN, AND THEIR ALLOYS 229

hardened by cold work and not by any lost or secret process. The A.S.T.M. specifications for annealed and hard-drawn copper wire are given in Table 25. The wires with small diameter have a higher tensile strength in the hard-drawn condition than those of larger sizes. The effect of cold work may be removed by annealing at relatively low temperatures. Pure copper will recrystallize if held for a long time at 300°F. Commercial grades of copper require higher temperatures, and 400 to 700°F are usual annealing temperatures to remove the effects of cold work and to cause recrystallization.

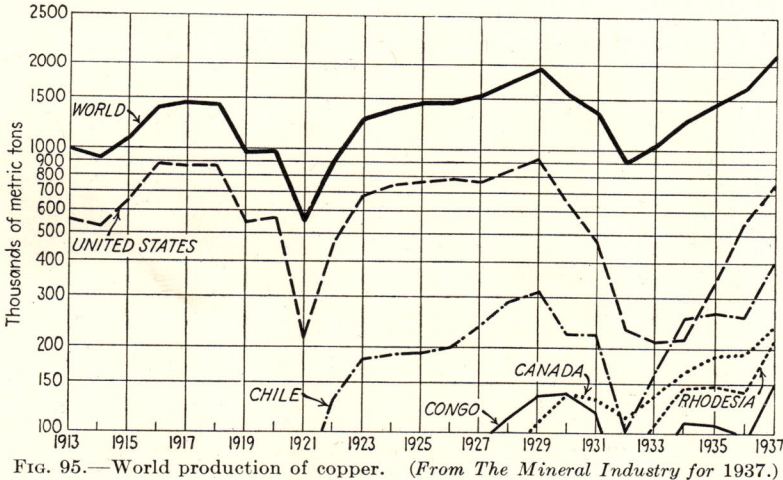

FIG. 95.—World production of copper. (*From The Mineral Industry for* 1937.)

Copper is valued as a structural material because of its ductility and resistance to corrosion rather than because of its strength. Water pipes of copper do not corrode nor do they impart rust to the water, and so they are used in the construction of residences where permanence and quality rather than low initial cost is the deciding factor. Copper is also used for gutters and shingles. Its red color changes quite quickly to a greenish gray, but corrosion does not proceed further.

The main use of copper is in the electrical industry where its high electrical conductivity makes it indispensable. In 1913, an international standard of conductivity was established and rated as 100. Improved refining methods now permit wire to be made with a conductivity as high as 102. Copper ranks next to iron as the world's most important metal for engineering purposes. The world production of copper is shown in the graphs of Fig. 95. The United States was by far the largest producer of copper up to 1929. It is still the largest producer, but Chile, Canada, and Rhodesia are all increasing their output.

It is estimated that 75 to 82 per cent of the copper produced in the United States is used as copper and that the balance is used in the form of alloys. The American Institute of Metals reports that 48 per cent of the total copper was used as such in the construction of electrical machinery, in transmission lines, and for other strictly electrical purposes. The automobile and building industries used 24 per cent for construction purposes, excluding electrical equipment, but including that used both as copper and in the form of alloys.

Metallurgy of Nickel.—The chief ores of nickel are sulfides, where the nickel is usually associated with copper and iron and sometimes with arsenic and other metals. The ore is roasted and reduced to matte like copper. The matte is then bessemerized in a way similar to copper matte, but the process is carried only far enough to oxidize the iron and part of the copper. The nickel-copper matte from the converter, which still contains other metals, is treated to separate the copper and nickel sulfides, then roasted, and after several other operations, is reduced to metal in a hearth furnace, and refined electrolytically, using nickel sulfate as the electrolyte. The electrolytic nickel contains 0.30 to 0.40 per cent cobalt, which is so similar to nickel that it is not objectionable for most purposes. If the cobalt is counted as nickel, the purity of the electrolytic nickel is 99.95 per cent. The world used 74,000 tons of nickel in 1935, and of this 62,831 tons came from Canada.

Properties and Uses of Nickel.—The composition and some of the properties of commercial nickel are given in Table 26. It resembles iron in many of its physical properties, and its use as an alloying constituent in steel has already been discussed. Like iron, it is ferromagnetic at room temperatures and loses its magnetism when heated, but unlike iron its crystals are face-centered at all temperatures. It has a white color which stays bright on exposure to the air and is extensively used as nickel plate to protect steel from corrosion. Its use in this field will be discussed in the chapter on Corrosion. Most of the nickel

COPPER, NICKEL, ZINC, TIN, AND THEIR ALLOYS   231

of the world is used for alloys. The American Bureau of Metal Statistics, in its Yearbook for 1936, reports that the 1935 production of the International Nickel Company, which produces

TABLE 26.—CHEMICAL COMPOSITION AND PHYSICAL PROPERTIES OF COMMERCIAL NICKEL*

Chemical composition:
- Nickel plus cobalt.................... 99.40 per cent
- Carbon........................... 0.10
- Silicon........................... 0.05
- Sulfur............................ 0.005
- Copper........................... 0.10
- Iron.............................. 0.15
- Manganese....................... 0.20

Melting point........................ 2615–2635°F
Lattice face-centered cubic............. 3.51 A°
Magnetic transformation............... 625–660°F
Annealing temperature range........... 1100–1750°F
Forging and rolling temperature range.. 1600–2300°F
Mechanical properties in rolled and annealed condition:
- Yield point....................... 20,000–30,000 psi
- Tensile strength.................. 65,000–75,000 psi
- Elongation in 2 in................ 50–30 per cent
- Brinell hardness.................. 100–150

* Abstracted from articles on Physical and Mechanical Properties of Nickel by P. D. Merica in Metals Handbook, 1936 ed., p. 1257.

about 85 per cent of the world's nickel, was used for the following purposes:

	Per Cent
Alloy steel for motor vehicles	20
Alloy steel for other purposes	27
Nickel-silver, etc	12
Rolled and drawn nickel	8
Electroplating	10
Monel metal	8
Cast iron	4
Heat-resistant electrical alloys	5
Other alloys	6

Metallurgy of Zinc.—Zinc occurs in nature largely as a sulfide. If the ores contain both lead and zinc, selective flotation is employed to give concentrates which are worked up for the respective metals. The sulfides are roasted to form oxides, which may be reduced with carbon without an excessively high temperature. The boiling point of zinc is so low, 1661°F

(905°C), that the metal would be volatilized and pass out with the flue gases in blast-furnace operations. This prevents its recovery in a blast furnace in the way that iron and copper are smelted. The zinc from a blast furnace could be recovered as zinc oxide in the flue dust, and part of the zinc oxide used as a pigment comes from that source. Metallic zinc is made by heating a mixture of the roasted ore and crushed coal in small inclined retorts only about 4 ft long and 8 in. in internal diameter. Several hundred retorts may be ranged in rows in a single furnace heated to about 2000°F. When the retort has been filled, a conical mouthpiece is cemented to the front end and the mouth-

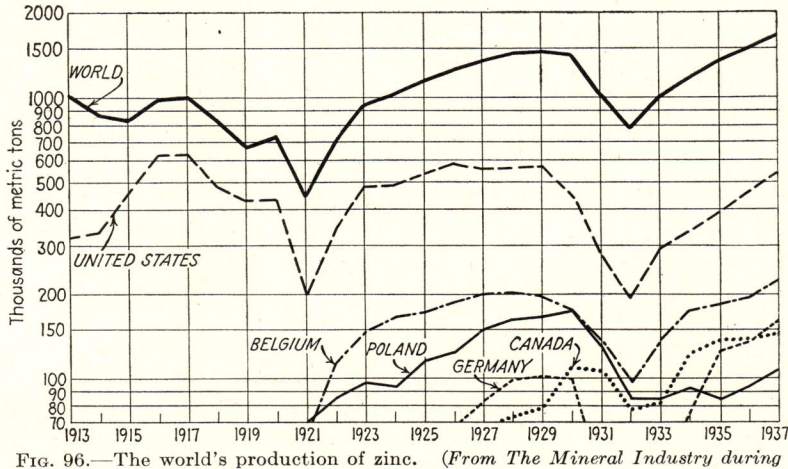

FIG. 96.—The world's production of zinc. (*From The Mineral Industry during 1937.*)

piece is in turn connected to an air condenser. The melting point of zinc is 787°F (419.5°C), and the condenser must be operated somewhat above that temperature in order that liquid zinc may be tapped off at intervals. This molten zinc is cast into slabs which are known commercially as "spelter."

The process of distillation eliminates almost all of the other metals that may have been in the roasted ore. The vapor pressures of lead and cadmium are high enough so that commercial grades of zinc may contain as much as 0.75 per cent cadmium and 1.60 per cent lead. Some commercial specifications require that each of these metals be below 0.07 per cent. The vapor pressure of iron is so low that only traces will distill with the zinc vapor, but iron is used so universally in tools and machinery that the zinc almost always picks up a few hundredths of a per cent of it.

In recent years, the small retorts have been partly replaced by continuous shaft furnaces which are internally heated by electricity. Some zinc is also produced by electrodeposition from aqueous solutions.

The United States produces about one-third of the zinc of the world as shown in the graphs of Fig. 96. Belgium ranks next, and Germany is now third. The principal use of zinc is as a metallic coating to protect articles of iron and steel from corrosion. This process is known as "galvanizing" and will be referred to again in the chapter on Corrosion and Protective Castings.

Properties and Uses of Zinc.—Zinc is so soft that it is difficult to use the usual machines for measuring its hardness. It is harder than tin and softer than annealed copper. The tensile strength of cast zinc varies from 8000 psi with coarse grain to 14,000 with fine grain.[1] The tensile strength of drawn zinc may vary from 22,000 to 40,000 lb. The A.S.T.M. standard specifications do not demand any of the usual tests for strength and ductility but substitute a progressive distortion test until the metal ruptures.

The American Metals Institute reports that of the 585,000 tons of zinc produced in the United States in 1936, the galvanizing industry used 242,000 tons as a protective coating on iron and steel products. Rolled zinc was manufactured to the extent of 55,000 tons and found its largest market in the manufacture of the tops of glass jars (15,500 tons) and battery cans (18,700 tons). The automobile industry used 6,000 tons of rolled zinc, and 3,000 tons were used as sheets by the photoengravers. Brass manufacture took 168,000 tons of zinc, and alloys for die-casting used 72,000 tons.

Metallurgy of Tin.—The main commercial ore of tin is the oxide SnO_2 which is found mainly in the East Indies, Siam, China, Bolivia, and Nigeria. Tin is the most expensive of the metals commonly used in manufacturing operations, and on that account a large proportion of it is reclaimed from scrap metal for re-use. The principal producers of tin are shown in the graph of Fig. 97. Malaya, Netherlands, India, Bolivia, and Siam are the principal

[1] HOFMAN, Metallurgy of Zinc and Cadmium, p. 10.

producing countries. The United States has no domestic tin ores, but consumes about half of the world's total output. In addition, 4,265 tons of tin were recovered from tin plate either in the metallic form or as compounds of tin. Much of the tin ore is of high purity, and reduction in a reverberatory furnace is all that is ordinarily necessary to produce a marketable grade of tin.

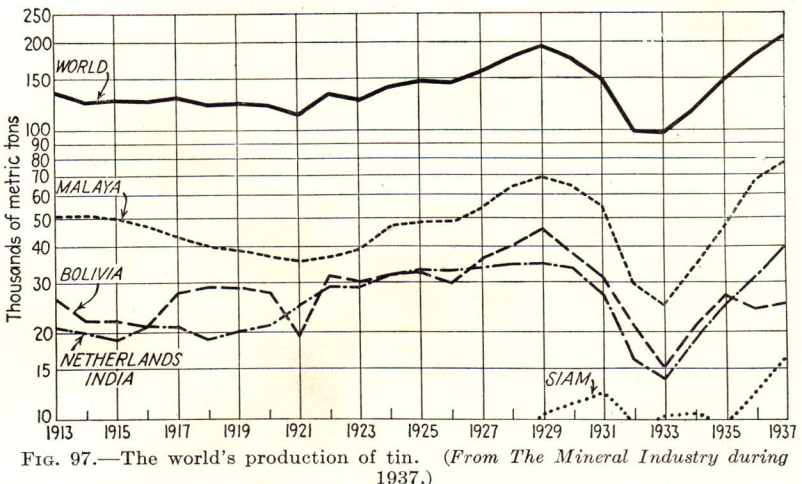

Fig. 97.—The world's production of tin. (*From The Mineral Industry during 1937.*)

Properties and Uses of Tin.—Tin has a low freezing point 449.5°F (231.9°C). It solidifies as gamma tin which at 322°F (161°C) passes into the beta modification which at 64°F (18°C) changes to alpha tin. It is the beta tin that is the white and useful modification. The alpha tin is a gray powder, and though the transition is very slow, articles of tin that are kept a long time, as in museums, sometimes decompose to a powder of the gray tin. The elastic limit of tin is only 200 and the tensile strength 2,000 psi.[1] Its softness, weakness, and high price limit the use of the pure metal for structural purposes. Nearly 40 per cent of the tin consumed in the United States is used in making tin plate. Tin is very resistant to corrosion, and steel sheets coated with tin are used in making cans for the food industry. The value of tin as a protective coating will be discussed in the chapter on Corrosion and Protective Coatings. Tin is also used

[1] Metals Handbook, 1936 ed., p. 1307.

in alloys with lead and other metals to produce solder and bearing metals. These two materials use nearly as much tin as the tin-plate industry, and they will be discussed under the alloys of lead. Bronze, the alloy of copper and tin, takes only about 6.0 per cent of the United States consumption.[1]

Alloys of Copper and Nickel.—Copper and nickel alloy with each other to form solid solutions in all proportions. The equilibrium diagram and a graph of the tensile strength of the

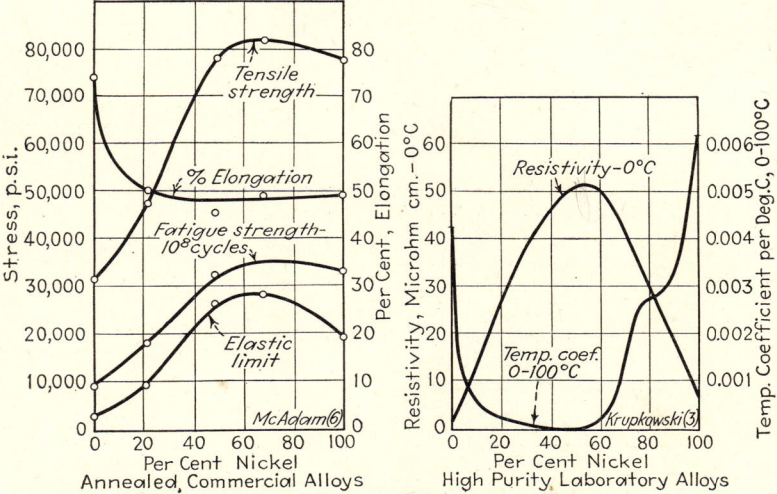

FIG. 98.—Mechanical and electrical properties of annealed copper-nickel alloys. (*Courtesy of International Nickel Co.*)

alloys has been given as Fig. 4 in Chap. I. Even a rather small amount of nickel causes the red color of the copper to disappear, and so almost all of the nickel alloys are white. Both copper and nickel are resistant to corrosion, and their alloys are also resistant. Since the price of copper is only one-third that of nickel, as little nickel is used as will answer the purpose. Nickel is used as a ternary alloying constituent with zinc and tin in some of the brasses and bronzes to be described later.

The mechanical and electrical properties of annealed nickel-copper alloys are shown in the graphs of Fig. 98.[2] Both the

[1] Metal Industries Handbook, 1936, p. 1288.
[2] Personal communication of Dr. E. M. Wise of International Nickel Company.

strength and elastic limit reach a maximum with about 65 per cent of nickel. The elongation is quite constant within the range of 20 to 100 per cent nickel. The graph showing the electrical resistance of alloys of high purity has a marked peak at about 55 per cent nickel and an almost zero temperature coefficient at 45 per cent nickel. Resistance coils made of this wire, constantan, change their resistance very little even when their temperature rises materially. Alloys of copper with 67 per cent nickel are used for the blades of steam turbines and those with 25 to 30 per cent nickel for condenser tubes handling sea water. The five-cent nickel coin of the United States contains 25 per cent of nickel.

TABLE 27.—CHEMICAL COMPOSITION AND PHYSICAL PROPERTIES OF MONEL METAL*

Chemical Composition
- Nickel 67
- Copper 30
- Iron 1.4
- Manganese 1.0
- Silicon 0.1
- Carbon 0.15

Melting point .... 2370–2460°F

Mechanical Properties of Sheet and Strip

	Annealed	Full hard
Tensile strength, psi	65,000–80,000	100,000–120,000
Yield strength, psi	25,000–35,000	90,000–110,000
Elongation in 2 in. per cent	40–25	8–2
Brinell hardness	110–150	210–270

Creep Strength
The stress necessary to produce 0.1 per cent elongation in 1000 hr. is

Temperature	Stress, Psi
600°F	36,000
800	23,500
1000	4,300

* Abstracted from article on Properties of Monel Metal by W. F. Burchfield in the Metals Handbook, 1936 ed., p. 1263.

The most important single alloy of copper and nickel is Monel metal, an alloy in the range of maximum strength, whose composition and properties are summarized in Table 27. The alloy may be worked readily both hot and cold and possesses high resistance to corrosion. This combination of properties makes it

COPPER, NICKEL, ZINC, TIN, AND THEIR ALLOYS 237

widely used. A modification known as K Monel metal contains about 3.5 per cent of aluminum. This alloy may be hardened by heat-treatment in somewhat the same manner as Duralumin, which will be discussed as one of the alloys of aluminum.

FIG. 99.—Architectural shapes extruded from nickel silver. (*From International Nickel Co.'s booklet on Nickel Silver in Architecture.*)

Nickel silver, often called German silver, is the name given to a series of alloys containing 5 to 30 per cent nickel and 55 to 75 per cent copper with the remainder zinc. Its tensile strength will vary from 25,000 to 65,000 psi. Alloys with 10 to 13 per cent nickel may be extruded hot in a variety of shapes as indicated in Fig. 99. If nickel silver is to be used as a casting alloy, small amounts of lead and tin are sometimes incorporated.

Alloys of Copper and Zinc. *Brass.*—When zinc is alloyed with copper, a solid solution results for all compositions up to 39.0 per cent zinc. The equilibrium diagram of Fig. 100 shows this large area of alpha solid solution. Next to this is an area in which, at temperatures above 453°C (847°F), there exists a mixture of alpha and beta solid solutions. When alloys within this area cool below 847°F, the beta solid solution changes to a beta prime modification which is harder and more brittle than the beta modification. The latter is harder and more brittle than the

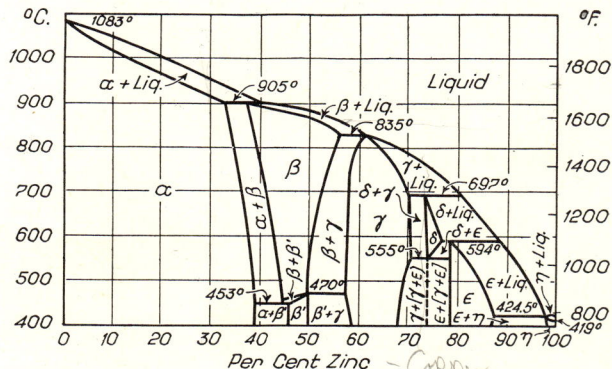

Fig. 100.—Equilibrium diagram of copper-zinc alloys. (*Metals Handbook*, 1939 ed.)

alpha phase and probably consists of a solution of the compound CuZn in copper. The right-hand half of the diagram is complicated and of little industrial importance. The left-hand side is however of great importance as all of the commercial binary brasses are found in this range of composition.

Properties of 70-30 Brass.—The tensile strength, hardness, and elongation of brasses with composition of 63 to 100 per cent copper is given in Fig. 101 from data by D. K. Crampton.

The figures refer to sheets 0.04 in. in thickness which have been cold-drawn to various degrees of hardness, and also to sheets of the same thickness after annealing. It will be observed that the strength increases for all compositions, until it levels off at a composition of about 70 copper and 30 zinc. The tensile strength of this 70-30 alloy is roughly 50 per cent greater than that of copper which has received the same mechanical treatment. The hardness has also increased uniformly. The elongation of the hard-drawn alloys is not very different from that of copper, but that of the annealed specimens is distinctly improved by the zinc. This 70-30 brass therefore is superior to copper when judged by all of the three major criteria of strength, ductility, and hardness.

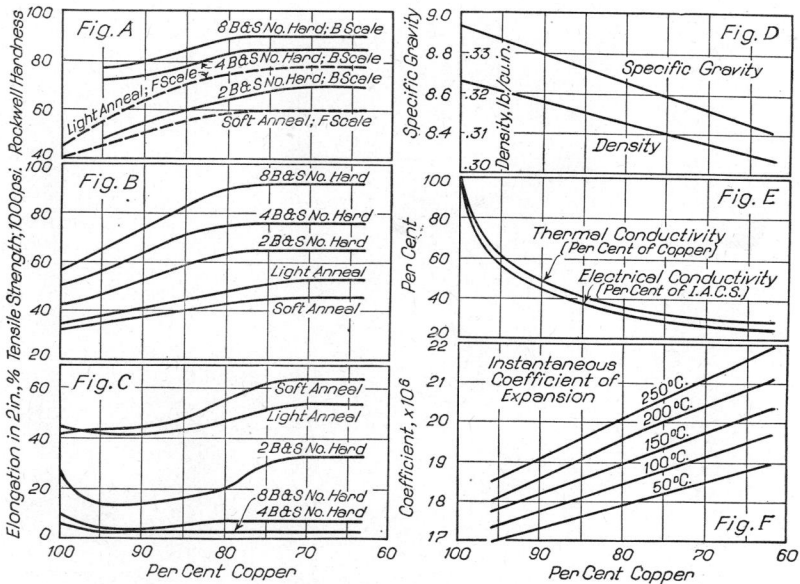

Fig. 101.—Physical properties of copper-zinc alloys in the form of thin sheets. *A*, Rockwell hardness of copper-zinc alloys (0.040 in. sheet); *B*, tensile strength of copper-zinc alloys (0.040 in. sheet); *C*, elongation of copper-zinc alloys (0.040 in. sheet); *D*, specific gravity and density of copper-zinc alloys; *E*, electrical and thermal conductivity of copper-zinc alloys (*C. S. Smith*); *F*, thermal expansion of copper-zinc alloys (*Bureau of Standards Sci. Paper* 410). (*Metals Handbook*, 1939 ed.)

It also offers the advantage of cheapness since zinc costs only about half as much as copper, and the melting point of the alloy is 350°F lower than copper. Another advantage is that the density is about 6 per cent less, and so a smaller weight of metal is required to fill a given volume. This alloy may be worked both hot and cold, but for hot work, lead must be below 0.04 per cent.

Since zinc forms a solid solution with copper up to 39 per cent, it follows that all of the alloys within this range of composition will be useful. The 70-30 alloy possesses the maximum advan-

240 *ENGINEERING MATERIALS*

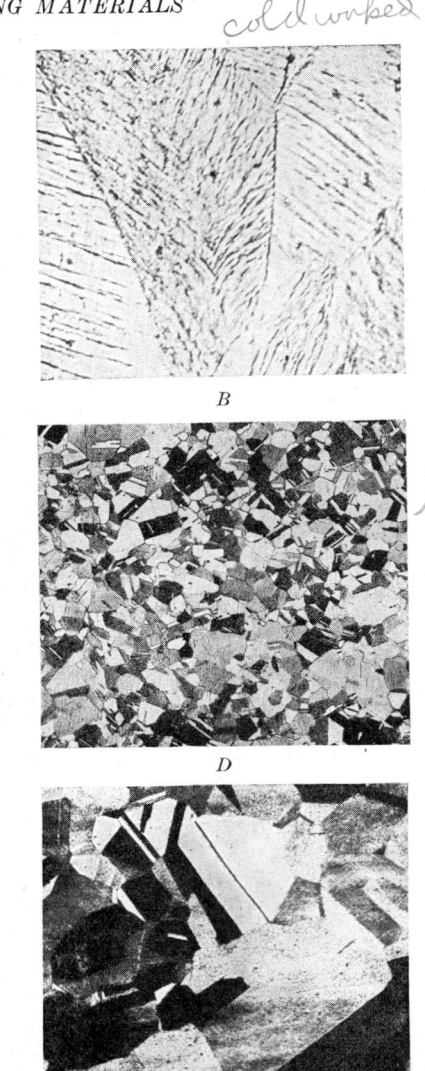

Fig. 102.—Photomicrographs showing effect of cold work and annealing on alpha brass containing 68 copper and 32 zinc. *A*, cold-worked to the extent of 38 per cent reduction in thickness, ×75; *B*, cold-worked to 60 per cent reduction, ×500; *C*, cold-worked to 37 per cent reduction and annealed for 30 minutes at 770°F (410°C), ×75; *D*, cold-worked to 60 per cent reduction and annealed for 30 minutes at 1022°F (550°C), ×75; *E*, cold-worked to 60 per cent reduction and annealed for 30 minutes at 1202°F (650°C), ×75; *F*, cold-worked to 60 per cent reduction and annealed for 30 minutes at 1337°F (725°C), ×75. (*Courtesy of Professor C. Upthegrove.*)

tages in properties and is certain to be all in the alpha state even on rather rapid cooling. According to the equilibrium diagram, the same may be said of the 66-34 composition, usually called "common high brass," which has the added advantage of being somewhat cheaper, but unless the composition is accurately controlled there is some danger of the undesirable beta modification persisting in the cold metal.

Cold Work and Recrystallization.—When brass is cold-worked, the grains become distorted and fragmented, as is the case with all metals. The formation of slip lines in alpha brass is shown in A and B of Fig. 102. This brass contained 68 per cent of copper and 32 per cent of zinc and so should have been, and probably was, composed entirely of alpha solid solution. The appearance of black and white crystals in the photomicrographs of this figure is due to the different orientations of the crystal units in the large crystal which may cause the incident light to be reflected into the microscope, when the crystal will appear white, or out of the microscope when the crystal will appear black.

The readjustment in the crystal structure during the annealing process is shown in the photomicrographs C, D, E, and F of Fig. 102, all taken at a magnification of 75 diameters, which is the same as A. Picture C, showing the effects of reheating to 770°F, depicts the alloy in the first stages of recrystallization. The slip lines have disappeared, and most of the old large crystal outlines are gone. New crystals appear rather clearly here and there, but the whole structure is rather indistinct.

Photomicrograph D shows the results of heating for 30 min at 1022°F. The crystals have completely reformed and appear as clear, small crystals. Photomicrograph E shows further crystal growth as the result of heating at 1202°F, and F shows very large grains due to carrying the temperature to 1337°F.

The changes in the physical properties of a brass during annealing correspond to the changes in the microscopic structure. The brass whose properties are given in Fig. 103 was severely cold-worked and therefore responds to annealing somewhat more readily than the brass shown in the photomicrographs of Fig. 102. Figure 103 shows that after annealing at 750°F the grain size is small, but that the strained conditions to the crystals have been relieved as shown by the marked increase in elongation, a lesser increase in reduction of area, and the decrease in tensile strength.

Most of the beneficial effects of annealing are obtained by heating to 1100°F.

Cast Alpha Brass.—In the discussion of the solidification of steel, it was mentioned that the first crystals to separate from the

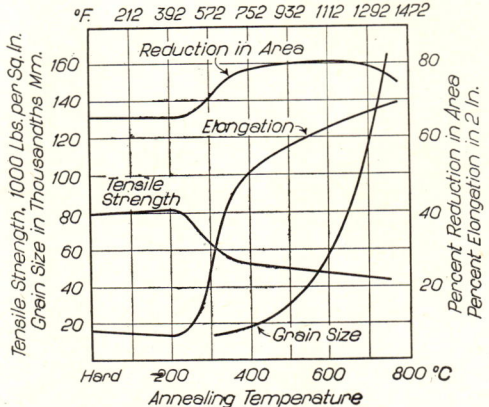

Fig. 103.—Effect of annealing temperatures on the properties of high brass. (*From Metals Handbook*, 1939 ed.)

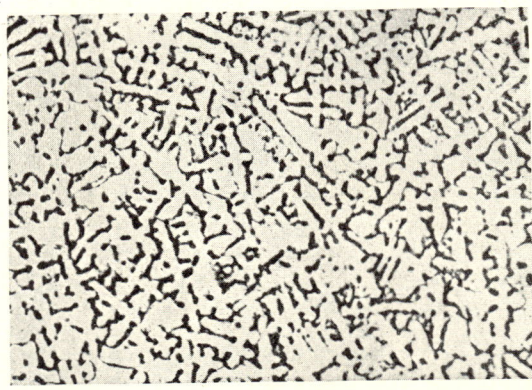

Fig. 104.—Microscopic structure of alpha brass (70 Cu, 30 Zn) when cast in sand. ×100. This shows the dendritic structure due to rapid cooling.

fused solution were nearly pure ferrite which grew by accretions of alloys progressively lower in carbon, so that unless the cooling was excessively slow the microscopic structure of a steel casting showed a nonuniform structure instead of the homogeneous solid solution, austenite, which equilibrium conditions demanded.

The same phenomenon is illustrated in Fig. 104, which pictures the microscopic structure of a cast brass with 70 copper and 30 zinc which should, if cooled at an equilibrium rate, have showed nothing but a single solid solution. The photograph shows a marked dendritic structure indicating the gradation in composition in the crystals as they formed. If this casting should be annealed for a long time, the structure should become homogeneous.

 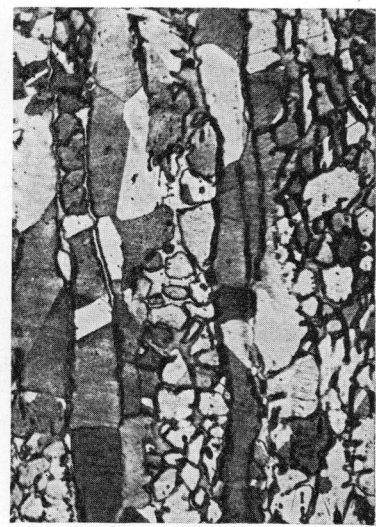

a   *b*
Fig. 105.—Microscopic structure of beta brass (60 Cu, 40 Zn). *a*, brass cast in sand, ×100; *b*, brass extruded at about 1500°F, ×100.

Beta Brass. Muntz Metal.—The alloy with 60 copper and 40 zinc contains enough of the beta prime constituent to make it quite different from the alpha brass. The equilibrium diagram shows that an alloy of this composition consists of two phases, both of which are solid solutions. The beta phase suffers a transformation when it cools below 847°F (453°C), changing to the beta prime modification which is harder and more brittle than either the alpha or the beta phase. The microscopic structure of cast beta brass is illustrated in Fig. 105 at a magnification of 100 diameters. It has almost the appearance of a eutectic structure of alternate plates of the alpha and beta prime phases.

When beta brass is reheated above 850°F, the more ductile beta phase again appears so that the alloy lends itself readily to forging and to extrusion at about 1500°F. The microscopic structure of such an extruded brass is shown in the right print of Fig. 105. The elongated crystals of alpha brass, showing some twinning, predominate in the picture. The beta crystals are fine stringers which are not prominent.

These two pictures show the marked directional influence given to the crystals by hot working, as compared with the random orientation of the cast structure. The lesser strength and ductility of a casting is in part due to this difference in structure.

The beta brass is somewhat harder, stronger, and less ductile than the standard alpha brass. It corrodes more readily and is more liable to "season cracks" which may develop after the alloy has been in use for some months or years. They will be discussed again in Chap. XVI on Corrosion.

Uses of Brass.—Since brass is stronger, more ductile, and cheaper than copper, it follows that it is used instead of copper where this is feasible. The electrical conductivity of 66-34 brass is only about 25 per cent that of copper, and so it is not used for electrical conductors. Neither is brass so resistant to corrosion as copper. The 90-10 alloy sometimes called "common bronze" and the 85-15 alloy called "red brass" are nearly as resistant as copper. The 70-30 and the 66-34 metal are used for spinning and drawing, as for cartridge cases, tubing, and automobile radiators. The 60-40 metal is used for much the same purposes where corrosive conditions are not to be feared. The tubes used in the condensers of steam power plants are sometimes of 60-40 composition, but the 70-30 alloy is preferred as being less liable to season cracks. Domestic water pipes are sometimes made of brass instead of copper, the composition depending on the corrosive nature of the water.

The American Society for Testing Materials lists two different alloys for condenser tubes with the chemical composition shown in Table 28. The specifications do not call for tensile tests but do call for flattening and expanding tests, and require that on microscopic examination the metal shall show sufficient annealing for complete recrystallization, without too coarse a grain.

Machinability of Copper and Brass.—Copper is such a ductile metal that it tears in machining and does not give a smooth cut.

COPPER, NICKEL, ZINC, TIN, AND THEIR ALLOYS

Brass cuts more freely, and its machining properties are improved by the addition of about 2 per cent of lead, which remains in the metal as fine droplets of lead distributed through the brass. The lead causes the chips to break off instead of rubbing over the face of the tool, an operation that evolves heat. If the chips break off as fast as the metal is cut, less heat is evolved, and so the machining operation can be carried on at higher speeds without overheating the tool. This leaded alloy is much used for automatic screwstock for small screws that must be cheap and well finished but do not need especial strength.

Table 28.—Composition of Brass Condenser Tubes

	Seamless 70–30 brass	Seamless Muntz metal
Copper not less than	70.00	59.00–63.00
Lead, not over	0.075	0.30
Iron, not over	0.06	0.07
Zinc	Remainder	Remainder

Alloys of Copper and Tin.—The alloys of copper and tin were known to the Greeks and Phoenicians from the earliest historical times and have been used ever since under the general name of "bronze." The alloys high in tin and low in copper do not have value, and the commercial bronzes all have less than 19 per cent of tin. The equilibrium diagram for the alloys up to 50 per cent tin, shown in Fig. 106, has a general resemblance to the copper-zinc diagram. The limit of the alpha solid solution is about 16 per cent of tin, but the solubility decreases very rapidly as the temperature drops below 1000°F. The addition of tin strengthens copper and also increases its resistance to corrosion up to the limits of the solid solution. An alloy with 8–10 per cent of tin was used for centuries as "gun metal" from which cannon were cast. Metal of approximately the same composition is used for statuary and for bells. The high cost of tin precludes the use of bronze where the cheaper brass may be substituted.

Alloys of Copper and Aluminum.—These alloys which are high in aluminum will be discussed in the chapter on aluminum. Mention will be made here only of the aluminum bronzes which consist of alloys with less than 11 per cent of aluminum. Aluminum forms a solid solution with copper up to 9.8 per cent, as shown in Fig. 107, and strengthens the alloy just as tin and zinc do. There

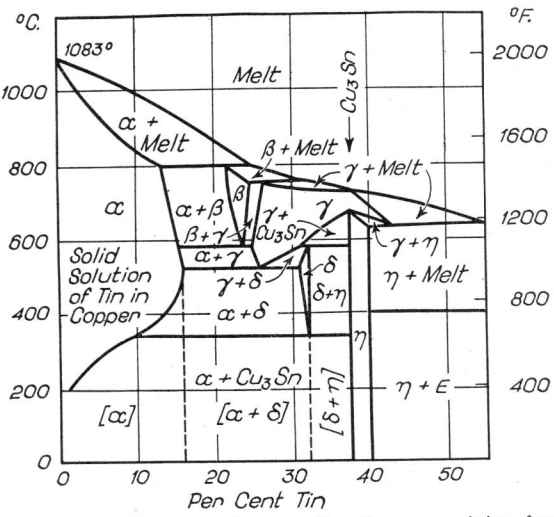

Fig. 106.—Equilibrium diagram of copper-tin alloys containing from 0–50 per cent tin. (*From Metals Handbook*, 1939 ed.)

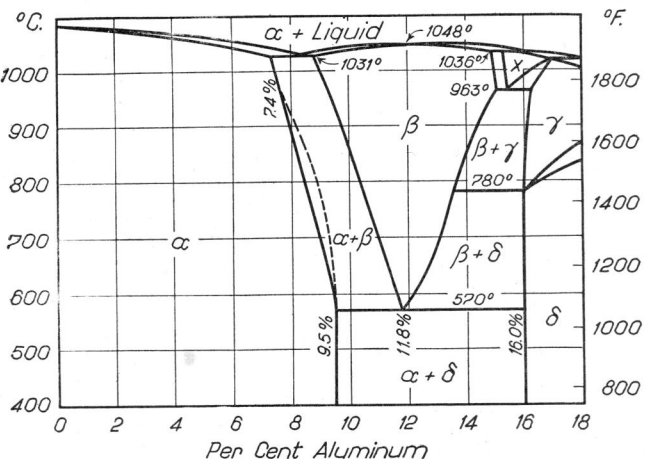

Fig. 107.—Equilibrium diagram of copper-aluminum alloys containing from 0–18 per cent aluminum. (*From Metals Handbook*, 1939 ed.)

is also the same possibility of heat-treatment for the alloys containing more than 8 per cent aluminum. They are not usually simple binary alloys but contain iron and smaller amounts of other metals. They will be discussed under the heading Aluminum Bronzes.

Ternary Alloys of Copper.—Since copper forms solid solutions with so many different metals, it would be expected that ternary and even more complicated alloys would be formed, with the constituent metals all remaining in solid solution. Lead is one of the few common metals that does not form a solid solution with copper. It is not possible to treat these complex alloys systematically. They are usually developed as the result of a series of trials which have shown that certain compositions have commercial value because of properties or price. A few of the more prominent alloys are listed below.

Iron, Silicon, Manganese, and Phosphorus As Minor Constituents.—Iron is so widely used for tools and machines that it is difficult to avoid its presence in small amount, particularly in secondary metal which has been recovered by remelting scrap. Iron remains in solid solution in copper up to a maximum of 4 per cent at the freezing point. The solubility decreases rapidly

TABLE 29.—CHEMICAL COMPOSITION OF MANGANESE BRONZE INGOTS*

	Maximum, per cent	Minimum, per cent
Copper	60.	55.
Zinc	42.	38.
Tin	1.5	0.0
Manganese	3.5	0.0
Aluminum	1.5	0.0
Iron	2.0	0.0
Lead	0.2	0.2

* A.S.T.M. Standards, 1936, p. 563.

as the temperature drops, until at 1100°F not over 0.3 per cent is in solution, and at room temperature the amount is even less. It hardens the metal somewhat but has little effect in amounts up to 2 per cent. Silicon, manganese, and phosphorus are all good deoxidizers and are sometimes added in small amounts for that purpose. If only a few tenths of a per cent remain in the alloy, they remain in solid solution and so strengthen and harden the metal somewhat. Antimony and bismuth cause red-shortness even when as little as 0.1 per cent is present.

Manganese Bronze.—Manganese bronze is really a special type of Muntz metal. The manganese is added primarily as a deoxidizer, but any additional amount remains in solid solution. The A.S.T.M. standard specification calls for a tensile strength of

TABLE 30.—PHOSPHOR BRONZE: CHEMICAL COMPOSITION AND PHYSICAL PROPERTIES IN SHEET AND STRIP FORM*

Chemical Composition, per cent

	Grade A	Grade C	Grade D
Copper	Remainder	Remainder	Remainder
Tin	3.80–5.80	7.0 –9.0	9.0 –11.0
Phosphorus	0.03–0.35	0.03–0.25	0.03– 0.25
Iron	−0.10	−0.10	−0.10
Lead	−0.05	−0.02	−0.02
Antimony	−0.01	−0.01	−0.01
Zinc	−0.30	−0.20	−0.20
Nickel	......	−0.15	
Copper + tin + phosphorus minimum	99.50	99.50	99.60

Physical Properties

Grade	Temper	Numbers hard	Nominal reduction by rolling, per cent	Tensile strength, psi.	Hardness rockwell "B" for sheets 0.040 in. in thickness
A	Soft	0	0	40,000–55,000	7–50
	Hard	4	37.1	72,000–87,000	82–90
	Spring	8	60.4	91,000–105,000	90–96
C	Soft	0	0	53,000–67,000	29–70
	Hard	4	37.1	85,000–100,000	91–97
	Spring	8	60.4	105,000–118,000	97–102
D	Soft	0	0	58,000–73,000	35–75
	Hard	4	37.1	94,000–109,000	94–101
	Spring	8	60.4	115,000–129,000	99–104

* Abridged from A.S.T.M. Tentative Standard, 1937 ed., p. 369.

70,000 psi and an elongation of 30 per cent. The limits of chemical composition are given in Table 29. It will be noted that the manufacturer may add at his discretion small amounts of tin, manganese, aluminum, and iron, all of which within the limits

COPPER, NICKEL, ZINC, TIN, AND THEIR ALLOYS 249

given, except perhaps iron, will remain in solid solution and increase the strength and ductility of the alloy. Iron exerts a

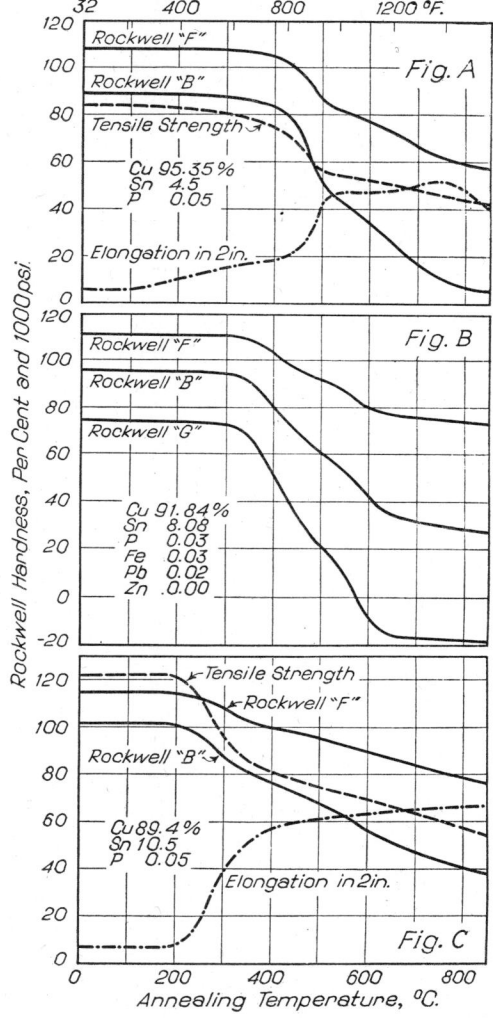

FIG. 108.—Physical properties of phosphor bronze. *A*, phosphor bronze grade A sheet, gage 0.040 in., reduced 50 per cent in thickness by rolling, annealed ½ hr at temperature noted; *B*, same as *A* but for grade C; *C*, same as *A* but for grade D. (*From Metals Handbook*, 1939 ed.)

powerful influence to refine the grains of castings, and aluminum is very effective in increasing strength.

Phosphor Bronze.—Phosphor bronze is high-grade copper-tin alloy which has been deoxidized with phosphorus and which carries a small amount (less than 0.35 per cent) of residual phosphorus. It is used, especially after cold-drawing, to make springs for electrical apparatus. There is also a very different alloy called "phosphor bronze" which carries 9 to 27 per cent of lead and is used for bearings. It will be discussed under the heading of Bearing Metals. The specifications for chemical composition and mechanical properties of sheet phosphor bronze are given in Table 30 and in Fig. 108. The additional strength and hardness imparted by increasing percentages of tin is to be noted and also the extraordinary tensile strength, 115,000 to 129,000 lb for the D composition with 10 per cent tin, after cold-working to a "spring" temper.

Silicon Bronze.—Silicon forms a solid solution with copper up to 5 per cent silicon at 1022°F. It is added in small amounts as a deoxidizing agent and is also used as a special alloying agent up to 4.0 per cent Si. Manganese is frequently added in amount of 1.0 per cent, and sometimes small amounts of zinc or tin, in addition to the silicon. These alloys can be worked either hot or cold and show unusual chemical resistance to some acids. The alloy with 3.0 per cent silicon and 1.0 per cent manganese when rolled into rods has a tensile strength of 50,000 psi and an elongation of 45 per cent. When cold-worked, rods up to $\frac{1}{4}$ in. in diameter show a yield point of 60,000 and a tensile strength of 90,000 psi, with an elongation of 8.0 per cent in 2 in.

Aluminum Bronze.—The aluminum bronze on the market contain 5.5 to 10.5 per cent of aluminum, with iron up to 4 per cent, nickel up to 8 per cent, and manganese up to 10 per cent. Two of the compositions specified by the U. S. Navy for wrought bronze and two as specified in the A.S.T.M. Standards for cast bronze are given in Table 31. In the wrought alloys, the increase in the percentage of aluminum and iron in the 88-9-3 alloy has increased the tensile strength and hardness without cutting down the elongation. The physical properties of these alloys can be duplicated by cheaper mild steel, except for the resistance to corrosion. Aluminum bronze is resistant to industrial atmospheres, salt water, and a number of dilute acids. The alloys for casting purposes do not differ widely from those to be wrought. The Grade B contains so much aluminum that on heating (see

COPPER, NICKEL, ZINC, TIN, AND THEIR ALLOYS

TABLE 31.—CHEMICAL COMPOSITION AND PHYSICAL PROPERTIES OF ALUMINUM BRONZES

1. Bronze to Be Wrought
   Metals Handbook, 1936 ed., p. 936.
   Chemical Composition, per cent

Type	88-9-3	95-5
Copper	84–93	92–96
Aluminum	7–10	4–7
Iron max	4.00	0.50
Other additions including nickel, tin, and manganese	2.00	
Impurities including Zn, Cd, and Pb, max	0.25	0.50

Physical Properties As Forged or Rolled

Tensile strength, psi	70,000–85,000	50,000–65,000
Yield point, psi	30,000–45,000	
Elongation, per cent in 2 in	20–40	15–40
Brinell hardness, 50-kg load	120–135	60–120

2. Bronze Castings
   From A.S.T.M. Standards, 1936, Part I, p. 544.
   Grades:
   A not responding to heat-treatment
   B responding to heat-treatment
   Chemical Composition, per cent

	Grade A	Grade B
Copper	87–89	89.5–90.5
Aluminum	7–9	9.5–10.5
Iron	2.5–4	1.25 max.
Total other impurities max	1.0	0.5

Physical Properties

	Grade A	Grade B	Grade B as heat-treated, quenched and drawn
Tensile strength, psi	65,000	65,000	80,000
Yield point, psi	25,000	25,000	50,000
Elongation in 2 in., per cent	20	15	4

Fig. 107) there will be complete solid solution, but on slow cooling there will be separation of a small amount of a harder eutectoid mixture of the alpha solid solution plus a harder solid solution containing Cu_2Al. The usual heat-treatment consists of quenching from 1500 to 1600°F followed by tempering between 700 and 1100°F.

Alloys for Casting.—Although any of the brasses may be used for castings, lead is usually added to those which are to be machined. Alloys with 75–85 copper, 5–10 zinc, 5–10 lead, and

TABLE 32.—LIMITS OF CHEMICAL COMPOSITION OF 88-8-4 ALLOY

	Desired	Minimum	Maximum
Copper	88.00	86.00	89.00
Tin	8.00	7.50	11.00
Lead	None	....	0.30
Zinc	4.00	1.50	4.50
Iron	....	....	0.25
Nickel	....	....	1.00
Phosphorus	....	....	0.05

occasionally tin and small amounts of nickel are used for pipe fittings, radiator valves, and other purposes where a reasonably strong and corrosion-resistant metal is required. Because of the low melting point of the lead, which is wholly in mechanical dispersion, the alloys are not recommended for temperatures much over 250°F.

An alloy containing tin and no lead known as 88-8-4 alloy contains 88 per cent of copper, 8 of tin, and 4 of zinc. It is used for valves and pipe fittings where good strength and resistance to steam and also to salt water are required. It is not recommended for temperatures above 500°F. The A.S.T.M. standard specifications require that it shall have a tensile strength of at least 38,000 psi, a yield point of 16,000, and an elongation of 22 per cent in 2 in. The limits of the permissible chemical composition is given in Table 32.

Bearing Metals.—Alloys of copper, zinc, and tin are used as bearing metals, but their discussion is reserved for the chapter on Lead and Tin Alloys where the whole subject of bearing metals will be considered.

COPPER, NICKEL, ZINC, TIN, AND THEIR ALLOYS 253

Zinc-alloy Die Castings.—Alloys containing 2.5 to 3.5 per cent copper and 3.5 to 4.5 per cent of aluminum with the balance zinc are used extensively for die castings. The A.S.T.M. tentative standard specifications for two of these alloys are given in Table 33. The tensile strength of cast zinc was stated in the

TABLE 33.—ZINC-BASE ALLOY DIE CASTINGS*
Chemical Composition, per cent

Alloy No.	XXI	XXIII
Copper	2.5–3.5	0.10 max
Aluminum	3.5–4.5	3.5–4.3
Magnesium	0.02–0.10	0.03–0.08
Iron, max	0.10	0.10
Zinc	Remainder†	Remainder†

Physical Properties Average of 5 Specimens

	XXI	XXIII
Tensile strength, min	44,000	35,000
Elongation in 2 in., per cent min	2.0	3.0
Charpy impact, ft-lb min	6.0	12.0

As an Optional Specification after Exposure to Water Vapor at 95°C for 10 Days

	XXI	XXIII
Tensile strength, psi min	30,000	30,000
Elongation in 2 in., per cent min	0.5	1.5
Charpy impact, ft.-lb min	0.75	12.0

* A.S.T.M. Tentative Specifications, 1937, p. 425.
† Except that lead, cadmium, and tin may be present in amounts less than 0.007 per cent for each.

last chapter to vary between 8,000 and 14,000 psi, depending on the grain size. The table shows that by adding only 3.5 to 4.0 per cent of aluminum a die casting may be expected with a tensile strength of 35,000 lb.

These zinc alloys change dimensions to only a small extent after solidification and are widely used for small parts where cheapness, accuracy of dimension, lightness in weight, and pleasing appearance are important factors. The illustrations of

254 ENGINEERING MATERIALS

Fig. 109 show the variety of these zinc-base die castings used in the mechanism of a price-indicating gasoline pump.

These alloys do not have good resistance to the weather. The optional specifications in Table 33 indicate that deterioration may be expected on exposure to water vapor at 95°C for 10 days.

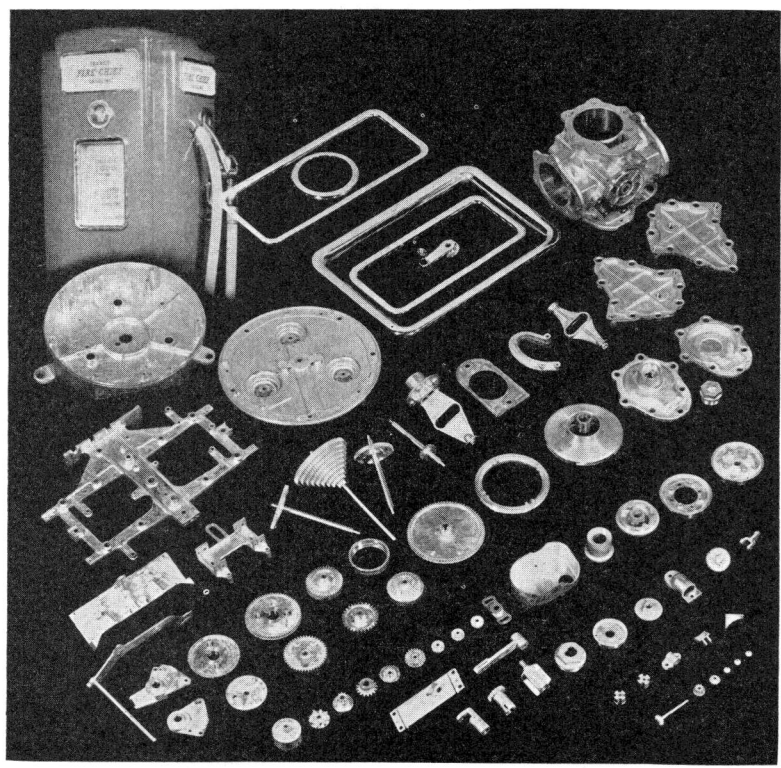

FIG. 109.—Die castings in a computing gasoline pump. (*From Catalog of New Jersey Zinc Co.*)

References

AMERICAN SOCIETY FOR METALS: Metals Handbook, 1939 ed., Cleveland.

HAYWARD, C. R.: An Outline of Metallurgical Practice, D. Van Nostrand Co., Inc., New York, 1929.

WYSOR, HENRY: Metallurgy, 3d ed. Chemical Publishing Co., Easton, Pa., 1927.

AUSTIN, L. S.: The Metallurgy of the Common Metals, 6th ed., John Wiley & Sons, Inc., New York, 1926.

LIDDELL and DOAN: The Principles of Metallurgy, McGraw-Hill Book Company, Inc., New York, 1933.

MATHEWSON, C. H., editor: Modern Uses of Non-ferrous Metals, published by American Institute of Mining and Metallurgical Engineers, 1935.

WOLDMAN and DORNBLATT: Engineering Alloys—Names, Properties, Uses, Published by American Society for Metals, 1936.

JEFFRIES, ZAY: Effect of Temperature, Deformation and Grain Size on the Mechanical Properties of Metals, *Trans. Am. Inst. Min. Met. Eng.*, **60,** 474 (1918–1919).

CRAMPTON, D. K.: Copper Alloys to Meet Severe Requirements, *Metal Progress*, May, 1936, p. 39.

WEBSTER, CHRISTIE, and PRATT: Comparative Properties of Oxygen-free High Conductivity, Phosphorized and Tough-pitch Coppers, *Trans. Am. Inst. Min. Eng., Inst. Metals Div.*, **104,** 166 (1933).

STANLEY, R. C.: Nickel—Past and Present, reprint *Canadian Inst. Min. Met., Bull.*, 1927, published by International Nickel Co., 1927.

MANTELL, C. L.: Tin, (Mining, Production, Technology and Applications), Reinhold Publishing Corporation, New York, 1929.

HOFMAN, H. O.: Metallurgy of Zinc and Cadmium, McGraw-Hill Book Company, Inc., New York, 1922.

CHAPTER XIV

ALUMINUM, MAGNESIUM, AND THE LIGHT ALLOYS

The metals of industrial importance that have already been discussed have been used by men for hundreds of years, although many of the valuable properties of their alloys are of recent discovery. In aluminum and magnesium, we deal with metals that

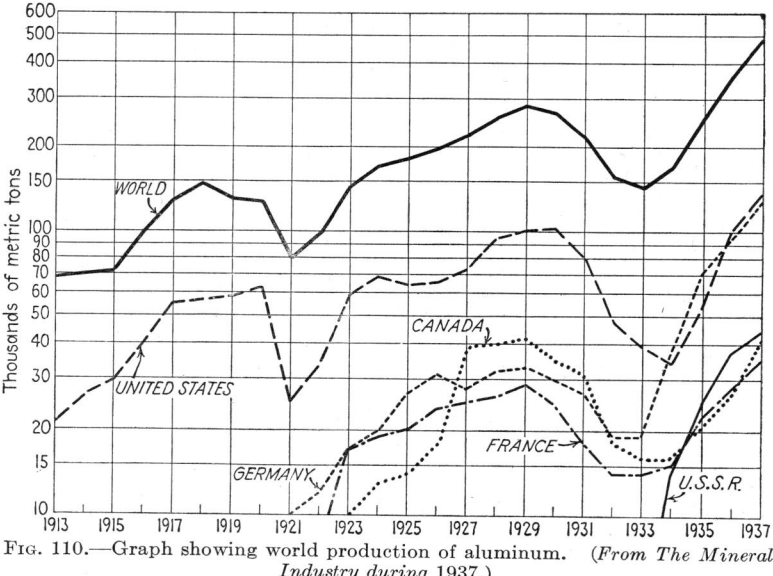

FIG. 110.—Graph showing world production of aluminum. (*From The Mineral Industry during* 1937.)

have been available for engineering purposes only during the past fifty years.

In spite of its tardy appearance, aluminum is now one of the world's most important metals, with a tonnage ranking next to copper. The graphs of Fig. 110 show that the United States and Germany are tied for first place and that together they produce over half of the world's production. The rise of Soviet Russia from a nominal production in 1933 to a position slightly above that of either France or Canada in 1937 is especially noteworthy.

Metallurgy of Aluminum.—The oxide of Aluminum Al_2O_3 is distributed widely on the surface of the earth. Some white clays contain over 30 per cent alumina in combination with silica, but no aluminum is being recovered from such low-grade materials. Bauxite, the hydrated oxide of alumina, mixed with iron oxide and silica, is found in various portions of the United States. The largest commercial sources are in the states of Arkansas, Georgia, and Tennessee. They contain 56 to 59 per cent alumina, 5 to 12 per cent silica, 1 to 3 per cent ferric oxide, and 27 to 30 per cent combined water. Large quantities are also mined in France, Hungary, Italy, Jugoslavia, British Guiana, and Dutch Guiana.

The tardy appearance of aluminum as a material cheap enough for engineering construction is due to the large amount of energy required to separate the metal from the oxide. This figure has already been given in Table 8, and attention was called, in the discussion of the iron blast furnace, to the failure of the high temperatures and strong reducing conditions in the hearth of the blast furnace to reduce any aluminum to metallic form, so that all of the alumina of the charge passed out in the slag.

Electrolytic Process.—The honor of finding a commercial process for the production of aluminum went to a young American chemist, Charles Martin Hall, who conceived the idea of finding a compound that, when fused, would be a solvent for aluminum oxide and permit the electrolysis of the dissolved oxide, metallic aluminum being liberated at the cathode and oxygen at the anode. He found this solvent in cryolite ($AlF_3 \cdot 3NaF$) and made his first aluminum on the small scale in 1886. Production on the industrial scale started 2 years later. This electrolytic process requires just as much energy to produce 1 lb of aluminum as would be required if it could be reduced by carbon in a blast furnace, and the energy is required in the expensive form of electricity. The process is however cheap enough to permit the widespread use of the metal.

Since it requires more energy to reduce alumina than to reduce silica or iron oxide, the electrolysis of impure alumina results in a metal contaminated with silicon and iron. An elaborate chemical purification of the bauxite must therefore precede the electrolysis, and the cost of this chemical purification is the factor that has, so far, prevented the commercial use of clays and other low-grade minerals as ores of aluminum.

258   ENGINEERING MATERIALS

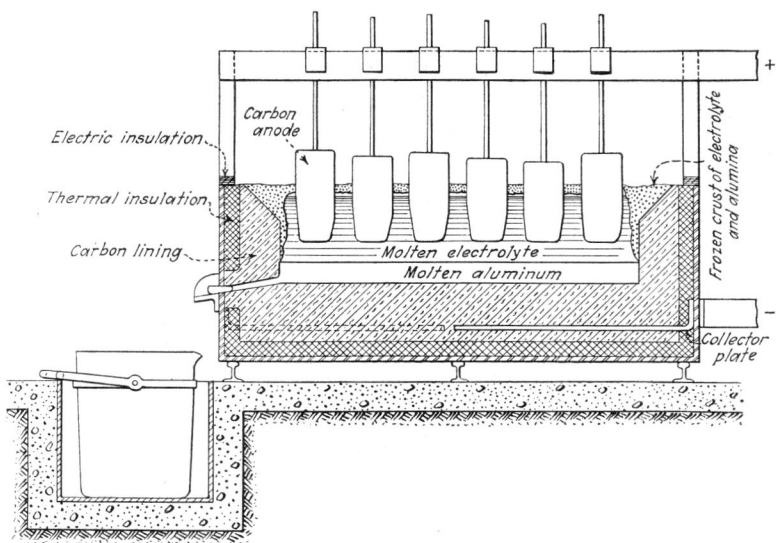

Fig. 111.—Cross section of electrolytic cell for manufacture of aluminum. (*Courtesy of Aluminum Company of America.*)

Fig. 112.—View of battery of electrolytic cells for manufacture of aluminum. (*Courtesy of Aluminum Company of America.*)

The simple construction of the electrolytic cells is shown in Fig. 111 and 112.[1] The container is a steel tank made of plates about 1 in. thick and lined with carbon which forms the cathode. The operating temperature is about 2000°F, and the energy required to keep the bath molten is supplied by the same electric current that performs the electrolysis. The anodes are of carbon, and since the oxygen from the electrolysis is liberated on the hot carbon anode it reacts at once, thus burning up about ¾ lb of carbon anode for each pound of aluminum set free at the cathode. This adds materially to the expense of the operation, for the electrode must be made of extremely pure carbon since any silica or iron oxide in the ash from the electrode passes into the bath and is reduced to silicon and iron which contaminate the aluminum. Cells of different sizes may each use 8000 to 30,000 amp at 5 to 7 volts, and 30 to 100 cells are connected in series, depending on the type of generating equipment employed. Since this is an electrolytic process, direct current must be used. A pound of aluminum requires the expenditure of 10 to 12 kw-hr. The electrolyte contains from 2 to 5 per cent alumina in solution. The cryolite does not suffer any alteration in the process, and the percentage of alumina is kept fairly constant by breaking the crust and shoveling in purified powdered alumina at intervals. The aluminum is tapped off once a day or even less often. The product may have a purity as high as 99.7, although most of the commercial product is less pure, perhaps 99.4, and standard specifications require only 99.0.

All of the common metals whose manufacture has been discussed in previous chapters could be refined by oxidation. It is evident that any attempt to purify aluminum alloys by such a method would result in oxidation of the aluminum itself rather than the silicon and iron which are the main impurities. It is possible by a process of electrolytic refining to produce a metal of 99.99 per cent purity, but so far it has not found large commercial applications.

Properties of Aluminum.—The density of aluminum at 68°F is 2.699 which makes a cubic foot weigh 163 lb, as compared with 557 lb for copper. The high heat of formation of its oxide indicates that it will oxidize in the air with great rapidity. This

[1] From EDWARDS, FRARY, and JEFFRIES, The Aluminum Industry, Vol. I, pp. 302 and 313.

is actually the case, but the film of oxide that forms on the surface protects the metal from further oxidation so that aluminum appears to be, and in practice is, resistant to atmospheric corrosion. The unoxidized metal has a brilliant luster, but the oxidized surface is a grayish white. It is a good conductor of electricity, being more than twice as good as copper on a weight basis, and 64 per cent as good on a volume basis.

The physical properties of high-purity aluminum and the commercial 99.0 per cent grade are compared for the annealed condition in Table 34. The purest aluminum is soft, weak, and ductile, having only one-quarter the tensile strength but twice

TABLE 34.—PHYSICAL PROPERTIES OF ALUMINUM*
Annealed Aluminum

	Purity 99.97 per cent	Purity 99.4 per cent
Tensile strength, psi	8,500	13,000
Elongation, per cent in 2 in	60	45
Reduction in area	95	80
Brinell number	16†	22†

Commercial Aluminum Sheet (2 S)

Temper designation	Tensile strength, psi	Yield strength, psi	Elongation, per cent in 2 in.	Brinell hardness number‡
Annealed −650°F	13,000	4,000	35	23
Half-hard	17,000	14,000	9	32
Hard	24,000	21,000	5	44

* From Metals Handbook, 1936 ed., pp. 926 and 928.
† With 0.125-in. ball and 50 kg pressure.
‡ With 10-mm. ball and 500 kg load.

the ductility of commercial copper. The commercial 99.4 aluminum alloy is somewhat stronger, because of the iron and silicon present, but has only a little over one-third of the tensile strength and 50 per cent more ductility than annealed commercial copper.

Aluminum is hardened and made stronger by cold work as is shown in Table 34 and may be annealed and have its grain refined by heating the cold-worked metal to 650°F. Its softness and ductility make it suitable for mechanical operations such as deep drawing and spinning. It may be welded by various processes, but care must be taken to prevent oxidation in the process. It becomes weaker at higher temperatures and at 400°F will have only about 60 per cent of the yield strength that it possesses at room temperatures. It does not become brittle even at temperatures as low as −100°F.

Aluminum powder is made by pounding aluminum foil into flakes of extreme thinness and fineness. It has a bright silvery color and is used as a pigment in paints and lacquers.

Aluminum cable is extensively used for the transmission of electric power, generally in the form of an aluminum cable surrounding a steel-reinforcing core. Over 730,000 miles of such cable have been installed in the United States.[1]

The thermal conductivity of aluminum is less than 60 per cent that of copper.

Aluminum-iron Alloys.—One of the common impurities in commercial aluminum is iron, which dissolves in molten aluminum but is almost completely insoluble in it in the solid states. A eutectic is formed at a composition of 98.3 per cent of aluminum. The two components of the eutectic after solidification are $FeAl_3$, a very hard and brittle compound, and pure aluminum. Iron that is present in aluminum in small amounts therefore makes it somewhat harder and more brittle.

Aluminum is added to steel to be used for nitriding in amounts between 0.9 to 1.5 per cent, but the alloy is not commercially useful without other alloying constituents. The addition of small percentages of chromium, molybdenum, and nickel have been recommended as beneficial in the nitriding operation. The properties of nitrided steel have been discussed in Chap. VIII. Alloys with 4 to 8 per cent of aluminum are forgeable, and those with 2 to 6 per cent of aluminum, 7 to 15 of chromium, and 1.0 per cent of carbon exhibit almost complete resistance to oxidation at 1550 to 1580°F.

Aluminum-silicon Alloys.—The second impurity that is usually present in commercial aluminum is silicon. Silicon will remain in solid solution in aluminum up to 1.6 per cent at 1071°F

---

[1] EDWARDS, J. D., 50 Years of Aluminum, *Metal Progress*, **29**, 34 (1936).

(577°C), but the solubility decreases to almost nothing at room temperature.

Silicon is added to aluminum in amounts up to 13 per cent in alloys to be used for castings. A eutectic with 11.7 per cent of silicon solidifies at 1071°F (577°C), which is 150° below the melting point of pure aluminum. Alloys with 5 to 13 per cent of silicon are used because of their freedom from hot-shortness and their tendency to form a sound and smooth skin. The alloy with 5 per cent silicon has a tensile strength of 9000 psi and an elongation of 35 to 50 per cent in 2 in. when cast in sand. If cast in

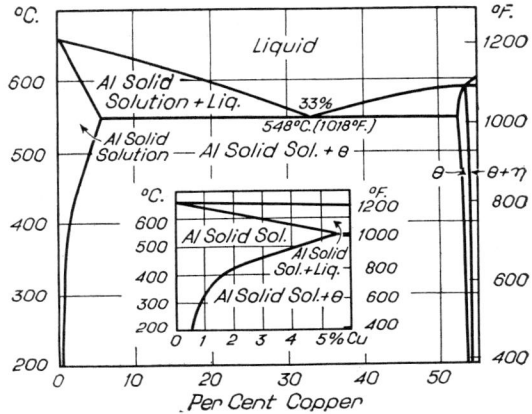

Fig. 113.—Equilibrium diagram for aluminum-copper alloys. (*From Metals Handbook,* 1939 ed.)

permanent molds, its tensile strength may be 10 to 20 per cent higher. It is well suited for marine castings, water jackets, and intricate castings that do not need much machining.

The alloy with 13 per cent of silicon, after modification with sodium, has a tensile strength of 24,000 to 26,000 and a yield strength of 11,000 psi, but its elongation is only 5.0 to 8.0 per cent in 2 in. It may be used for the same type of castings as the 5 per cent alloy and is preferred for die castings especially where the casting is intricate and the section thin.

Copper-aluminum Alloys.—The aluminum bronzes which contain from 4 to 11 per cent of aluminum were discussed with the copper alloys. Little commercial use is made of the alloys richer in aluminum until the range of alloys with more than 90 per cent aluminum is reached. The equilibrium diagram for the alloys of copper and aluminum with less than 50 per cent copper is shown in Fig. 113. When these alloys freeze, a eutectic is formed at 1018°F (548°C) with 67 per cent aluminum, the two constituents after solidification being a solid solution of copper in aluminum with 5.5 per cent copper, and a compound $CuAl_2$ which is quite hard. The eutectic is itself rather hard and brittle, and most of the alloys that are to be rolled or forged are in the range below 5.5 per cent copper. The diagram shows that the solubility decreases as the temperature drops, and therefore that $CuAl_2$ must slowly precipitate out. The separation of the hard $CuAl_2$ grains hardens and strengthens the alloy, and the term "precipitation hardening" was first used in describing the changes taking place in this alloy of aluminum and copper. The alloy with 95 per cent aluminum and about 4 per cent copper forms the basis of Duralumin, but since small amounts of other metals are also added, it will be discussed under the heading of the quaternary alloys.

Aluminum-manganese Alloys.—Manganese forms a solid solution up to 1.86 per cent manganese at the freezing point of the alloy. A harder compound Al_6Mn separates as the alloy cools, and so manganese, like copper, gives the same possibility of hardening by precipitation. The A.S.T.M. tentative specification for aluminum-manganese alloy sheet and plate calls for 1.0 to 1.5 per cent manganese. Since this alloy is to be used for cold-working, the sheet metal in the soft state is required to have a tensile strength of 19,000 psi as a maximum and an elongation of 20 to 25 per cent, depending on the thickness of the sheet. After being cold-worked to the hard condition, the tensile strength must be at least 27,000 lb and the elongation 1 to 4 per cent. This alloy is used in the manufacture of furniture, cooking utensils, in architectural work and in the construction of railway cars where parts are not stressed too highly.

Aluminum-zinc Alloys.—Zinc dissolves in aluminum to form a solid solution whose content of zinc decreases rapidly as the temperature drops until it is not more than 2 per cent and possibly much less at room temperature. The material separating out from the solid solution is not a harder constituent as is the case with copper and manganese but is approximately pure zinc. The binary alloys of aluminum and zinc find little application.

Magnesium-aluminum Alloys.—The complete diagram of the magnesium aluminum alloys shows an area of solid solution at each end of the diagram which contains the commercial alloys. The diagram for the system containing up to 40 per cent magnesium and also a more detailed sketch of the area with less than 20 per cent of magnesium is shown in Fig. 114. The maximum amount of solid solution is 14 per cent and occurs at 855°F. The solubility decreases rapidly to less than 4 per cent at 400°F. The solubility at room temperature is not known. The material

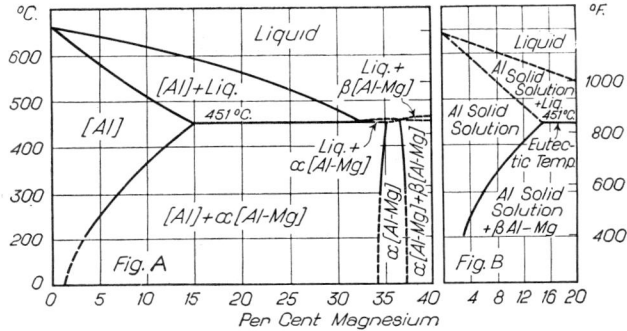

FIG. 114.—Equilibrium diagram for aluminum-magnesium alloys. (*From Metals Handbook*, 1939 ed.)

separating out from the solid solution seems to be another Al − Mg solid solution. The simple binary alloys of magnesium and aluminum find use in both cast and wrought alloys. The properties of the more complicated alloys high in magnesium are discussed in the section devoted to magnesium.

Aluminum-casting Alloys.—The aluminum manufactured for castings may be of somewhat lower purity than that required for rolling, since the common impurities silicon and iron both harden and strengthen the aluminum without causing great brittleness, if present in small percentages. Secondary aluminum may contain not only silicon and iron but also small amounts of copper and manganese. These elements again do not harm castings in small amounts, and may be helpful in specific cases. The Society of Automotive Engineers lists a number of chemical compositions from which several are selected for presentation in Table 35. Those used in the United States fall into three classes according to the major alloying constituent, magnesium, silicon,

ALUMINUM, MAGNESIUM, AND THE LIGHT ALLOYS

TABLE 35.—ALUMINUM CASTING ALLOYS*

S.A.E. number	Alloying constituents	Method of casting	Physical properties and uses
320	Magnesium, 3.25–4.25 Manganese, 0.60	Sand	Tensile strength, 22,000 psi. Elongation, 6.0 per cent in 2 in. High resistance to corrosion and readily machinable. Good for carburetor cases and pipe fittings.
324	Magnesium, 9.25–11.25	Sand	This alloy after heat-treatment has the highest mechanical properties of the casting alloys. Tensile strength of heat-treated castings, 40,000 psi. Elongation 11 per cent in 2 in. Used for parts of trucks, railway cars and aircraft.
35	Silicon, 4.5–6.0 Copper max., 0.4 Iron max., 0.8	Sand and permanent molds	Good for large, intricate castings. Good resistance to corrosion. Tensile strength, sand cast, 17,000 psi with 3 per cent elongation in 2 in. When cast in metal molds, tensile strength should be 21,000 and elongation 2.5 per cent.
37	Silicon, 12.0–13.0 Iron max., 0.8 Manganese max., 0.5	Sand	Good foundry characteristics and resistance to salt-spray corrosion. Tensile strength, sand cast, 24,000 psi and elongation 4 per cent in 2 in.
33	Copper, 6.0–8.0 Silicon max., 2.0 Iron max., 1.5 Zinc max., 2.5	Sand or permanent molds	General casting alloy. Used for crank cases, transmission cases, cylinder heads. Tensile strength, sand cast, 19,000 psi with elongation of 1.0 to 2.5 per cent. Tensile test cast in permanent molds, 23,000 lb.
34	Copper, 9.25–10.75 Iron max., 1.50 Iron and silicon max., 2.0 Magnesium, 0.15–0.35	Permanent molds and sand	Pistons and camshafts for automobile engines where hardness and resistance to wear are required. After heat-treatment, tensile strength, 26,000–34,000 lb.
38	Copper, 4.0–5.0 Silicon max., 1.2 Iron max., 1.2		Most widely used of the high-strength heat-treated alloys. Good resistance to salt spray and used for castings on shipboard. Also various parts in automobiles and aircraft. After heat-treatment, 29,000 lb. tensile strength with 6.0 per cent elongation or 32,000 lb. with 3.0 per cent elongation.
31	Copper, 2.25–3.25 Zinc, 12.50–14.50 Silicon, iron, manganese, and tin } max. 1.70		This alloy is used in Europe as a general casting alloy. It is not resistant to corrosion nor is it recommended for elevated temperatures. Its tensile strength may be 25,000 psi with elongation of 1–3 per cent.

* Condensed from S.A.E. Handbook, 1938 ed., pp. 367–378.

TABLE 36.—WROUGHT ALUMINUM ALLOYS*

Chemical Composition

Commercial aluminum (2 S)—At least 99.0 aluminum with balance mainly iron and silicon

Alloy 3 S—Commercial aluminum plus 1.0–1.5 per cent manganese and 0.2 per cent (max.) copper

Duralumin (17 S)—Commercial aluminum plus 4.0 per cent copper, 0.5 per cent manganese, and 0.5 per cent magnesium

Alloy 24 S—Commercial aluminum plus 4.2 per cent copper, 0.6 manganese and 1.5 per cent magnesium

Alloy 53 S—Commercial aluminum plus 0.7 per cent silicon, 1.25 per cent magnesium and 0.25 per cent chromium

Mechanical Properties

	Tensile strength, psi	Yield strength, psi	Elongation, per cent in 2 in.	Brinell hardness†	Endurance limit, psi
Commercial aluminum (2 S):					
Soft	13,000	5,000	35	23	5,000
Half-hard	17,000	14,000	9	32	7,000
Hard	24,000	21,000	5	44	8,500
Alloy 3 S:					
Soft	16,000	5,000	40	28	7,000
Half-hard	21,000	18,000	20	40	9,000
Hard	29,000	25,000	10	55	10,000
Duralumin:					
Soft	26,000	10,000	20	45	11,000
Heat-treated and aged	58,000	35,000	20	100	15,000
Heat-treated, aged and cold-worked	63,000	46,000	13	110	
Alloy 24 S:					
Heat-treated and aged	65,000	43,000	20	105	14,000
Heat-treated, aged and cold-rolled	68,000	53,000	13	116	14,500
Alloy 53 S:					
Soft	16,000	6,000	30	28	7,500
Heat-treated and aged	35,000	28,000	20	74	11,000

* From Report on Service Characteristics of Light Metals and their Alloys, *Proc. Am. Soc. Testing Materials*, **34**, I, 277 (1934).

† 50-kg load. 10-mm. ball.

ALUMINUM, MAGNESIUM, AND THE LIGHT ALLOYS 267

or copper. Iron and silicon are always present to the extent of a few tenths of a per cent but are often added intentionally in small amounts because of their strengthening effect. Manganese and magnesium are added as minor constituents for a similar reason. A fourth class of alloys containing 12.50 to 14.50 per cent of zinc with only 2.25 to 3.25 per cent of copper is used in Europe where

Fig. 115.—A 240-ft dredge boom made possible through the application of aluminum alloy structural shapes and plates. (*Courtesy of Aluminum Company of America.*)

it is desired to conserve the use of copper. It is not resistant to corrosion.

Wrought-aluminum Alloys.—The metals added to aluminum for alloys to be rolled or otherwise wrought into shapes comprise the same list as those added to make casting alloys. If the elements added can remain in solid solution at room temperature, they strengthen the metal but do not permit hardening by heat-treatment. The silicon and iron that are present in the commercial grades of aluminum to a maximum for 1.0 per cent for the two play their part in adding strength. Manganese up to 1.2 per cent may be added without conferring precipitation-hardening properties and so may magnesium up to 2.5 per cent. The composition and properties of selected alloys are given in Table 36. The alloying element that is most used to make the alloy respond to heat-treatment is copper added in amounts that are usually within the limits of 4.0 to 4.5 per cent. The value of these light and strong alloys is illustrated in the picture of the dredge with a boom 240 ft long which is illustrated in Fig. 115.

Duralumin or Dural.—This is the oldest of the aluminum alloys which respond successfully to heat-treatment. S.A.E. specification 26 calls for the following chemical composition:

	Per Cent
Copper	3.5–4.5
Magnesium	0.2–0.75
Manganese	0.4–1.0
Aluminum minimum	92

The possibilities of heat-treatment inherent in this alloy may be seen from the equilibrium diagram of Fig. 113 for the copper aluminum alloys. The presence of the small quantities of the alloying metals modify the diagram in details but not in general outline. The diagram indicates that the copper may be brought into solid solution, if present to not more than 5.0 per cent, by heating to 1000°F. It is probable that the small amounts of silicon, iron, manganese, and magnesium are also brought into solid solution at this temperature. If the alloy is quenched from 900 to 1000°F, the product will be a supersaturated solid solution comparable with austenite in steel. This supersaturated solid solution tends to return to equilibrium conditions, slowly at room temperatures, more rapidly if aged at temperatures about 200°F. As the solid solution decomposes, crystals of hard $CuAl_2$ and of a hard silicide separate. The size and distribution of these particles influence the strength and hardness of the alloy in the same way that the size and distribution of the carbides affect the strength and hardness of steel. The process of aging Duralumin is analogous to the tempering of steel, but the temperatures for treating Duralumin are lower than those for

ALUMINUM, MAGNESIUM, AND THE LIGHT ALLOYS

steel because of the lower temperatures at which recrystallization of aluminum occurs.

The Aluminum Company of America[1] emphasizes the need for accurate control of time and temperature to get good results. They direct that the alloy 17 S, which is the usual Duralumin, should be heated until the temperature at the center of the piece is 930 to 950°F and then quenched in cold water. The quenched metal is soft and ductile, but aging starts quite rapidly and

Fig. 116.—Group of die castings made from aluminum base alloy. (*Courtesy of Aluminum Company of America.*)

proceeds at a diminishing rate until it becomes practically complete after four days at room temperature. The mechanical properties of this alloy are given in Table 36. It is advisable that any cold-forming operation be undertaken within an hour after quenching unless the metal is stored in a refrigerator to retard the aging process. In the soft state, this alloy will have a yield strength of 10,000 psi and a Brinell hardness of 45. In assembling riveted structures, the rivets are driven cold and are kept in

[1] Alcoa Aluminum and Its Alloys, 1937 ed.

refrigerated containers to prevent hardening before they are driven. This alloy, after aging will have a tensile strength of 60,000 and a yield strength of 37,000 psi with an elongation of 22 per cent in 2 in. The cold-worked rivets will be even stronger. The yield strength decreases quite rapidly at higher temperatures, and at 400°F its tensile strength is 25,000, yield strength 20,000, and elongation 25 per cent. Several other alloys respond to heat-treatment in various degree. Some contain fractional percentages of nickel and chromium.

Alloys for Die Casting.—A die casting is one in which the metal, in the molten or pasty state, is forced by pressure into a permanent mold where it cools quickly and from which it is ejected as soon as it is solid. These castings have the advantages of rapid production, accurate dimension, and smooth finish. The steels used for the dies must not warp or wear too fast at the temperatures involved. The high melting point of brass has restricted the use of that metal for die castings. The alloys of aluminum are well adapted for die castings, and in general the silicon and copper-silicon alloys are used. The variety of shapes that may be produced by die-casting aluminum base alloys is shown in Fig. 116.

Resistance to Corrosion. Alclad Sheet.—The thin film of oxide that forms on aluminum is resistant to corrosion. Salt spray is detrimental, and electrolytic corrosion must be guarded against by avoiding contact with a dissimilar metal. Alloys of the Duralumin type, which contain copper, corrode somewhat more readily than the commercial aluminum. A product that is marketed under the name of Alclad consists of a rolled sandwich containing a center of a strong alloy covered with a surface layer of aluminum of high purity which is alloyed to the core. This coating of pure aluminum gives the whole piece the protection of pure aluminum.

Metallurgy of Magnesium.—Magnesium is found distributed widely throughout the world as the carbonate, magnesite, and is also found as an abundant constituent of the silicate rocks. The high heat of formation of magnesium oxide prevents the reduction in a blast furnace. The purified oxide may be dissolved in molten fluorides and electrolyzed in a manner similar to aluminum, but the only commercial method at present is to electrolyze fused magnesium chloride which is obtained in high purity as a by-product in working up some impure salt brines. The world production is about 11,000,000 lb per year, with Germany as the largest producer. The United States ranks second with a 1936

TABLE 37.—MAGNESIUM AND MAGNESIUM ALLOYS
Mechanical Properties of Pure Magnesium*

	As cast	As rolled
Tensile strength, psi	13,000	25,000
Elongation, per cent in 2 in	6	4
Brinell hardness (500 kg, 10-mm ball)	30	40

Dow Metal—Typical Compositions and Mechanical Properties†

Alloy	Aluminum	Manganese	Zinc	Magnesium
H	6.0	0.2	3.0	90.8
O	8.5	0.2	0.5	90.8
K	10.0	0.1	Silicon 0.5	89.4

	Tensile strength, psi	Yield strength, psi	Elongation, per cent in 2 in.	Brinell hardness
H as cast	27,000	12,000	5	50
Heat-treated	38,000	12,000	11	51
Heat-treated and aged	38,000	18,000	5	62
O press forged and aged	45,000	30,000	8	78
K	30,000	22,000	1	62

Characteristics and Uses
  H for sand castings and forgings with improved salt-water resistance
  O for simple press forgings and extruded sections of high-yield strength
  K for die castings. Good casting characteristics and good mechanical properties

  * Metals Handbook, 1936 ed., p. 1209.
  † Dow Chemical Company, Bulletins on Dow Metal, 1938.

production of 3,903,000 lb, all of which was produced by the Dow Chemical Company.

Properties of Magnesium.—Magnesium is the lightest of the commercial metals with a density of 1.74 at 68°F. Its weight per cubic foot is 108.5 lb, as compared with 175 for 99.0 per cent aluminum and 557 for copper. Its melting point is 1202°F (650°C). Magnesium may be cast and also extruded and rolled hot or cold.

The metal is plastic enough so that it can be extruded or rolled at 650°F. If the metal is worked cold, it must be annealed rather frequently, as it hardens rapidly with cold work. The A.S.T.M. tentative (1937) standard specification for magnesium ingot requires at least 99.80 per cent magnesium. The tabulation of physical properties in Table 37 shows it to have roughly the same tensile strength as aluminum but to be much less ductile.

The high heat of formation of magnesium oxide makes the metal a good deoxidizer, and it is added to many nonferrous alloys in small amounts to effect deoxidation. The brilliant light emitted by burning magnesium powder or ribbon makes it useful in photographic work.

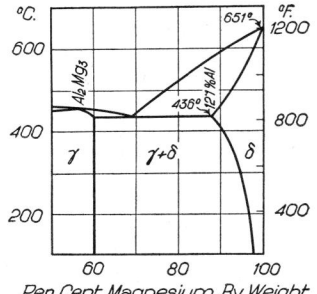

FIG. 117.—Equilibrium diagram for magnesium-aluminum alloys containing from 60 to 100 per cent magnesium. (*From Metals Handbook*, 1939 ed.)

Alloys of Magnesium and Aluminum.—Magnesium dissolves in aluminum to form a solid solution with a maximum of 15.3 per cent magnesium at the eutectic temperature of 844°F (451°C) and a decreasing solubility at lower temperatures to 3.0 per cent at 400°F. The solubility at room temperatures has not been accurately determined. The presence of small amounts of magnesium in various aluminum alloys has already been mentioned. At the high magnesium end of the diagram, there is also a solid solution with a maximum of 12.1 per cent of aluminum at the eutectic temperature of 817°F (436°C) and a decreasing solubility at lower temperatures to about 2 per cent at room temperature as indicated by the diagram of Fig. 117. Other investigators have placed the solubility at room temperature at 5 to 7 per cent. The effect of the aluminum in solid solution is to strengthen the alloy as is usual with solid solutions. The excess constituent which separates contains the harder Al_2Mg_3 as one of its constituents. These compositions therefore possess the possibility of precipitation hardening and have commercial importance.

ALUMINUM, MAGNESIUM, AND THE LIGHT ALLOYS 273

Alloys of Magnesium and Manganese.—The equilibrium diagram for these two metals has not been worked out, but there is evidence that as much as 3.3 per cent of manganese may exist in solid solution at 1193°F (645°C) but that the solubility drops

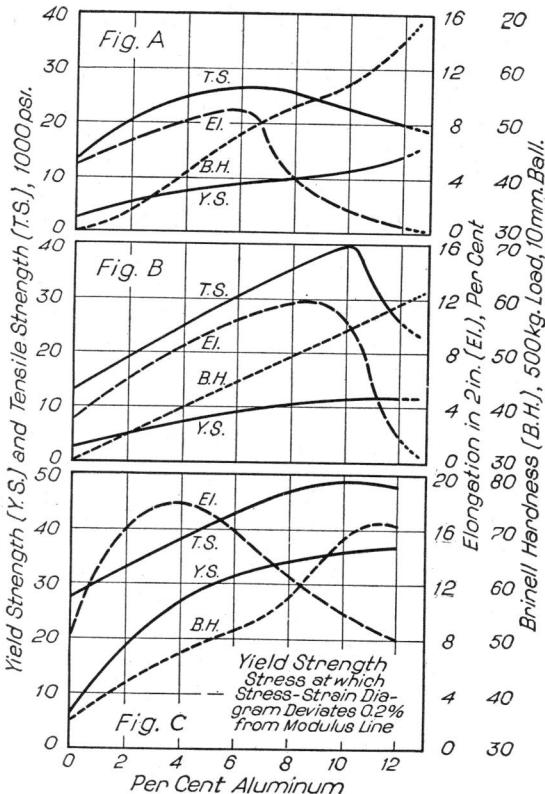

Fig. 118.—Physical properties of magnesium-aluminum alloys. *A*, tensile strength of sand cast magnesium-aluminum alloy; *B*, same as *A*, but after solution heat treatment; *C*, mechanical properties of extruded metal. (*From Metals Handbook*, 1939 ed.)

to practically zero at 400°F. An alloy of 98.5 magnesium and 1.5 manganese is recommended for its resistance to salt water.

Alloys of Magnesium, Aluminum, and Manganese.—The important commercial alloys of magnesium belong in this system and contain from 4 to 12 per cent of aluminum and 0.10 to 0.30

per cent of manganese. The largest producer of these alloys is the Dow Chemical Company which markets them as various grades of Dowmetal. The change in physical properties that takes place with increasing percentages of aluminum in alloys of magnesium containing a few tenths of a per cent of manganese is shown in Fig. 118.

The sand-cast alloy shows a maximum tensile strength and elongation with a little over 6 per cent of aluminum, but after heat-treatment of the castings, the maximum elongation is found with 9 per cent and the maximum tensile strength with 10 per cent of aluminum. These percentages approach the limit of the quantity of aluminum that can be held in solid solution. The yield strength and Brinell hardness show little change with heat-treatment. The extruded metal shows higher yield strength, tensile strength, and hardness than the cast alloy. The elongation shows an extraordinarily high value for the alloy with 4 per cent aluminum, and although it decreases with the higher percentages of aluminum, it still remains higher than either of the cast forms. Illustrations of the properties of Dowmetal are given in Table 37 taken from a bulletin of the Dow Chemical Company. It is remarkable that the addition of 4 per cent of weak and soft aluminum to weak and soft magnesium can produce an alloy which, in the annealed state, is twice as strong as either one alone. These alloys find their major uses in the aircraft industry as castings and rolled or extruded shapes. They are also used in automotive equipment and as die castings.

References

EDWARDS, FRARY, and JEFFRIES: The Aluminum Industry, 2 vols., McGraw-Hill Book Company, Inc., New York, 1930.

EDWARDS, J. D.: 50 Years of Aluminum, *Metal Progress*, **29**, 34 (1936).

AMERICAN SOCIETY FOR TESTING MATERIALS: Service Characteristics of the Light Metals and Their Alloys, reprinted from *Proc. Am. Soc. Testing Materials*, Vol. **34**, Part I, 1934.

ZEERLEDER, ALFRED VON: The Technology of Aluminum and Its Light Alloys, Gustav Fock, New York, 1936.

Light Metals and Alloys, *U. S. Bur. Standards Circ.* 346, 1927.

ALUMINUM COMPANY OF AMERICA: Alcoa Aluminum and Its Alloys—1937, Pittsburgh.

TEMPLIN and PAUL: The Mechanical Properties of Aluminum and Magnesium Alloys at Elevated Temperatures, Symposium on Effect of Temperature on the Properties of Metals, published by American

Society for Testing Materials and American Society of Mechanical Engineers, 1931.

MUTCHLER, WILLARD: The Weathering of Aluminum Alloy Sheet Materials Used in Aircraft, National Advisory Committee for Aeronautics Report 490, 1934.

EDWARDS, J. D.: Aluminum Paint and Powder, 2d ed., Reinhold Publishing Corporation, New York, 1936.

HAUGHTON and PRYTHERCH: Magnesium and Its Alloys, His Majesty's Stationery Office, London, 1937.

GANN, J. A.: The Magnesium Industry, *Ind. Eng. Chem.*, **22,** 694 (1930).

GANN, J. A.: Magnesium Industry's Lightest Structural Metal, *Jour. Soc. Automotive Eng.*, **28,** 653 (1931).

DOW CHEMICAL COMPANY: Dow Data Book and Bulletins, Midland, Mich.

WELTY, G. D.: Magnesium Alloys in Aircraft-engine Construction, *Jour. Soc. Automotive Eng.*, **30,** 112 (1932).

HARVEY, W. G.: Magnesium and Its Alloys in Aircraft, *Trans. Am. Electrochem. Soc.*, **56,** 57 (1930).

BENGOUGH and WHITBY: The Corrosion and Protection of Magnesium and Its Light Alloys, *Trans. Inst. Chem. Eng. (Great Britain)*, **11,** 176 (1934).

STERN, MARC: Die-casting Practice, McGraw-Hill Book Company, Inc., New York, 1930.

CHAPTER XV

LEAD AND ITS ALLOYS
SOLDERS AND BEARING METALS

Lead is a soft and fusible metal whose use goes back to remote antiquity. It resists corrosion well, and pieces of lead pipe and sheet uncovered in the ruins of ancient Rome are still in good condition.

Metallurgy of Lead.—The principal ore of lead is galena (PbS) which is widely distributed throughout the world. The ore is

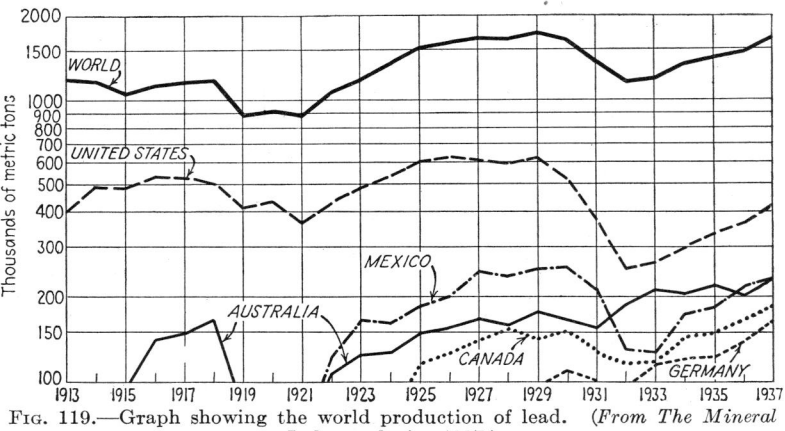

FIG. 119.—Graph showing the world production of lead. (*From The Mineral Industry during* 1937.)

roasted and reduced in a blast furnace which is similar in principle to that used for smelting copper, the products being metallic lead, with some matte, and slag. Flue dust must be recovered not only because of its value as a source of lead and also gold and silver, but because of its poisonous properties. The lead fume and the arsenic oxide, which frequently accompanies it, poison water supplies and also grass and crops and so cause the death of cattle. Lead is refined by careful oxidation on a hearth or in a kettle lined with brick. The copper, tin, and zinc oxidize and are removed from the surface by skimming.

LEAD AND ITS ALLOYS

An electrolytic process somewhat similar to that for copper may also be used to refine lead.

Uses of Lead.—The graphs of Fig. 119 show the quantity of lead produced in the world from 1913 to 1937. The United States furnishes about one-fourth of the world's production, with Mexico and Australia tied for second place. The United States production in 1937 came mainly from Missouri, Utah, and Idaho with Nevada, New Mexico, and Arizona contributing lesser amounts. The amount of secondary lead recovered in the United States in 1936 amounted to 262,900 tons.

TABLE 38.—USES OF LEAD IN THE UNITED STATES IN 1936*

	Tons of 2000 Lb.
White lead	86,500
Red lead and litharge (excluding storage batteries)	54,000
Storage batteries	191,000
Cable covering	61,400
Building (including chemical plants)	40,000
Automobiles	11,100
Railway equipment	2,400
Shipbuilding	200
Ammunition	32,500
Terne plate	6,200
Foil	28,500
Bearing metal	16,500
Solder	22,000
Type metal	17,000
Calking	13,500
Castings	5,750
Other uses including lead tetraethyl	46,000
	633,550

* Yearbook of American Bureau of Metal Statistics, 1936, p. 55.

The largest single use for lead in the United States is in the manufacture of storage batteries, which, as shown in Table 38, took 30 per cent of the total consumption of the United States in 1936. This figure includes the metallic lead used in the grids of the batteries and also the red lead (Pb_3O_4) and litharge (PbO) used as paste in the filling of the plates. The pigments white lead, red lead, and litharge take the next largest amount of lead. Much of the commercial lead whose uses are given in the table has been alloyed with antimony to make it harder and stronger.

Properties of Lead.—Lead is one of the heaviest metals, its density being 11.34 and its weight per cubic foot 706 lb. Two specifications for the chemical composition of commercial leads are given in Table 39. The purer Grade I, also called "corroding lead," which is used for the manufacture of white lead pigment must contain at least 99.94 per cent lead. The common lead

TABLE 39.—COMPOSITION AND PROPERTIES OF COMMERCIAL LEAD

Chemical Composition of Pig Lead*

	Grade I corroding lead, per cent	Grade III common lead, per cent
Silver, max	0.0015	0.002
Copper, max	0.0015	0.0025
Copper plus silver, max	0.0025	
Arsenic, max	0.0015	0.015
Antimony and tin, max	0.0095	
Zinc, max	0.0015	0.002
Iron, max	0.002	0.002
Bismuth, max	0.05	0.15
Lead by difference, min	99.94	99.85

Physical Properties of Cast Lead†

	Desilverized lead‡	Chemical lead§	Very pure lead
Percentage of lead	99.99	99.90	99.999
Yield point, psi	861	1643	714
Tensile strength, psi	1966	2765	1609
Elongation, per cent	64.2	50.2	68.6
Reduction in area, per cent	92.4	87.9	100.0
Brinell hardness number (10-mm ball, 100 kg, 30 sec):			
1 hr after casting	4.2	5.5	2.9
10 days after casting	4.1	5.4	3.0

* A.S.T.M. Standards, 1936, p. 678.
† HIERS, G. O., Trans. Am. Inst. Chem. Eng., **20,** 131 (1927).
‡ Desilverized lead from southeastern Missouri.
§ Undesilverized lead from southeastern Missouri.

must contain at least 99.85 per cent, bismuth being the only impurity that is tolerated in more than traces. The physical tests of the cast leads given in Table 39 show the metal to be very soft and ductile. The equicohesive temperature of lead is probably below the freezing point of water so that lead stiffens slightly with cold work but anneals itself continuously and creeps under very slight loads. Lead sheet and pipe of pure lead will stretch and bend unless they are supported almost continuously along their length. The low heat of formation of lead oxide indicates that lead should be resistant to atmospheric corrosion, and this is actually the case. Some acids, notably sulfuric, form a protecting film, but the organic acids and even carbon dioxide in the presence of moisture cause rapid corrosion. Lead pipe

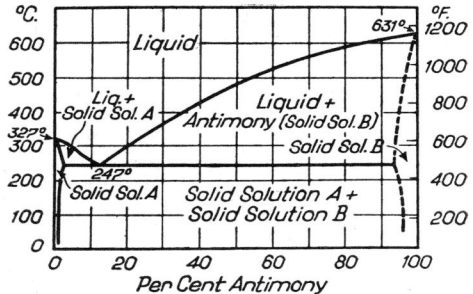

Fig. 120.—Equilibrium diagrams for lead-antimony alloys. (*From Metals Handbook*, 1939 ed.)

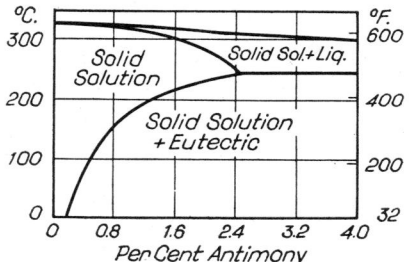

Fig. 121.—Equilibrium diagrams for lead-antimony alloys. (*From Metals Handbook*, 1939 ed.)

should not be used to transport drinking water unless careful tests have shown the water to be noncorrosive, because of the danger of lead poisoning among those who drink the water. Lead is a cumulative poison which is not eliminated by the human body and so may build up to a poisonous amount when taken in minute quantities over a long period of time.

Alloys of Lead and Antimony.—The chief metallurgical importance of antimony is as an alloying constituent of lead. Its price is roughly that of copper and therefore higher than lead so that its use is mainly as an addition in percentages of less than 15 to harden the lead. The equilibrium diagram of the antimony-lead alloys is shown in Fig 120, and the portion with less than 4.0 antimony is shown in grater detail in Fig. 121. It is a diagram of a simple type with alpha solid solution containing 2.4 per cent of antimony as a maximum at the eutectic temperature of 476°F (247°C) and diminishing solubility to not over 0.2 per cent at room temperature. At the other end of the diagram, there is a beta solid solution whose limits are not so well known but which

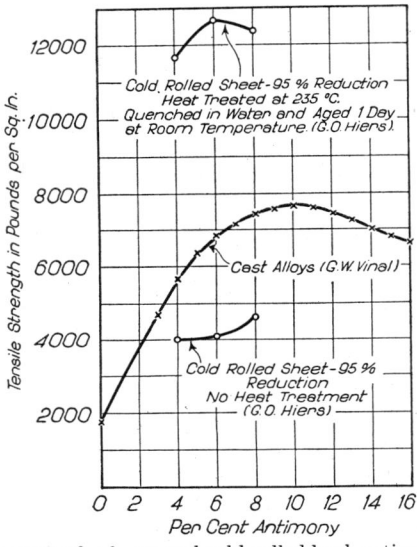

Fig. 122.—Tensile strength of cast and cold-rolled lead-antimony alloys. (*From Metals Handbook*, 1939 ed.)

at room temperatures contains very little lead. There is a eutectic containing 11.5 per cent of antimony. It is evident from the diagram that the alpha solid solution gives a possibility of age-hardening through the separation of harder particles from a quickly cooled alloy. The annealing temperature of lead is so low, substantially room temperature, that the final hardness of the metal depends in part on the temperature of aging.

Uses of Antimonial Lead.—The greater strength imparted by small percentages of antimony, as shown in Fig. 122, makes it logical to incorporate that metal where strength is at all important. The grids for the plates of storage batteries contain 7 to

12 per cent. The lead used in bullets carries about 12 per cent of antimony, and hard lead sheets and pipes contain more than 6 per cent.

The effect of varying percentages of antimony and of heat-treatment on the tensile strength of extruded wire is shown in Fig. 123. The lower curve of the lower diagram shows the effect of increasing amounts of antimony on wire which after extrusion was annealed at 230°F (110°C), a temperature high enough to permit the dispersed antimony to coalesce to rather large particles. The maximum tensile strength occurs at about 2.5 per cent antimony, which represents the maximum amount that can exist in solid solutions at any temperature. Larger percentages of antimony appear in the eutectic, and their effect is actually to decrease the strength of the annealed metal. Other samples of the wire were heated to 455°F (235°C) to bring the maximum amount of antimony into solid solution and were then quenched and tested at once. This series gave a somewhat higher maximum strength with a slow increase to 12 per cent of antimony, probably because the quenching was so fast that a more effective distribution of the hard particles was obtained. The highest tensile values were obtained by aging this quenched alloy for 70 days at room temperature. The solid solution decomposed to give fine particles of antimony which exerted a large reenforcing effect. The maximum strength, over 10,000 psi, was obtained by aging a quenched alloy containing 2.5 per cent antimony. The lead used for cable sheaths contains 1 per cent of antimony. Higher percentages of antimony which appeared in the form of a eutectic cut the tensile strength to less than 7,000 lb.

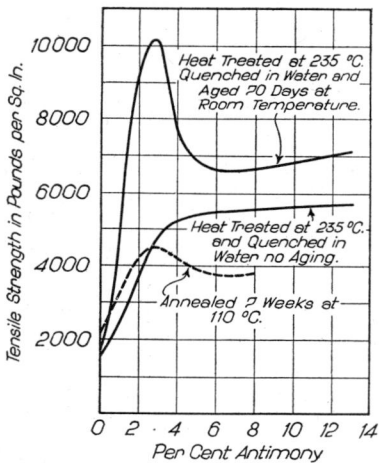

Fig. 123.—Tensile strength of lead-antimony alloys in the form of extruded wires. (*From Metals Handbook*, 1939 ed.)

Alloys of Lead and Tin.—The equilibrium diagram of the lead-tin alloys was presented in Chap. I as an illustration of a simple system involving a solid solution at each end of the diagram with a single eutectic between them. It is shown again in Fig. 124. The addition of tin strengthens lead as shown in Table 2 in Chap. I. In this respect, it acts in the same way as antimony, but since tin is the more expensive metal, it is not used for hard lead. The alloys of lead and tin are used extensively as solders, and their properties are discussed in a following paragraph.

Pewter is an alloy containing 75 to 85 per cent of tin, which has been used for more than a thousand years for making household pitchers, platters, and other vessels. Its low melting point, its white color, and the ease with which it could be cast made it a favorite material in the early days, but its use is now very limited.

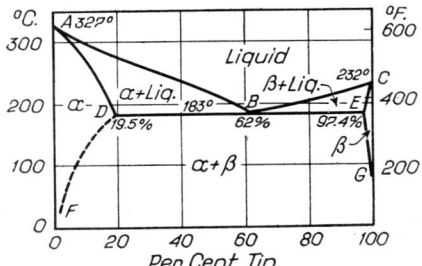

FIG. 124.—Equilibrium diagram of lead-tin alloys. (*From Metals Handbook*, 1939 ed.)

Tin foil may be made of pure tin, but it is also sometimes made by rolling out a sandwich of two sheets of tin with a sheet of lead between them. The two metals adhere in the process of rolling so that a compound sheet is formed. Lead may also be added to the tin used in coating steel, and the product is then known as "terne plate" rather than tin plate. The danger of lead poisoning is so great that lead should not be used as an alloy in materials that are to come in contact with food.

Solders.—Soldering is a process that is used extensively in joining metal sheets like tin plate, galvanized iron, and copper. Solder is an alloy whose melting point is lower than that of the materials to be soldered, and which when molten wets and forms an alloy with the two surfaces to be joined. Brazing is a form of soldering at high temperatures, using brass alloys as the solder. Fusion welding differs from soldering in that the surfaces to be joined are actually fused and flow together.

Soft Solders. *Lead-tin Alloys.*—The soft solders that constitute the type most widely used are all alloys of lead and tin. The specifications for solders as given by the American Society for Testing Materials are abstracted in Table 40. They can best

TABLE 40.—COMPOSITION AND MELTING POINTS OF SOLDER*

Desired composition in percentage for Grade A solders to be used for galvanized iron and zinc. The maximum amounts of impurities that may be permitted are: antimony 0.12, copper 0.08, zinc and aluminum none, and all others 0.10 per cent.

Grade	1	2	3	4	5
Tin	50.00	45.0	40	37.5	33.0
Lead	50.0	55.0	60	62.5	67.0
Initial melting point, °F	358	358	358	358	358
Complete liquefaction, °F	415	437	458	468	485

* Abstracted from A.S.T.M. Standards, 1936 ed., p. 695.

be understood by comparing them with the equilibrium diagram of the lead-tin system given in Fig. 124. Each of the permissible compositions lies in the range that give as the microscopic constituents the alpha solid solution with 19.5 per cent tin and the eutectic with 62.0 per cent tin. All of the compositions therefore attain complete solidification at 358°F and commence to solidify from 57 to 127° higher than that. This gives a range of temperatures in which the alloy is a pasty mixture of liquid and solid which is a useful property in wiping joints of lead pipe, illustrated in Fig. 8 of Chap. I. Most of the nonferrous metals may be united by this solder if the surfaces are clean. A flux is frequently helpful in providing a clean surface. Steel must be coated with one of the other metals such as tin or zinc before it can be soldered. In uniting two surfaces, each must be heated at least momentarily to the melting point of the solder at the time the solder is applied, so that the solder will flow between the two surfaces, alloy with them, and bind them together on cooling. The heating element in small operations is the plumber's soldering iron (copper) or a small blowpipe used frequently by electricians. Since tin is expensive, that alloy is to be chosen which will have the least tin and yet possess suitable flowing and adhesive properties. The Society of Automotive Engineers recommends an additional grade of solder with only 25 per cent of tin to be used on work that is to be coated with enamel and then baked, since it will withstand higher baking temperatures than solders containing more tin.

Hard Solders. *Brass and Silver Solders.*—There are no cheap and suitable alloys for solder whose melting point lies between that of the lead-tin group 500°F and the brasses melting at 1600 to 1650°F. In considering the brazing compounds, which are brasses, reference should be made to the equilibrium diagram of the copper-zinc alloys shown in Fig. 100. The customary brazing alloys contain 50 to 52 per cent copper and 50 to 48 per cent zinc. They solidify at a little above 1600°F to the beta solid solution which is plastic until a temperature of 900°F is reached. The solder therefore will yield to cooling stresses without tearing.

The silver solders are ternary alloys of copper, zinc, and silver. An alloy with 20 silver, 45 copper, and 35 zinc has a melting point of 1430°F, and an increase in the percentage of silver up to 45 per cent lowers the melting point still further. In some cases, cadmium is incorporated to give a still lower melting point. Alloys of many compositions are in use, and some of them have melting points as low as 1200°F.

In the brazing processes, the alloy is usually supplied as fine grains which are placed between the two surfaces to be joined and melted by heating with a torch or by placing in a furnace. The surfaces must be clean, and fluxes are usually used.

Bronze Welding Rods.—Any of the alpha brasses and bronzes may be used as welding rods with an acetylene torch or the electric arc as the source of heat. Since copper forms a solid solution with iron, these high-copper alloys may be used to weld cracks or to fill up cavities in castings. Their melting point, 1600 to 2000°F, is below that of steel or cast iron, and there is not so much formation of austenite with subsequent formation of a hard spot and perhaps a shrinkage crack on cooling as would have been the case had torch or electric welding been employed. The alloys used are ductile at all temperatures during the cooling process and so accommodate themselves to the changes in volume of the steel or cast iron.

Type Metal.—The modern method of typesetting by machine involves a die-casting process whereby each line or other unit of type is set by the machine as a mold, into which molten metal is forced. In printing newspapers, these slugs of metal are then clamped together to form a plate onto which successive sheets of damp paper are pressed until a layer of considerable thickness has been applied. This matrix sheet is then removed and placed on a cylinder of the proper diameter to dry. Another casting is made from this paper matrix, and the resulting curved plate is locked onto the cylinder of the printing press. All of these plates are remelted as soon as they have served their purpose. The metals used for this purpose are all alloys of lead, tin, and antimony. One composition of linotype metal is given as 85 lead, 3 tin, and 12 antimony.

Bearing Metals.—When two moving parts are in apparent contact as is the case when machinery is in motion, it is necessary that a film of oil or other lubricant be kept between the two metal surfaces to avoid undue friction which would be accompanied by heating, scoring of the metal surfaces, and ultimately "seizing" of the two parts. If the contacts between the two surfaces are almost instantaneous, as is the case with ball bearings, the oil film has an opportunity to rebuild itself after every contact. If the surfaces are in approximately continuous contact, as with a rotating shaft, it is helpful and at times almost necessary to choose a metal for one of the bearing surfaces that will make it easier to maintain a film of oil between the two surfaces.

A bearing metal is usually an alloy whose microscopic structure shows two sets of crystals. Each of them should be somewhat softer than the material of the rotating shaft, and one of them should be softer than the other. As the shaft rotates, the softer constituent of the bearing metal wears away slightly and leaves very shallow valleys that serve as pathways for the oil films, which constantly replenish those which may be squeezed out when the load of the shaft comes on the elevated portions of the bearing. Gray cast iron has been used as a bearing metal for slowly moving machines. The ferrite granules are fairly soft, and the graphite flakes wear away to leave cracks which provide for the movement of the lubricant.

It is impossible to line up a shaft so accurately that it will run perfectly truly through several bearings. A bearing should therefore possess enough plasticity so that it will yield slightly without cracking, and accommodate itself to the shaft. In setting up a long line of shafting, it is desirable to have an alloy that can be poured into the journal boxes of the bearing blocks after the shaft is in place. This bearing metal must not alloy with the steel shaft nor have such a high melting point that it will draw the temper of the shaft or cause it to warp. The choice of a bearing metal will depend on the speed of rotation, the load on the shaft, the method of lubrication, and other factors. The grain size of the alloy affects its properties, and so not only the composition of the alloy, but also the method of its application must be adapted to the particular purpose.

The coefficient of thermal expansion of the bearing metal must also be considered. As the bearing becomes warmer in operation, the shaft and also the bearing expand. The rigid housing usually prevents the expansion of the bearing outward so that the shaft and bearing approach each other more closely as the temperature rises. In a bearing that is not properly designed, this heat may cause the bearing metal to melt with the result that the bearing is "burned out."

White Bearing Metals. *Babbitt Metal.*—The white bearing metals are ternary or quaternary alloys of tin, lead, antimony, and copper. These alloys were developed in the earlier days by a process of trial and error, and it is only in recent years that a systematic study of microscopic structures and physical proper-

TABLE 41.—COMPOSITION AND PROPERTIES OF WHITE BEARING METALS*
Desired Composition, per Cent †

Alloy number	1	3	5	7	9	11
Copper	4.5	8.3	2.0			
Tin	91.0	83.3	65.0	10.0	5.0	
Antimony	4.5	8.3	15.0	15.0	10.0	15.0
Lead	....	....	18.0	75.0	85.0	85.0

Physical Properties

Yield point, psi	4,400	6,600	5,050	3,550	3,400	3,050
Tensile strength, psi	12,850	17,600	15,050	15,650	14,700	12,800
Brinell hardness:						
10-mm ball, 500 kg, 30 sec	17.0	27.0	22.5	22.5	19.0	15.0
Initial melting point, °F	433	464	358	464	459	471
Complete liquefaction, °F	......	792	565	514	493	504

* A.S.T.M. Standards, 1936 ed., p. 704.
† Zinc and aluminum must be completely absent, arsenic may not be above 0.10 per cent in some grades nor above 0.25 per cent in any, and iron must be below 0.08 per cent in numbers 1 to 6.

ties has permitted some systematic classification. The values given in Table 41 are selected from these given as standards by the American Society for Testing Materials. The Society of Automotive Engineers lists some of these same compositions and gives others that are intermediate. The name "white bearing metals" is applied to these alloys to distinguish them from the bearing bronzes high in copper. The name "Babbitts" have been applied to alloys high in tin of the general composition of

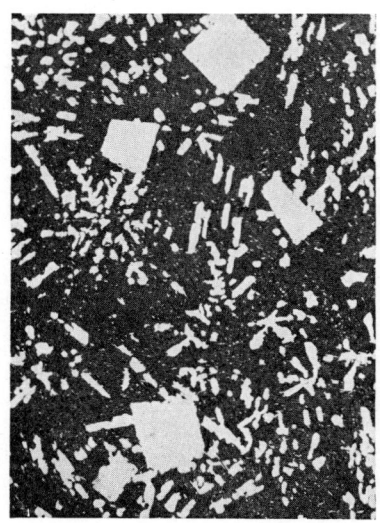 

a   *b*

FIG. 125.—Microscopic structure of Babbitt metal. Composition: tin 85, antimony 7.5, copper 7.5. ×100. *a*, coarse crystals due to slow cooling; *b*, finer crystals due to more rapid cooling. (*Courtesy Professor C. Upthegrove.*)

alloy number 1 of Table 41 because of the pioneer work that Isaac Babbitt did on bearings and bearing metal. His work resulted in a United States patent issued to him in 1839 for a shell lined with a soft alloy to be used as a bearing. The formula that he suggested was composed of 50 lb tin, 5 lb antimony, and 1 lb of copper. The general name of Babbitts has been extended to cover a wide range of compositions used for bearing metals.

It will be noted that the alloys given in Table 41 vary in composition from 85 of lead and zero tin to zero lead and 91 of tin. Copper is present in those with high tin content, and antimony is present in all, in amounts varying from 4.5 to 15.0 per cent. The strongest and hardest alloy is number 3 with 83 per cent of tin and 8.3 per cent each of antimony and copper. It is recommended for lining connecting rod and shaft bearings that are subject to heavy pressures. The high content of tin makes it expensive. If the bearings are large and the service light, the cheaper alloys with little or no tin, like numbers 7, 9, and 11 are recommended.

The microscopic structure of a hard Babbitt metal, not very different in composition from the number 3 alloy given above, is shown in the two pictures of Fig. 125. In each of these pictures, the cubes are composed of hard tin-antimony particles, the stars and rodlike particles are hard copper-tin alloy, and the black background is a softer eutectic rich in tin. Both pictures are magnified to 100 diameters, and the difference in the size of the crystals is due to the rate of cooling. The coarser structure results from pouring the alloy at a higher temperature into a hot metal mold, and the finer structure from pouring at a lower temperature into a cold metal mold.

Bearing Bronzes.—These alloys are used where the pressures and temperatures of operation are so high as to rule out the lead or tin alloys. They are usually alloys of copper and tin that have been deoxidized with phosphorus, although sometimes no more than traces of the phosphorus may remain in the finished bronze. They also all contain lead which is present as a finely divided dispersion and gives the soft constituent to the bearing. One of the well-known alloys contains copper 80, tin 10, and lead 10, with phosphorus varying from traces up to as high as 1.0 per cent. This alloy shows a tensile strength of 27,000 to 33,000 lb with an elongation of 7 to 12 per cent in 2 in. and a Brinell hardness of 47 to 52 (500 kg for 30 sec).

Fusible Alloys.—The eutectic mixture of lead and tin melts at 358°F. Lead and bismuth form a eutectic melting at 257°F. The ternary alloy of lead, tin, and bismuth has a eutectic at 205°F. The quaternary alloy has a eutectic melting at 150°F with a composition of bismuth 49.5, lead 27.3, tin 13.1, and cadmium 10.1. This is approximately the composition of the alloy known for years as Wood's metal. These alloys are used where solders of low melting point are desired. Wood's metal wets glass and is used in making connections in glass apparatus. The low-melting alloys are also used in automatic fire-alarm and sprinkler systems where the alloy on melting breaks an electrical circuit or releases the water.

References

HAYWARD, C. R.: An Outline of Metallurgical Practice, D. Van Nostrand Company, Inc., New York, 1929.

SMYTHE, J. A.: Lead, Longmans, Green & Company, New York, 1923.

MANTELL, C. L.: Tin, Reinhold Publishing Corporation, New York, 1929.

MOORE, BETTY, and DOLLINS: The Creep and Fracture of Lead and Lead Alloys, *Univ. Illinois Bull.*, p. 272, 1935.

HIERS, G. O.: Soft Solders and Their Application, *Metals and Alloys*, **2**, 257 (1931).

LEAD INDUSTRIES ASSOCIATION: Useful Information about Lead, 1st ed. New York, 1931.

HIERS, G. O.: Characteristics of Very Pure and Commercial Lead, *Trans. Am. Inst. Chem. Eng.*, **20**, 131 (1927).

BASSETT, H. N.: Bearing Metals and Alloys, Edward Arnold & Company, London, 1937.

LUMEN BEARING COMPANY: Handbook for Engineers and Machine Designers, Buffalo, New York, 1930.

CORSE, W. M.: Bearing Metals and Bearings, Reinhold Publishing Corporation, New York, 1930.

CHAPTER XVI

CORROSION OF METALS AND PROTECTION BY METALLIC COATINGS

Introduction.—Corrosion involves a distintegration of the surface because of a chemical action. Abrasion by a sand blast or by friction is not usually classed as corrosion. The chemical action may be due to a number of reactants and may manifest itself in various ways. The most common instance of corrosion is the formation of iron rust in damp air or in water. Some other metals are more, and some are less, easily corroded than iron, but no definite scale of relative corrodibility can be made because each metal varies in its resistance to different corrosive conditions. There is no single cause of corrosion, and it can be explained only by a careful study of individual cases.

Acidity and the pH System.—The intensity factor in an acid solution is a function of the concentration of the hydrogen ions (H^+) that are present. A solution that is "normal" in hydrogen ions contains one gram equivalent, which is substantially one gram, of hydrogen ions in a liter. A normal solution of hydrochloric acid contains one gram mol, or 36.5 g, of HCl in a liter of water. A solution that is one-tenth normal contains 3.65 g of HCl per liter, and since in this dilution a solution of hydrochloric acid is ionized almost completely, a liter of this solution will contain one-tenth gram mol of hydrogen ion. If the solution were dilute enough, we could have a solution one-millionth normal, where the quantity of hydrogen ions in a liter of solution would be one millionth of a mol, or more conveniently 10^{-6} gram mol.

A convenient system of nomenclature called the "pH system" has been devised to indicate these small concentrations. It uses the logarithmic exponent without the negative sign to denote the degree of acidity, and gives it the name pH. In the illustration of the solution with the concentration of H^+ of 10^{-6} mol per liter, the pH would be stated as 6. A solution that is one-tenth normal will have 10^{-1} mol H^+ per liter, or a pH of 1.

The system is not used for solutions more acid than pH = 1. Grapefruit juice and sour milk have a pH of about 3.5.

Pure water is slightly dissociated at room temperature. At 77°F, a liter contains 10^{-7} gram mol H^+ and 10^{-7} gram mol OH^- has a pH of 7. Since the number of hydrogen and hydroxyl ions is the same, the solution is neutral. If the solution were made alkaline, the number of hydroxyl ions would increase and the number of hydrogen ions would decrease, and so the pH values would rise above 7. The pH of saturated limewater is about 12.0 and that of ordinary soapy water varies from 10.0 to 11.5.

This system is almost universally used to indicate the variations in feebly acid and alkaline solutions, but as was stated before, it is not adapted to the measurement of strongly acid or alkaline solutions.

One of the characteristics of an acid in water solution is its ability to attack metals, the hydrogen ion of the solution giving up its electrical charge at the surface of the metal to become hydrogen gas and the metal going into solution as a metal ion. Most of the common metals are attacked by strong acids, but not many of the ordinary materials are used by engineers in an environment where they must resist strong acids. Most of the corrosion that is of industrial importance takes place in solutions which are feebly acid, with oxygen as a cooperating agent. Oxygen in water solution tends to be corrosive, for every metal is soluble in water to a slight extent. If water should be placed in a bowl of gold, a minute amount of gold would go into solution until the water became saturated for gold. The reaction would then stop even if oxygen were present because, as shown in Table 8, gold oxide has a negative heat of formation, and gold oxide will not be formed in water solution. If water containing dilute acid should be placed in a gold bowl, it would dissolve somewhat more gold than pure water would, but the action would soon stop.

Rusting of Iron. The Functions of Oxygen.—Let us assume that a boiler in a house-heating plant was made of perfectly pure iron and that in the summer it was filled with absolutely pure water and closed tightly. Iron would at once start to dissolve and would continue to go into solution until the water was saturated with iron when the reaction would stop, and no further corrosion would occur. A second assumption may be made that the boiler was closed tightly when the lower part was filled with water and the upper part with air, which for this purpose will be considered to be a mixture of oxygen and nitrogen. The water will contain some dissolved oxygen which will react with the ferrous ions to form the less soluble ferric hydroxide. The formation of this precipitate (rust) will leave the water unsaturated for iron ions, and so more iron will go into solution. The corrosion and rust formation will continue until substantially all of the gaseous oxygen present in the boiler will have become converted to the hydroxide, and then, on the assumption that the boiler is tightly sealed, the corrosion will stop. The nitrogen in the vapor space will be inert, and not affect the corrosion.

If a third assumption is made that the boiler is half-full of water and that a valve on top of the boiler is open to the air, then oxygen in the boiler will be replenished by diffusion from the outside, and corrosion will continue below the water line. If a long enough time should elapse, the boiler might be corroded through at one or more points. The points of most active corrosion in this hypothetical case would be at the water line because the concentration of the oxygen would be greatest at the surface of contact of the water with the air. Iron exposed to dry air at room temperature does not corrode. When the relative humidity of the air rises above 40 per cent, corrosion starts and proceeds with greater rapidity as the relative humidity rises to higher figures. There would be some corrosion in the upper part of the boiler under the third set of conditions, especially if alternating temperatures caused occasional condensation of moisture on the surface of the metal.

If the temperature of the boiler was above room temperature, the corrosion would be more rapid than at room temperature, provided the supply of air was adequate to keep the water supplied with dissolved oxygen. If the temperature rose to the boiling point of water, the steam evolved would drive off the air, and corrosion would stop because of lack of oxygen. It would soon become necessary to add water to the boiler, and if this added water contained air, corrosion would be resumed. In a household heating plant, the steam is usually condensed in the radiators and the condensed water is returned to the boiler. There is almost always some air in the piping system and the radiators, so that the hot water returning to the boiler is corrosive both to the pipes and the boiler itself.

Rusting of Iron in Water and Air.—Air contains, in round numbers, 20.9 per cent of oxygen and 79.1 per cent of nitrogen by volume. It also contains carbon dioxide to the amount of 0.04 per cent by volume. Rain water always becomes saturated with air as it falls, and at a temperature of 60°F will contain 20.5 cc of dissolved gas per liter of water. The volume of each of the gases and their relative proportion are given in Table 42.

TABLE 42.—COMPOSITION OF RAIN WATER SATURATED WITH AIR AT 60°F

	Dissolved gases expressed as cc per liter of water	Percentage of total gas
CO_2	0.4	2.1
O_2	7.1	34.2
N_2	13.0	63.7
Air	20.5	100.0

It is to be noted that the percentage of dissolved carbon dioxide has risen to 2.1 per cent and that of oxygen to 34 per cent of the total gases so that rain water is a rather powerful corrosive agent. If, in the illustration of the steam boiler, the boiler was half full of water saturated with air and there was free access of air to the upper part of the boiler, there would have been two corrosive agents present. The hydrogen ion from the carbonic acid would accelerate the solution of the iron as the carbonate, which would be changed by the oxygen to the hydroxide, regenerating the carbon dioxide. The carbon dioxide therefore acts as a catalyst to increase the rate of corrosion. The statement that iron rust is composed of iron hydroxide is not strictly correct, as it always contains a small amount of loosely held carbon dioxide which continues to act as a catalyst, so that steel which has a film of rust corrodes faster than if it were clean metal.

The explanation of this combined effect of carbon dioxide and oxygen may also be stated in terms of ionic reactions. In an acid solution, when an H^+ ion discharges on the metal an equivalent of metal goes into solution as Fe^{++}, and free hydrogen gas collects on the metal as an adherent film. If the concentration of the hydrogen ions in the solution is very low, pH 6 to pH 9, the driving force of the ions in solution will be too slight to break through the hydrogen film, and so corrosion will stop. If oxygen and carbon dioxide are present simultaneously in solution, the oxygen will oxidize the film of gaseous hydrogen, thus removing the resistance to the discharge of more hydrogen ions. The oxygen is said to act as a depolarizer.

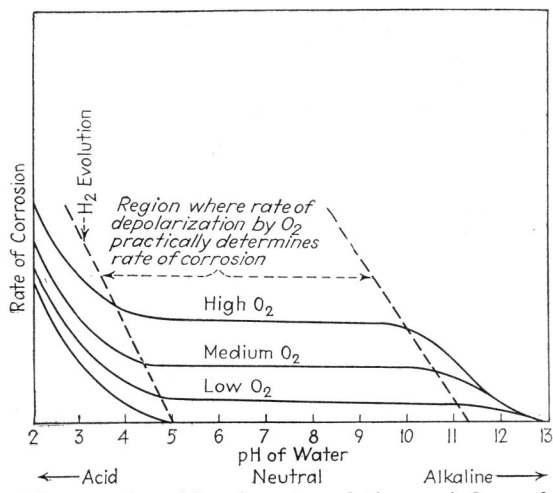

FIG. 126.—The corrosion of iron in water solutions as influenced by pH and concentration of dissolved oxygen. (*From McKay and Worthington, Corrosion Resistance of Metals and Alloys.*)

The corrosion of steel in water containing dissolved oxygen is accelerated still further if the acidity is increased. The rain of industrial cities carries appreciably higher acidity than that of the country districts due to sulfuric acid present in the coal smoke. The interdependence of acidity and oxygen concentration on corrosion is shown in Fig. 126, taken from McKay and Worthington's book. In waters more acid than pH 5, corrosion will proceed whether oxygen is present or not. Above pH 12, there will not be enough hydrogen ions to cause measurable corrosion even in presence of abundant oxygen. Between pH 5 and pH 11, the corrosion is almost proportional to the amount of oxygen in solution at the surface of the metal where it can act as a depolarizer. Water that is perfectly still will be much less corrosive than water in motion, because in the former case the layer of water next to the metal may have new oxygen conveyed to it only

Fig. 127.—Concentration cell corrosion. The stagnant film of solution, where the wires crossed, became depleted in oxygen and formed a concentration cell with local corrosion of the wires at the point where they crossed. (*From McKay and Worthington.*)

slowly by diffusion, whereas if the water is in motion, the film next to the metal is being constantly replaced by water containing new supplies of oxygen.

Corrosion of Iron Due to Concentration Cells. (Solution Cells).—This type of corrosion is due to unequal distribution of chemical reagents within a single solution. Copper is insoluble in dilute hydrochloric acid, but if one part of a solution containing a piece of copper is aerated so that there is a local concentration of dissolved oxygen, the copper will be corroded locally. If a spot of iron rust is formed on a sheet of iron, the gaseous oxygen in the layer of rust next to the metal becomes exhausted because the incoming oxygen must diffuse through the rust already formed. The edges of the film of rust are richer in oxygen, and if moisture is present, a concentration cell is established which accelerates the corrosion under the thicker part of the rust spot. This action becomes more pronounced as the spot of rust becomes thicker, and so a pit forms under the rust which extends and deepens indefinitely so long as moisture and air are present. The puzzling local corrosion of iron pipes in contact with cinders or soil may sometimes be direct chemical corrosion or at least accelerated by chemical agents, but is often due mainly to some form of oxygen concentration cell.

Fig. 128.—Corrosion of a screen wire caused by a seam within the wire. The solution filling this seam was stagnant and became depleted in oxygen. *a*, a screen wire in which corrosion is caused by a seam fails completely while adjacent wires are relatively unattacked; *b*, section through corroded wire in *a* showing the defects which caused corrosion. ×150. (*From McKay and Worthington.*)

The wires crossing each other in the screen shown in Fig. 127 were of the same composition but corroded irregularly because of a concentration-cell effect. The film of water between the wires where they crossed was stagnant and became depleted in oxygen. Each junction therefore became anodic and was corroded more rapidly than the portions of the wire exposed freely to the corroding solution. The corrosion of the screen wire of Fig. 128 was due to a seam shown on an enlarged scale on the same figure. The solution filling this seam was stagnant and deficient in oxygen, and so the metal surface next to the seam was corroded.

Protective Films.—In the case of iron rust which has just been cited, the coating of rust caused an acceleration of corrosion, partly because of its thickness which permitted local differences in the concentration of the oxygen at the surface of the metal. If iron is heated in steam or air at controlled temperatures somewhat below a red heat, a thin blue film of oxide is formed which is quire resistant to corrosion. A film of this sort may be formed as one of the incidents of heat-treatment of steel. Its protective action is due, at least in part, to its thinness which prevents concentration cells from forming. Some experiments have indicated that the thinner the film, the more effective it is. The great financial loss through corrosion of steel would be largely prevented if iron rust formed a protective film. Metal that has been exposed to the weather, as is the case with steel bridges, must be carefully cleaned, preferably with a sand blast, before a new coat of paint is applied because no paint is impervious to moisture, and if paint is applied over a rusted metal surface, corrosion will continue beneath the paint film. Some metal oxides form protective coatings, but iron rust is not one of them. Other metals, notably chromium and, to a lesser extent, aluminum and magnesium are more resistant to atmospheric corrosion because of thin protective films that are formed on exposure to water and air.

The heat evolved when metals react with oxygen to form oxides is one factor that measures the tendency of a metal to corrode through oxidation. The values for the heat of formation of the oxides given in Table 8 show that gold would not corrode in air at room temperature because the heat of formation of its oxide is negative, that copper would have a slight tendency, iron a stronger tendency, and aluminum and magnesium a very strong tendency to oxidize in presence of air. This tendency actually exists but is masked by the fact that both aluminum and magnesium form a very thin protective film of oxide.

Galvanic or Two-metal Corrosion.—If two pieces of pure iron should be immersed in a dilute salt solution that is saturated with air, they would not corrode much faster because of the NaCl in solution. If one of the two pieces of iron was connected to the positive and the other to the negative pole of a battery giving a very low electromotive force—less than 1 volt—and there was no dissolved oxygen in the solution, current would flow momentarily, causing chlorine (and hydroxyl) ions to migrate to the piece of iron that was the anode and sodium (and hydrogen) ions to the piece that formed the cathode. The current would flow only momentarily because the low voltage of the battery would be too small to overcome the backward force of polarization exerted by the products deposited on the electrodes. If, however, this solution was open to the air, the dissolved oxygen would act as a chemical depolarizer to remove the hydrogen film from the cathode, so that the current would flow continuously and the iron at the anode would go into solution continuously, even though the electromotive force of the battery was extremely weak. If there was only one piece of iron in the solution and the two terminals of the battery were connected to this one piece of metal, there would be local corrosion at the area that was connected to the negative pole of the battery.

The source of the electric current need not be located in a separate battery but may be generated by a primary cell formed within the corroding solution. The Italian scientist Galvani discovered that an electric current could be generated in a solution by the contact of two dissimilar metals, and this effect was later named "galvanism" in his honor. In a galvanic circuit, one of the metals acts as a cathode on which the hydrogen ions discharge and which thereby becomes protected. The oxidation of the hydrogen ions causes metal ions to go into solution from the anode. If a piece of zinc and a piece of iron should be placed in contact in a dish of water exposed to the air, there would be a feeble galvanic action established which would cause the zinc to corrode more rapidly than if the iron were not present. If a piece of tin and a piece of iron were placed in contact in a similar solution, it would be the iron that would be corroded. The electrical conductivity of pure water saturated with air is small compared with the conductivity of a dilute salt solution. The greater corrosive power of sea water which contains about

4 per cent of salts, principally NaCl, is largely due to its greater electrical conductivity which accelerates galvanic corrosion and also the action of concentration cells.

Relative Resistance of Metals to Galvanic Corrosion.—The energy evolved through the formation of oxides has been mentioned as a measure of the tendency of a metal to corrode under oxidizing conditions. A comparison of minimum electromotive forces required to deposit a metal coating from a normal solution of its salt permits the formation of an electrochemical series which ranks the metals in much the same order as that of the heats of formation of oxides. This is natural since both tables are based on the changes in energy. Corrosion is, however, too complex a phenomenon to be classified according to a single function. McKay and Worthington[1] have compiled a table that they have developed as a result of extensive experimental work, which lists some of the more common metals and alloys in the order of resistance to corrosion. They believe this table to be accurate for metals exposed to many common dilute water solutions, such as sea water, and dilute acids and alkalies. Their list which is reproduced as Table 43 divides the metals and alloys into minor subgroups according to the galvanic action that they exert on

TABLE 43.—THE GALVANIC SERIES OF METALS AND ALLOYS*

This series arranges the metals according to their tendency to corrode galvanically and has some analogies to the electrochemical series. It is however based upon actual experience with corrosion and laboratory measurements. Metals grouped together have no strong tendency to produce galvanic corrosion on each other. When two metals distant on the list are connected, it is the metal that stands higher on the list which becomes anodic and is corroded. The first member in each group is the most readily corroded.

    Corroded end. Anodic.
    Magnesium, aluminum, duralumin
    Zinc, cadmium
    Iron, chromium-iron (active), chromium-nickel-iron (active)
    Soft solder, tin, lead
    Nickel, brasses, bronzes, nickel-copper alloys, copper
    Chromium-iron (passive), chromium-nickel-iron (passive)
    Silver solder
    Silver, gold, platinum
    Protected end. Cathodic.

* McKay and Worthington, Corrosion Resistance of Metals and Alloys, p. 33.

[1] Corrosion Resistance of Metals and Alloys.

each other when put into contact in a water solution. The members of one subgroup will exert relatively little action on the other members of that group but will cause a more powerful galvanic effect if in contact with metals more remote in the table. If a screen should be woven with nickel wires running in one direction and copper wires in the other, the galvanic action would be so weak that there would be little corrosion where the wires crossed, when this screen was immersed in salt solution or dilute acids. If the wires were of copper and iron, the iron wire would be badly corroded at the contacts. If tin and iron wires were used, the iron would be corroded, but if zinc and iron wires were crossed, it would be the zinc that would corrode. Attempts have been made to protect steel boilers from corrosion by placing slabs of zinc in various places below the water line and connecting these slabs to the tubes and other steel parts of the boiler by metal conductors. The zinc will protect the steel at a small distance from the point of contact of the two metals, but not at the distances involved in any ordinary distribution of zinc plates in a boiler.

Lack of Homogeneity as a Cause of Corrosion of Metals.—In discussing the manufacture of bessemer steel, it was stated that the ferromanganese or spiegel added in the ladle to cause deoxidation had only a few moments in which to react, and that bessemer steel was therefore less homogeneous than open-hearth steel which could be held a longer time to permit complete deoxidation. A local spot high in manganese or high in dissolved oxides on the surface of a steel sheet exposed to the weather will form one element of a galvanic cell which will induce local corrosion.

The additive effect of various agents is shown in Fig. 129, taken from McKay and Worthington's work. They explain that the original pitting was due to slight surface irregularities or floating particles from the solution and that pitting continued due to the adhering corrosion product, which probably acted to form concentration cells.

An interesting illustration of the variation in corrosion of steel after various heat-treatments is given in Fig. 130 from Speller. The dispersion of the carbides in troostite gives the condition most favorable to rapid corrosion. The finer dispersion of martensite gives greater resistance to corrosion, as does also the coarser aggregation of carbides found in sorbite and pearlite.

CORROSION OF METALS AND PROTECTION 301

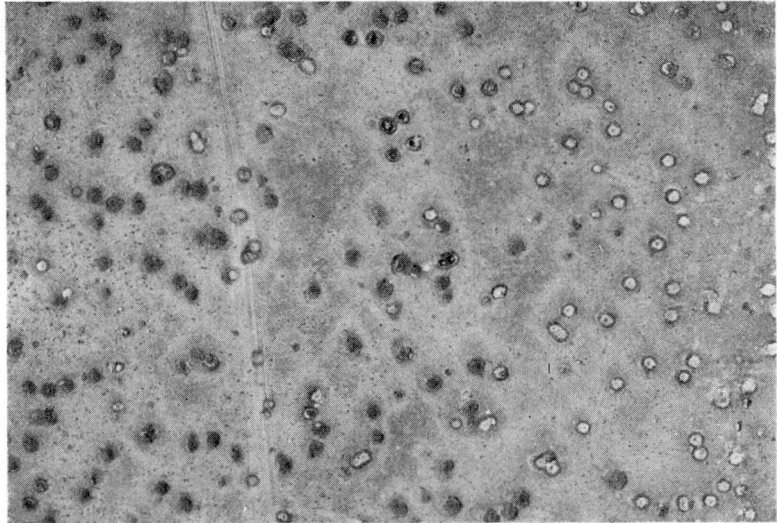

Fig. 129.—Pitting corrosion. The commercially homogeneous surface of this alloy sheet was pitted due to slight surface inequalities or floating particles from the solution. Pitting continued due to the adhering corrosion product. (*From McKay and Worthington.*)

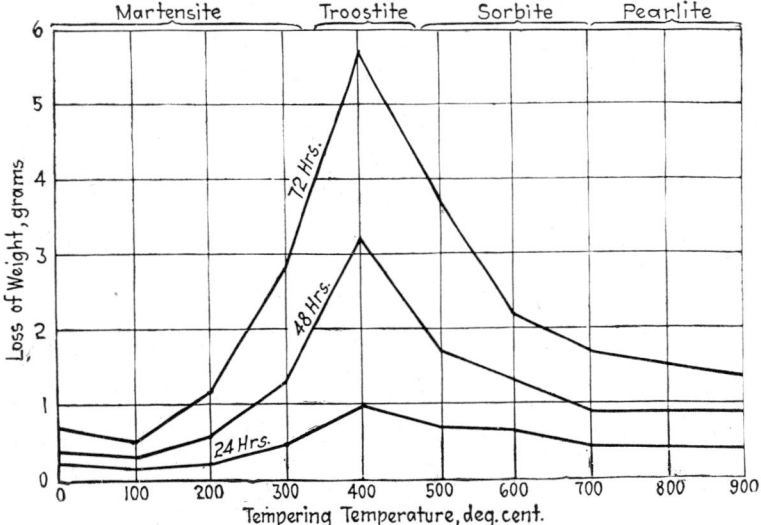

Fig. 130.—Influence of distribution of the carbides on the solubility of steel in 1 per cent sulfuric acid. (*From Speller, Corrosion Causes and Prevention.*)

The greater tendency to corrosion that Duralumin shows over aluminum may be laid to the separation of the $CuAl_2$ particles during the age-hardening process. The stainless cutlery steels must be especially free from segregation and inclusions if they are to be really stainless.

Strains as a Cause of Corrosion. Corrosion Fatigue. Season Cracking.—A piece of metal such as a rotating shaft is subject to alternating stresses as it revolves, and the resulting strains are greatest at the circumference of the shaft. The surface layers are therefore subject to the greatest strain and also to corrosive influences. A small pit due to corrosion of the surface may develop into a crack due to the alternate stresses and give rise to the phenomenon sometimes known as "corrosion fatigue." Metal that has been cold-worked is more apt to corrode than unstrained metal.

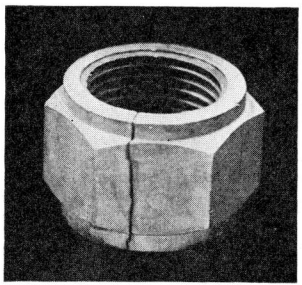

FIG. 131.—Season crack in a cold-worked brass fitting which had been exposed to ammonia fumes. Composition: copper 60, zinc 40. (*Courtesy Professor C. Upthegrove.*)

In the manufacture of cartridge cases, disks of brass are deformed cold in successive operations with occasional annealing operations to remove the effects of cold work. It is necessary that the brass be left somewhat hard after the last drawing operation so that it will spring back to its original diameter after firing and so be loose enough to be removed from the gun easily. Cartridge cases occasionally develop "season cracks," due to a combination of surface corrosion and internal strains due to cold work.

The cracked brass fitting reproduced in Fig. 131 had been machined from a rod 60-40 brass which had been extruded hot and then drawn cold. It was used in the piping of a refrigeration machine where it was exposed to the fumes of ammonia. The combination of strains due to the cold work, together with the slightly corrosive effect of the ammonia, caused the crack to develop while the fitting was in service.

The combined effect of corrosion and alternating stress on steel sheets is shown in the microscopic cracks of Fig. 132.

Resistance of Copper Alloys. Dezincification.—It has been indicated that alloys that are not uniform in composition are apt to be corroded. It follows that pure metals, and solid solutions that are homogeneous throughout, are apt to be most resistant to corrosion. Brass with not less than 67 per cent copper consists

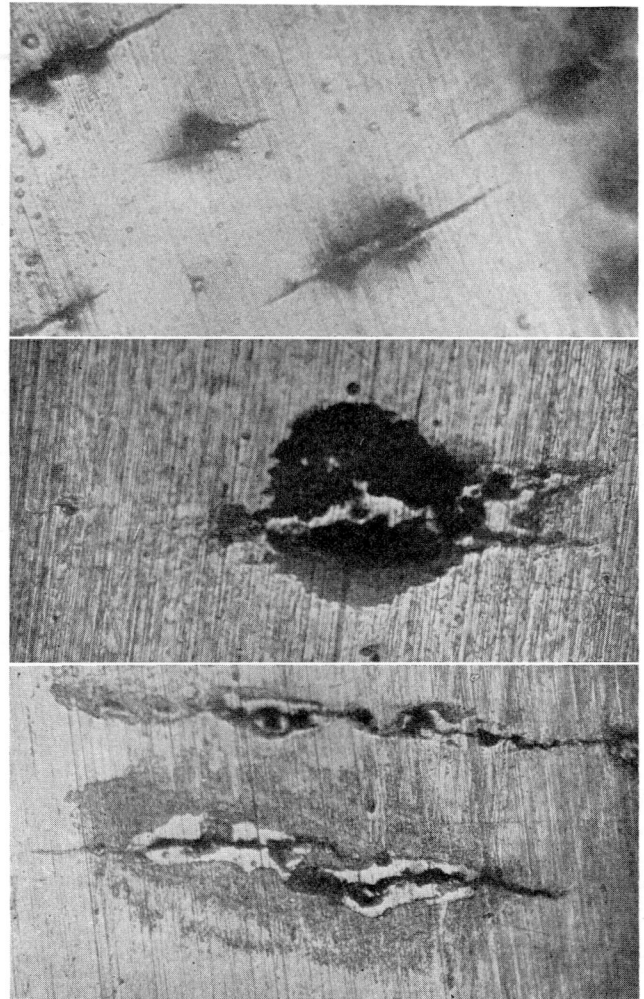

Fig. 132.—Microscopic cracks forming on steel surfaces by combined action of corrosion and alternating stress. ×100. (*From McKay and Worthington.*)

wholly of the alpha solid solution and is preferred in condenser tubes to the cheaper 60-40 brass because it is less subject to corrosion and season cracking. The beta brass, Muntz metal, or admiralty brass is subject to a form of corrosion called dezincification. This is a form of galvanic corrosion in which the beta phase dissolves, the zinc going into solution and the copper plating out on the alpha phase with the result that the metal becomes porous. This type of brass is considered unsatisfactory for service in salt water and is sometimes corroded even in fresh water.

TABLE 44.—RELATIVE CORROSION OF NICKEL-COPPER ALLOYS*

	Metal Dissolved, Mg per Sq Dm. per Day
Nickel†	10–11
Monel metal†	2– 8
70 Cu 30 Ni	5–23
Copper†	22–28

These specimens were immersed in a slow-tide stream of pure sea water for 87 days. The samples marked † showed pitting.

* From McKay and Worthington, Corrosion Resistance of Metals and Alloys, p. 396.

Copper and nickel are both quite resistant to corrosion, and as might be expected their alloys which form solid solutions in all proportions are also resistant, and sometimes more resistant than either metal. McKay and Worthington cite the results given in

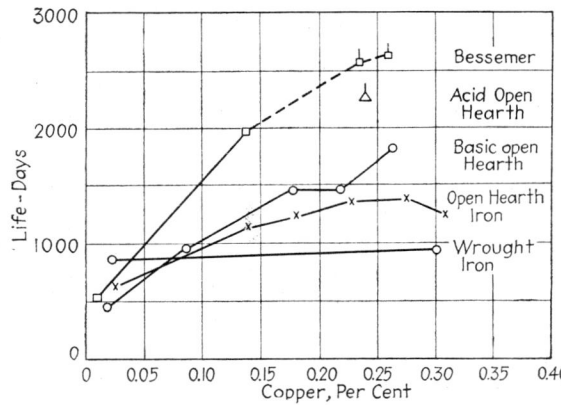

FIG. 133.—The effect of copper in reducing the corrosion of steel sheets exposed to the weather. (*From McKay and Worthington.*)

Table 44 to show the comparative resistance of Monel metal and another alloy not much different in composition.

The incorporation of one-quarter of one per cent of copper triples the life of steel sheets exposed to the atmosphere of

Pittsburgh as shown in Fig. 133. The copper is in solid solution and so may increase the resistance to corrosion, but the main effect of the copper seems to be to form a uniform hard film which is a protective coating rather than an accelerating coating like ordinary rust. When copper-bearing steel is immersed in water, its resistance to corrosion is not much greater than that of ordinary steel.

Stainless Steel.—In order to place a steel in the stainless class, the percentage of chromium must be at least 12 per cent, and preferably 25 to 30 per cent. In the chromium ferrites, the carbon should be very low, because carbon in the form of chromium carbides is apt to cause galvanic corrosion, and any chromium in combination as carbide reduces the amount that remains in solid solution. The stainless cutlery steels that do not contain nickel, but rely on the 12.0 to 15.0 per cent chromium to impart stainless properties to a steel with 0.30 to 0.40 per cent carbon, must be quenched, tempered, and carefully polished if they are to be resistant to corrosion.

Selective Solution. Intergranular Corrosion.—In preparing specimens for metallographic examination, an etching agent is chosen that will dissolve the metal at the grain boundaries at a different rate from that of the body of the grain. When metal is corroded, the solution may be selective and along grain boundaries or it may affect the whole surface fairly uniformly. When metal is tested for endurance under alternating stresses in the presence of corroding mediums, the endurance limit is frequently cut down because of intergranular corrosion. The effect is sometimes very serious because the cracks are not visible to the naked eye and failure of the metal may take place before the cracks are discovered. This type of corrosion sometimes causes failures in steam boilers, and further reference to corrosion by boiler waters will be made in the chapter dealing with water.

Protective Metal Coatings.—If steel should be coated with gold or platinum so that the coating was absolutely continuous, there could be no corrosion of the steel so long as the coating remained unbroken. If, however, a scratch was made with a file on such a surface some of the iron would have its protective coating removed and would corrode. Copper or nickel are less effective than gold as the protective coating because they are not themselves so resistant to corrosion and are reactive enough to stimulate a galvanic action at a point where the coating is imperfect. It is difficult to secure a perfectly continuous metal coating of nickel or copper by ordinary electroplating methods. In plating objects like the bumpers for automobiles, it was formerly the practice to clean the metal very carefully, give it a very thin electroplate of copper and then one of nickel, and repeat the process with another of copper and a second of nickel. Each of the plated coatings might have a few pinholes, but the chance that the pinholes in four successive coatings would coincide became very small. Such a coating will protect the steel of the bumper from corrosion so long as it remains perfect.

The lack of continuity of the older metallic films has been largely remedied by improved technique, and it is customary now to plate a single coat of nickel directly onto the steel. The protective effect is a function of the thickness of the plate. A coating of nickel or nickel plus copper with a thickness of 0.002 in. gives prolonged protection against corrosion. This is a somewhat thicker coating than is usually demanded by the automobile companies. It is customary to test the efficiency of the protective coating by the salt-spray test, in which finished specimens are exposed to a fog of salt water saturated with air, and the number of hours exposure before visible rust appears on the article is noted. In general, the efficiency of protection increases with the number of coats and their thickness. Chromium is harder and more resistant to atmospheric corrosion than nickel, but it is also more expensive. It is customary to apply it as a thin final coat over nickel plate. A thickness of 0.00002 in. of chromium over nickel adds considerably to the protection, but a thicker coat is better. Its resistance to corrosion is discussed in a separate paragraph.

Zinc and cadmium stand higher than iron in Table 43 and will therefore be more readily corroded. Zinc is the cheapest of the metals used for protective coatings, but is also the most readily corroded. It may be applied by an electroplating process but is more usually applied by dipping the metal into molten zinc. This process has for years been incorrectly called "galvanizing," and galvanized iron as a trade term denotes sheets of mild steel that have been coated with zinc by passing through a bath of molten zinc. The zinc dissolves to a small extent in the iron, and this thin film of alloy permits the outer coating of zinc to adhere firmly to the metal. If a scratch is made on a sheet of galvanized steel, the zinc along the edges will suffer preferential corrosion and the iron will be protected even if the zinc has been removed from a strip ⅛ in. in width. Zinc-coated steel (galvanized) is used largely for wire fences, gutters and roofs on houses, water pipes, and utensils such as tubs and buckets. Elbows, T's, and other pipe-fittings made from cast or malleable iron are protected in a similar way. Zinc is more soluble in some natural waters than in others, and water that has been standing overnight in the small pipes of a home may have dissolved enough zinc to make it advisable to flush the pipes before using the water for drinking purposes. Zinc-coated metal cannot be used to replace tin plate for cans in which fruit and vegetables are preserved because of its rather high solubility. Zinc is not a cumulative poison like lead, but it is not desirable to take much of it into the body.

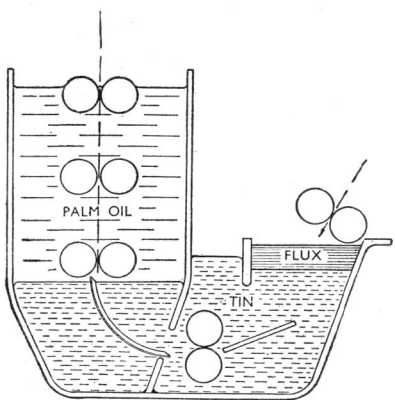

Fig. 134.—Diagrammatic sketch of machine for tinning steel sheets. (*From International Tin and Development Council Bulletin No. 4.*)

Tin Plate.—Steel sheets containing less than 0.1 per cent carbon are pickled in dilute sulfuric acid to remove the mill scale and then passed through a bath of fused zinc chloride, a bath of molten tin, and a bath of palm oil, all in one operation as indicated in Fig. 134. The molten tin is maintained at a temperature of 575 to 650°F, and the flux of zinc chloride, with sometimes ammonium chloride added to it, is heated only by the contact with the molten tin. The amount of tin picked up by the sheet will depend upon the temperature of the bath and the time of contact. The amount of tin remaining on the sheet is controlled by passing through asbestos brushes on rolls running in a tank of oil kept at a temperature of 460 to 465°F or only 10 to 15° above the melting point of tin. The best oil is palm oil which is pressed from the fruit of the palm tree. Hydrogenated cottonseed oil similar to the Crisco used in the household kitchens may also be used. The tin plates after leaving the grease pot are cleaned of excess of oil and polished with bran. A standard grade of tin plate will have 0.7 lb of tin applied to 100 sq ft of steel sheet.

Tin is not corroded by fruit juices or the vegetables that are customarily used for food, and so tin cans are widely used in the food industry. If the coating is imperfect, corrosion of the steel will be accelerated by galvanic action as shown in Table 43. When tin plate is to be used for structural purposes like roofs or gutters, an alloy of 12 to 25 parts of tin to 88 to 75 parts of lead is frequently used. This is called "terne plate." It is cheaper and more resistant to the weather than a coating of pure tin.

Protective Coatings of Inorganic Salts.—It has been mentioned that thin films of oxides afford protection against corrosion if they are continuous. Almost all of the common metals form better protecting films when exposed to the weather than iron. Aluminum and magnesium form the most striking examples, because they should be the most readily corroded of all of the metals and alloys listed in Table 43, and yet they resist atmospheric corrosion much better than iron. Tin, nickel, and copper do not have as high a tendency to corrode as iron and also form thin protective films. The red color of copper changes slowly in the air to a greenish black, and the bronzes and brasses weather to a greenish tinge. Freshly cut lead has a bright surface but it quickly forms a gray-black film.

Artificial protective coatings of oxides are sometimes applied. Steel may be "blued" by heating articles in steam or air at temperatures somewhat below a red heat. The formation of the blue film in tempering has been mentioned. The method has been widely used on rifle barrels and also on razor blades. Copper may also have an artificial film produced by heat-treatment which may vary in color from a dull red to a blue. It has been used to produce ornamental effects on copper shingles. An oxidized coating has been produced on aluminum which will adsorb organic dyes strongly and produce a brightly colored finish which is fairly permanent. Aluminum that has been protected in this manner is sometimes referred to as "anodized aluminum."

Artificial coatings of phosphates may be produced upon steel by immersing articles in hot dilute solutions of phosphoric acid or acid salts of phosphates. This coating is not itself extremely resistant to the weather but is helpful in improving the bond between varnishes and enamels and steel. During the World War, the United States Navy protected its submarine mines by a phosphate coating over which asphalt was applied. The production of a thin phosphate coating as a base for the later application of enamels or lacquers is known in the automobile trade as "bonderizing."

Effect of Acidity and Alkalinity on Corrosion.—The realization of the importance of films in preventing or accelerating corrosion permits a clearer understanding of the effects of acids and alkalies. An increase in alkalinity, which involves a decrease in the number of hydrogen ions, tends usually to promote the stability of oxide films. The effect of acidity of water on the rate of corrosion of iron is shown graphically in Fig. 126, to which reference has already been made. If oxygen is entirely absent, the water may have an acidity as great as pH 5 without causing corrosion, because the hydrogen film on the metal remains intact. Oxygen causes depolarization of this hydrogen film, and when oxygen is present there will be corrosion throughout the range of pH 4 to pH 11 to an extent depending mainly on the amount of oxygen present. When the pH becomes greater than 11, the number of hydrogen ions is very small and the number of hydroxyl ions is large enough to stabilize an oxide film and stop corrosion. Steel that is imbedded in concrete is protected from corrosion by the alkalinity of the products formed when cement reacts with water. If the concrete cracks or changes chemically through aging, the protection disappears. This will be discussed in the chapter on concrete.

The behavior of zinc in dilute acids and alkalies is shown in Fig. 135, also taken from McKay and Worthington. Zinc reacts more energetically than iron in acid solution, and its protective film is not stable with a higher acidity than pH 6. The metal is corroded least at a pH of 10, but at a pH of 12 the oxide film commences to dissolve in the alkaline solution and corrosion proceeds rapidly. Lead resists sulfuric acid, even when quite hot and concentrated, because a resistant film of lead sulfate is formed. But lead may not be imbedded in lime plaster or concrete because, like zinc, its oxide film is not stable in alkaline solution.

Substances may be present in the corroding solution that will attach themselves to a metal surface and form a protective film.

Oxidizing agents such as chromates help to stabilize the oxide film. Some coal-tar derivatives will hinder the corrosion of steel even in rather strong acids by forming a protective film on the metal. Steel sheets that are to be tinned or galvanized must have the mill scale removed by pickling in hot sulfuric acid containing 2 to 15 per cent H_2SO_4. A chemical inhibitor added to the acid protects the metal but permits the scale to be dissolved. The yield of petroleum and natural gas may often be increased by

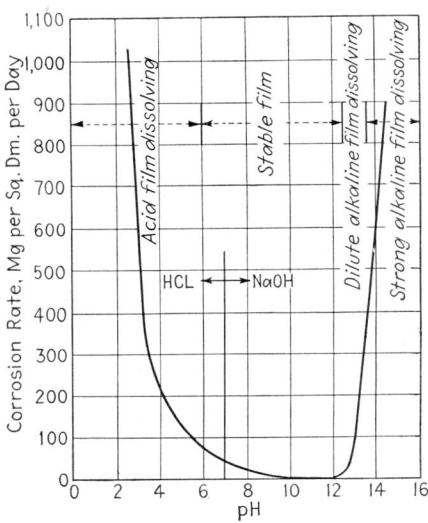

FIG. 135.—Effect of pH value on corrosion of zinc. (*From McKay and Worthington.*)

pumping acid solutions under high pressure into the rock at the bottom of the well. This only became commercially feasible after an effective inhibitor was developed that would protect the steel casing of the well from corrosion by the acid pumped down to dissolve the rock.

Chromium in the Active and Passive States.—Metals on whose surface a resistant film of oxide has formed do not corrode rapidly in acids until that film has been broken down. They are said to be in a "passive state." If the corroding agents contain oxygen, the passive state may persist and the metal continue strongly resistant to corrosion. Chromium is resistant to corrosive conditions in the presence of air whether the chromium is applied as a thin film of pure chromium or is incorporated in sufficient amount into an alloy of the stainless-steel type. The chromium irons and the stainless steels are listed in Table 43 as more resistant to corrosion than the nickel-copper alloys when the chromium is in the passive condition, but less resistant than the nickel-copper alloys and than lead and tin when the chromium is in the active state. Brine solutions may cause pitting of stainless steel under one set of conditions and be inert under slightly different circumstances. The line between the sets of conditions is sometimes difficult to trace.

Corrosion at High Temperatures.—The types of corrosion that have been discussed have all involved the hydrogen ion. At

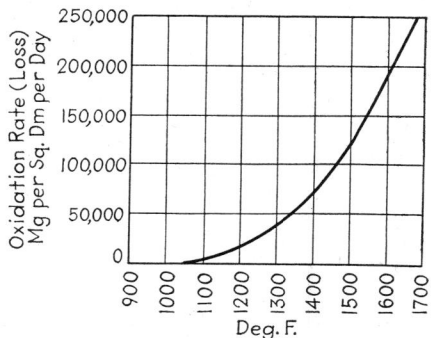

FIG. 136.—Rate of oxidation of steel in air at high temperatures. (*From McKay and Worthington.*)

temperatures above 212°F where the corroding agents are all in the gas phase, there must be a different mechanism. Almost all metals undergo oxidation when heated to redness in air, and the rate increases rapidly with temperature as shown by the curve of Fig. 136. Ordinary steel and iron commence to suffer progressive oxidation and scaling at temperatures of 1000 to 1200°F. Alloys with 5 per cent chromium and 1.0 to 1.5 per cent silicon may be used for a long time at 1500°F without serious oxidation. The addition of 0.5 per cent aluminum to a 5 per cent chromium alloy permits its use up to 1750°F. Alloys with 14 per cent of chromium and also the 18-8 stainless steels do not scale much below 1500°F. Alloys of nickel and chromium containing 15-20 chromium and 60-80 nickel may be used for considerable periods at 2000 to 2200°F.

Gases containing sulfur as SO_2 or H_2S are especially corrosive and are more harmful to nickel than to chromium.

Organic Chemical Compounds as Protective Coatings.—Coatings such as paint, varnish, lacquer, asphalt, and synthetic resins are produced by compounding materials of complicated chemical structure which are made up mainly of carbon, hydrogen, and oxygen and which do not often contain metals in the free form. They act as protective coatings through their water-repellent nature. Few of them are able wholly to prevent the penetration of water to the metal, but they do offer a resistance to its passage and limit the amount that reaches the metallic surface. They also offer a high resistance to the passage of galvanic and electrical currents and so tend to prevent solution concentration cells and galvanic corrosion. They will be discussed somewhat more fully in a later chapter.

References

McKay and Worthington: Corrosion Resistance of Metals and Alloys, Reinhold Publishing Corporation, New York, 1936.

Speller, F. N.: Corrosion: Causes and Prevention, McGraw-Hill Book Company, Inc., New York, 1935.

Rawdon, H. S.: Protective Metallic Coatings, Reinhold Publishing Corporation, New York, 1928.

Blum and Hogaboom: Principles of Electroplating and Electroforming, 2d ed., McGraw-Hill Book Company, Inc., New York, 1930.

CHAPTER XVII

ROCKS AND THEIR DECOMPOSITION PRODUCTS. CLAY PRODUCTS

Composition of the Earth.—The ground upon which we walk is composed in part of partially decomposed vegetable and animal matter but is made up mainly of a mixture of mineral substances consisting either of fragments of rocks or of products that have been formed from the rocks by the action of water and the air.

In its earlier geological history, our planet was very hot, and due to its rotating motion, the heavier substances like metallic iron found their way to the center of the mass while the lighter materials such as the oxides worked their way to the surface. Dr. H. S. Washington of the Geophysical Laboratory of the Carnegie Institute has compiled data as to the varying composition of the earth from the center to the surface.[1] The illustration of Fig. 137 taken from his paper shows that the central core of the earth with a radius of about 2100 miles is composed mainly of an iron-nickel alloy and that silicate rocks are found in increasing amount as the surface is approached. The deeper layers of silicate rocks are composed of the basic silicates of lime, magnesium, and iron, and it is only the surface layer, about 12 miles thick, that carries rocks high in silica and containing alkalies of which feldspar is a prominent example. The typical rocks of this outer layer are granites.

These zones are not of uniform composition or thickness, and intrusions of material that normally belongs in a deeper layer are occasionally found in an outer layer. Many of our ore deposits owe their formation to such intrusions, although the deposits as they appear today have usually been much altered by secondary changes.

The Outer Crust of the Earth.—The outer granitic zone whose thickness varies from 8 to 12 miles is the only portion of the earth with which man can come in contact. The composition of these

[1] The Chemical Composition of the Earth, *Am. Jour. Sci.*, **209**, 351 (1925).

rocks has been summarized by F. W. Clarke[1] of the U. S. Geological Survey. The most plentiful element in the igneous rocks is oxygen (46.5 per cent) with silicon next (27.6 per cent), then

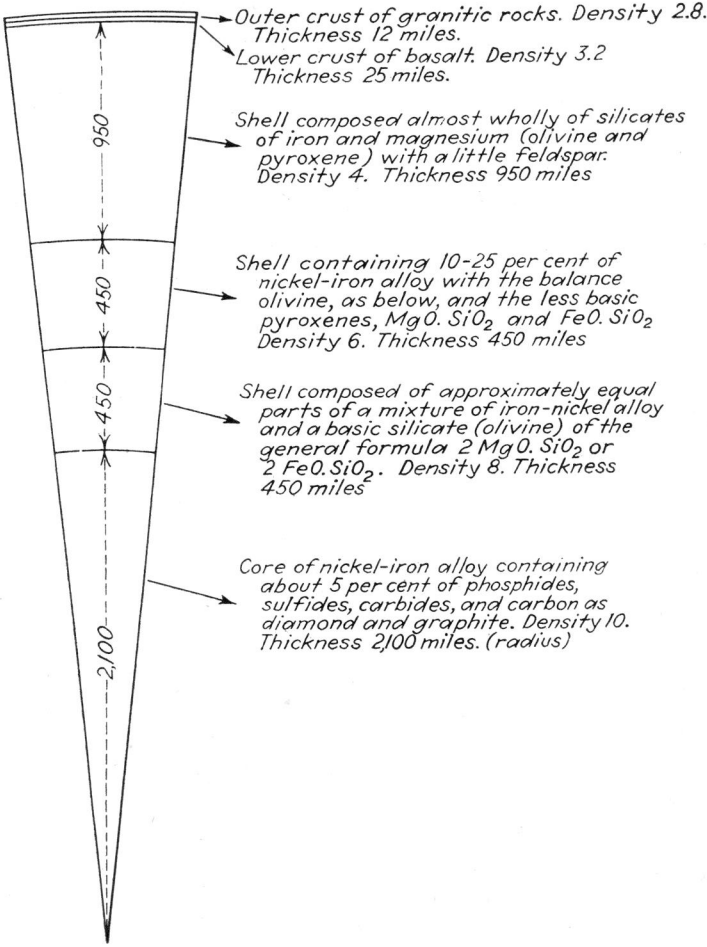

Fig. 137.—The chemical composition of the earth. [*From H. S. Washington, Am. J. Sci.*, **209**, 351 (1925).]

aluminum (8.1), iron (5.1), calcium (3.6), sodium (2.8), potassium (2.6), and magnesium (2.1). These are the eight elements that

[1] The Data of Geochemistry, *U. S. Geol. Survey*, Bull. 776, 5th ed., 1924.

are present to the extent of more than 1 per cent. Together they account for 98.2 per cent of all of the material in the igneous rocks of the crust of the earth. The abundance of oxygen indicates that almost all of the elements will be combined with it as oxides. The oxides present in the largest amount will be SiO_2, Al_2O_3, Fe_2O_3, and FeO, MgO, CaO, Na_2O, and K_2O. Their relative amounts and also the amounts of some of the minor constituents of the outer crust are given in Table 45 compiled from Clarke's data.

TABLE 45.—AVERAGE COMPOSITION OF IGNEOUS ROCKS*

Name of compound	Chemical formula	Percentage
Silica	SiO_2	59.14
Alumina	Al_2O_3	15.34
Iron oxide (ferric)	Fe_2O_3	3.08
Iron oxide (ferrous)	FeO	3.80
Magnesia	MgO	3.49
Lime	CaO	5.08
Sodium oxide	Na_2O	3.84
Potassium oxide	K_2O	3.13
Water	H_2O	1.15
Titanium oxide	TiO_2	1.05
Phosphoric anhydride	P_2O_5	0.299
Manganese oxide	MnO	0.124
Carbon dioxide	CO_2	0.101
Chromium oxide	Cr_2O_3	0.055
Sulfur	S	0.052
Minor compounds	.....	0.269
		100.000

* From CLARKE, F. W., Data of Geochemistry, 5th ed., p. 29.

The solid crust of the earth is relatively thin and rests upon a viscous molten magma. In some places this molten magma has forced its way up through joints and cracks in the outer crust and flowed out as lava, which upon cooling has formed the volcanic igneous rocks. If the lava cooled quickly, a glassy mass often resulted. Basalt or traprock is an example of a lava that cooled rather quickly to a stone which is finely crystalline. Granite is typical of a lava that has cooled extremely slowly and so has formed large crystals. The slow cooling can have taken place only under a protective coating of surface rocks which have been removed later by erosion in those places where the granites now appear as surface rocks.

When the magma was in the molten state and under pressure, it contained steam and dissolved gases. When the pressure was released, as during a volcanic eruption, the expanding gases blew out fragments of lava ranging in size from masses of several pounds to particles of dust so fine that they were carried into the stratosphere and did not fall back to earth for several years. The lava which flowed as a stream from the volcano frequently contained gas bubbles which resulted in a porous rock.

TABLE 46.—COMMON MINERALS IN IGNEOUS ROCKS*

Name of mineral	Average percentage	Chemical composition
Quartz	12.0	Pure SiO_2
Feldspars	59.5	A family of minerals, silicates of alumina with potash, soda, or lime. The common forms are: Orthoclase, $K_2O.Al_2O_3.6SiO_2$ Albite, $Na_2O.Al_2O_3.6SiO_2$ Anorthite, $CaO.Al_2O_3.2SiO_2$
Hornblendes and pyroxenes	16.8	Complex silicates of CaO, MgO, and FeO with one molecule of the base RO to one molecule of SiO_2
Mica	3.8	Complex silicates of Al_2O_3 with K_2O and H_2O, MgO, FeO and Li_2O. Biotite has the formula $(K,H)_2O.2(Mg,Fe)O.Al_2O_3.SiO_2$
Minor minerals	7.9	
	100.0	

* Adapted from Clarke, F. W., Data of Geochemistry, 5th ed., p. 423.

Under other circumstances, the steam may have condensed to liquid water far below the surface of the ground, and made its way to the surface carrying in solution mineral constituents from the lower levels and depositing them as the temperature dropped or as the soluble constituents interacted with some of the rocks nearer the surface. Many ore deposits have been formed in this manner.

Minerals in Igneous Rocks.—The minerals in the granite rocks forming the outer crust of the earth consist of feldspars, hornblendes, pyroxenes, quartz, and micas which together form 92.1 per cent of the minerals of unaltered igneous rocks. Table 46 adapted from Clarke's Data of Geochemistry gives the proportion and a brief statement of the composition of these minerals. Mica splits readily into thin flakes, but the flakes themselves are resistant to further disintegration. Ignorant prospectors for gold are sometimes deceived by the glittering flakes of yellow mica which are occasionally found in sands.

Properties of Granites.—Granites are igneous rocks composed of the three constituents quartz, feldspar, and mica that are present as crystals which are usually large enough to be plainly visible to the naked eye. They are hard, and therefore it is costly to cut and polish granites for use as building stones. They are strong with a compressive strength of 15,000 to 30,000 psi. They absorb very little water and resist weathering so well that some of the advertisements speak of granite as "the stone eternal." The colors vary from gray to brown, and the more finely crystalline varieties take a high polish. These qualities make granite a favored material for tombstones and for monumental buildings that are intended to suggest stability and permanence, such as banks and public buildings. The strength and durability of granite also make it desirable in the form of large blocks for the facing of canal locks and the construction of sea walls. In the days of horse-drawn vehicles, granite blocks a little larger than common brick were much used for paving streets where there was heavy trucking. Modern buildings constructed of steel or reinforced concrete do not need granite for its strength, and it is not used to the extent it once was as a building material. Granite does not resist fire well. The three minerals of which it is composed have different coefficients of thermal expansion, and the stone cracks and spalls badly, especially if cold water is thrown upon it while it is hot.

Traprock or Basalt.—The igneous rocks that have considerably less silica than the granites show as their dominant crystalline constituents feldspars and pyroxenes with little or no quartz. They are usually fine-grained gray or black stones which lack the beauty of the granites and so are not much used for building stones. Their fine-grained structure does make them tough and well adapted for paving blocks. After crushing, they make good material for unpaved highways, for railroad ballast, and for aggregates in concrete.

Weathering of Rocks.—All rocks become disintegrated, some more and some less rapidly, on exposure to the weather. Variations in temperature cause differential expansion and contraction of the different minerals composing the rock and ultimately disintegrate the surface. Such a physical process is the major cause of weathering in arid regions and also in the regions where continuous cold prevails. The ultimate product is a rock flour whose composition is the same as that of the parent rock.

The processes of weathering in which liquid water plays a part are much more important.

Water will dissolve small amounts of the minerals of rocks just as it will dissolve metals and all other materials with which it comes in contact. Rain, with its carbon dioxide and oxygen content, not only dissolves but changes the composition of the minerals. The changes are slow but, when continued during geological periods measured in millions of years, are sufficient to disintegrate and wear away whole mountain ranges. The corroding effect of water increases with the extent of surface of the rock that is exposed to its action. When the sun shines directly on a rock, the rapid expansion of the surface tends to cause surface cracks. If the stone is exposed to freezing temperatures when these cracks are filled with water, the expansion due to ice formation will increase the size of the cracks and may cause chips to break off. The attrition of rocks in the beds of streams or by glaciers increases the amount of fine material and hence the rate of solution and weathering.

Products of Weathering Igneous Rocks.—The first stage of the chemical weathering of silicate rocks involves hydrolysis or the decomposition of the outer surface of each mineral with the introduction of combined water into the products formed. The carbon dioxide of the air will also frequently enter into the reaction. The decomposition of the feldspar, orthoclase ($K_2O.Al_2O_3.6SiO_2$), is frequently written

$$(K_2O.Al_2O_3.6SiO_2) + CO_2 + XH_2O = K_2CO_3 +$$
Orthoclase

$$(Al_2O_3.2SiO_2.2H_2O) + 4SiO_2.XH_2O$$
Kaolinite

The potassium carbonate is very soluble and will be carried away in solution. The hydrated silica is more soluble than the mineral kaolinite and will be slowly removed by selective solution, leaving a residue richer in kaolin. The water containing silica in true or colloidal solution may deposit it as concretions of partially dehydrated silica known as chert, flint, opal, or even, when well crystallized, as secondary quartz. Other portions of this water may deposit the silica as a cement to bond particles of sand to each other to form sandstones.

The oxides of aluminum and iron also tend to go into colloidal solution and under favorable circumstances may be deposited as bauxite, a hydrated oxide of alumina, or as iron ores.

In our own temperate climate, the weathering has rarely proceeded so far and the silica has remained in combination with alumina (or iron oxide), often in hydrated compounds and in particles of colloidal size. These minute hydrated particles are recognized as the fundamental components of all clays. The distinguishing characteristic of clay is its extreme fineness, and a comparison of the dimensions of the classes of particles ranging from coarse sand through fine sand, silt, and clay is given in Table 47.

TABLE 47.—CLASSIFICATION OF SOIL CONSTITUENTS ACCORDING TO THE U. S. BUREAU OF CHEMISTRY AND SOILS

Grade	Name	Size, mm
7	Clay	0.002
6	Silt	0.002–0.050
5	Very fine sand	0.050–0.10
4	Fine sand	0.10 –0.25
3	Medium sand	0.25 –0.50
2	Coarse sand	0.50 –1.0
1	Fine gravel or very coarse sand	1.0 –2.0

No commercial clay consists wholly of the very fine particles which, according to the table, must be less than 0.002 mm in size (0.00008 in.). The analyses of Table 48 show that some materials rated as clays may contain as little as 22 per cent of this very fine clay substance.

Silicates of the hornblende or pyroxene type that do not contain alkalies but do contain lime, magnesia, and iron oxide will yield a

TABLE 48.—MECHANICAL ANALYSIS AND TENSILE STRENGTH OF SOME NEW JERSEY CLAYS*

Designation	1	2	3	4	5
Mechanical analysis, per cent:					
Clay substance	59.00	44.00	22.00	30.64	87.96
Fine silt	11.00	7.11	5.66	14.21	6.95
Silt and fine sand	14.70	24.35	26.55	5.58	3.00
Medium sand	3.50	7.80	11.45	6.40	1.00
Sand	11.40	16.35	33.44	42.95	
Total	99.60	99.61	99.10	99.79	98.91
Water for maximum plasticity	32.1	20.5	25.2	.....	39.1
Air shrinkage, per cent	8.6	5.0	10.0	.....	5.0
Tensile strength of dried clay, psi	453	297	289	105	<20

Description of clays
  1. Very plastic, slightly gritty, dense, red-burning clay.
  2. Gritty and plastic.
  3. Gritty and plastic.
  4. Sandy, micaceous character.
  5. A soft, powdery washed ball clay. Plastic.

*RIES and KUMMEL, The Clays and Clay Industry of New Jersey, *Geol. Survey of New Jersey*, **6**, 87–88 (1904).

hydrated silicate on weathering and, in addition, calcium carbonate, magnesium carbonate, or ferrous carbonate, depending on the base in the original mineral. The mineral enstatite (MgO, SiO_2) breaks down on weathering, according to Ries and Watson,[1] to talc and magnesite, according to the equation

$$4(MgO.SiO_2) + H_2O + CO_2 = (3MgO.4SiO_2.H_2O) + MgCO_3$$
$$\text{Enstatite} \qquad\qquad\qquad\qquad \text{Talc} \qquad\qquad \text{Magnesite}$$

The $FeCO_3$ formed from rocks that contain FeO may be dissolved by water and later oxidized to $Fe(OH)_3$. The SiO_2 which is also formed in the decomposition of the rocks may be removed by solution in circulating water, leaving the iron hydroxide in a more concentrated form. The great iron-ore deposits of the Lake Superior region were probably enriched in this manner.

Limestone and Marl. Dolomite and Magnesite.—When one of the lime silicates is decomposed by weathering, the lime that it contains is converted to calcium carbonate by the carbon dioxide of the air. This $CaCO_3$ is fairly soluble

[1] Engineering Geology, p. 26.

in rain water because the CO_2 in the water forms calcium bicarbonate $Ca(HCO_3)_2$ which is considerably more soluble than $CaCO_3$. Some of the lower forms of vegetable life absorb the soluble bicarbonate and use it in building their skeletons. Coral reefs are composed of calcium carbonate and have been built up in this manner in the ocean, and marl is deposited in fresh-water lakes in a similar way. If these deposits of soft marl are, through later geological changes, subjected to high pressure, they become compacted and yield limestones and even crystalline marbles.

Magnesium carbonate may be dissolved and reprecipitated in a similar manner. Pure deposits are called "magnesite," and a limestone containing much magnesium carbonate is termed a "dolomite." Theoretically a dolomite contains one molecule of $MgCO_3$ to each molecule of $CaCO_3$.

Selective Sedimentation.—A stream in rapid motion carries sand and finer particles of mineral matter in suspension, as well as fragments of wood and vegetation. If the stream flows into a pond where its velocity becomes much less, the coarser particles of the rock and sand are the first to settle out and frequently form a gravel or sand bar. The finer particles settle later in accordance with their fineness, specific gravity, shape, and degree of hydration so that deposits of varied composition are formed through selective sedimentation. A process such as this never makes a sharp division of constituents, but occasionally sediments have been subjected to secondary erosion and a second selective sedimentation, which may give deposits of more uniform composition.

Sedimentary Rocks.—The products of the decomposition of rocks that have been deposited by water tend to arrange themselves in horizontal layers made up of particles of approximately the same size and density. The layers, or beds, may be compacted by pressure, altered by heat, and perhaps cemented together by the deposition of material carried by water percolating through the mass. The general name of "sedimentary rocks" is given to the whole group of rocks, regardless of chemical composition, that has been laid down by sedimentation. It is evident that there will be great variation in the properties, composition, and value of sedimentary rocks.

Metamorphic Rocks.—Both the igneous and sedimentary rocks may become subjected to high pressures and temperatures during the mountain-building processes in the earth's crust. The chemical composition of the rocks is not changed, and the most apparent results of the alteration in structure, called "metamorphism," are the development of crystallinity and the arrangement of minerals in pseudo layers. Granites become gneisses, basalts change into schists, limestone and marls into marble, sandstone into quartzites, and shale into slate. Similar processes change soft coal into anthracite and graphite.

Durability of Building Stones.—The geologist classifies building stones according to their origin. The engineer is interested mainly in the properties of a stone that make it useful for his purposes, and the preceding brief outline of some of the processes involved in the formation and disintegration of rocks has been sketched merely to provide background for the discussion of properties. Building stones must have hardness and strength, but these properties are not the most important because, as will be seen later, the strength of masonry walls is limited by the strength of the mortar rather than by that of the stone. The most important property of a building stone is reliability and durability when exposed to its two greatest enemies, fire and frost. The harmful effect of fire is due to the changes in volume and sometimes in chemical composition caused by the high temperature of the outer layers of the stone. The harmful effect of freezing is not usually due to the low temperature, although shrinkage cracks may form through contraction in cold weather. The major damage popularly attributed to "frost" is due to the formation of ice within the surface pores, with consequent expansion and rupture of the outer layers of the stone. The combined effects of alternating high and low temperatures together with some solvent action due to rain water results in the weathering of stone which is sometimes noticeable in even a few years. This weathering action is most severe in locations where the rainfall is high and the winters are cold.

Properties of Limestone and Marble.—Limestone is, when pure, composed entirely of calcium carbonate ($CaCO_3$), but it frequently contains magnesium carbonate ($MgCO_3$), and it may also contain varying amounts of silica and clay. The names "marl" and "chalk" are given to soft varieties not adapted for building stone but usable as raw materials for portland cement. When limestone has become dense and crystalline through the action of heat and pressure during past geologic periods, it is called "marble." In order that limestone may be of commercial value as a building stone, it must have a compressive strength of 5,000 to 10,000 psi. There are many deposits of limestone which will satisfy this requirement but not so many which are uniform in color and structure and have good resistance to weathering. Tests to determine water absorption have some value in estimating resistance to weathering, and a series of alternate freezing and thawing tests has greater value. It must be remembered, however, that the quality of stone will vary from one part of a quarry to another and that careful inspection at the quarry is necessary if a uniform product is to be obtained.

Limestone can be sawed readily and is much used for dimension stone in building operations. Marble will take a polish, but ordinary limestone is not dense enough. Both marble and limestone are corroded by the atmosphere, especially in cities where the rain carries sulfuric acid from coal smoke. This corrosion is sufficient to dull the polish on marble but not enough to wear away a good limestone appreciably in a generation. Limestone is porous enough to absorb some rain water which drags particles of soot into the pores of the stone. A limestone building that when new was almost white may in 20 years become almost black. The most effective way to restore the fresh appearance to the stone is to cut off the outer surface with a sandblast. Some quarries yield a limestone that contains a small amount of petroleum, enough to make the surface water repellent. The beautiful Mellon Institute building in Pittsburgh is built from such a limestone, and its builders hope that the soot will not stick to it. Buildings that have been cleaned by sand-blasting are sometimes treated with paraffin to make the new surface water repellent.

Sandstones.—When igneous rocks are decomposed by weathering, the quartz crystals are among the most resistant constituents, and since they are also hard, they survive the abrasion due to stream transportation and form the largest constituent of our sands. Beds of sand cannot be consolidated to rock by pressure alone, and the formation of sandstones requires some bonding agent to be present in water percolating through the beds. Water containing calcium bicarbonate may deposit calcium carbonate as a cementing medium. Water containing silica may percolate through a sand bed and evaporate, depositing silica as a bonding agent. If the sand contains some clay, the clay may serve as a bonding agent.

Sandstones may therefore differ widely in composition and properties. The sandstones of commerce must be homogeneous, fine grained, and dense. The crushing strength of acceptable sandstones may vary from 4,000 to 12,000 psi. The resistance to weathering also varies within wide limits. The silica bond gives some of the hardest and best sandstones, but these hard stones do not cut readily. The stone from some quarries splits rather readily along the bedding planes, and flagstones split in this manner were widely used for sidewalks and curbs before concrete became so generally used. Sandstone is used for building construction in the same way as limestone. Its resistance to weathering is of the same order of magnitude. Care must be exercised in using sandstone bonded with $CaCO_3$ in cities. The acid rain water dissolves the bond just as it dissolves limestone, but since the calcium carbonate bond constitutes but a small percentage by weight of the sandstone, the solution of the bond is accompanied by large disintegration of the stone.

Sandstones of uniform composition with a bond that is not too hard are used for grindstones. The quartz grains must tear out to give a fresh cutting surface before the pores have become filled up with fine particles of steel. The production of grinding wheels with synthetic abrasives and synthetic bonding agents has greatly decreased the use of the natural stones.

Shale and Slate.—When clays are compacted by pressure and moderate heat, nonplastic masses of shale may be formed. Shale disintegrates rather quickly on exposure to the weather, and so is not usable as a building stone. It is sometimes used as a raw material in the manufacture of brick and portland cement. Slates are formed from deposits of fine-grained clay that have been subjected to long-continued pressure in a single direction. Under favorable conditions, slipbands will form in such a homogeneous material and the resultant stone can be split into thin plates. The resistance of slates to the weather depends upon their density and other factors which cannot be evaluated definitely. Some roofing slates will last for 100 years, and others must be replaced in half that time.

Sand and Gravel. Crushed Stone. Importance of Graded Size of Particles.—Sand and gravel are both materials that have resisted the weathering of igneous rocks and the abrasion of streams and glaciers. They differ only in their particle size, the fine material being called "sand" and the coarser being named "gravel." The principal constituent of sand is quartz, but fragments of other stones are present. Surface deposits of both sand and gravel may contain clay and also surface soil carrying partially decomposed vegetable matter.

Only tough and weather-resistant rocks are suitable for crushing. Traprock with its fine grain, toughness, and low water absorption is excellent. Limestone and sandstone may be good or poor depending upon their physical properties. Crushed stone, gravel, and sand are all used as aggregates in concrete, and the special requirements for that purpose are discussed further in the chapter on Concrete. They are also used extensively in making gravel or macadamized roads.

The material for a good road should consist of a mixture of coarse and fine material, because such a material will pack to a mass with few voids. It is simple to visualize this by imagining a box filled with stones the size of baseballs. The empty spaces between the balls could be filled with gravel of pea size, and the spaces between the gravel could be filled with sand. Wet clay might then be flowed into the box to coat all of the surfaces and help to fill the remaining voids, the excess water being allowed to flow out of the bottom of the box. Such a mass of graded aggregates if used to form a road surface, either alone as a macadamized road or in concrete, would be much firmer and less liable to distortion under the pressures and impacts of traffic than one composed of particles of a single size.

Clay as a Bonding Agent.—In the illustration of the box full of stones of graded size coated with wet clay, the provision that the excess water should be allowed to drain off was important because wet clay is a lubricant, whereas a thin film of damp clay is a cement. One of the first requisites of highway construction is adequate drainage so that the particles composing the road surface will not be immersed in water. A small amount of a claylike substance is desirable as a cementing material in the construction of gravel roads. Some gravels and sands carry enough clay, 1 to 3 per cent, to form a cement, but others may be improved for highway purposes by the incorporation of clay. When the stone and gravel wear under traffic, some stones yield a very fine powder which acts like clay as a bonding agent.

Foundry Sands.—Mention has already been made of the use of sand for molds in the foundry. A desirable foundry sand is one that is coated with a small amount of clay which contains

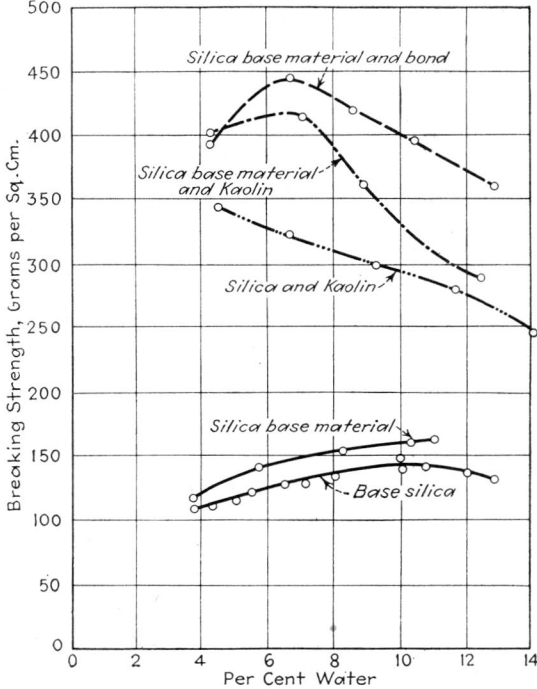

FIG. 138.—Synthesis of a molding sand showing compressive strength of various compositions. (*From G. G. Brown, Molding Sands of Michigan.*)

some colloidal iron hydroxide. The effect of these added materials has been shown by G. G. Brown[1] who started with powdered fused silica and added to it kaolin and hydrated iron oxide. The results are given in Fig. 138. The coated sand showed three times the compressive strength of the untreated base silica. It will be noted that for each sand there is an optimum amount of water that gives maximum strength. Too little water does not

[1] *State of Michigan, Geol. Survey Div., Geol. Series* 35, *Pub.* 41, p. 113, 1936.

make the clay sticky enough, and too much gives the clay somewhat the properties of a lubricant rather than a cement.

Clay as a Colloid.—It has been mentioned that kaolin ($Al_2O_3 \cdot 2SiO_2 \cdot 2H_2O$) is the typical clay substance derived from the weathering of the feldspars. It is always found associated with other decomposition products of rocks, and these may be of a varied nature. It is not possible to assign any definite chemical composition to clay, but it is characterized by physical properties that depend largely on its fineness of division. When particles of mineral matter become so small that they can no longer be seen with an ordinary microscope, they are called "colloidal particles." Their surface becomes exceedingly large in proportion to their mass, and the layer of adsorbed water on the surface also becomes very large in proportion to the mass. The small particle size and the film of adsorbed water give to suspensions of clay in water the properties of a viscous liquid.

When dry clay is moistened with the right amount of water, it becomes plastic and can be molded by the fingers into a shape such as a brick or even into a simple hollow article such as a cup. If this damp article is allowed to dry slowly, it will shrink somewhat but will retain its shape and attain considerable strength due to the adhesion of these colloidal particles to each other and to the larger particles of silt and sand in the clay.

Plasticity of Clays.—A plastic body has been previously defined as one that may be continuously deformed by a slight pressure without rupturing. It possesses no elastic limit and does not harden by cold work. If water is added slowly to a sample of clay while it is worked with the hands, the clay soon becomes damp enough to be pressed into a solid mass if considerable pressure is exerted. With more water, a condition will be reached where the clay may be worked freely without cracking but without sticking to the fingers. Somewhere in this range occurs the region of greatest plasticity, which can be determined with fair accuracy by an experienced clayworker, but may be determined more accurately by apparatus designed for the purpose. The amount of water required for maximum plasticity will vary from 10 per cent for clays with low plasticity to 50 per cent for very plastic clays. When still more water is added, the clay becomes sticky, and with further amounts of water, it becomes a viscous fluid termed a "slip."

When wet clay is dried, the reverse changes occur and a loose dry powder will finally result, provided the material was worked while it dried. In commercial operations such as the manufacture of brick or pottery, the wet clay is molded and dried quietly and slowly, so that the article will retain its shape. It will shrink in volume as the water evaporates but will become stronger, until in its air-dried condition it will have considerable strength. If air-dried clay is wetted, it will revert to the plastic condition.

The Strength of Dried Clay.—Clay is a mechanical mixture of rock fragments of various small sizes, but its characteristic property of plasticity when wet and strength when dry is due only to the finest particles that approach colloidal dimensions. The mechanical analyses and tensile strength of five New Jersey clays are given in Table 48. The amount of true clay substance ranges from 22 to 88 per cent, and at the other extreme in the scale of fineness, the amount of sand varies from nothing to 43 per cent.

The tensile strength of these clays in the dried condition was determined by adding water to maximum plasticity and forming briquettes in molds similar to those described later for portland cement. The briquettes were allowed to dry slowly in the air and were then dried in an oven at 221°F and tested in a tensile machine like that used for portland cement. The strength of the briquettes from these five clays varied from less than 20 psi for clay 5, to 453 psi for clay 1. Since the tensile strength is probably due almost entirely to the very finest particles listed as clay substance, it might be expected that the strongest clay would be the one with the most clay substance. On the contrary, clay 5 with 88 per cent of clay substance had so little strength that it could not be determined accurately and was merely reported as less than 20 psi. These fine particles with their large amount of adsorbed water made up such a large percentage of the total volume that they pulled away from each other in drying and destroyed the bond. The clay with the highest tensile strength after drying carried an intermediate amount of clay substance (59 per cent) and the smallest amount of sand (11.4 per cent). The remainder of the material was divided in particle size between silt and fine sand. This clay had a graded particle size which permitted the fine clay to exert its maximum bonding action.

Graded particle size in a clay is therefore extremely important. Clays for common brick may be used just as they come from the ground, but for pottery and other ware of high quality, clays are nearly always prepared by "washing," a process involving suspension of the clay in water, followed by sedimentation, or filtration, to remove coarse sand. Several clays are then blended to secure a mixture with the best combination of plasticity, tensile strength, and other properties of importance.

Preparation of Clay.—Clay for common brick is often used almost as it is dug, but clay for more expensive ware is often prepared very carefully. Surface clays are usually quite plastic, but the clays from deeper levels which have been compacted for centuries sometimes have little plasticity when first mined. The plasticity increases if the clays are stored damp. A mixture of clays prepared for porcelain manufacture had its dry transverse strength increased from 140 to 268 psi by aging in the damp condition.[1] It has been reported that the Chinese potters, who make extremely thin porcelain, age their clays in the damp state for a generation. Weak organic acids increase plasticity, and organic matter like straw, when decomposed by bacteria, aids plasticity. When the Pharaoh of the Exodus ordered the Israelites to produce their full quota of bricks without their usual allowance of straw, he was undoubtedly inflicting a real punishment. A slight change in the pH of the clay will vary the plasticity. A small amount of an alkaline solution will convert a sticky clay into a thin liquid which will run through a filter cloth. A small amount of acid will coagulate clay so that it will settle out rapidly and leave a layer of clear water above it. Salts may either coagulate a clay or increase the dispersion of the particles.

Forming Clay Wares.—Clay wares may be formed by one of four processes. The oldest is the soft mud process where soft plastic clay is formed by the hands, or pressed into a wooden mold to make a brick, or into a porous mold to make ornamental architectural terra cotta. The potter's wheel as an aid to the fingers in forming hollow ware is almost as old as civilization.

A modern development of the soft-mud process is to use a mud that is stiffer than can be worked by hand and force it through a die as a continuous block or tube which is later cut into lengths to form brick, drain tile, or other simple shapes.

[1] RIDDLE and McDANIEL, *Jour. Am. Ceramic Soc.*, **1**, 617 (1918).

330   ENGINEERING MATERIALS

Fig. 139.—Pugmill for working and extruding clay. (*From Patterson Foundry and Machine Co.*)

Fig. 140.—Architectural tile immediately after extrusion. The pieces are being sprayed with a ceramic glaze by the two nozzles shown. (*Courtesy National Fireproofing Corporation.*)

ROCKS AND THEIR DECOMPOSITION PRODUCTS 331

A machine for mixing and extruding stiff clay is shown in Fig. 139. The vertical barrel of the machine known as a "pugmill" is kept filled with clay containing enough water to make it stiffly plastic. It acts as a mixer and forces the clay down against the coarse spiral threads of the horizontal shaft. The clay is forced forward by the interrupted threads of the "auger" and

FIG. 141.—Structural tile showing effect of deaeration before burning. The specimen at the left was made and burned in the usual manner. The specimen at the right was made from deaerated clay and burned in the usual manner. [*From Ohio State Univ. Engineering Studies*, **1**, VI (1932).]

through a die, from which it emerges as a continuous block or tube onto a conveyor where the block is cut into pieces of the required length. The appearance of architectural tile immediately after extrusion is shown in Fig. 140. These tile are to be glazed on one surface during the firing process. The nozzles spraying the suspension of the glaze are shown at the left of the picture. The clay must be plastic enough to extrude smoothly and yet be stiff enough so that the products will not be disturbed by careful handling immediately after extrusion. It is evident from the construction of the pugmill that the knives will tend to drag films of air into the clay. In recent years, the body of the pugmill has been made tight and a vacuum has been applied during the pugging process to remove the air and prevent the formation of film. The improvement in the quality of structural tile produced by evacuation is shown in Fig. 141. Another modern development is to use clay in the form of a slightly damp powder and compress it under a pressure of 5 or 6 tons per square

FIG. 142.—Shaping blast furnace brick in a power press, and stacking the brick on cars to be conveyed through the tunnel kiln for drying and firing. (*From Harbison-Walker, Modern Refractory Practice.*)

inch into simple shapes such as brick or floor tile, as is illustrated in Fig. 142.

Hollow articles such as teapots are produced in quantity by making patterns and then a hollow mold out of gypsum plaster. This mold is porous and is split into two parts to facilitate removal of the teapot. The clay is mixed with water to a creamy consistency known as a "casting slip" whose pH should be somewhat on the alkaline side to reduce the viscosity of the mixture and ensure a maximum amount of clay in suspension, while still maintaining a pourable mixture. A measured amount is poured into

ROCKS AND THEIR DECOMPOSITION PRODUCTS

the mold which is shaken vigorously while the water is being absorbed by the porous plaster of the mold. In a few minutes, a layer of wet clay will have been deposited uniformly over the interior of the mold. The excess quantity of slip may then be poured out of the mold which is then set aside for several days, while the water diffuses slowly to the outer surface of the mold where it evaporates. The result is that the wet clay in the interior of the mold dries gradually and shrinks away from the surrounding walls so that the two parts of the mold may be separated and the teapot lifted out.

Drying Clay Ware.—When a brick of wet clay stands in the air of a room, it loses moisture. At first, the rate of evaporation is the same as from a surface of water equal to the area of the exposed surfaces of the brick. The rate of drying becomes progressively slower, since the moisture in the interior has to diffuse through the pores of the brick before it can be evaporated from the surface. This loss of moisture is accompanied by a shrinkage of the brick, the greater shrinkage occurring with the most plastic clays. There is a wide variation of the amount of shrinkage even in a single class of clays. Ries states that the linear shrinkage of washed kaolin on drying may vary from 3.3 to 10.80 per cent and that for paving brick clays may vary from 0.9 to 5.82 per cent.

If the drying is very rapid, the moisture will be removed from the outer layers and they will become dry while the center of the brick is still wet. Fine shrinkage cracks will be formed on the surface of the brick which is said to be "checked." If the newly formed mud brick should be piled close together on a non-absorbent plate so that the drying would take place only on one exposed surface, the shrinkage of the outer surface would warp the whole brick. Drying must therefore be slow and uniform so that the brick will not be checked, cracked, or deformed in the process. Soft-mud brick will shrink more than stiff-mud brick made from the same clay, and both will shrink more than the dry-pressed brick with its low percentage of water. The quality of the clay will also influence the drying rate. A sandy non-plastic clay with only a small amount of colloidal material will shrink less and may be dried much faster than a plastic clay.

Sun-dried or Adobe Brick.—A study of the preceding data shows that sun-dried brick may have considerable strength.

The compressive strength of dried clays is rarely determined, but figures by Ries indicate that the compressive strength may be almost five times the tensile strength, so that compressive strengths of 500 to 1000 psi will not be unusual. This is ample for building simple structures, and buildings of air-dried brick are preserved in the adobe houses of prehistoric Indians in Arizona as well as in the ruins of Babylonia and Assyria. Brick dried in this way will disintegrate in rain and so are not adapted to any except desert conditions.

Effect of Moderate Heat on Clays.—The shrinkage that clays undergo while drying at room temperature has been discussed. Since room temperature and humidity vary, the figures for shrinkage given in the tables are obtained by drying in an oven at either 221 or 230°F. At this temperature, all of the moisture is driven off. A small amount of adsorbed water may remain. Water that is chemically combined will not be driven off with much rapidity until a very low red heat (1000°F) is reached. Clays burned at this temperature will slowly rehydrate in contact with water at room temperature, but in contact with superheated water, 400 to 500°F, rehydration may be obtained in 8 to 48 hr with regeneration of the plastic clay.

Chemical Composition of Clays.—The preceding discussion has stated that clay nearly always contains kaolin as its plastic material, and that in addition it may contain a wide range of other minerals and also partially decomposed vegetable matter. The physical properties of the clay are very important to the brickmaker, but the chemical composition becomes of importance only during the burning process. It will be discussed in the next chapter.

Effect of High Temperatures on Clay.—When clay is heated above a dull red heat, chemical changes commence to take place in increasing degree as the temperature is raised. Combined water is driven off, organic matter oxidizes and disappears, and compounds such as calcium and magnesium carbonate decompose to form oxides. The most important change, however, is the formation of a small quantity of fusible glass which bonds together the mineral particles and causes profound changes in the properties of the brick. The importance of this formation of glass is so great that its consideration is deferred to the next chapter, where the whole question of burning clay wares will be discussed.

References

RIES and WATSON, Engineering Geology, 5th ed., John Wiley & Sons, Inc., New York, 1936.

TARR, W. A.: Introductory Economic Geology, 3d ed., McGraw-Hill Book Company, Inc., New York, 1930.

CLARKE, F. W.: The Data of Geochemistry, 5th ed., Government Printing Office, Washington, D. C., 1924.

WASHINGTON, H. S.: The Chemical Composition of the Earth, *Am. Jour. Sci.*, **209**, 351–378 (1925).

BOWLES, OLIVER: The Stone Industries, 1st ed., McGraw-Hill Book Company, Inc., New York, 1934.

BROWN, G. G.: Molding Sands of Michigan and Their Uses, *State of Michigan Geol. Survey Division, Geol. Series* 35, *Pub.* 41, 1936.

ECKEL, E. C.: Building Stones and Clays, 1st ed., John Wiley & Sons, Inc., New York, 1912.

RIES, HEINRICH: Building Stones and Clay Products, 1st ed., John Wiley & Sons, Inc., New York, 1912.

RIES, H.: Clays, Occurrence, Properties and Uses, 3d ed., John Wiley & Sons, Inc., New York, 1927.

WILSON, H.: Ceramics—Clay Technology, 1st ed., McGraw-Hill Book Company, Inc., New York, 1927.

SEARLE, A. B.: The Chemistry and Physics of Clays and Other Ceramic Materials, 2d ed., Ernest Benn, Ltd., London, 1933.

BROWN, G. G.: Clays and Shales of Michigan and Their Uses, State of Michigan, *Geol. Survey Division, Geol. Series* 30, *Pub.* 36, 1924.

SHAND, S. J.: Useful Aspects of Geology, 2d ed., T. Murby and Co., London, 1927.

SCHAFFER, R. J.: The Weathering of Natural Building Stones, His Majesty's Stationery Department, London, 1933.

MERRILL, G. P.: Rocks, Rock-Weathering and Soils, 2d ed., The Macmillan Company, New York, 1906.

SEARLE, A. B.: Clay and What We Get from It, The Macmillan Company, New York, 1925.

ROBINSON, G. W.: Soils: Their Origin, Constitution and Classification, 2d ed., T. Murby and Co., London, 1936.

ROSS and KERR: The Kaolin Minerals, *U. S. Geol. Survey, Professional Paper* 165-E, 1931.

PARMELEE, C. W.: Clays and Some Other Ceramic Materials, Edwards Bros., Ann Arbor, Mich., 1937.

CHAPTER XVIII

FUSED SILICATES. VITRIFIED CLAY PRODUCTS GLASS, SLAGS, AND REFRACTORIES

Importance of Fused Silicates.—The preceding chapter discussed brick and other clay wares but postponed discussion of the changes taking place at temperatures above a dull red heat. The increasing hardness, strength, and density that come to brick as a result of exposure to higher temperatures are due mainly to the formation of a small amount of glass which bonds the mineral particles together. The strength of brick and its resistance to weathering increase with the amount of glass formed.

If a brick, or a clay dish, is heated very carefully to continually higher temperatures, so much glass may be formed that the product after cooling will be composed of a mass of mineral particles each completely imbedded in glass so that the product is almost free from pores and absorbs very little water. Such products are said to be vitrified. Paving brick are burned until vitrified and so are porcelain wash bowls and the dishes used on the dinner table. The smooth and resistant surface of such articles is produced by coating them with a powdered glaze, also a glass, which is melted at the temperature of the final firing.

The transparent glass used for windows and electric light bulbs is a fused silicate carefully formulated to pass, on cooling, through a viscous state which will allow it to be blown into a bulb or rolled or drawn into a flat sheet of window glass.

The earthy impurities of ores are eliminated in the blast furnace by additions of fluxes which form glasses whose fusing point and specific gravity are both lower than that of the metal to be made in the furnace, so that the slag can be tapped off in the molten state.

The linings for the blast furnace and for steel-melting and other high temperature furnaces are usually silicates formulated and manufactured so that they will not melt at the operating temperatures of the furnaces in which they are used. These silicate linings are built up of bricks whose particles have been bonded together during their own manufacture by a small amount of fused silicate of very high melting point.

The materials for furnace linings resist high temperatures and are called for that reason "refractory materials" or more often "refractories." Some of the basic refractories contain so little silica that the bonding agent cannot be called a silicate. It is usually, however, a glass in which the silica has become a minor constituent.

Crystalline Quartz and Vitreous Silica.—Quartz is a crystalline form of pure silica (SiO_2) which has already been referred to as one of the minerals composing granite rocks. It occurs, in rare cases, as large clear transparent crystals used for optical purposes. It occurs much more abundantly as silica sands which are sometimes so closely cemented together as to form the rock quartzite. When the crystals are of submicroscopic dimensions, a rock may be formed that is at times translucent, as in the semiprecious stones carnelian and agate, or it may be gray to black as in chert. The latter is sometimes found as a constituent in glacial gravels and gives difficulties when it is used as an aggregate in concrete pavements because it disintegrates after the concrete has hardened.

Silica melts to a clear liquid at 3110°F and, when cooled, will solidify to clear silica glass. It is difficult to get this product free from bubbles. Most of the commercial fused quartz, also called "vitreous silica," is translucent or milky, and fused quartz that is truly transparent is expensive. Quartz is very transparent to ultraviolet light and is used for the tubes of therapeutic lamps.

Quartz exists in a number of crystalline modifications which are stable only within definite temperature ranges but which remain in the metastable form for long periods. Vitreous silica after it has been fused and cooled is not in the same crystalline form in which it existed before fusion. It has a thermal coefficient of expansion which is so low that it is almost zero. Vitreous silica may be heated to redness and plunged into cold water without cracking. This low coefficient of expansion makes it valuable for some forms of scientific apparatus, and the combination of low coefficient of expansion and resistance to corrosion by acids makes it useful for equipment in chemical plants.

Transition Forms of Quartz. Tridymite and Cristobalite.—There are actually eight different varieties of silica, but the two important intermediates are tridymite and cristobalite. The temperature ranges in which these are stable are

	Degrees Fahrenheit
Quartz	Up to 1598
High tridymite	1598–2678
High cristobalite	2678–3110
Silica fuses	3110

The transformation from one modification to the other takes a number of hours, and on cooling fairly rapidly, the form that was stable at the high temperature persists after cooling. Thus, vitreous silica should not persist below 3110°, but actually the fused quartz glass is stable for many years at room temperature.

The commercial importance of the rate at which these transformations take place lies in the restrictions they impose in the manufacture and use of silica brick for high-temperature duty. When quartz changes to tridymite there is marked expansion, but there is not much change when tridymite changes to cristobalite. Both tridymite and cristobalite show an expansion of about 1 per cent in passing through the temperature range of 300° to 600°F with much slower expansion above those temperatures as is shown in Fig. 151. Silica brick make good arched roofs for furnaces because their expansion wedges the bricks tightly into place while the furnace is hot. The arch must be constructed so that it can rise and fall as the furnace becomes hotter and colder. The manufacture and behavior of silica brick will be discussed later in this chapter.

Glass.—Pure silica when melted gives a glass that would be not only satisfactory, but preferable in many ways to our ordinary window glass, if it could only be fabricated readily. The melting point of silica is high, and the resultant product is viscous and full of bubbles unless unusual precautions are taken. It is necessary to make additions to lower the melting point and also the viscosity of the melt in order to have a workable manufacturing process. A considerable amount of viscosity is necessary in the solidifying mass so that it can be blown into shapes such as bottles. It is remarkable that the Persian and Egyptian glassmakers of 3000 years ago had discovered the rather narrow range of composition of usable glass as shown in Table 49. The ancient glassmakers used rather more soda than we do and so made glass that melted more readily but was not so resistant to weathering. Otherwise their glass formula was not much different from that used today.

Table 49.—Composition of Ancient and Modern Glass*

Source	Ancient Egyptian	Modern bottle
SiO_2	63.86	69.42
$CaO + MgO$	12.04	9.19
$K_2O + Na_2O$	23.46	18.22
$Al_2O_3 + Fe_2O_3$	1.32	2.71

The Egyptian sample is a transparent glass made about 1400 B.C.
The modern bottle glass is not as resistant to the weather as window glass but it is satisfactory for its purpose.

* Morey, The Mystery of Ancient Glassware, *Art and Archeology*, **28**, 199 (1929).

The most powerful agents to reduce the melting point of silica are the alkalies sodium and potassium carbonates. Sodium carbonate is much the cheaper and is generally used. Unfortunately the combination of soda and silica gives glasses that are soft and too soluble in water to be resistant to weathering. If enough alkali is incorporated, soluble water glass is formed which finds industrial use as an adhesive and as a cleaning agent in laundries, besides serving in many other useful capacities. In order to counteract the softening action of soda and render the glass less soluble, lime is used today as it was 4000 years ago. If too much lime is added, the glass becomes too fluid to be blown well, and tends to crystallize instead of remaining as a solid solution.

A usual molecular formula for window glass approaches $Na_2O.CaO.5SiO_2$ which in percentage is equivalent to Na_2O 15, CaO 13, and SiO_2 71.5 Audley[1] says that a glass of the formula 0.94 Na_2O, 1.06 CaO, and 4.90 SiO_2 becomes quite soft at 1550°F and is so stiff as to be almost rigid at 1060°. Cooling strains in this glass may be removed at 1185°.

Optical glasses may deviate widely from this formula and so do glasses with low coefficient of thermal expansion and glasses for special purposes, but the great tonnage of glass approximates the composition given above.

[1] Silica and the Silicates.

340   ENGINEERING MATERIALS

Up to 25 years ago, glass was melted in batches in clay pots holding only about 1000 lb of glass. Since that time, the continuous-tank furnace has been developed which may hold as much as 2000 tons at a time. An illustration of the cross section of such a furnace is given in Fig. 143. A generation ago, a workman dipped his blow pipe into a pot of molten glass and drew out a small gob that he worked and rolled on an iron plate until it was the right consistency, then with his breath and sometimes with the aid of a mold, he blew a bottle, an electric light

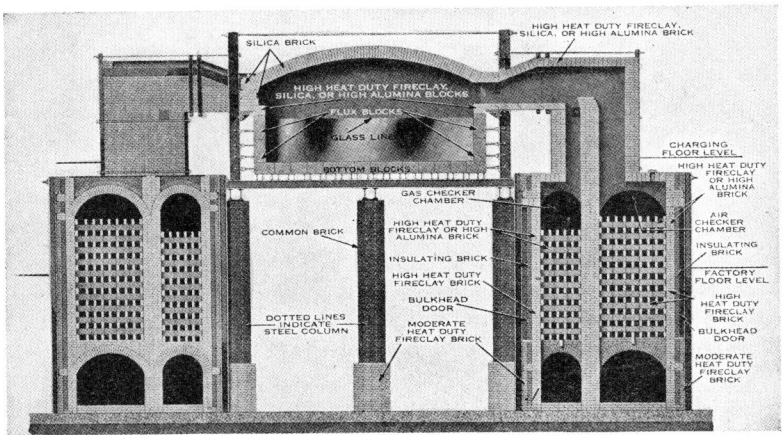

Fig. 143.—Cross section of glass tank with regenerators. (*From Harbison-Walker, Modern Refractory Practice.*)

bulb, or other article. Now the raw materials are fed into one end of a tank furnace over 100 ft long, along which the melting product slowly flows as a sluggish stream of glass 4 ft deep. The temperature is hot enough near the outlet end so that the glass becomes thinly fluid and homogeneous. The temperature slowly falls as the outlet of the tank is approached so that the glass emerges at just the right viscosity to form a continuous ribbon which may be drawn into a thin sheet for window glass, or a thicker sheet for plate glass; or the rapidly revolving arms of an automatic bottle machine may dip into the tank, suck up the right amount of glass, form it into a bottle, and discharge it onto the conveyor at a rate of more than one bottle per second. All glassware must be annealed to remove shrinkage strains, and this is done in continuous ovens called "lehrs" which take the hot glass and cool it slowly. Bottles are handled entirely by automatic machinery until they come to the inspector. No machine has yet been made to make the observations and exercise the judgment required of an inspector.

The sheets of glass for window glass move continuously from the rolls through the lehr and out before they are cut up into the sizes that the market demands. Drawn window glass is never perfectly flat, and so there is always a slight distortion of objects seen through it. Plate glass is ground and polished on each face so that it is flat and is therefore more desirable, but more expensive.

Recent developments in glass technology have produced hollow blocks for construction of buildings and, in contrast, fine fibers that may be spun like silk and look like silk.

Enamels.—Many kitchen utensils are made from stamped sheet steel that has been coated with a vitreous enamel. Bath tubs and sinks are made from cast iron and coated with a similar material. The enamel is essentially a glass whose chemical composition has been modified somewhat to make its coefficient of thermal expansion approach that of cast iron or steel as closely as is possible. The glass may contain oxides to impart color, such as cobalt oxide which dissolves to give a deep blue. Other materials may be added that do not go into solution but remain as fine suspended particles or droplets which make the glass opaque. Oxides of tin, calcium phosphate, calcium fluoride, and clay are used as opacifiers. The enamel is first melted in a pot and then poured into water to make it grind more readily. It is ground to a powder, dried, and dusted on to the red-hot vessel that is to be coated. The vessel is then put back in a furnace until the enamel melts. Three successive coats with intermediate firings are frequently applied. The formula for the enamel is usually rather high in soda to lower the melting point, and so the enamel is not very resistant to acids. White-enameled sinks and bath tubs stain readily when water containing iron is allowed to drip on them. The iron replaces some of the soda in the enamel and so penetrates deeply into it. Tubs and sinks of vitrified clay possess a more resistant glaze and do not absorb iron.

These fused-silicate enamels must not be confused with the type of varnish that is sometimes called enamel. The modern household refrigerator is usually white both inside and outside.

The steel sheets on the inside are almost always coated with a fused vitreous enamel that will not be stained by foods which may be spilled and will not impart any odor to the food. The outside of the refrigerator is frequently coated with a varnish or a lacquer.

Slags.—One of the first steps in extracting iron, copper, lead, and many other metals from their ores is to subject them to a smelting operation to separate the valuable metallic constituents from the useless rock and clay (gangue) that accompany them. Fluxes are mixed with the ore as it is charged into the furnace in such proportions as to produce a slag that will be fluid at the tem-

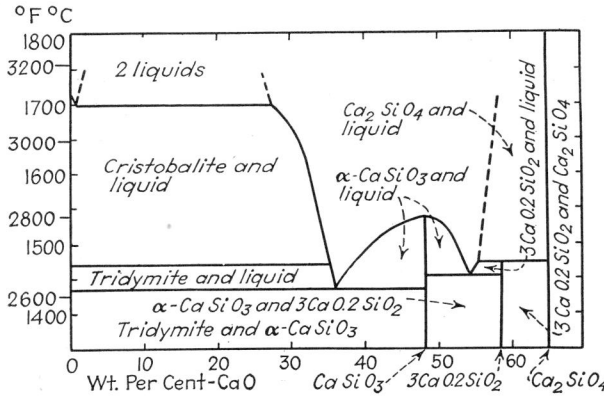

Fig. 144.—Portion of the equilibrium diagram of the system $CaO-SiO_2$. Temperatures are given in both centigrade and Fahrenheit scales. [*From G. W. Morey, J. Am. Ceram. Soc.*, **17**, 145 (1934).]

perature of the furnace operation. Most gangues are high in silica, and their melting point is too high for economical operation. Sodium carbonate could be added to reduce the melting point, as was done in the manufacture of glass, but slag should melt to a thin liquid without passing through the viscous state which is so necessary for working glass. Soda is also relatively expensive. Lime is better and cheaper than soda and is almost always used. An understanding of the function of lime demands a knowledge of the combinations of lime and silica.

The Lime-silica Equilibrium Diagram.—Lime and silica react to form three definite compounds, and the equilibrium diagram up to 70 per cent CaO shown in Fig. 144 shows these three compounds with three eutectics.

FUSED SILICATES. VITRIFIED CLAY PRODUCTS

The points of inflection on the complete diagram are as follows:

Composition	Melting Point, °F
Pure SiO_2	3110
Eutectic, 99 SiO_2, 1 CaO	3088
Eutectic, 63 SiO_2, 37 CaO	2617
$CaO \cdot SiO_2$, 52 SiO_2, 48 CaO	2804
Eutectic, 46 SiO_2, 54 CaO	2651
$2CaO \cdot SiO_2$, 35 SiO_2, 65 CaO	3866
Eutectic, 30 SiO_2, 70 CaO	3749
Pure CaO	4661

The importance of the equilibrium diagram in any systematic study of slag formation may be seen by a study of the two eutectics with 54 and 37 per cent of lime which have almost the same melting point but are separated by the compound $CaO \cdot SiO_2$ with a melting point nearly 200°F higher than either of the neighboring eutectics.

Balancing Acidic and Basic Constituents in Slags.—Magnesium oxide behaves much like lime in its relations to silica, but the melting points of its eutectics are higher than those with lime. Figures show that it would be impossible to make a slag that would be fusible at 2400°F, the maximum temperature of the blast furnace, from CaO, MgO, and SiO_2 alone. Alumina is however always a constituent of the gangue of iron ores, and fortunately it tends to lower the melting point of slags. A study of the equilibrium diagram of the lime-alumina-silica series[1] shows the following eutectic compositions that would be fusible in the iron blast furnace:

Melting point, °F	Percentage composition		
	SiO_2	Al_2O_3	CaO
2309	43	20	37
2138	62	15	23
2390	42	11	47

The addition of 2 or 3 per cent of iron oxide would lower the melting point of this mixture still more.

In discussing the iron blast furnace, it was stated that the slag was made up roughly of equal percentages of the basic con-

[1] International Critical Tables, Vol. IV.

stituents CaO and MgO and the acidic constituents SiO_2 and Al_2O_3. The figures cited above indicate the basis on which slag calculations are made. It is not necessarily the slag with the lowest melting point that is most desirable, since it must be so proportioned as to have only a slight corrosive effect on the refractories. The composition of desirable slags for blast furnaces smelting the ores of lead, copper, and other metals may be calculated from the equilibrium diagrams of the oxides that will be present in the slag.

Utilization of Slags.—Slags may be considered as synthetic igneous rocks which have been cooled so rapidly that there has been little opportunity for differential crystallization, and so they have remained in the glassy state, with perhaps some crystals of microscopic size. An iron blast furnace produces 1 ton of slag for each ton of pig iron, so that many million tons of this material are available each year. It has been proposed to cast the molten slag into blocks for pavements or other construction purposes, and the hardened slag has sometimes been crushed and used as a substitute for crushed stone. One unfortunate property is the lack of stability of some of the slags, which were cooled so quickly that equilibrium was not obtained. Slow crystalline changes sometimes take place after the slag has cooled, with consequent development of internal strains which cause pieces to crack and disintegrate, after some months or even years. The presence of sulfides in slag increases the tendency to disintegrate when exposed to the weather. Some slags are entirely stable and are used satisfactorily for slag wool and other construction purposes. The slag from the iron blast furnace finds considerable use as one of the raw materials in the manufacture of portland cement.

Slag Wool, Rock Wool, and Glass Fiber.—Slag wool has been prepared for many years by allowing molten slag to drip before a jet of high-pressure steam which blows the molten slag into short filaments somewhat like coarse wool. It has been used as a material for thermal insulation, but has sometimes been unsatisfactory because of a tendency to break down to a powder as mentioned in the preceding paragraph. Research has shown that some slags are entirely reliable. Rock wool is the name given to a product of controlled composition which is synthesized especially for the production of a fiber for thermal insulation.

Glass, with its greater viscosity, may be drawn into long fibers which are finer than silk and woven into textile fabrics which possess the beauty and pliability of silk. This material is still in the development stage, but it has found a definite use as a filter cloth for acids which disintegrate cotton in a short time.

The Corrosive Action of Molten Slag on Furnace Walls.— It has been pointed out that the eutectics in the systems that are made up of CaO and MgO as the basic constituents and SiO_2 and Al_2O_3 as the acidic constituents lie on either side of the composition of 50 parts of base to 50 of acid. It follows that if a molten basic slag should be in contact with a firebrick wall high in silica the two would combine to form a more fusible compound, and the firebrick wall would be rapidly corroded. A similar result would be obtained if a molten acid slag should be in contact with a basic refractory material. Therefore in the basic open-hearth furnace and in other basic furnaces, the lining of the hearth is made of basic material to lessen corrosion by the basic slag, and in the acid open-hearth both the slag and the lining are high in silica.

Coal Ash as a Slagging Agent.—The mineral matter in coal is frequently clay which was carried by streams of past ages into the swamps where vegetation was growing and decaying to form the deposit that was ultimately to become coal. Coal ash may be largely kaolin and have a softening point above 2600°F or have enough iron oxide mixed with the clay to make it fusible at 2000°F. When coal is burned on grates, some coals will yield a powdery ash and others will form a mass of clinkers. The iron in coal is sometimes present as iron pyrites FeS_2 which on combustion yields FeO, or Fe_2O_3, and SO_2. The ferrous oxide (FeO) lowers the melting point of the slag much more than the ferric oxide (Fe_2O_3). The method of conducting the combustion process has therefore an important bearing on the formation of clinkers. This is a subject that will be discussed more fully in the chapter on Fuels and Combustion.

In large industrial plants, coal is frequently powdered and blown into the furnace with a jet of air so that the coal burns while the particles are in suspension. The temperature of the intense combustion is usually high enough to fuse the ash, much of which is carried through the furnace and out of the stack as a fine powder. The collection and economical disposal of this "fly" ash offers a difficult problem. The ash that does not go up the stack may adhere as a sticky mass to the firebrick walls and to the metal tubes of a boiler or it may form a fusible slag and corrode the walls. When powdered coal is being burned, part of the ash will collect in the ash pit. Lime is sometimes added to this material to make a slag fluid enough to be tapped off.

Fire Clay and the Alumina-silica Equilibrium Diagram.—Fire clay consists largely of kaolinite with associated substances which may consist of any of the minerals of the igneous rocks or their decomposition products. It is evident from what has preceded that lime, magnesia, and iron oxide, no matter how they are combined, will lower the fusion point of a fire clay. Not so much emphasis has been placed on the alkalies, but their effect on lowering the melting point of silica to make a commercial glass has been mentioned. Alkalies are actually much more harmful in a fire clay than are lime, magnesia, or iron oxide in that they lower the melting point more than an equal amount of any of the other compounds. Of the other minor constituents, titanium oxide (TiO_2) is similar to and no more harmful than silica. Water, whether present as moisture or as water of crystallization, is all driven off at a dull red heat and so does not need to be considered in any study of refractories.

The two important components of fire clay are alumina and silica. The mineral kaolinite with the formula $Al_2O_3.2SiO_2.2H_2O$ contains SiO_2 46.5, Al_2O_3 39.5, and H_2O 14.0 per cent. After removal of the water, the dehydrated mineral contains 54.1 per cent SiO_2 and 45.9 per cent Al_2O_3. When this mineral is dried in an oven at 220°F and then heated, very little of the combined water is evolved until about 750°F, and it is almost all driven off by 900°. The mineral apparently dissociates at 1200 to 1400°F, but there is no clear evidence as to the nature of the products. At temperatures of 2000 to 2600°F, a new mineral, mullite ($3Al_2O_3.2SiO_2$), forms, and the silica that is left over takes the form of tridymite if the heating has been slow enough to permit the transformation of quartz to take place.

The equilibrium diagram of the alumina-silica series is shown in Fig. 145.[1] There is a eutectic with 5.5 per cent Al_2O_3 at 2820°F, which is the lowest melting point in the whole series. Any

[1] From Harbison-Walker's Refractories. Redrawn from data by Bowen and Grieg.

refractory containing only Al_2O_3 and SiO_2 may be used up to 2800° without any liquid forming. The eutectic continues over the whole range of composition from substantially 100 per cent SiO_2 to 71.8 per cent Al_2O_3. If bricks composed of 5 to 20 per cent alumina with 95 to 80 per cent silica should be made up and tested, the proportion of the eutectic would be found to become less with increasing amounts of alumina, and since the eutectic is a stiff liquid, the safe operating temperature would rise with increasing alumina until with 40 per cent Al_2O_3 it might be 3100°F.

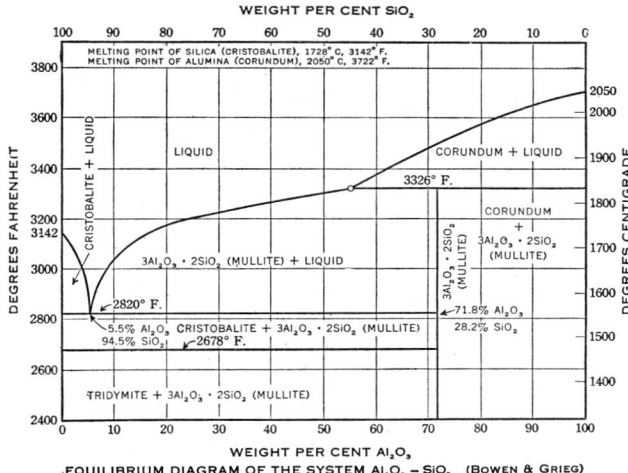

FIG. 145.—Equilibrium diagram of the system Al_2O_3-SiO_2. (*From Harbison-Walker, Modern Refractory Practice.*)

Changes in Clay While Burning. Glass Formation.—The manufacture of brick and other clay wares was described briefly in the last chapter up to the point where the product was air-dried. It was shown that drying had to be slow and uniform throughout the various portions of the piece if shrinkage cracks were to be avoided. The strength and also the shrinkage of the air-dried ware was indicated to be a function of the amount of colloidal material in the clay. Another factor influencing strength and shrinkage was the size distribution of the particles in the clay.

When brick or other articles of clay are fired, the heat must be applied slowly and evenly, for there is a variable amount of water (usually 5 to 10 per cent) that is in a state of combination and is not completely driven off until a temperature of 1000 to 1200°F is reached. Any carbonaceous material that may be present in the clay should also be burned off in this temperature range.

These changes for three New Jersey clays are shown in Table 50. The sandy clay had a low air shrinkage, lost only 3.95 per

TABLE 50.—PROGRESSIVE LOSS OF WEIGHT AND LENGTH OF CLAYS WHEN DRIED AND BURNED*

	Sandy clay, per cent		Plastic clay, per cent		Black clay, per cent	
	Wt. loss	Linear shrinkage	Wt. loss	Linear shrinkage	Wt. loss	Linear shrinkage
Air shrinkage.......	....	1.0	....	8.0	....	5.6
Dried at 230°F.....	0.63	...	3.29	...	3.48	
Fired to 932°F......	2.52	...	5.32	...	9.42	
1112	1.05	0.0	1.70	0.3	2.61	0.4
1292	0.26	0.0	0.83	0.0	1.61	0.0
1472	0.10	0.0	0.41	0.0	0.46	0.0
1652	0.02	0.0	0.49	0.0	0.33	0.0
1832	0.09	1.4	0.34	1.3	0.14	1.3
2012	0.03	0.0	0.24	4.0	0.22	4.7

The loss in weight at 230°F is moisture that remained in the bricklets, which had stood in a warm room for several weeks, but still contained moisture which was driven off when heated in an oven to 230°F. The losses in weight on firing are based on the oven-dry weight.

* From RIES, KUMMEL, and KNAPP, The Clays and Clay Industry of New Jersey. *Final Report of the State Geologist,* **6,** 94 (1904).

cent in weight on firing to 1652°F, and did not shrink a measurable amount during the process. The plastic clay had a high air shrinkage and also a large loss in weight at 230°F. On firing to 1652°, it lost 8.75 per cent in weight but shrank only 0.3 per cent in length. The black clay contained considerable organic matter. On firing to 1652°, it lost 14.43 per cent in weight, the high figure being due to the organic matter, but it shrank only 0.4 per cent in length.

These figures illustrate the general principle that the air-dried clay does not shrink much during the initial stages of the burning process. The shrinkage due to the drying of the colloid takes place during the air-drying process, and the air-dried ware is stiff enough so that loss of chemically combined water or organic matter changes its dimensions only slightly.

On heating the test bricklets from 1652 to 1832°F, all of them showed a shrinkage of 1.3 to 1.4 per cent in length with very little change in weight. The red color also developed more fully during this period, and the brick became much harder. The samples fired to the next step, 2012°F, were all "steel hard" and could not be scratched with a knife. The sandy clay did not show any further shrinkage at this higher temperature, but the other two both shrank an additional 4 per cent.

These changes in length and hardness occurring above 1600°F were due to a liquid film of glass which formed through interaction between some of the very fine constituents of the clay and cemented the coarser particles together. A clay that contains considerable iron oxide forms this fusible glass readily. Ordinary red brick are burned at a low temperature because the glass forms at a low temperature. Brick that burn hard at a low temperature are cheaper to manufacture, and therefore the common brick of the market are almost all red brick.

The sandy clay of Table 50 did not contain much of this fusible clay, for there was no further shrinkage in the sample burned to 2012°. The other two clays showed a continuing shrinkage and probably had reached the point where the bricklets would have commenced to soften and lose their shape. This phenomenon of formation of glass in such amount that the films become substantially continuous is known as "vitrification." A brick that is thoroughly vitrified is strong, dense, and almost nonporous.

Pyrometric Cones as Indicators of Burning Conditions.—The glass that appears during the burning process is formed by the interaction of some of the constituents of the clay, and it continues to grow in quantity through corrosion of, and interaction with, other materials of the clay with which it comes in contact. The quantity of glass formed will be a function of the coarseness of the particles, of the temperature, and also of the time. Fifty years ago, Seger made up a series of mixtures of kaolin with various chemicals, to give definite softening temperatures, which he formed into slender pyramids. A series of these were placed in a pottery kiln where they could be seen through a peephole, and as the temperature rose, one cone after another commenced to bend over and finally to slump. These cones are still used, not as an accurate indication of temperature, but as an indication of how the combination of time and temperature is affecting the products in the kiln.

Updraft Kilns for Burning Brick.—The simplest method of burning brick is in a temporary structure erected out of the bricks to be burned. Air-dried brick are piled crisscross on a level piece of ground and built up into a pile with arches about 18 in. wide and 3 ft high running through at the ground level to serve as combustion chambers. The outside surface of the pile is usually faced with imperfect brick from a previous run. Clay mud is then plastered over the outside faces of the pile to keep the products of combustion confined to useful channels. This method of daubing or plastering the outside of the kiln gives it the name of a "scove kiln." A fire of wood, coal, or oil is kindled in each arch and kept low for a few days to permit the mass to warm slowly and uniformly. About a week is required to heat the kiln, and it is kept at full heat for several days, after which it is allowed to cool slowly. When the brick are cold enough to handle, the kiln is torn down as the bricks are needed for shipment. It is evident that during the burning there must have been a higher temperature just above the arches of the combustion chamber than at the top of the kiln. If the brick at the top of the kiln are to be burned hard, the brick next the arch will be overburned. Such a kiln may therefore yield a proportion of vitrified brick near the arches, and the greater proportion of the brick may be well enough burned to be resistant to the weather, but a proportion of those on top will be underburned "salmon" brick which are too soft and porous to be used for exposure to the weather, but may be used for interior partitions where neither great strength nor weather resistance are required.

The next step in the evolution of the kiln was to use permanent brick walls for the outside of the kiln, and from that the updraft kiln developed. All updraft kilns however have the disadvantage of hot spots nearest to the fire and where the draft is strongest.

Downdraft Kilns.—The downdraft kiln has a closed dome-shaped roof and takes the combustion gases through holes in the floor to a subterranean flue and a separate stack. A cross section of such a kiln is shown in Fig. 146 taken from the *U. S.*

FUSED SILICATES. VITRIFIED CLAY PRODUCTS 351

Bureau of Mines Bulletin 271. This kiln has an inside diameter of 38 ft and is heated by coal burned in eight fire boxes, of which one is shown, spaced around the circumference of the kiln. The combustion gases rise under the domed roof and are sucked down through channels left between the bricks to the openings in the floor, through which they pass to collecting flues and then to the stack which rises to a height of 42 ft above the floor level. The kiln is reinforced structurally by four external steel hoops as shown.

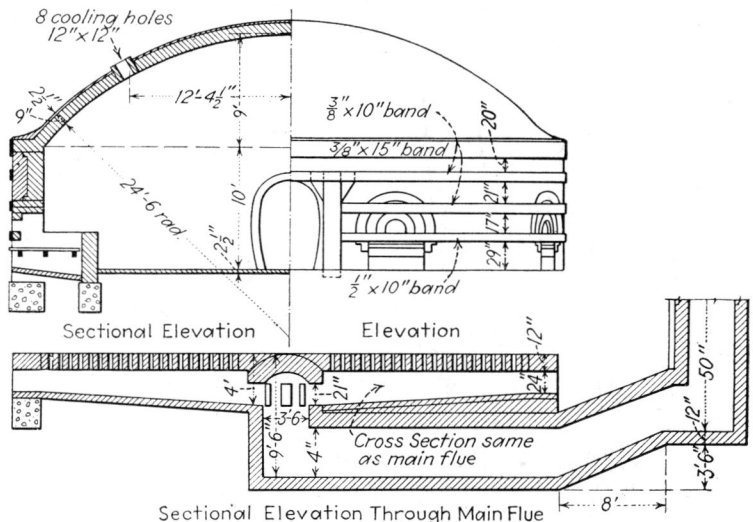

Fig. 146.—Partial cross section and elevation of downdraft kiln. [*From Bur. Mines Bull.* 271, 38 (1927).]

The great advantage of the downdraft kiln is the uniform temperature which may be maintained. The hot gases are forced to descend evenly by the distribution of the holes in the floor. If conditions were more favorable to a higher temperature over one area of the floor, the hotter gases being lighter would offer more resistance to the pull of the stack, and so the volume of hot gases passing through the hotter area would be automatically reduced.

In the updraft kiln, on the other hand, if one area in the kiln receives more of its share of the hot gases, these hotter gases tend to increase the draft in that region and so automatically increase the rate of flow of the gases and the temperature in that particular area. The brick from an updraft kiln will therefore vary in the degree of burning according to their position in the kiln, whereas the brick from a downdraft kiln may be burned so evenly that they may all be sold as a single grade.

Continuous Kilns.—One great disadvantage of the single downdraft kiln is the low fuel economy, since the gases escape up the stack at the full heat of the kiln. The extent of the fuel

Fig. 147.—View of an annular ceramic kiln. The workman at the right is stacking dried tile which are about to enter the kiln. The workman at the left is removing burned tile as they come out of the kiln. (*Courtesy National Fireproofing Corporation.*)

loss will be better understood after the chapter on Fuels and Combustion has been studied. Greater fuel economy was obtained by operating several kilns in series so that the hot gases from one passed to another which was less advanced in the heating process. The most modern and efficient development is the tunnel kiln which may either be straight or circular. The latter type is illustrated in Fig. 147. The workman at the right is stacking dried tile onto a platform which rotates slowly so that the tile are carried into the kiln, heated to the necessary temperature, and cooled again before they emerge and are removed by the workman shown at the left. When dry-pressed brick are being made, as illustrated in Figure 142, they may be loaded on a car as illustrated in that picture, passed through the drying oven, and then through the kiln and emerge as finished brick without being touched until they are unloaded.

Influence of Method and Temperature of Firing on Properties of Building Brick.—The dried brick must be stacked in the kiln in such a way as to allow free circulation of the fire gases around them. They must be slowly heated. The shrinkage, as they are heated to a dull red heat, is due to the evolution of combined water and the consequent shrinkage of the colloidal material. At some higher temperature depending on the chemical composition and particle size of the constituents of the clay, glass will commence to form and continue to form in larger amounts as the temperature rises. The increase in the amount of glass will cause the brick to shrink and become less porous. When the amount of glass is so great that the brick is almost ready to slump in the kiln, it is said to be vitrified. Further heating would cause it to melt to a slag.

The crushing strength of a brick will increase with the amount of the glass bond that is formed. Since the formation of the glass is also accompanied by a diminution of porosity, a relationship has been sought between strength and water absorption. A statement of such a relationship formed a part of the standard specifications of the American Society for Testing Materials for many years, but was removed in 1930 as not being reliable enough

TABLE 51.—RELATION BETWEEN WATER ABSORPTION AND COMPRESSIVE STRENGTH OF BUILDING BRICKS*

Brick	Mean of five tests	
	Water absorption, per cent	Compressive strength, psi
Vitrified	5 or less	5000 or over
Hard	5–12	2500 or over
Medium	12–20	2000 or over
Soft	20 or over	1000 or over

* A.S.T.M. Standards, 1924 ed., p. 670. This table has been dropped from more recent issues of the Standards.

for a standard specification. It is presented in Table 51 as a matter of information.

The durability of brick when exposed to the weather in our northern climates is associated with the factors of strength and water absorption. A soft brick that absorbs 20 per cent of water and has a compressive strength of only 1000 psi will go to pieces if it is frozen when saturated with water. A hard brick absorbing 5 to 12 per cent of water and with a compressive strength of over 3500 lb would probably last almost indefinitely in the outer wall of a building, but might not last many years if set in a sidewalk where ice formation would be more severe.

Bricks to be used in pavements subject to the impacts and abrasion of traffic must be vitrified in order to be strong and nonporous. It is not desirable to carry the vitrification to the state where the brick is substantially a homogeneous glass because it becomes brittle and liable to chip.

Color of Burned-clay Products.—The ordinary brick is red because of the iron oxide in the clay. If the burning temperature is carried so high that the iron oxide reacts with the clay to form a silicate, the red color changes to purple, and then to a greenish black when actual fusion has taken place. A clay that contains considerable lime as well as iron burns to a yellow or brown color. Clay that does not contain iron gives a white product. The subject of glazes will be discussed in a subsequent paragraph.

TABLE 52.—CHANGES IN PHYSICAL PROPERTIES OF A CLAY WHILE BEING BURNED TO FORM A BUILDING BRICK*

Water required for maximum plasticity, per cent...... 25.2
Air shrinkage, per cent.......................... 10
Average tensile strength, psi..................... 289

Temperature of burning:					
Cone number.........	05	03	1	3	5
Corresponding temperature, °F.......	1922	1994	2102	2174	2246
Fire shrinkage, per cent.	2	2	4	4	4.3
Water absorption, per cent.............	13.13	9.05	6.29	4.24	2.86
Color...............	Light red	Light red	Red	Red	Deep red
Hardness............	Nearly steel hard	Steel hard			

* From RIES and KÜMMEL, The Clays and Clay Industry of New Jersey, Vol. VI of the Final Report of the State Geologist, 1904, p. 415.

Burning Building Brick.—The changes during the manufacture and burning of a clay used for making building brick may be illustrated by the behavior of a New Jersey clay as studied by Ries and Kummel and presented in Table 52.

This clay required 25.2 per cent water for maximum plasticity, had 10 per cent air shrinkage, and showed a tensile strength of 289 psi in the air-dried condition. The brick burned to cone 05 (1922°F) would have been classed as medium brick. If burned 70° hotter to cone 03, the brick would have been harder and would have absorbed only 9.05 per cent water. It would be classed as a hard brick. Brick burned to cones 1, 3, and 5 (2102 to 2246°F) would be classed as vitrified brick. The highest of the three temperatures is probably as much as the brick would stand without softening.

Harmful Constituents of Clays for Building Brick.—Attention has been focussed on the physical properties of clays for building bricks, and little has been said about the chemical composition. There are very few materials present in native clays that make them unusable for the manufacture of brick. Sand, and even larger pebbles, hinder the manufacture of a smooth and uniform brick but do not necessarily injure anything but the appearance. The one material that causes serious trouble is limestone. As will be seen in the next chapter, limestone ($CaCO_3$) burns to lime (CaO) at temperatures of about 1800°F. If the limestone in the clay is finely divided, the lime will combine with the clay in the burning process and a sound brick will result. If there is much lime, the color tends to be yellow rather than red. If however the limestone is present in lumps as large as the head of a small pin, part of it will remain as lumps of CaO in the finished brick. When the brick becomes wet, the lime will slowly hydrate and expand, breaking out the surface of the brick in what is called a "lime pop."

Decayed vegetation or other organic matter in a clay does not preclude its use for brick manufacture, but it does necessitate some precautions in burning. The organic matter must be burned completely out of the brick before the formation of glass begins, or else the gas evolved on combustion of the organic matter may puff the brick. Gas may also be evolved, if the clay contains iron oxide, through formation of carbon monoxide from the reduction of the ferric oxide by the carbon of the clay.

The progress of the combustion of the carbon may be followed by taking a brick out of the kiln and breaking it. Figure 148 shows the stages during the oxidation of the carbonaceous matter in a brick, which before firing was quite dark as shown by the bottom brick, and which became light colored first near the surface and then at greater depths as air diffused into the brick to oxidize the carbon and the carbon dioxide diffused out.

FIG. 148.—Progressive oxidation of carbon in a brick during burning process. [*From Geol. Survey of New Jersey*, **6,** 141 (1904).]

Properties of Various Clay Products for Structural Purposes.— Common brick is often made from surface clays by the soft-mud process and burned in scove kilns. A brickyard, operating only in summer, can be started with very little capital and furnish brick for a local market at a low price. The product of each kiln of such an establishment will range from soft salmon to fully vitrified brick. The soft brick may be used for interior partitions and that portion of the chimney which is below the roof. The harder brick will be good for almost any structural purposes.

"Face brick" is the name given to any brick that is resistant enough to the weather to be used on the outside of a wall. A common brick that is well burned may be used as a face brick. Face brick are however often made with special care to give architectural effects. Brick that have been partially dried may be repressed to give a smooth surface, sharp corners, and more accurate dimensions. If rough-surfaced brick are desired, the effect may be obtained as they are extruded from the brick machine by slicing off the outside surface with a wire.

FUSED SILICATES. VITRIFIED CLAY PRODUCTS

Structural clay tile are made in a variety of grades and shapes. If they are to carry a load, they must be burned hard so as to have strength. If they are to be used in foundations, they must be vitrified so that water will not work through them. If they are intended as fire-protective members for steel beams, they should be burned rather lightly so as to remain porous and have a high thermal insulating value.

Drain tile are burned at a low temperature and are not flanged, so as to permit water to enter the line as freely as possible.

Sewer tile are burned harder and are often glazed in addition. They are made with a flange so that the units may be cemented together to form a tight sewer.

Floor tile and roof tile must be dense and hard. They are frequently made by the dry-press process so as to have exact dimensions and high density. They may however be made exactly like any brick and burned to have low water absorption.

The word "terra cotta" means burned clay, but the name has come to be applied only to ornamental architectural units usually made by pressing plastic clay by hand into a porous mold. In the drying process, the unit shrinks enough to be withdrawn from the mold, after which it is dried further and burned.

Paving brick must be vitrified so as to have a maximum resistance to impact, abrasion, and freezing. They are usually made by the stiff-mud process from clays with considerable iron oxide. Such clays are usually plastic, extrude well, and vitrify at a relatively low temperature with consequent economy in the fuel used to fire the kiln.

Sanitary ware is the general name given to water closets, urinals, and bath tubs made of vitrified clay. The ware must be vitrified so as to be nonabsorbent, and the customer usually demands that the color must be white. White clays have a high vitrifying temperature, and the burning is therefore expensive. The customer also wants the surface smooth and that calls for a glaze. The product is very much like that in high-grade dishes, whose manufacture will be described in a subsequent paragraph.

Glazes and Glazed Ware.—A glaze is a glass of special composition that is ground to a powder, suspended in water, and applied to the surface of a clay product, usually after it has been burned at a low temperature and is still porous. If a green-colored roof tile is wanted, it may be obtained by dipping a porous red clay tile into a water suspension of a powder of an opaque green glass. The porous clay sucks the water from the suspension, and when the tile is withdrawn from its momentary immersion, it is evenly covered with a coating of the powdered glass. The coated tile is then put into a kiln and fired a second time until the glaze melts. If the melting point of the glaze is less than the vitrifying temperature of the clay, the product will consist of a porous body covered by a green glaze. This will be resistant to the weather so long as the glaze does not crack. It is hard to make the coefficient of thermal expansion of the glaze exactly the same as that of the body, and so on exposure to the weather, fine cracks form. The glaze is said to "craze." When the cracks become large enough to permit water to work into the porous body so that ice may form, the green glaze will be split off in spots, the red tile will commence to show through, and the tile will be on its way to destruction.

A better way to glaze roof tile, sewer tile, or sanitary ware is to make the glaze of such a composition that it melts at the same temperature as that at which the body of the ware vitrifies, so that in the second firing the body will vitrify and the glaze will melt simultaneously. This calls for great skill. The larger pieces of sanitary ware may have the water suspension of the glaze sprayed on with an air jet.

Porcelain is the name give to plates and dishes which are so thin that the glaze, on melting, penetrates right through the body so that the finished piece becomes translucent. In making fine wares of this sort, plastic and nonplastic clays are carefully selected and mixed with feldspar and other materials so that the plasticity, shrinkage, and vitrifying temperature will conform to the desired standard.

Delicate dishes cannot be stacked in a kiln, and so each dish is put in a fire-clay box called a "sagger" which protects it from physical contacts and from dust. These saggers are then stacked in the kiln just as if they were brick.

Influence of Chemical Composition on Vitrifying Temperature.—The complicated chemical composition of clays is illustrated in Table 53 from the work of Ries. The chemical analysis does not give any information on such important factors as the amount of water for maximum plasticity, which varies in these

TABLE 53.—CHEMICAL ANALYSES AND PHYSICAL PROPERTIES OF WEST VIRGINIA CLAYS*

Chemical Analysis

Serial number		II	V	XI	XII
Silica	SiO_2	57.7	61.4	66.7	56.2
Alumina	Al_2O_3	20.2	26.2	21.8	26.3
Ferric oxide	Fe_2O_3	7.0	0.3	0.4	2.8
Ferrous oxide	FeO	0.3	0.4	1.0	1.0
Lime	CaO	0.2	0.1	0.3	0.4
Magnesia	MgO	1.2	....	0.1	1.4
Soda	Na_2O	0.6	....	0.1	0.5
Potash	K_2O	2.6	....	0.5	3.9
Titanic oxide	TiO_2	0.9	1.4	1.1	0.6
Moisture		2.7	0.8	1.0	1.4
Phosphoric acid	P_2O_5	0.1			
Loss on ignition		5.9	9.1	7.1	5.5

Physical Tests

	II	V	XI	XII
Water for plasticity, per cent	28	21	20	24
Tensile strength when air-dry, psi	122	32	75–90	89–100
Air shrinkage, per cent	4	3	4	4
Temperatures for incipient vitrification				
Cone number	1	....	....	1
Temperature, °F	2102			2102
Vitrification:				
Cone number	5	30	30	5
Temperature, °F	2246	3146	3146	2246
Fire shrinkage, per cent	11	....	0	6
Color when burned	....	Buff	Buff	Red

* RIES, H., Clays, Occurrence, Properties and Uses, 3d ed., p. 570.

four clays from 21 to 28, nor the air shrinkage, which is almost the same for the four, nor the tensile strength when air-dried, which varies from 32 to 122 psi. The chemical analysis does permit a qualitative appraisal of the way these clays will behave on burning. The compounds of Al_2O_3, SiO_2, and TiO_2 all have a high softening point, and have been called "nondetrimentals." This softening point is lowered by the addition of Fe_2O_3, FeO, CaO, MgO, Na_2O, and K_2O, which have been called "detrimentals." Clay II of Table 53 shows a ratio of nondetrimental to detrimentals of 6.7 and vitrifies at cone 5. Clay XII is not much different with a ratio of 8.3 and a vitrification also at cone 5.

Clay XI shows a ratio of 36 and does not vitrify until cone 30. Clay V does not have the alkalies reported, but the other detrimentals are low, and it also vitrifies at cone 30. This chemical analysis suggests in a general way that clays V and XI would probably make good firebrick and that clays II and XII would have low vitrifying temperatures. Actual burning tests are however necessary to obtain quantitative data.

Fire-clay Brick.—Fire clay is composed almost wholly of kaolinite and silica, and is one of the major raw materials in the

Fig. 149.—Special shapes made from fire clay. (*From Harbison-Walker, Modern Refractory Practice.*)

manufacture of vitrified porcelain. Fire-clay brick, however, must not vitrify even if used at the high temperatures demanded for the lining of the kiln or for the sagger enclosing a porcelain dish. Reference to the equilibrium diagram of the alumina-silica series will show that the lowest liquefying point is the eutectic temperature of 2820°F. Even the best commercial fire clays are contaminated to a slight extent by lime, magnesia, iron oxide, and alkalies so that a glass may commence to form at somewhat lower temperatures.

It is desirable that fire-clay brick as well as all other refractories have accurate dimensions, since the shapes are often complicated, as shown in Fig. 149, and they must fit together closely. It is desirable that the shrinkage be small, and therefore fire clay that has already been burned and preshrunk and imperfect bricks are ground up coarsely and put back into the mix. This preshrunk material is called "grog." The amount of plastic clay is kept low to lessen shrinkage, and the result is a brick that is physically weak. This does not make much difference, because a wall of firebrick should never be expected to carry more than a small load.

Fire-clay brick are therefore made from a mixture of burned and raw clays, molded and dried carefully, and burned at as high a temperature as they are to meet in service so that they will not shrink after they have been built into the furnace. The temperatures of the combustion gases in furnaces are sometimes higher than the softening temperature of the brick, but fortunately it is only the surface of the brick that reaches the full temperature of the flame. One of the points to be observed in designing a furnace is to provide for cooling the backs of the brick exposed to the highest temperatures so that the main portion of the wall will be kept below the softening point of the brick and so remain stiff and capable of bearing the small load put upon it.

Mortar for Fire-clay Brick.—The mortar for fire-clay brick must be a plastic material that will have some strength when air-dry, and must burn to be strong even at the high temperatures to which the wall will be subjected. The usual material is a fire clay of approximately the same composition as the brick with which it is to be used. Since the mortar must be plastic, it follows that there must be colloidal water present and that the mortar will shrink when the furnace is first heated. Thick joints are to be avoided, and that is one reason why firebrick shapes should be accurate in dimension. In some cases, it is specified that each brick shall be rubbed into place as it is being set, and that only a thin film of mortar will be permitted.

Additions of portland cement, lime, sodium silicate, and salt are sometimes suggested as additions to fire-clay cement. These all lower the melting point as is indicated in Fig. 150.

High-alumina Refractories.—The mineral kaolinite after dehydration contains 45.9 per cent Al_2O_3 and 54.1 per cent SiO_2. Refractories with higher percentages of Al_2O_3 may be made by mixing bauxite or diaspore, both forms of hydrated aluminum oxide, with the clay. There will still be a eutectic formed at 2820°F as may be seen from the equilibrium diagram for all

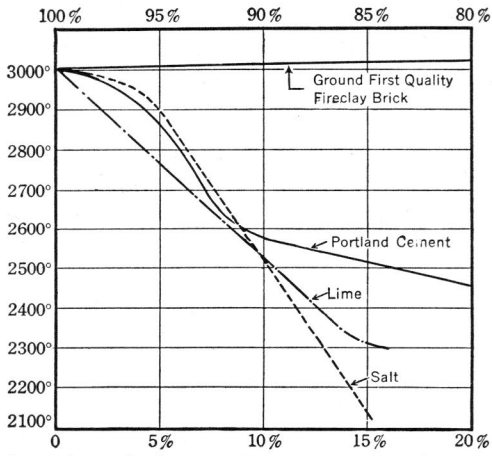

FIG. 150.—Fusion points of mixtures of a plastic fire clay and other materials. (*From Harbison-Walker, Modern Refractory Practice.*)

compositions up to a 71.8 per cent alumina. However the proportion of eutectic decreases as the percentage of alumina rises, and so the brick with 50, 60, and 70 per cent of Al_2O_3 may be used at temperatures of 3200 to 3300°F. These brick are also corroded less readily by most slags than are fire-clay brick.

At all compositions above 71.8 per cent Al_2O_3, mullite ($3Al_2O_3 \cdot 2SiO_2$) and corundum (Al_2O_3) become the stable phases and no glass is formed on heating, the mass remaining entirely solid until the melting point of mullite, 3326°F, is reached. Since no glass is formed in the burning process to serve as a bond, the manufacture is somewhat difficult, and these mullite refractories are often melted in an electric furnace and cast into blocks of the shape required. They are expensive but have proved of great value in lining the tank furnaces in which glass is melted.

FUSED SILICATES. VITRIFIED CLAY PRODUCTS

Silica Brick. Ganister.—The lime-silica equilibrium diagram shows that with the addition of more than 1 per cent of lime a small amount of eutectic will form at 2597°F (1425°C). Silica brick is made by crushing a native quartzite, often called "ganister," mixing it with about 2 per cent of lime, and pressing in a power press.

Silica brick, after burning, contain approximately 55 to 70 per cent cristobalite, with the remainder tridymite, residual quartz, and a small percentage of a highly siliceous glass which softens

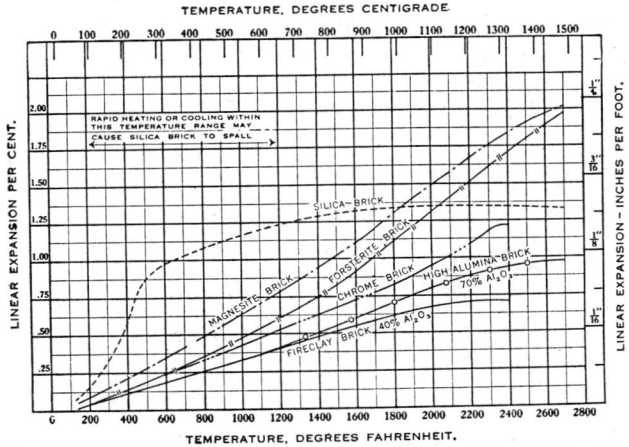

FIG. 151.—Approximate reversible thermal expansion of refractories in linear per cent. Mean values. (*From Harbison-Walker, Modern Refractory Practice.*)

about 2600°F. The crystalline portion forms a skeleton that retains its rigidity at 2800°F and even higher. Continued exposure to high furnace temperatures increases the amount of cristobalite with a slight additional permanent expansion. Silica brick find extensive use in arched roofs of furnaces because of the expansion in the temperature range of 500 to 1200°F which is a characteristic of silica brick, as is shown by Fig. 151. This expansion causes the brick to expand and so wedge themselves more firmly into the arch.

Basic Refractories. *Dolomite. Magnesite.*—Lime and magnesia are the two materials available for basic refractories. Lime however reacts with the moisture of the air to form calcium hydroxide and increases so much in volume that brick made from it disintegrate in the air. Dolomite ($CaCO_3 \cdot MgCO_3$) may be burned to form mixed oxides, and burned dolomite is used in crushed form in building up the linings of open-hearth steel furnaces. Magnesite ($MgCO_3$) may be burned to the oxide and subsequently calcined at a high temperature to ensure complete shrinkage. It does not hydrate in the air if it has been burned to 3000°F. Iron oxide and chromium oxide unite with magnesite at high temperatures and form a bond.

Neutral Refractories. *Chrome and Alumina Brick. Carborundum.*—The oxides of chromium and aluminum do not react readily with either silica or with magnesia and so are sometimes called "neutral refractories." Chrome ore, as mined, always contains other minerals, and when made into a brick and fired, the bond is usually due to a glass of complex composition.

Aluminum oxide may be added to fire-clay brick as has been mentioned. These brick not only have a higher softening point but are also more inert to slags than the fire-clay brick.

Carborundum (silicon carbide) is a product of the electric furnace that may be used at higher temperatures than any of the materials mentioned. It is inert to slags. Its expense precludes its use under any but exceptional circumstances.

Bricks with High- and Low-thermal Conductivity.—Small air spaces interfere with the transmission of heat. A brick, to be a good insulator, should have a maximum porosity, and a brick to transfer heat well should be dense. Silica brick usually has a higher thermal conductivity than fire-clay brick, and magnesite brick has a conductivity that is much higher than either of the others.

Porous brick for insulating purposes may be made by mixing sawdust or ground cork with clay while the brick is being molded. When the brick is fired, the organic matter burns out and leaves a brick that is very porous and light but weak structurally.

Diatomaceous earth consists of microscopic shells of diatoms and other marine organisms whose composition is almost pure hydrated silica. It is found in deposits as a very soft and light rock which may be sawed into blocks for use as insulating brick or crushed and used as an insulating powder.

Selection of a Refractory Brick.—The cheapest brick are those made of fire clay, and those made to withstand the highest temperatures are more expensive than those intended only for

FUSED SILICATES. VITRIFIED CLAY PRODUCTS 365

lower temperatures. Fire-clay brick shrink during the burning process, but after they are made they expand when heated and contract when cooled as shown in Fig. 151. Other brick show greater volume changes than fire-clay brick. Silica brick are unique in their large volume change in the temperature range of 200 to 1000°F, which makes them liable to spall, unless the cooling and heating are conducted very gradually. This expansion and contraction make silica brick undesirable for furnaces which are heated and cooled frequently.

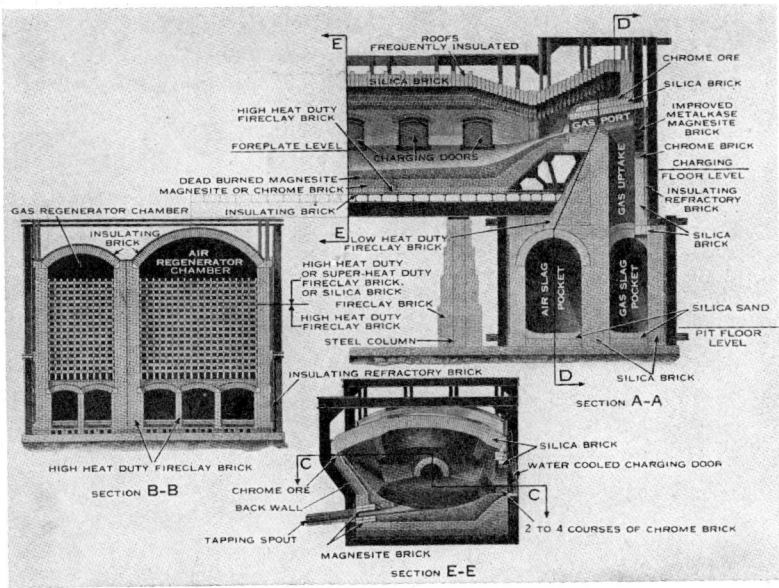

FIG. 152.—Partial section of basic open-hearth furnace. (*From Harbison-Walker, Modern Refractory Practice.*)

If brick are to be subjected to the action of slags, their composition must be such as to give good resistance to corrosion.

The variety of brick used in the construction of a basic open-hearth furnace is shown in Fig. 152. Other illustrations of various furnaces given in the text will indicate where the various types of refractories are used.

Precautions in Heating and Cooling Furnaces.—The illustrations of furnaces in the preceding chapters have indicated the complexity of the structures built out of firebrick and other refractory materials. The linear expansion and contraction of the various types of refractory materials are shown in Fig. 151. It will be fairly evident from these data that furnaces must be heated and cooled slowly so that the thick walls will expand and contract at substantially the same rate throughout their cross section. The longest life will be attained by a furnace if it is kept hot continuously after it is put into service. If a blast furnace or a battery of coke ovens is to be idle a month, it is usually considered economical to keep it hot, though not up to full operating temperature, during its period of idleness.

References

SOSMAN, R. B.: The Properties of Silica, Reinhold Publishing Corporation, New York, 1927.

AUDLEY, J. A.: Silica and the Silicates, Baillière, Tindall & Cox, London, 1921.

NORTON, F. H.: Refractories, 1st ed., McGraw-Hill Book Company, Inc., New York, 1931.

BOLE, G. A., and others: Problems in the Firing of Refractories, *U. S. Bur. Mines Bull.* 271, 1927.

EITEL, WILHELM: Physikalische Chemie der Silikate, Leopold Voss, Leipzig, 1929.

ASCH and ASCH: Die Silikate, Julius Springer, Berlin, 1911.

MOREY, G. W.: Properties of Glass, Reinhold Publishing Corporation, New York, 1938.

CHAPTER XIX

LIME, GYPSUM, AND MAGNESIUM OXYCHLORIDE PRODUCTS

Converting Limestone to Lime.—When limestone or other form of calcium carbonate is heated (calcined or burned) to a high enough temperature, it dissociates according to the equation

$$CaCO_3 \rightleftarrows CaO + CO_2$$

Heat is absorbed in the dissociation to the extent of 772 British thermal units (Btu) per pound $CaCO_3$, or 1380 Btu per pound CaO. The degree of dissociation of $CaCO_3$ under equilibrium conditions is, like all chemical reactions, a function of the temperature, the pressure, and the concentration of the reacting substances. If calcium carbonate is heated in a closed vessel in which there is a small opening so that there will be no accumulation of pressure, no carbon dioxide can be detected in the gas phase until a temperature of about 900°F is reached.

If the temperature is slowly raised, the concentration of the CO_2 in the gas phase will increase as shown in Table 54, until at a

TABLE 54.—EXTENT OF DISSOCIATION OF $CaCO_3$ AT VARIOUS TEMPERATURES, AND ATMOSPHERIC PRESSURE*

Temperature, °F.	Equilibrium Pressure CO_2 Mm. Mercury
932	0.11
1112	2.35
1292	25.3
1472	168.
1652	773.

* JOHNSON, JOHN, *Jour. Am. Chem. Soc.*, **32**, 944 (1910).

temperature of about 1650°F, the partial pressure of the CO_2 within the vessel will become greater than that of the atmosphere, and CO_2 will be evolved in a continuous stream through the small aperture which has been assumed to be present in the reaction vessel. If the temperature had been held constant at some lower temperature, say 1500°F, the reaction would have come to a standstill, under the conditions we have assumed, owing to the reversal of the reaction by the CO_2 present in the vessel.

If the conditions of calcining should be changed so as to blow a continuous stream of air through the vessel and thus remove the carbon dioxide as fast as it was formed, the equilibrium would be disturbed and the reaction might go to completion at any temperature above 900°F. There is thus no fixed temperature for calcining or burning lime, but since the reaction proceeds more rapidly at higher temperatures, it is usually carried out at temperatures of 1600 to 2300°F. Theoretically there should be no limit to the calcining temperature except the melting point of CaO, which is so high, 4658°F, that it can never be reached. In practice, the upper temperature is usually set by secondary reactions which involve the silica, alumina, and magnesia that may be contained in the limestone. These will be discussed later.

Pure limestone loses 44 per cent of its weight when it is burned to CaO, but shrinks in volume only 12 to 20 per cent. Lumps of limestone retain their shape and become more porous on burning.

Limekilns.—Theory shows that limestone will be burned more rapidly and economically in an open furnace than in a closed vessel. No damage will ordinarily be done to the lime by contact with clean smoke gases, and the heat transfer will be much better if there is direct contact between the hot gases and the limestone, than if they are separated by a wall. Lime is therefore almost always burned in direct-fired kilns, with the smoke gases passing about and between the lumps of lime.

Old-style Pot Kiln.—The art of burning lime is an old one and can be carried out with very simple equipment. An old-style pot kiln is illustrated in Fig. 153, copied from Meade.[1] These kilns were usually built into the side of a hill so that the limestone could be dumped in at the top and the burned lime raked out at the bottom. The kiln itself was constructed of rough stone, preferably with a lining of firebrick. An arched opening about 5 ft high permitted the operator to feed the wood fire and pull out the lime. In charging a kiln, a falsework of wood was built up inside of the opening, and on top of this falsework, large lumps

---

[1] Manufacture of Lime for Chemical Purposes, *Trans. Am. Inst. Chem. Eng.*, **13**, I, 288 (1930).

of limestone were placed so as to form a self-supporting arch. The kiln was then filled with lumps of limestone ranging from 2 to 8 in. in diameter so as to permit a free circulation of the smoke gases. The wood fire was lighted and maintained for 3 or 4 days until all of the stone was heated to a bright red heat, after which the kiln was permitted to cool and the product was raked out. The expense for labor and fuel was high in a kiln of this sort, and no adequate control could be maintained over the temperature of burning. Fortunately the process of slaking eliminates the overburned and underburned material, as will be

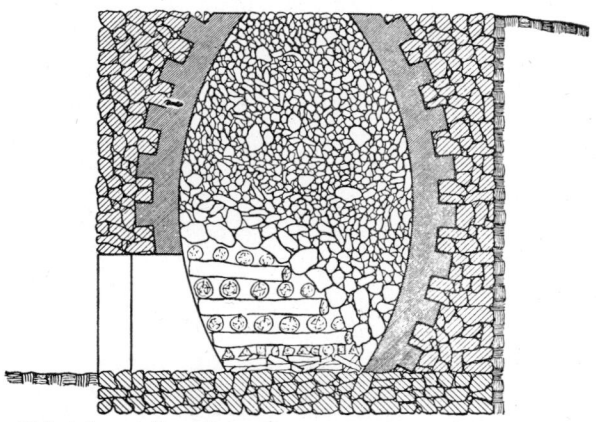

FIG. 153.—Old-style pot limekiln. [*From Meade, Trans. Am. Inst. Chem. Eng.*, **13**, 1, 288 (1920).]

explained later, so that although a kiln of this type was inefficient, it furnished a usable product.

Modern Shaft Kilns.—The old-style pot kiln was improved by making it a permanent structure with separate fireboxes and by keeping it in continuous operation by withdrawing small amount of burned lime and adding an equivalent amount of fresh limestone at frequent intervals. Such a kiln is represented in Fig. 154, also taken from Meade. This kiln has a steel shell 11 ft in diameter and 38 ft high which rests on a concrete foundation and terminates in a steel cooling cone. The upper 5 or 6 ft is not lined and serves as a storage chamber in which the limestone becomes gradually dried and warmed. The illustration shows two hand-fired grates for coal, but powdered coal, oil, or gas may be substituted if these fuels are more economical. The constricted portion in the kiln opposite the fireboxes is partly to take the load of the limestone in the stack off of the cooler, and partly to make the cross section small enough so that there will not be a cold central column of limestone coming down the stack. Portions of burned lime are drawn off at intervals of a few hours into a car which runs on a track below the cooling cone. A kiln

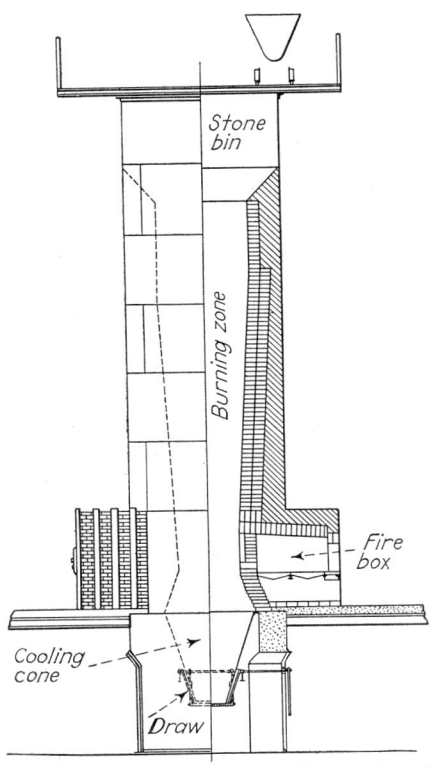

Fig. 154.—Vertical limekiln. [*From Meade, Trans. Am. Inst. Chem. Eng.*, **13**, 1, 290 (1920).]

of this size burning coal will produce 8 to 12 tons of lime a day. If gas is used as the fuel, the output may be doubled.

Limekilns in chemical plants, beet-sugar mills, and other plants that wish to use the CO_2 gas as well as the lime do not have external fireboxes. The fuel is coke which is charged into the top of the limekiln along with the limestone. The gases from the dissociation of the $CaCO_3$ and the smoke gases are drawn off the top, and the lime is drawn out of the bottom substantially as in the kiln shown in the figure.

Rotary Kilns.—The rotary kiln was transferred to the lime industry after having been developed by the manufacturers of portland cement. It consists of an inclined cylinder 5 to 8 ft in diameter and 50 to 150 ft long lined with refractory brick. The illustration of Fig. 155 shows a kiln 8 by 120 ft, fired with producer gas, which may be expected to produce 75 to 80 tons of lime daily. The limestone is crushed, before feeding, to a size

FIG. 155.—Rotary limekiln. (*Courtesy Vulcan Iron Works.*)

that will all pass through a 2-in. screen. It is fed continuously into the upper end of the kiln and works its way as a rather thin layer to the bottom of the kiln where it falls into a rotary cooler.

Influence of Chemical Composition of Limestone.—It will be recalled that limestone is a sedimentary rock that may contain clay and other decomposed rock products, and that magnesium carbonate may also be deposited in the same way as calcium carbonate and so be mixed with the limestone. Magnesium carbonate may be calcined to the oxide at a somewhat lower temperature than calcium carbonate. The MgO is similar chemically to CaO, slakes like lime, and does not injure lime as a structural material provided the temperature of burning has not been too high. The injurious properties of overburned magnesia will be considered when the hydration of lime is being discussed.

Silica and alumina unite with lime at the temperature of the limekiln to form products of indefinite composition, some of which are probably glasses. The active constituent of lime is CaO (or MgO), and any lime in combination as $CaCO_3$, as a glass or in other form, will not form $Ca(OH)_2$. One molecule of silica or alumina will render several molecules of lime or magnesia inactive, especially if the temperature of burning is too high. The overburning temperatures for various grades of limes have been said to be as follows:

	Degrees Fahrenheit
High calcium lime	2300
Impure calcium lime	1900–2100
Pure magnesium limestones	1800–1900
Impure magnesium limestones	1300–1800

Standard Specifications.—The Standard Specifications for quicklime for structural purposes are quoted in part in Table 55

TABLE 55.—STANDARD SPECIFICATIONS FOR QUICKLIME FOR STRUCTURAL PURPOSES*

The quicklime shall conform to the following requirements as to chemical composition, calculated to the nonvolatile basis.

	Calcium lime	Magnesium lime
Calcium oxide, min. per cent	75	
Magnesium oxide, min. per cent		25
Calcium and magnesium oxides, min. per cent	95	95
Silica, alumina, and oxide of iron, max. per cent	5	5
Carbon dioxide, max. per cent:		
(a) If sample is taken at the kiln	3	3
(b) If sample is taken at any other place	10	10

* Abstracted from A.S.T.M. Standards, 1936 ed., Part II, p. 27.

from the 1936 A.S.T.M. Standards. When a sample comes freshly from the kiln, it must not contain over 3 per cent CO_2 which is an index of undecomposed carbonates, nor more than 5 per cent of SiO_2, Al_2O_3, and Fe_2O_3 taken together. The sum of the CaO and MgO must be at least 95 per cent. Quicklime absorbs CO_2 readily when exposed to the air, and so the amount of CO_2, if sampled at any other place than the kiln, may rise as high as 10 per cent, while still complying with the specifications.

The specifications also provide that there shall not be over 15 per cent of residue on slaking, which demands further explanation.

Slaking or Hydrating Lime.—Quicklime reacts with water according to the equation

$$CaO + H_2O \rightleftarrows Ca(OH)_2$$

The heat evolved in the formation of the hydrate is 488 Btu per pound CaO which is enough to raise the temperature of an insulated sample up to a dull red heat. Dry hydrated lime is fluffy and a good heat insulator. If a barrel of quicklime should be stored where rain could reach it, and conditions as to the rate of rainfall should be favorable, the wood of the barrel might catch fire. Freight cars and storehouses occasionally burn up from this cause.

The heat evolved when lime reacts with water is so great as to create a strong driving force to the right of the equation. The reaction will therefore go completely to the right provided an excess of moisture is present. In order to reverse the reaction, the temperature must be raised, and if hydrated lime is heated to redness, the CaO will be regenerated.

Quicklime is never used for structural purposes, but is always hydrated first. The hydrated lime is mixed with sand to form a plastic mass which may be used by the mason in laying brick or by the plasterer in plastering a wall. The plaster hardens partly through evaporation of the water but to a greater extent through combination of the hydrated lime with the carbon dioxide of the air to form crystalline calcium carbonate. If the particles of hydrated lime are to be most effective in promoting plasticity, they must be so small as to be almost of colloidal dimensions, just as was the case with clay particles. The size of the particles of hydrated lime is dependent, to a considerable degree, on the method of hydration, and the technique of this operation has been deemed sufficiently important to warrant discussion in the Standard Specifications.

Slaking for Lime Putty.—A generation ago, quicklime was the only form of lime on the market, and the slaking of the lime was one of the early operations conducted at the site of a new building. The mortar box was about 4 ft wide, 6 to 8 ft long, and 1½ ft deep, made of boards so as to be watertight. Lump lime was shoveled into the box to form a loose layer about 4 in. deep, and several buckets of water were thrown over it. Much of the water was soaked up by the lump lime, but some collected in the bottom of the box. The workman watched the operation, but did nothing more until signs of reaction became evident in the crumbling of some of the lumps of lime with evolution of steam. A small amount of water was thrown upon the lumps that were reacting, for the double purpose of lowering the temperature and providing the additional water needed for the reaction. When the whole mass started to become active, the workman added more water and stirred the mixture with a hoe, keeping the reactive lumps constantly wet. The heat generated made the water boil in places, and constant stirring was necessary. In about half an hour after the first reaction was evident, the violence of the reaction was over, and if the operation had been properly conducted, the box was almost half-full of a snow-white paste or putty consisting of the hydrated lime with some excess water. The box was then covered and allowed to stand, with occasional dampening, until the time came to mix it with sand.

If the workman was careless or inexpert and added too much water at the beginning of the operation, the lime was "drowned" and hydrated slowly in cold water, with the result that the resulting putty was not as plastic as it should have been. If too little water was added, or the stirring was neglected, a dry hydrate formed in spots at a higher temperature and this caused loss of plasticity.

The rate at which the lime slakes and the plasticity of the putty is a function of the purity of the lime and temperature of burning, as well as of the method of slaking. A lime of high purity will react almost instantly with water, and the Standard Specifications direct that quick-slaking lime be added to the water, not the water to the lime, and that sufficient water be present to submerge the lumps completely. For slow-slaking limes, the water should be added to the lime in small portions, and it may even be necessary to add warm water to get the reaction started in cold weather.

Slow-slaking limes are those which are less pure and have been overburned. The product formed by combination of a portion of the lime with silica acts in some unexplained manner to slow down the rate of hydration of the whole mass. Magnesia hydrates much more slowly than lime, and if the magnesia has been overburned, it will not hydrate for days or even weeks. The harmful effects of unhydrated magnesia will be discussed when considering the volume changes in mortars. The Standard Specifications state that for plasterer's mortar the putty should stand at least 2 weeks. This specification is to ensure complete hydration of all of the lime and magnesia and also to develop greater plasticity. For mason's mortar, the recommendation is for a minimum of 24 hr storage of the putty before use. The lower requirement for mason's mortar is because of the lower plasticity required.

The Standard Specifications recommend that the lime putty for plasterers' use be passed through a number 10 sieve which has wires spaced about 0.09 in. apart. This sieve retains the large particles of unburned limestone and also of overburned lime that had not hydrated. In making mason's mortar, smoothness is not so important but all large lumps of unburned limestone or overburned lime should be detected and rejected during the working of the putty. It is this almost automatic rejection of over- and under-burned material that permitted the old pot kilns to deliver a usable product.

The amount of lime putty will vary with the quality of the lime, but one barrel of good lime weighing 200 lb will produce about 8 cu ft of lime putty.

Hydrated Lime.—Lime is hydrated during the process of slaking, but the term "hydrated lime" is restricted by the Standard Specifications to a dry powder "obtained by treating quicklime with water enough to satisfy its chemical affinity under the conditions of its hydration." It consists chemically of the dry hydrates of lime and magnesia. The hydrated-lime industry developed because of the nuisance of the slaking process on large construction jobs, and of the inefficiency and expense of the hand labor required.

Hydrated lime is made by adding just enough water to lime so that the chemical reactions are completed without any excess of either quicklime or of water remaining. Provision must be made for carrying off the heat liberated in the hydration process. The product is sifted and the hydrate is packed as a white powder into paper bags holding 40 or 50 lb each.

When this powder is mixed with water, it forms a lime putty ready for immediate use. The sacks of hydrated lime may be stored without danger of heating or slaking. The paper sack retards the access of air to the contents, but the carbon dioxide of the air does gradually change the powdered hydrate to powdered carbonate which is valueless for mortar.

Lime Mortar.—Mason's mortar is made by mixing 1 volume of lime putty with 2 or $2\frac{1}{2}$ volumes of sand. One volume of hydrated lime is equivalent to one volume of putty. The mortar must be plastic enough to work freely under the trowel, but stiff enough to stand up under the weight of a single brick. Some lime putties have greater sand-carrying capacity than others.

Plasterer's mortar is usually applied in three coats. The first, called the "scratch" coat, is applied directly to the lath or to the masonry wall. It must be pressed firmly against the wall so that it works into the crevices of the masonry and the spaces between the laths, so as to give better adherence to the wall. Before it has hardened, it is scratched with a tool to produce grooves about $\frac{1}{8}$ in. deep. After the scratch coat has hardened, the "brown" coat is applied, and after that has hardened, the "finishing" coat is applied, if one is specified. Hair and wood pulp fillers are sometimes added to the plaster to improve its strength when freshly applied to the wall.

For the scratch coat on lath, 1 volume of lime, either putty or hydrated, is used with $1\frac{1}{2}$ of sand. For the scratch coat on masonry, less lime is used, the proportions of 1 lime to 3 sand being sufficient. For the brown coat, 1 lime to 3 sand is adequate. When a sanded surface is desired on a wall, the brown coat is the last coat applied. In case a smooth white surface is required, a putty coat is applied over the brown coat. In former days, this consisted of lime putty diluted somewhat and applied without any other admixture as a thin coating over the brown coat. In more modern practice, gypsum plaster is nearly always mixed with the hydrated lime.

Hydrated lime shrinks so much on drying that it cannot be used by itself as a plaster or as a mortar. Sand grains are strong, and if the mixing is well done, and the proportions of lime and sand are correct, the mixture will have adequate strength. The shrinkage is reduced, and the porosity of the finished plaster is increased by the sand. Increased porosity permits the plaster to harden more rapidly.

Hardening of Lime Mortar.—When the mason places a trowel full of soft mortar on a wall and sets a brick on it, he settles the brick into place with a light tap from the handle of his trowel. The mortar is soft enough to flow readily under the weight of the brick plus the tap of the trowel. It will however not flow under the weight of the brick alone. After a few minutes, the mortar will have stiffened considerably owing to the absorption of water by the brick. Porous common brick absorb water much more rapidly than the less porous face brick. The hardening of lime mortar as distinguished from the setting is due to the carbon dioxide of the air reacting with the calcium hydroxide to form crystals of calcium carbonate according to the equation

$$Ca(OH)_2 + CO_2 \rightleftarrows CaCO_3 + H_2O$$

This reaction proceeds very slowly if the plaster and the carbon dioxide are both dried artificially, and it is probable that it proceeds best in the presence of enough moisture to form a film of liquid water which becomes saturated with calcium hydroxide and from which the less soluble calcium carbonate separates to form crystals on the sand grains. These crystals grow slowly and ultimately bridge the gap from one sand grain to the next.

One of the most favorable conditions for rapid hardening of mortar occurs in walls where the lime plaster has been applied over wooden or metal lath. The total thickness of plaster is only about half an inch, and there is circulation of air over both surfaces. About 10 days is allowed between coats, and a three-coat job requires about a month. The plaster will not have attained nearly its maximum strength by that time, and it will continue to increase slowly in strength and hardness, although in winter when the humidity is low, the increase will almost cease. It is to be noted that the walls of a new house plastered with lime mortar will always be alkaline. Paint and wallpaper must be applied with caution.

Masonry walls must harden from the outside to the center, and the rate of hardening becomes very slow in the center of thick walls. Walls of mediaeval castles were sometimes 10 ft thick, and the story has been told of finding soft mortar in the center of such walls after the lapse of 100 years.

The effect of age on the strength of mortar can be noted wherever brick buildings are being pulled down. If a wall is toppled over after it has been built only a few years, the shock knocks the mortar off most of the brick. On the other hand, if a wall is pulled down after it has been built 50 years, the mortar is sometimes so strong and adherent to the brick that the brick will split before the mortar joint gives way. This is not a proof that better mortar was used 50 years ago, but proof that the recrystallization of the calcium carbonate continues for many years.

When brick piers are tested under compression at the age of 6 months, failure always occurs at a the mortar joints at values representing only 10 to 20 per cent of the crushing strength of the brick. In modern practice, portland-cement mortar is always used on important work for reasons that will be discussed in the next chapter.

Since the hardening of lime mortar is due to the reaction with carbon dioxide, and the amount of carbon dioxide in the air is only 0.04 per cent, it would appear logical to accelerate the rate of hardening by increasing the amount of CO_2 in the air. This may be accomplished by placing braziers containing burning coke in a room that has been recently plastered. Both the increased temperature and the increased concentration of CO_2 will accelerate the rate of formation of $CaCO_3$. Unfortunately, however, the strength of the mortar is due to the formation of rather large crystals of calcium carbonate which grow from one sand grain to the next and bond the two together. An increase in the concentration of carbon dioxide causes the formation of many small crystals and a plaster that lacks strength. The temperature should not be allowed to go below freezing, for crystals of $CaCO_3.5H_2O$, an unstable hydrated carbonate of lime, form.[1]

The use of lime mortar as an external plaster coat or stucco will also be considered after a study has been made of portland cement.

Durability of Lime Mortar and Plaster.—Fully hardened lime mortar and plaster consist of grains of sand bonded together by crystalline calcium carbonate. They are thus very similar to some sandstones. When lime mortar is used in masonry construction exposed to the weather, the mortar disintegrates more

[1] WHITE, A. H.: *Proc. Am. Soc. Testing Materials*, **9**, 530 (1909).

rapidly than the brick and it is necessary to go over the wall every few years and "point up" the joints with fresh mortar. In interior construction, lime mortar is extremely reliable and durable. The cracks that occur in the plaster of old houses are usually due to settlement, or twisting of a frame structure by wind. The plaster itself resists water well. The damage caused by water leaking through a ceiling, where the plaster was applied over wooden lath, is due to the swelling of the lath. The plasterer pressed the fresh mortar between the laths far enough so that it curled over and locked behind the lath. This held the plaster firmly in place until water caused the lath to swell and break off the plaster.

The cracking of plaster due to the slow hydration of magnesium oxide after the plaster has become hardened will be considered in connection with the behavior of magnesium oxide in portland cement.

Gypsum Plaster.—Gypsum plasters are widely used for plastering walls, and are in direct competition with lime plasters for this purpose. They belong however in an entirely different chemical classification, and harden in a very different way. The use of gypsum plaster has been known for thousands of years in Egypt, and the very word gypsum is derived from the name of that country.

Gypsum and Its Dehydration Products.—The mineral gypsum is a hydrated calcium sulfate with the formula $CaSO_4 \cdot 2H_2O$, which occurs in large deposits in many parts of the world. The water of crystallization is not very firmly held, and if powdered gypsum is heated slightly in dry air it will lose part of its water, which it will regain if allowed to stand at room temperature in moist air. When gypsum is heated to higher temperatures, it parts with its water more readily, and gradually loses all of it to become the anhydrous $CaSO_4$ which is called "anhydrite."

There is also a fairly definite stopping point when half of the water has been driven off, and the residue is called the "half-hydrate." The equations are usually written

$$CaSO_4 \cdot 2H_2O \rightleftarrows CaSO_4 \cdot \tfrac{1}{2}H_2O + 1\tfrac{1}{2}H_2O$$
Half-hydrate

$$CaSO_4 \cdot 2H_2O \rightleftarrows CaSO_4 + 2H_2O$$
Anhydrite

This involves the absurdity of eliminating a half molecule of water, but it is arithmetically correct and corresponds to the usual nomenclature. The manufacturing process consists of calcining the gypsum to drive off part or all of its water of crystallization, and the hardening of the plasters when used is due to a reversal of the chemical reaction, water being taken into combination to form $CaSO_4.2H_2O$.

Calcination of Gypsum.—The temperatures involved in the calcination of gypsum are below a red heat, and the older method of manufacture, which is still widely used, consists in grinding the gypsum rock to a fine powder and heating it in a large steel kettle which is provided with a stirrer and set in brickwork, so that the hot gases from the firebox circulate around it and through several flues which pass through the kettle. A kettle 8 ft in diameter and 10 ft high will hold about 10 tons of ground gypsum and will permit the completion of the heating operation in about 4 hr.

The ground rock is run into the kettle, which is usually hot from the previous batch, as the stirrer slowly revolves so as to give more uniform temperature throughout the mass. When the temperature rises to about 230 to 270°F (depending on the rate of heating), steam is evolved so rapidly that the mass "boils." When the boiling ceases, the powder settles down again in the kettle.

This marks the end of the first step in the dehydration process, and if the powder is withdrawn after this stage is completed, it will be found to be approximately the half-hydrate $CaSO_4.\frac{1}{2}H_2O$. Some commercial plants withdraw the plaster at a temperature of about 350°F. To the manufacturer, this is known as "first-settle" plaster. To the consumer, it is known as plaster of Paris, or merely as gypsum plaster. Almost all of the gypsum plaster that reaches the market consists of first-settle plaster with various additions, such as sand or wood pulp.

If the gypsum is not withdrawn from the kettle after the first settle, it commences to boil again at about 360°F, owing to the evolution of the remaining water of crystallization. The product, after this step is finished at about 400°F, is known to the manufacturer as "second-settle" plaster, and is the material used by the large manufacturers of plaster board and other gypsum products. It gives a stronger product, but it is not stable when stored in damp air and is not sold in package form to retailers. The material after the second settle has lost all of its water of crystallization and is known as "soluble anhydrite" to distinguish it from a more stable and less soluble form of anhydrite that is formed by longer heating or heating to a higher temperature.

A more economical method of calcining gypsum, which is available to large plants, is to use a rotary kiln similar to the limekiln. The gypsum rock, crushed to pieces about the size of a nut, is passed through the kiln at such a speed that a pyrometer in the stream of solid material at the outlet of the kiln will register about 550°F. The center of these lumps has however not become heated very hot, so the lumps are conveyed into storage pits where the temperature throughout the lumps is equalized and the product becomes fairly uniform in composition. It is ground to powder and mixed with other ingredients after it is drawn from the storage pits.

The Hardening of Gypsum Plaster.—The hardening of all grades of gypsum plaster is due to recombination of the plaster with the water that is added to make it plastic enough for application as a plaster or other purpose. The equation may be written as follows:

$$CaSO_4 \cdot \tfrac{1}{2}H_2O + 1\tfrac{1}{2}H_2O \rightleftarrows CaSO_4 \cdot 2H_2O$$

or

$$CaSO_4 + 2H_2O \rightleftarrows CaSO_4 \cdot 2H_2O$$

They are identical with those previously written for the dehydration of gypsum. The equations as written above proceed to the right at room temperature. The plaster sets and hardens because the liquid water reacts with the plaster to form the solid crystalline hydrate. In order that the product shall set and harden, the hydrated product must be less soluble than the anhydrous material. The solubility of the gypsum plaster $CaSO_4 \cdot \tfrac{1}{2}H_2O$ is about 9 g per liter at room temperature. The solubility of the hydrated crystalline gypsum $CaSO_4 \cdot 2H_2O$ is 2 g per liter. In the process of setting and hardening, the half-hydrate dissolves to form a solution that may at its maximum hold 9 g per liter of the half-hydrate. Such a solution is however supersaturated for the dihydrate, and so some of the latter crystallizes out leaving the water with a lower percentage of half-hydrate. More half-hydrate then goes into solution, and the process is kept up until either the water is all used up, or the half-hydrate has all reacted. In practice, the mixture frequently contains more than enough plaster to combine with the water present, so that the hardened product consists of gypsum with a small excess of unconverted half-hydrate.

This process of hardening through reaction with water is the mark of hydraulic cements. Gypsum plaster is scientifically a hydraulic cement, although in the trade the term is often restricted to the silicate cements which will be discussed in the next chapter.

Rate of Setting of Gypsum Plasters.—The term "setting" is used to indicate the initial phase of the hardening process, and a plaster is said to have set when it has become stiff. This is determined with equipment and methods standardized by the American Society for Testing Materials. The fingernail may be used as a rough testing instrument, and the appearance of the initial set approximately determined as the condition when the plaster is no longer indented readily by the fingernail. If pure gypsum is calcined at a low temperature and mixed with warm water, the time of set may be only 2 min. This is the type of material used by dentists in taking impressions of the mouth. Fine grinding also accelerates the rate of setting. A large amount of water retards the set, because more liquid water must be changed to the solid crystalline state before the mass can stiffen.

Another factor affecting the rate of setting is the presence of small amounts of substances that either accelerate or retard the set. The final product is to be $CaSO_4.2H_2O$, and if the calcination has been so thorough that none of the original gypsum has come through unchanged, the solution of $CaSO_4.\frac{1}{2}H_2O$ may remain for some time as a saturated solution before crystals of $CaSO_4.2H_2O$ commence to form. A small amount of the crystalline gypsum will furnish seed crystals and ensure a prompt formation of new crystals. The addition of common salt to the water used in making up the mixture is said to accelerate the set, although no good explanation for its action has been presented.

In manufacturing plaster for commercial use, it is ordinarily necessary to retard the set so that the product after mixing with water will remain a plastic mass for an hour or more so as to give opportunity for the plasterer to apply it to the wall and get it smoothed before it sets. The retardation of the time of set may be accomplished by a little glue added to the water, or more cheaply by a commercial retarder made from hair and tankage from the stockyards. The retarder probably acts by retarding the formation of the initial crystals. Clay in rather large proportions also retards the rate of setting.

Fibers of wood pulp, hair, or asbestos are sometimes added to increase the strength of the wet plaster when it is first applied to a wall.

Specifications for Calcined Gypsum and Gypsum Plaster.—The A.S.T.M. Standards contains a number of specifications for gypsum products. Calcined gypsum is defined as having the approximate formula of $CaSO_4.\tfrac{1}{2}H_2O$. It must all pass a No. 14 sieve (sieve opening 0.0555 in.), and according to one specification not less than 75 per cent must pass a No. 100 sieve (sieve opening 0.0059 in.). This rather coarse size is permissible because of the relatively high solubility of the gypsum. Portland cement, as will be seen later, must be ground very much more finely. The tensile strength must be not less than 200 psi and the compressive strength not less than 1000 psi, when determined according to a method that is rigidly prescribed. Gypsum plasters react rapidly enough so that they gain their full strength in less than 24 hr.

Gypsum plasters consist of calcined gypsum mixed with sand, wood fiber, or other materials. Ready-sanded plaster for the scratch coat may not contain more than two-thirds of its weight of sand and must contain 20 per cent of calcined gypsum. It must set in not less than $1\tfrac{1}{2}$ nor more than 7 hr and shall have a tensile strength of not less than 75 psi.

Gypsum Wallboards.—The A.S.T.M. Standards for 1936 define wallboard as a gypsum-plaster board designed to be used, without the addition of plaster, for walls, ceilings, or partitions and affording a surface suitable to receive decoration. It consists of an incombustible core of gypsum, with or without fiber, but not exceeding 15 per cent fiber by weight, and surfaced with paper or other fibrous material firmly bonded to the core. The paper used is somewhat similar to blotting paper since it must be porous in order that the plaster may adhere to it strongly. The outer surface of the paper is usually sized or coated to lessen the porosity. The plaster may contain sawdust, or in some cases starch, to lighten the weight. The fiber and gypsum are mixed dry, then wetted and mixed further in a continuous machine that feeds the wet mix onto a moving sheet of paper. The top sheet is applied in the next step and the wet sandwich passed between rolls that give the proper thickness. The board continues to travel for about 200 ft at a speed of 10 ft per minute until it is set, when it is cut up and sent to the driers.

Gypsum Tile.—Hollow tile for partitions may be extruded much like clay tile onto a moving belt that carries the block until it has set sufficiently to be cut into lengths and lifted off the belt to be conveyed to a drier. Reinforced gypsum roof tile may be cast by hand. Gypsum plaster may also be poured like concrete into forms for roofs.

Keene's Cement.—Keene's cement is anhydrous calcined gypsum whose set has been accelerated by the addition of other materials. When gypsum is heated rapidly to 400°F, it will have lost its water of hydration and have the formula $CaSO_4$, but it will still retain the crystal structure of the half-hydrate, will react readily with water, and so it is called "soluble anhydrite" or "second-settle gypsum." If the temperature of calcination is raised to a red heat, the soluble anhydrite changes to a modification that is much less soluble. Its solubility is however greater than that of gypsum $CaSO_4.2H_2O$, and so it possesses the same capabilities of hardening through reaction with water.

This product was originally made under an English patent which expired many years ago, and the name Keene's has become recognized as the designation for this dehydrated product. The A.S.T.M. Standards require that its time of setting shall be between 1 and 4 hr and that its tensile strength shall be not less than 450 psi. The materials used to accelerate the set are kept as trade secrets. Sodium sulfate, potassium sulfate, and borax have been used.

The ordinary gypsum forms a porous mass of interlocking crystals. Keene's cement has become a dense material because of the higher temperature in the kiln. Each particle reacts slowly, and so the crystals of the hydrated compounds become large and strong. The water required to mix Keene's cement to a thick paste is insufficient to hydrate all of the cement, and so if the material is broken up soon after it has set and mixed with a little more water, it will set again. It makes such a hard wall and floor plaster that its surface may be ground and polished.

Imitation marble may be made by burning very pure gypsum and mixing tinting materials with different batches. This material is then spattered on to a wall or column so as to give local color effects, and the surface is then polished and waxed. The large monolithic columns found in the older and rather ornate hotels consisted usually of a steel column around which plaster of this sort had been applied.

Magnesium Oxychloride Cement.—The discovery of a strong cement produced by the interaction of magnesium oxide and a solution of magnesium chloride was made by Stanislaus Sorel, a French engineer, in 1867, and the product is sometimes called "Sorel cement." The precise nature of the chemical compound formed is still in dispute, and it is probable that the reaction is not a definite one. It may be written

$$3MgO + MgCl_2 + 7H_2O \rightleftarrows 3MgO.MgCl_2.7H_2O$$

The reaction is reversible, and by washing with successive portions of water, substantially all of the $MgCl_2$ may be washed out leaving a residue of $Mg(OH)_2$.

The calcination of magnesite has been mentioned in the discussion of lime, and it was stated that its dissociation temperature was lower than that of calcium carbonate. Brief reference was made to the danger of overburning magnesite because it slowed up the process of hydration, and it was stated that it would be discussed further when the effect of magnesium oxide in portland cement was considered. Magnesia burned at a low temperature hydrates readily to form a gelatinous hydrate, and is, on that account, sometimes called "plastic magnesia" or "caustic magnesia." The magnesia that is to be used for oxychloride cement must be a high-grade stone carefully burned at a low temperature and ground to a powder almost as fine as portland cement.

The magnesium chloride is used as a rather concentrated solution, containing about 20 per cent anhydrous $MgCl_2$.

Inert materials of various types may be incorporated. Sand, asbestos, and clay are sometimes used when a hard tile is desired. Sawdust and wood flour may be used if a softer tile is wanted.

The dry ingredients are mixed thoroughly, and sufficient of the magnesium chloride added to make it plastic. The mixture may then be applied to a floor or wall. It sets in a few hours and gains strength rapidly. A mixture of straight magnesium oxide and chloride may be expected to give a tensile strength of 250 psi after 24 hr, and 350 psi after 7 days, with further increases up to 60 days. These values are higher than those required by the Standard Specifications for the regular grade of portland cement.

Magnesium oxychloride cements are not very durable when exposed to the weather because of the leaching of the magnesium chloride by rain. Unless the magnesite has been very carefully prepared, its delayed hydration will cause expansion and disintegration. These cements lend themselves admirably to the manufacture of soft tile or plaster which will not reflect sound. Sawdust and wood pulp give a good product with the magnesium oxychloride mix but do not behave well when incorporated in lime or portland-cement mortar. Colors can also be readily incorporated. The expense of the magnesium oxychloride cements restricts their use to special purposes. The cement is more resilient than concrete, and the impact of feet does not make so much noise as on concrete. It retains some plasticity after it has hardened. It may be laid over a wooden floor, and if the floor settles somewhat, the cement will accommodate itself to it without cracking.

The Addition of Copper to Magnesium Oxychloride Cements.— Hubbell[1] has reported that the addition of 10 per cent of finely divided metallic copper to the mixture produces a material that has superior characteristics. The copper reacts slowly and forms an insoluble basic copper chloride. It is claimed that the new material is much superior to the magnesium oxychloride cements in constancy of volume and weather resistance.

References

EMLEY, W. E.: Lime: Its Properties and Uses, *U. S. Bur. Standards, Circ.* 30, 1920.

ECKEL, E. C.: Cements, Limes and Plasters, 2d ed., John Wiley & Sons, Inc., New York, 1922.

KNIBBS, N. V. S.: Lime and Magnesia, Ernest Benn, Ltd., London, 1924.

Physical Properties of the Principal Commercial Limestones Used for Building Construction in the United States, *U. S. Bur. Standards, Tech.* Paper 349, 1927.

[1] *Ind. and Eng. Chem.*, **29**, 123 (1937).

MEADE, R. K.: The Manufacture of Lime for Chemical and Metallurgical Purposes, *Trans. Am. Inst. Chem. Eng.*, **13**, I, 287 (1920).

PORTER, J. M.: The Technology of the Manufacture of Gypsum Products, U. S. Bur. Standards, *Circ.* 281, 1926.

Gypsum—Properties, Definitions and Uses, *U. S. Bur. Standards, Circ.* 108, 1921.

Wall Plaster: Its Ingredients, Preparation and Properties, *U. S. Bur. Standards, Circ.* 151, 1924.

WHITE, A. H.: Volume Changes in Gypsum Structures Due to Atmospheric Humidity, *Univ. Michigan, Dept. Eng. Research, Bull.* 2, 1926.

Caustic Magnesia Cement, *U. S. Bur. Standards, Circ.* 135, 1922.

RALSTON, PIKE, and DUSCHAK: Plastic Magnesia, *U. S. Bur. Mines,* Bull. 236, 1925.

HUBBELL, D. S.: A New Inorganic Cement and Adhesive, *Ind. and Eng. Chem.*, **29**, 123 (1937).

WIG, PEARSON, and EMLEY: Durability of Stucco and Plaster Construction, *U. S. Bur. Standards Technologic Paper* 70, 1917.

CHAPTER XX

THE SILICATE CEMENTS: POZZUOLANIC CEMENTS, HYDRAULIC LIMES, NATURAL CEMENTS, PORTLAND CEMENT

Types of Silicate Cements.—With the exception of calcined gypsum and the magnesium oxychloride cements, all of our hydraulic cements are silicates of lime, with alumina, iron oxide, and magnesium oxide playing secondary but sometimes important roles. The Romans, and possibly other peoples before them, made some of these cements in an empiric manner. Scientific knowledge of these cements has come only within the past generation. It is still incomplete for all classes of the cements.

These cements are all formed by the action of heat on a mixture of silica, alumina, iron oxide, lime, and magnesia. Sometimes the product is ready for use after it has been burned and ground. Sometimes an additional step is necessary. In the pozzuolanic group, the cement must be mixed with hydrated lime after it has been burned. Portland cement is by far the most important member of the group, but all of the types are still used.

Pozzuolanic Cements.—The art of burning lime and making lime mortar was known before the days of the Roman Empire. There is a little village on the Bay of Naples called Pozzuoli, and it was found that if the sand from this village was mixed with lime paste the resulting mortar would set under water. This sand was one of the products of an eruption of Vesuvius. It had been blown out of the volcano as droplets of molten lava which, cooling quickly in the air, had fallen as a sandy deposit near the foot of the mountain. The hydraulic cement made from this product was not of high quality as judged by modern standards, but it did good service when used under water or below ground where it would always stay damp. The Romans knew it would not be permanent above ground, and so the superstructures of their concrete buildings were always faced with clay brick or tile. Structures built of their concrete are still in good condition after two thousand years exposure to the mild Italian climate.

An artificial pozzuolanic cement has been made from the slag of the iron blast furnace. If this slag is run, while molten, into water so as to chill it and then dried and ground with dry hydrated lime, a pozzuolanic cement will be formed. This cement is not suitable for use aboveground, and its manufacture has been discontinued. The slag is now used as an ingredient in true portland cement.

Pozzuolanic material is sometimes added to portland cement. When portland cement hydrates, calcium hydrate is set free, as will be shown later. Therefore the addition of pozzuolanic material to portland cement will decrease the amount of hydrated lime in the hardened mortar, and perhaps make the cement more resistant to corrosive agents. The theory of such an addition seems sound, but little practical application has been made of it in this country. Cements in which additions of this sort are incorporated are known as "blended cements."

No adequate investigation has ever been made of the reactions taking place when pozzuolanic cements harden. Almost any siliceous slag, if chilled and ground finely, will react with hydrated lime, but if the slag is slowly cooled, stable and inactive minerals are formed that will not react with hydrated lime. Chilled slag remains as an active supercooled glass. The lack of stability of this cement when used aboveground is probably due to a large amount of colloidal water contained in the hardened cement. When the cement becomes dry, the shrinkage caused by loss of colloidal water causes cracks to form.

Hydraulic Limes and Natural Cements.—With the fall of the Roman Empire came the darkness of the Middle Ages which lasted nearly a thousand years. The art of burning lime and making mortar was not lost, and it was observed that some limes had the ability to harden under water. The marl from the bed of streams in the chalk country of England was found to yield a hydraulic lime, and one explanation which was advanced was that the calcium carbonate had, because of its long submersion, become so habituated to water that it could harden even when submerged.

The first attempt at a more rational explanation came from John Smeaton, a civil engineer in England and a contemporary and friend of James Watt, the inventor of the steam engine. Smeaton had been commissioned in 1756 to build a lighthouse on the partially submerged Eddystone reef off the coast of England and realized that he could not hope to succeed without a reliable hydraulic cement. He made a study of the hydraulic limes which were known and came to the correct conclusion that all limestones or marls that yielded a hydraulic lime contained a proportion of clay.

The various seams from a limestone quarry do not contain a uniform amount of clay, and in burning the stone for hydraulic lime, it was found that, on slaking with a small amount of water, some of the lumps remained hard and did not break down to powder. They were thrown away and only the powder was used. Forty years later, Joseph Parker in England took out a patent on the process of burning clayey nodules in a limekiln and grinding up the calcined lumps which came from the kiln and which would not slake with water. He called this ground cement "Roman cement," although the Romans never knew cement of this sort, and the name is still occasionally found in the literature.

The cement industry of the United States commenced during the construction of the Erie Canal in New York State in 1818, when a suitable limestone for making hydraulic cement was found near the middle section of the canal.

Modern Hydraulic Limes and Natural Cements.—The reactions between calcium carbonate and clay (SiO_2, Al_2O_3, and Fe_2O_3) have already been mentioned. In burning brick, it was stated that finely divided calcium carbonate reacted with the clay during the burning process and that a sound brick resulted. The standard specification for builders' lime requires that the amount of $SiO_2 + Al_2O_3 + Fe_2O_3$ shall not be over 5 per cent. These materials are usually present in the limestone as a finely divided clay which will combine with the lime at 2000°F and form a compound of unknown composition, but one that is hydraulic. The lime becomes progressively less plastic as the percentage of these acidic compounds increases, and their amount was therefore limited to 5 per cent in the specification for builders lime. Eckels[1] cites analyses of feebly hydraulic limes in which the sum of the $SiO_2 + Al_2O_3 + Fe_2O_3$ ranges from 17 to 24 per cent, the balance being CaO and MgO. Such a product will contain enough free lime so that if it is slaked with steam there will be enough expan-

[1] Cements, Limes and Plasters, p. 195.

sion to break the lumps to a fine powder which will be a mixture of hydrated lime and a hydraulic cement.

If the sum of the $SiO_2 + Al_2O_3 + Fe_2O_3$ rises much above 30 per cent, but not usually above 40 per cent, the product as it comes from the limekiln will no longer break down to a powder with steam but if it is ground finely, it will form a hydraulic cement which is marketed under the name "natural cement."

Fortunately for the engineers and lime manufacturers of an earlier day, the reactions are such that they were almost certain to obtain a usable product. Limestone of any composition will give a useful product, provided the kiln temperature is kept within the limits specified for burning lime. The product will be either a builder's lime, a hydraulic lime, or a natural cement.

Specifications for Natural Cement.—The A.S.T.M. Standards for 1936 define natural cement to be the finely pulverized product resulting from the calcination of an argillaceous limestone at a temperature only sufficient to drive off the carbonic acid gas. The word "argillaceous" means claylike, and it is used in the cement industry to denote any mixture of $SiO_2 + Al_2O_3 + Fe_2O_3$. Another somewhat uncommon word frequently used in the cement industry is "neat" in the sense of undiluted. A pat of neat cement is made from a paste that contains cement and water, with no sand or other aggregate or diluent.

Tests for time of setting are made on pats of neat cement, and tests of tensile strength are made on briquets of neat cement, frequently also on briquets of mortar made by mixing the cement with a specified volume of standard sand. The tensile strength demanded of natural cements is less than one-fifth that of portland cements. Briquets made of 1 part of cement and 3 of standard sand, after storage for 7 days (1 day in moist air and 6 days in water), need show a tensile strength of only 50 psi for natural cement, as compared with 275 psi required of portland cement.

Minor Importance of Natural Cements.—The classes of hydraulic cements which have been considered have all been of a type that could be made with simple equipment operating without scientific control. They gave a product that was usable, but not so good or economical as the portland cement of modern days. These cements are still made but in small quantities.

Masonry Cements.—There is one purpose for which hydraulic limes and natural cements still hold their own—in making mortar for brick and stone masonry. Lime mortar hardens slowly, is rather weak, and weathers rapidly so that it must be repointed rather often. Portland cement does not give a plastic enough mortar for masonry work, but the plasticity may be improved by the addition of hydrated lime. The color of portland cement is greenish gray, although white cement may be made from selected raw materials at a higher cost. This is because portland cement is burned at such a high temperature that the iron in the cement is in combination as a fused silicate. The same phenomenon was noted in burning red brick where the normal red color changed to greenish black on overheating beyond the normal vitrifying range. The hydraulic limes and natural rock cements burned at the temperature of the limekiln retain the iron in the state of ferric oxide and so have a yellow tint. These products also retain enough free lime so that, after they are hydrated, they will give a mortar which will be plastic enough to spread properly. Portland cement mortar is objectionable for marble or limestone not only because of the color but also because it tends to stain the stone. The hydraulic limes are free from this tendency. There are a few mills operating under scientific control that produce hydraulic limes and natural cements as masonry cements.

Portland Cement. Early Development.—The name portland cement was given to a product patented by Joseph Aspdin, a bricklayer of Leeds, England, in 1824. He called it portland cement because, after hardening, it resembled in color the stone quarried near Portland in England. His patent covers an artificial mixture of limestone and clay but does not mention proportions or temperature of burning. His product was probably about the same as a natural cement, although the product was a synthetic one, and there is no evidence that he carried his temperatures to the point of incipient vitrification. He did however make cement that was usable and probably gradually raised his kiln temperatures.

In Germany, the first portland cement was made in 1852, and in the United States in 1872. This first mill was located near Kalamazoo, Michigan, and operated for about 10 years. In the early years, the manufacture was on an entirely empiric basis, the quality was uneven, the price was high, and the whole industry operated on a small scale. For many years, natural cement was considered preferable except where great strength was required.

Scientific Foundations of Portland-cement Manufacture.—In 1887, Henri Le Châtelier, a young French chemist who was to become one of the world's leaders in physical chemistry, investigated the constitution of portland cement for his doctoral dissertation. Many investigators have studied the subject since Le Châtelier laid the foundation, and the structure of portland-cement clinker and its products of hydration are now understood quite thoroughly.

The Microscopic Structure of Portland-cement Clinker.—The product that comes from the rotary kiln in the manufacture of portland cement consists of lumps, approximately spherical, which are frequently about the size of a pea. They have been heated to incipient fusion in the kiln, and the product is called "clinker." If a piece of this clinker is ground to a thin section so that light will be transmitted through it and it is examined under the microscope, it will be seen to be composed of several different types of crystals and some glass. The four important crystalline minerals and their chemical compositions are given in Table 56.

TABLE 56.—IMPORTANT CONSTITUENTS OF PORTLAND-CEMENT CLINKER

Tricalcium silicate	$3CaO.SiO_2$
Beta dicalcium silicate	$2CaO.SiO_2$
Tricalcium aluminate	$3CaO.Al_2O_3$
Tetracalcium alumino ferrite	$4CaO.Al_2O_3.Fe_2O_3$

Percentage Composition

	CaO	SiO$_2$	Al$_2$O$_3$	Fe$_2$O$_3$
$3CaO.SiO_2$	73.7	26.3		
$2CaO.SiO_2$	65.1	34.9		
$3CaO.Al_2O_3$	62.3	....	37.7	
$4CaO.Al_2O_3.Fe_2O_3$	46.2	....	21.0	32.8

Raw Materials for Portland Cement.—The older A.S.T.M. Standard Specifications define portland cement as being made from calcareous and argillaceous materials. Calcareous includes all compounds of lime and magnesia, and argillaceous includes all compounds of silica, alumina, and iron oxide, with minor amounts of alkalies. The calcareous materials are usually limestone or marl, and the argillaceous materials clay or shale. There are some limestones which contain so much clay that they have nearly the composition required for portland cement. Blast-furnace slag rates as an argillaceous material because additional lime must be incorporated with it for the manufacture of portland cement. There is a wide variety in the possible raw materials, and no limitation is put upon them. The identity of the raw materials disappears in the burning process, and it is only the final product that is of importance. There are specific limitations on magnesia and sulfates, and they will be discussed later.

The Standard Specifications do not even say that the clinker shall contain any definite amounts of tricalcium silicate or aluminate. The physical tests that are imposed on the finished product and the highly competitive conditions in the industry do, however, limit both the raw materials and the chemical composition of the finished cement.

It is possible, in the laboratory, to make the pure mineral constituents mentioned in Table 56, but it is not easy to do so. Each of them is a hydraulic cement, but not in itself altogether desirable as a commercial product. It is desirable to have a small amount of iron oxide and a somewhat larger amount of alumina to form a fusible glass during the burning process. This glass acts as a solvent for the other materials and facilitates the formation of the definite minerals that characterize portland cement.

Chemical Composition of Clinker.—The chemist must have at his disposal at least two raw materials, one of which is too high in lime and one which is too low in lime for his purpose. He starts with the silica and alumina and calculates how he must combine them to obtain the compounds $3CaO.SiO_2$ and $3CaO.Al_2O_3$. He does not, however, use as much lime as this formula will call for, because experience has shown that it is not possible, on the large scale, to get complete combination of these constituents in the ratio of the full molecular formula without leaving some lime in the free CaO form. This is detrimental. The chemist therefore decreases the lime in his formula to a figure that experience has shown to be safe. A mill that is well equipped and operated can run closer to the full lime formula than a mill that is not so efficient. Since the raw materials will contain variable proportions of silica and alumina, it is evident that there can be no standardization of chemical composition.

The average composition of 32 American cements is given in Table 57. It will be noted that the sum of the acidic constituents (SiO_2, Al_2O_3, Fe_2O_3) is 30.7 per cent and that the lime (CaO) is

TABLE 57.—AVERAGE COMPOSITION AND STRENGTH OF 32 AMERICAN CEMENTS*

Chemical Composition, Per Cent

SiO_2	21.92 ⎫
Al_2O_3	5.91 ⎬ 30.7
Fe_2O_3	2.91 ⎭
CaO	62.92
MgO	2.54
SO_3	1.72
Loss on ignition	1.50
Insoluble residue	0.20
	99.62

Calculated Percentage of Mineral Constituents

$3CaO.SiO_2$	40.7 per cent
$2CaO.SiO_2$	32.1
$3CaO.Al_2O_3$	10.7
$4CaO.Al_2O_3.Fe_2O_3$	8.9
$CaSO_4$	2.9

Physical Properties

Tensile strength, psi

	1:3 Mortar	Neat
3 days	215	200
7 days	290	295
28 days	390	445
3 months	430	500

Compressive strength, psi
Neat Cubes

3 days	1590
7 days	2720
28 days	5230
3 months	7100

Compressive strength, psi
6 × 12 Cylinders†

3 days	1100
7 days	1850
28 days	3120

* *Proc. Am. Soc. Testing Materials*, **28**, I, 228 and 261 (1928).
† Materials for one cylinder:—5 lbs. cement, 12 lbs. dry sand, 18 lbs. dry gravel or crushed stone and 3 lbs. water.

62.9, slightly more than twice that of the acids. The calculated percentages of the mineral constituents shows 40.7 per cent of $3CaO.SiO_2$ and 32.1 per cent of $2CaO.SiO_2$. Theoretically, more lime might well have been used in the formula to increase the proportion of $3CaO.SiO_2$. There is no official specification requiring any ratio of lime to silica, but any attempt to push the lime much higher causes danger of free lime. There is no official statement of the relative proportions of SiO_2, Al_2O_3, and Fe_2O_3 that are permitted, but the behavior of the clinker in the kiln and other manufacturing conditions make it economical to keep the Fe_2O_3 about half the Al_2O_3 and the sum of the two (R_2O_3) about 40 per cent of the SiO_2.

It would be theoretically possible to make a rough mixture of the raw materials and heat it long enough at the clinkering temperature to permit uniformity to be attained through diffusion. Practically, it is possible to get complete combination only if the raw materials are finely ground and intimately mixed before burning.

Burning Portland Cement.—The material going into the cement kiln is an intimate mixture of materials so proportioned that the main constituents when they leave the kiln are calcium silicates, with lesser amounts of aluminates, and still smaller amounts of compounds containing iron oxide, magnesia, and alkalies. The clinker must, after grinding and mixing with water, yield a hydraulic cement with the required strength, a reasonable time of setting, and complete soundness. The soundness test has been mentioned in the discussion of natural cements. It is the most important of the tests made on portland cement.

The changes that take place on burning a cement mixture were studied by E. D. Campbell and S. Ball[1] who burned a properly proportioned mixture of limestone and clay in a laboratory rotary kiln whose temperature was advanced by steps of about 50°F. Some of the data are given in Table 58. The first samples were collected through a normal temperature range for a lime-kiln, 1872 to 1960°F, and yielded cements that were perfectly sound and had reasonable setting times. These first three samples would have made acceptable cements of the "natural-cement" grade. The samples of cement collected during the next 15 steps as the temperature rose from 1960 to 2640° were

[1] *Jour. Am. Chem. Soc.*, **25**, 1104 (1903).

TABLE 58.—CHANGES IN PROPERTIES OF A PORTLAND CEMENT MIXTURE BURNED TO DIFFERENT TEMPERATURES*

The mixture was burned in a laboratory rotary kiln whose temperature was advanced by small steps. Samples were taken for test at each step of the temperature. The results on the 24 samples are summarized below.

Samples Nos.	Temp. of burning, °F.	Soundness	Initial set	Final set
1–3	1872–1960	Perfect	No. 3 = 23 min.	7 hr. 20 min.
4–13	2014–2465	Growing worse to complete disintegration	No. 9 = ½ min.	4 min.
14–16	2465–2554	Complete disintegration		
17–18	2597–2644	Growing better		
19–24	2644–2960	Perfect pats	No. 20 = 32 min.	4 hr. 22 min.

* From CAMPBELL and BALL, *Jour. Am. Chem. Soc.*, **25**, 1104 (1903).

entirely unacceptable. They were all unsound, and many of the samples were so bad that the pats went completely to pieces during the steaming test. The time of set was excessively fast on these same samples. The samples taken on the last five steps 2644 to 2960°F were all sound, had a reasonable setting time, and would have made acceptable portland cements.

The raw materials had entered into combination at the 1872 to 1960° range to give a hydraulic cement, but the nature of the compounds formed at that temperature is entirely unknown. As the temperature rose, the cement became bad, again for a reason not well understood. At temperatures above 2500°F, enough glass had been formed so that the product from the kiln commenced to show vitrification, and as the temperature rose further, the clinker came out of the kiln as hard, black, rounded, vitrified pellets which, in microscopic examination, showed the characteristic crystalline structure of portland cement.

One of the reasons for the unsoundness at temperatures of 2000 to 2600°F was the presence of free lime. At temperatures below 1950, free lime hydrates so rapidly after it is ground finely that hydration is complete before the cement has taken its initial set, and the expansion during hydration does no harm. At temperatures above 2000°, the lime hydrates so slowly that some expansion takes place after the pat has set and been placed in the steam bath, with the result that the pat becomes cracked. The excess of lime in this mixture was not brought into combination until a high temperature—with this particular composition 2640°F—was reached.

It would seem that an easy and logical modern method would be to heat the raw materials to fusion and so obtain complete combination. Unfortunately, tricalcium silicate, the chief component of portland cement, dissociates at 3450°F, which is below its melting point. It is possible to make a fused cement that is of quite a different composition from portland cement, but it cannot be sold as portland cement.

The difficulties encountered by the early manufacturers of portland cement can be better understood in view of the necessity of attaining a much higher temperature range than was required for the natural cement, and of controlling chemical composition accurately on a basis that has been worked out scientifically only in recent years.

Hydration of Portland Cement.—If a small amount of portland cement should be mixed with a large amount of water and the mixture kept in constant agitation, the cement would react with the water and form a voluminous jellylike mass but would not yield a strong hydraulic cement. When portland cement is mixed for concrete, the amount of water is usually less than that required to hydrate all of the cement, and the cement must not be disturbed after it has taken its initial set.

The reactions that take place under these circumstances are usually written as follows:

$$3CaO.Al_2O_3 + 6H_2O = 3CaO.Al_2O_3.6H_2O$$
$$3CaO.SiO_2 + XH_2O = 2CaO.SiO_2.XH_2O + Ca(OH)_2$$
$$2CaO.SiO_2 + XH_2O = 2CaO.SiO_2.XH_2O$$
$$4CaO.Al_2O_3.Fe_2O_3 + XH_2O = 3CaO.Al_2O_3.6H_2O + \text{amorphous}$$
$$\text{paste of undetermined composition.}$$

In the study of gypsum plasters, it was stated that the anhydrous substance must be more soluble than the hydrated compound if the substance was to form a hydraulic cement. This could be easily proved in the case of gypsum plasters since the solubility of the gypsum was great enough to permit accurate measurements and the rate of solution was so rapid that the hydration became complete in less than 24 hr.

Measurements made on portland cement indicate that the solubility of the hydrated products is less than that of the material in the clinker, but the solubility is very small and the rate of reaction so slow that months and even years may be required to complete the hydration of a fine particle. Bogue and Lerch[1] made pure products, ground them to the standard fineness for portland cements, and determined the rate at which they took up water in fixed combination. Summaries of their results are given in Table 59.

TABLE 59.—PROGRESSIVE HYDRATION OF PORTLAND CEMENT*
Fixed Water in Cement Compounds Calculated as Percentage of Original Anhydrous Material

	1 day	28 days	1 year
$3CaO.SiO_2$	8.6	14.6	19.0
Beta $2CaO.SiO_2$	0.8	3.4	12.2
$3CaO.Al_2O_3$	30.2	34.9	36.9
$4CaO.Al_2O_3.Fe_2O_3$	25.7	27.9	29.4

* From BOGUE and LERCH, Portland Cement Association Fellowship at the Bureau of Standards, *Paper* 27, 1934.

The products that hydrate most rapidly are the $3CaO.Al_2O_3$ and the $4CaO.Al_2O_3.Fe_2O_3$ whose hydration, when ground very finely, approaches completion in 1 day. The $3CaO.SiO_2$, the most important constituent in portland cement, fixed 8.6 per cent of water in 1 day, 14.8 in 28 days, and 19.0 in 1 year. The beta dicalcium silicate reacted so slowly that the amount of fixed water was only 0.8 per cent after 1 day, 3.4 at 28 days, and 12.2 at the end of a year. It is evident therefore that the hydration of portland cement proceeds very slowly and that it may require more than 1 year to attain completion.

The progressive increase in strength of these pure compounds is shown in Fig. 156 by the same authors. The aluminates attained almost their full strength in 28 days, but their final strength was not very high. The $3CaO.SiO_2$ made the most impressive showing with a compressive strength of 6000 lb at 7 days and of 10,000 lb at the end of a year. The $2CaO.SiO_2$ hardly showed any strength at 7 days but at the end of a year

[1] Portland Cement Association Fellowship at the U. S. Bureau of Standards, *Paper* 27, 1934.

stood almost even with the 3CaO.SiO₂ at 10,000 lb. At the end of two years, the compressive strengths, not shown on the chart, were 11,300 psi for the 3CaO.SiO₂ and 14,350 for the 2CaO.SiO₂.

Controlling the Time of Set.—Portland cement usually sets too fast, and it is customary practice to add a retarder during the grinding process. The standard retarder is gypsum, and it is

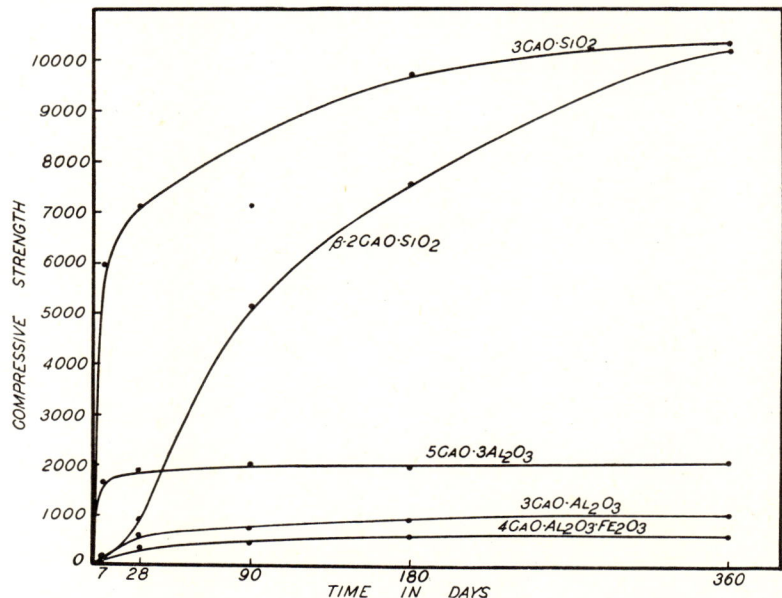

Fig. 156.—Comparison of compressive strength of cement compounds in psi. (*From Bogue and Lerch. Portland Cement Association Fellowship Paper 27. National Bureau of Standards, 1924.*)

relatively immaterial whether it is added in the calcined or uncalcined form. The gypsum acts by combining with the tricalcium aluminate as it goes into solution to form a complex sulfoaluminate. The equation is written

$$3CaO.Al_2O_3 + 3CaSO_4 + XH_2O = 3CaO.Al_2O_3.3CaSO_4.31H_2O.$$

This sulfoaluminate is very insoluble and precipitates, thus taking the 3CaO.Al₂O₃ out of solution and rendering it unavailable for crystal formation. The tricalcium aluminate is the first material to hydrate and the constituent that causes the initial set. Standard specifications demand that the initial set shall not be developed in less than 45 min. and the final set shall not be delayed more than 10 hr. The specifications also limit the permissible SO_3 in the finished cement to 2.0 per cent which corresponds to 4.3 per cent gypsum—$CaSO_4.2H_2O$.

Fineness of Grinding.—The solubility of the constituents of portland-cement clinker is so small that the clinker must be ground extremely fine if it is to gain strength rapidly. The A.S.T.M. Standards for 1936 specify that the residue on a No. 200 sieve shall not exceed 22 per cent by weight. A No. 200 sieve is one that has 200 meshes to the linear inch. It is more precisely defined as one in which the width of the opening is 0.0029 in. and the diameter of the wire is 0.0021 in. It would be desirable to use even a finer sieve, but the wires of the 200 sieve are so delicate that there is much difficulty in keeping the screen openings accurate.

A No. 325 sieve with approximately 325 meshes per linear inch is used when it is desired to determine the percentage of particles that are somewhat finer than those which will be retained on a No. 200 sieve. This sieve is so delicate that it can be used only with special precautions and must be calibrated frequently by use of a standard reference sample.

The gradation of still finer particles of cement may be determined by observing the rate at which they settle through an inert liquid such as kerosene. Light from a standard source passes through the suspension of the cement in kerosene and then into a photoelectric cell. The current generated in the cell will vary with the intensity of the light and therefore with the turbidity of the solution, and a series of readings made at various heights of the suspension permits the calculation of the number of particles at each level. It is assumed that each particle is a sphere, and so the surface of the particles can be calculated. The mean specific surface is calculated by an integration of all of the readings. This method of determining fineness by determining turbidity was adopted as an A.S.T.M. Standard in 1937. In 1938 however, the American Society for Testing Materials[1] decided that tests for fineness were no longer necessary and eliminated all reference to them from their standard specifications.

Test for Soundness.—The A.S.T.M. Standards state: "A pat of neat cement shall remain firm and hard, and show no signs of

[1] *Proc. Am. Soc. Testing Materials*, **1,** 303 (1938).

distortion, checking or disintegration in the steam test." This is the most important test to be made in passing upon the acceptance of cement, because the results are available within 24 hr, and failure to pass the test gives definite ground for rejection of the cement, even though it has already been delivered on the job. In making the test, cement powder, without any

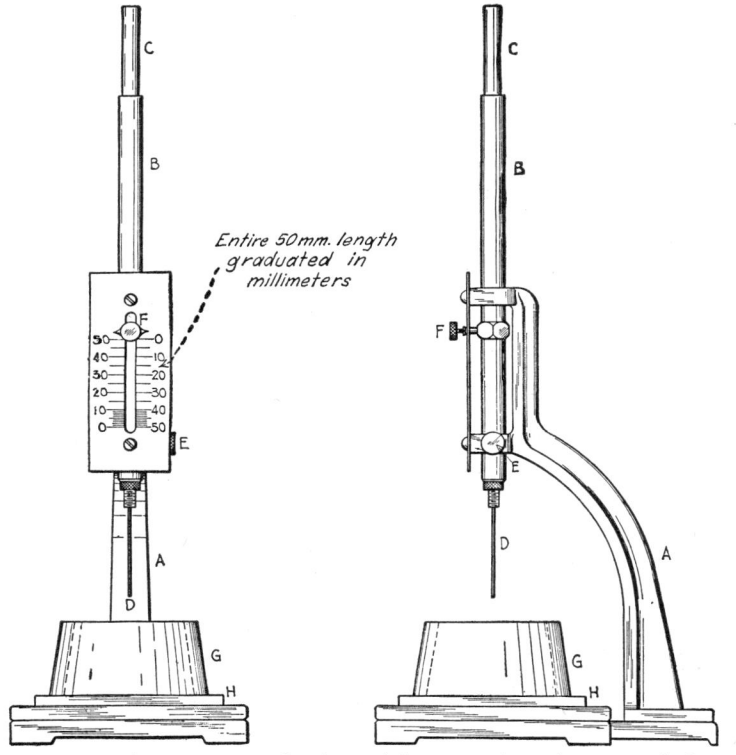

FIG. 157.—Vicat apparatus for determining normal consistency and time of set of portland cement. [*From A. S. T. M. Standards*, II, 17 (1936).]

admixture of sand (neat cement), is mixed with water enough to form a plastic mass that can be rolled into a ball without cracking or slumping. The exact amount of water to make the required normal consistency is determined by the penetration of the needle of the Vicat apparatus illustrated in Fig. 157. A pat of neat cement paste about 3 in. in diameter, ½ in. thick at the center, and tapering to thin edges is formed on a glass plate. This pat is allowed to set and harden at room temperature in a moist closet of specified construction for 24 hr, and is then placed in a steam bath where it remains in an atmosphere of steam over a bath of boiling water at a temperature of 205 to 212°F for 5 hr. The pat when examined on removal from the steam bath shall, as stated above, show no signs of distortion, checking, or disintegration. Slight unsoundness will be shown by a small amount of warping or fine cracks at the edges of the

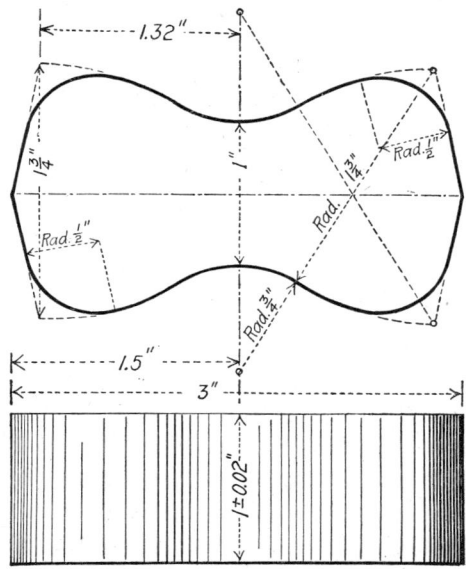

Fig. 158.—Details of form of briquet for tensile strength. [*From A. S. T. M. Standards*, II, 23 (1936).]

pat after it has been removed from the steam bath. More serious unsoundness will be shown by crumbling of the pat.

This test gives an accelerated indication as to what would probably happen in a much longer time in water of room temperature. A failure on this test is almost always due to expansion, with free lime as the most frequent cause. Unless the manufacturing process is conducted with skill and care, a small amount of lime will be left uncombined. This lime, burned at the high temperature of the cement kiln, will not become completely hydrated in water of room temperature for weeks or even months. The steam test is, however, relied on to detect it.

Strength Requirements.—The tensile strength of the cement is determined by mixing it with 3 parts by weight of a standard sand, moistening the mixture with water, and forcing the mortar into briquet molds of specified dimensions, all according to a procedure that is carefully standardized. The form of the briquet is illustrated in Fig. 158. The briquets are allowed to remain in the molds in a standard moist closet for 24 hr, after which they are removed from the molds and immersed in water for further aging. At least three briquets must be broken for each test and the figures averaged. The tensile strength of these 1:3 mortar briquets shall be at least as follows:

Age at test days	Storage of briquets	Tensile strength, psi
7	1 day in moist air, 6 days in water	275
28	1 day in moist air, 27 days in water	350

It is further specified that the average tensile strength shall be higher at 28 days than at 7 days.

Standard Specifications for Portland Cement.—The groundwork has now been laid sufficiently so that the standard specifications may be discussed intelligently. The 1936 A.S.T.M. Standards gives a definition of portland cement that has stood unchanged for many years. It is awkward and hard to understand. The A.S.T.M. Committee on Cement (C-1) has recommended a much clearer definition[1] which is quoted below:

Portland cement is the product obtained by pulverizing clinker consisting essentially of calcium silicates, to which no additions have been made subsequent to calcination other than water and/or untreated calcium sulfate except that additions not to exceed 1 per cent of other materials may be added, provided such materials have been shown not to be harmful by tests prescribed and carried out by Committee C-1 on Cement.

This definition seems very loose, but when considered with the other restrictions imposed in the specification it is adequate. Calcium sulfate is added to control the time of setting, and water is allowed because a small amount of water added in the grinding

---

[1] *Proc. Am. Soc. Testing Materials,* **38,** 303 (1938).

mill lessens the power required for grinding and facilitates the hydration of a small amount of free lime which is almost invariably present in the clinker. The amount of water is limited by the later clause which restricts the loss on ignition to 4.0 per cent.

The clause permitting the addition of other substances, in amount not greater than 1 per cent and provided they have been shown not to be harmful, is to authorize the additions of catalysts to control the setting time or the rate of attainment of strength. Calcium chloride and tannic acid are instances of substances that have been proposed. Under the older official definition, no substance can be sold as portland cement if it contains any added material other than water or gypsum.

The chemical limitations are all contained in the following lines:

	Maximum Limit
Loss on ignition, per cent	4.00
Insoluble residue, per cent	0.85
Sulfuric anhydride (SO_3) per cent	2.00
Magnesia (MgO) per cent	5.00

When the clinker comes from the kiln at a bright white heat, it has no loss on ignition. The water added in the grinding process, either as the water of crystallization of gypsum, or as liquid water, will all be driven off again at a red heat in the test for loss on ignition which involves heating a weighed sample of the cement to redness. If the finished cement stands in a humid atmosphere, it will pick up moisture and also carbon dioxide from the air, and may ultimately set hard while it is still in the sack. If any attempt should be made to regrind and put on the market cement that had deteriorated in this way, the excessive loss on ignition would detect it. The average loss on ignition of the 32 American cements was 1.50 per cent.

Fresh portland cement is almost completely soluble in dilute acid. The insoluble residue in the 32 cements averaged only 0.20 per cent. The restrictive clause in the specification would detect adulteration by addition of finely ground sand or other inert material.

The addition of gypsum to retard the set has already been discussed. If the time of setting of a cement cannot be controlled by the amount of gypsum permitted, it ought to be discarded as a bad cement.

Magnesia is not considered to have any value in increasing the strength of portland cement. It is never added intentionally, but it exists so generally in the raw materials that a small amount is permitted. If it is combined as a silicate or in the form of a glass, it does no harm, but if it remains in the form of free MgO, it hydrates very slowly and expands. The dangers of free magnesia in hydrated lime have been alluded to, and the subject will be discussed more fully in a subsequent paragraph when volume changes are being considered. The steaming test for soundness does not detect free magnesia, although a proposed autoclave test with superheated steam does show it. The latter is not yet official, and the only guard against free magnesia is the limit of 5.0 per cent as the total amount that is permitted in the cement.

Aggregates for Mortar and Concrete.—The term "aggregate" is applied to the inert material such as sand, gravel, and crushed stone which is to be mixed with cement. A mixture of cement, water, and sand is termed "mortar." A mixture of cement, water, sand, and coarser material such as gravel or crushed stone is termed "concrete."

The aggregates should be clean, strong, and durable when exposed to the weather. The particles of sands and gravels as dug from open pits near the surface of the ground are sometimes coated with clay or organic matter which prevent good adherence of the cement to the aggregate. The film may be removed by washing. When crushed stone is used, it should be selected for strength and weather resistance. Sand and gravel from surface deposits have been exposed to the weather for so many centuries that they would be expected to be durable. However frost rarely penetrates more than 5 ft. into the ground, and so there is no absolute assurance that sand and gravel from deeper layers will be reliable. Mica is to be avoided because it splits so readily. Some forms of chert, although a form of quartz, disintegrate in winter. Cinders should be used with care, and if possible, only after they have been exposed to the weather for a year.

The gradation in size of the particles of aggregate is very important. It has already been discussed somewhat in connection with gravel roads.

Cement Mortar.—A mixture of cement, sand, and water is not plastic enough to be well adapted to the purposes of the mason or the plasterer. Fortunately, hydrated lime is a good plasticizer and does not interfere with the hardening of the cement. It will be remembered that calcium hydroxide is set free during the hardening of tricalcium silicate. Portland-cement mortar is stronger than lime mortar and hardens in the center of a thick wall just as rapidly as on the surface.

Portland cement and hydraulic lime plasters are much used for the external plaster coats on buildings, called "stucco." Stucco made with portland cement hardens quickly and is strong. The disadvantages due to volume changes in the finished stucco on exposure to the weather will be discussed later.

Designing Concrete Mixtures.—The aggregate used in concrete is much cheaper than the cement, and in order that the cement may be used to maximum efficiency, the aggregate should be so chosen that, after the concrete is mixed, a minimum amount of cement will be needed to bond the particles of aggregate to each other. There is no simple way of determining just how the coarse and fine aggregates available for a particular job should be mixed to give the best results, and in important work a series of trial cylinders should be made up, using different proportions of mixture, sufficiently long in advance so that their compressive tests may be available before work starts.

It is evident that, in general, a concrete rich in cement will be stronger but more expensive than one poor in cement.

The proportions for a mix in the laboratory are frequently expressed in weight, with the amount of the finest material cement being given first and the coarsest material last. Thus a 1:2:4 mix would mean 1 weight of cement to 2 weights of sand and 4 weights of gravel. In field work, the proportions are frequently expressed by volume because of the greater ease of proportioning by measure. A 1:2:4 mix will, in the field, usually mean 1 cu ft of cement (one sack), 2 cu ft of sand, and 4 cu ft of gravel or crushed stone.

Water in Concrete.—Water performs two distinct functions in concrete. When the concrete is first mixed, it wets all the surfaces and provides a lubricating film between the particles. With a small amount of water, a concrete may be so stiff that it must be rammed into place. With more water, it will become plastic enough to flow into place with a little assistance, and with still more water, it will become a thick mush.

The importance of a correct amount of water may be visualized by imagining the conditions that might arise in pouring a reinforced concrete column. If the mix is the right consistency, it will flow smoothly around the reinforcing steel and fill up the form as it is poured in. If it is too stiff, it will not flow smoothly and may leave empty spaces. If it is too wet, the coarse aggregate will settle to the bottom and water will rise to the top.

The second function of the water is to react with the cement to form the bonding agent between the particles of aggregate. The water commences to perform this function as soon as it comes in contact with the cement, and the very finest particles of cement become hydrated quite completely in the few minutes required to mix the concrete and deposit it in the forms. This part of the cement helps to make a viscous mass but does not contribute much to the final strength of the concrete.

After the cement has taken its initial set, the hardened mass will contain both liquid water and undecomposed cement. If the mass is kept damp, the water will continue to react with the cement for months. The volume of the reaction products is almost identically the same as the volume of the clinker plus the water which is being combined, so that the reaction does not cause strains in the concrete. If the amount of water added in the concrete mixer was too great, there will be drops of surplus water in the hardened concrete. If the concrete dries out, these will leave empty spaces. If not enough water was added in the concrete mixer, there will be unused cement. The amount of water to be added to the mixture should therefore be carefully proportioned.

The Water-cement Ratio.—The importance of the ratio of water to cement was first brought out fully by Abrams in the Portland Cement Association's Research Laboratory. He showed that, for plastic mixtures, the strength of concrete was more nearly proportional to the ratio of water to cement than to any other single variable. He expressed his values in terms of volumes of water for one volume of cement and also in gallons of water for one sack of cement. A sack of cement weighs 94 lb and contains approximately 1 cu ft of cement. There are 7.5 gal of water in

1 cu ft, and therefore a water-cement ratio of 1 corresponds to 7.5 gal of water for each sack of cement used.

The values for compressive strengths after 28 days of moist storage are plotted against water-cement ratios in Fig. 159. The greater the amount of mixing water per sack of cement, the weaker will be the concrete.

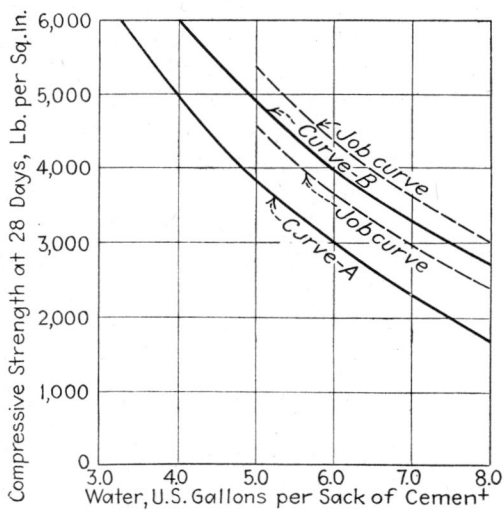

Fig. 159.—Influence of water-cement ratio on compressive strength of concrete cylinders. Curve A was published at the time the water-cement ratio strength law was announced in 1918. Curve B is representative of present-day cements. In the absence of preliminary tests, lower values than curve B should be used for design. (*From Portland Cement Ass. Design and Control of Concrete Mixtures*, 1938 ed.)

Slump Test.—A simple test to measure the plasticity of a mixture is to measure the amount of "slump" that a cone of the wet concrete undergoes when the supporting conical form is withdrawn. This is illustrated in Fig. 160, where the illustration at the left shows a cone that was made in a conical form 12 in. high, which slumped 1 in. when the mold was withdrawn.

The other illustrations show progressively greater slumps because more water was used per unit of aggregate. The strength remained approximately constant because the ratio of water to cement was kept constant. The compressive strength of the test cylinders does not vary much from an average of 4100 psi, but the cement used per cubic yard of concrete increases from

4.7 to 7.6 sacks. The use of the water-cement ratio may be sufficient to ensure concrete of a given strength, but the contractor who wishes to obtain economical results must study the gradation of his aggregates and the effect of varying mixtures if he wishes to obtain economical results.

FIG. 160.—Influence of varying aggregates on slump, and constancy of strength with constant water-cement ratio.

Specimen	1	2	3	4	5	6
Water, in gal per sack of cement	7	7	7	7	7	7
Mixture, by volume	1:2½:4	1:2½:3	1:2½:2	1:2:4	1:2:3	1:1½:2
Slump, in in	1	5¼	7½	7	8½	9½
Strength, psi	3980	4050	4110	3960	4290	4130
Sacks of cement per cu yd of concrete	4.7	5.3	6.1	5.1	5.8	7.6

Concretes for Different Degrees of Exposure.—The Portland Cement Association has made a short compilation of the uses to which concrete is put and the kind of concrete demanded which is reproduced as Table 60. It bases the classification on the resistance to weather in a winter climate. Concrete with a high water-cement ratio will be both weak and porous, and so absorptive of water that it will disintegrate through formation of ice if exposed to winter weather. A richer concrete will be stronger, will absorb less water, and will not disintegrate when frozen. But the volume changes that rich concrete undergoes are powerful destructive agencies which affect rich concrete more strongly than lean concrete. The cause and effect of these volume changes will be discussed later.

Increase of Strength with Age.—Concrete structures gain strength slowly because of the very slight solubility of the active constituents of the clinker. If the concrete becomes dried, all hardening stops, since the processes all involve the reaction of water with cement. Water vapor also reacts with cement, and the columns, floors, and walls of a concrete building continue to gain in strength slowly, but more rapidly in summer, owing to the moisture in the air. The rate at which various mixes of

TABLE 60.—RECOMMENDED WATER-CEMENT RATIOS FOR CONCRETE TO MEET DIFFERENT DEGREES OF EXPOSURE*

These requirements are predicated on the use of concrete mixtures in which the cement meets the present standard specifications of the A.S.T.M. and to which an early curing is given that will be equivalent to that obtained when protected from the loss of moisture for at least 7 days at a temperature of 70°F. For curing conditions less favorable than this, correspondingly lower water-cement ratios should be used. The values are also based on the assumption that the concrete is of such consistency and is so placed that the space between the aggregate particles is completely filled with cement paste of the given water ratio.

Exposure \ Class of structure	Reinforced piles, thin walls, light structural members, exterior columns, and beams in buildings	Reinforced reservoirs, water tanks, pressure pipes, sewers, canal linings, dams of thin sections	Heavy walls, piers, foundations, dams of heavy sections
Extreme: 1. In severe climates like in northern United States, exposure to alternate wetting and drying, freezing and thawing, as at the water line in hydraulic structures 2. Exposure to sea and strong sulfate waters in both severe and moderate climates	5½	5½	6
Severe: 3. In severe climates like in northern United States, exposure to rain and snow, and freezing and thawing, but not continuously in contact with water 4. In moderate climates like southern United States, exposure to alternate wetting and drying, as at water line in hydraulic structures	6	6	6¾
Moderate: 5. In climates like southern United States, exposure to ordinary weather, but not continuously in contact with water 6. Concrete completely submerged, but protected from freezing	6¾	6	7½
Protected: 7. Ordinary inclosed structural members; concrete below the ground and not subject to action of corrosive groundwaters or freezing and thawing	7½	6	8¼

* From Portland Cement Association's Design and Control of Concrete Mixtures, 6th ed., 1938.
† Surface water or moisture carried by the aggregate must be included as part of the mixing water.

concrete are expected to gain in strength when kept continuously damp is shown in Fig. 161, also furnished through the courtesy of the Portland Cement Association.

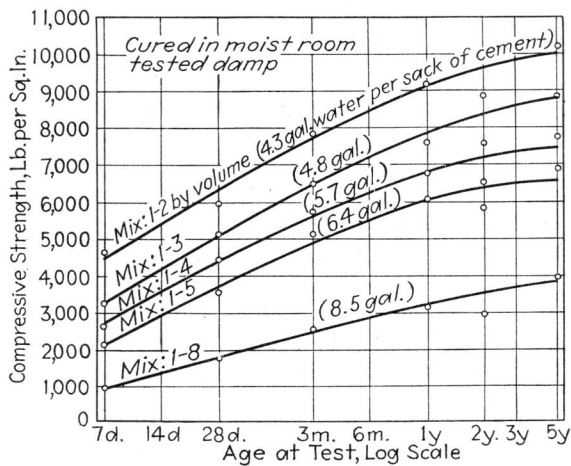

FIG. 161.—Increase in strength of concrete with age. Moist curing. (*Courtesy of the Portland Cement Ass.*)

Effect of Temperature on Hardening of Concrete.—The rate at which chemical reactions take place is accelerated by increase in temperature, and the hardening of cement conforms to the general rule. The effect of the temperature of storage on a series of concrete cylinders that were tested at the University of Illinois is shown in Fig. 162. The compressive strengths of the cylinders stored at 70°F is rated as 100 and all other strengths expressed as percentages. Cylinders stored at 90°F showed a relative strength of 110 and those at 30°F had a relative strength of only 57 at the end of 28 days. The temperature of 30°F was the temperature of the curing room, and since heat is evolved in the hydration of cement, the blocks probably did not become frozen during the test.

The curve at 20°F is dotted to indicate the weakening effect and the uncertainty due to freezing of the concrete. The effect of freezing will be discussed later.

Hydrated Portland Cement As a Colloid.—If a few particles of portland cement are mixed with a drop of water on a glass slide and the reactions are examined through the microscope, crystals will be seen to form on some of the particles, but the whole field soon becomes cloudy owing to the formation of an amorphous white substance which prevents further inspection of the process. A briquet of neat cement that is kept continually in water will gain in strength very slowly after 1 year. If such a 1-year briquet is dried, ground finely, and worked into a paste with additional water, it will set and harden and attain considerable strength again. If a slice should be sawed from a briquet of neat cement which had been 1 year in water, and the slide should

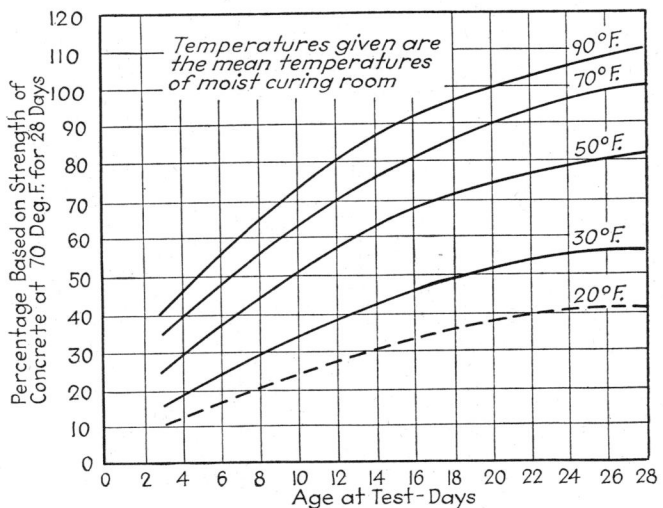

Fig. 162.—Effect of temperature during curing period on the compressive strength of concrete. (*From Bull.* 81, *Eng. Exp. Sta., Univ. of Ill.*)

be ground down to a thin section and examined under a microscope, it would appear as a dense white mass in which could be seen particles of unchanged clinker.

There are several reasons why the hydration of cement proceeds at an increasingly slow rate and finally ceases altogether, before all of the particles of cement have been hydrated. The solubility of the minerals in the cement clinker is so small that the reactions all take place on the surface of the particles. The finest particles of the tricalcium aluminate hydrate promptly and quite completely to give the strength at the end of 24 hr. The coarser particles become surrounded with a layer of hydrated product through which water must diffuse to react with the surface of the unchanged clinker. In a rich mortar or concrete, the reaction products become so closely packed that no more water can force its way to the unchanged clinker, and so the reaction proceeds excessively slowly or stops altogether, although there may still be considerable unhydrated clinker present.

In writing the equations for the reactions occurring during the hardening of cement, some of the products were written as containing XH_2O. These products may contain some definite number of molecules of water of crystallization, but they also contain water in a loose form of combination. In many respects, these hydrated products are like clay that contains the mineral kaolinite, whose formula is written $Al_2O_3.2SiO_2.2H_2O$ and whose water of crystallization is not driven off completely until a red heat. Clay also contains colloidal water which is partly removed by drying in the air and partly by drying in an oven. The loss of this colloid water is accompanied by marked shrinkage. If the clay that has been air-dried is brought in contact with water, it will rehydrate, regain its colloidal water, and expand.

A bar of neat portland cement owes its strength, in part, to interlocking crystals of definite composition, and in this respect it resembles gypsum plaster or lime plaster. It also owes part of its strength to the colloidal material which forms through the reaction of the clinker with water. This colloidal material gives up water and shrinks when it is dried, and takes up water and expands when it is wetted.

Volume Changes Due to Changing Moisture Content.—When portland cement reacts with water and sets, there is first a very slight decrease in volume as the liquid water enters into combination. This is followed by a small expansion. If a bar of neat cement is removed from the mold and measured after the first day, and the bar is then kept immersed in water and measured at intervals, it will be found to be expanding at a decreasing rate, and the length will become constant after about a year's immersion in water.

The behavior of four experimental bars of 1 in. cross section is shown in Fig. 163. The two upper graphs show that the bars expanded 0.10 per cent in length during 1 year in water and did not increase their length while lying in water for 2 more years. When these two bars were then taken out of water and placed in the air of the room where they slowly became dried and lost their

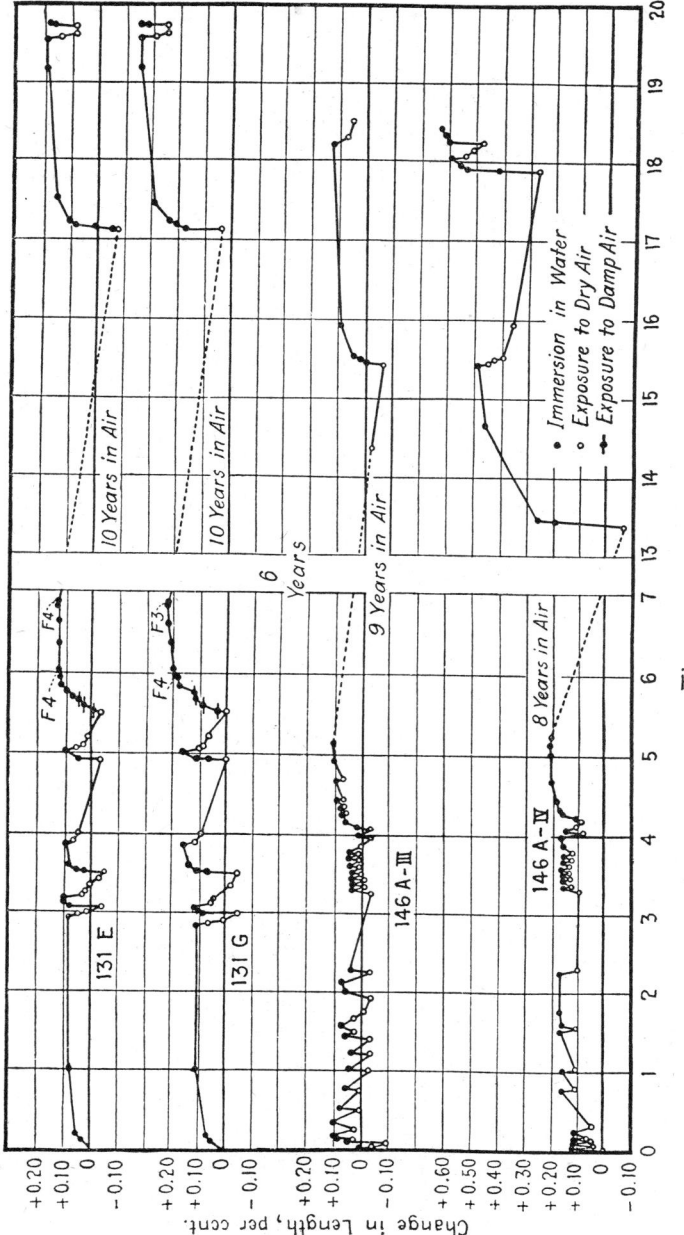

Fig. 163.—Changes in length of bars of commercial neat cements at room temperature with change in moisture. [*From A. H. White, Proc. A. S. T. M.*, **28**, II, 398 (1928).]

colloidal water, they shrank not only to their initial 1-day length but even further, so that their length changed from +0.10 to −0.05 per cent. All substances with fine pores such as limestone and brick exhibit this phenomenon but in a much smaller degree. The action of the colloidal cement is shown diagrammatically in Fig. 164, where the sand grains are depicted being pushed apart by the swollen colloid and pulled together by the dry colloid.

In the illustration of Fig. 163, the bars of neat cement were kept in water 3 years before they were allowed to become dry. In the third graph, Bar 146 A III was placed in dry air as soon as

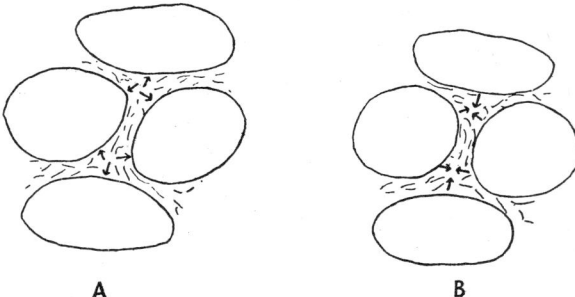

Fig. 164.—Diagrammatic representation of stresses in cement mortar when wet and dry. *A* represents four sand grains with the colloid between them wet and swollen. The arrows show that the grains are being pushed apart and that the colloidal cement is in compression: *B* represents the same situation with the colloid dry and contracted. The grains are being pulled together and the colloidal cement is in tension. [*From A. H. White, Proc. Am. Concrete Inst.*, **22**, 190 (1928).]

it was removed from the mold after 1 day. It shrank 0.07 per cent in 3 weeks and then was placed in water where it soon expanded to +0.10 per cent, a change in length of 0.17 per cent from the air-dried to the wet state. Alternations of length kept up in all these bars as often as the environment was changed from wet to dry, or dry to wet, even up to an age of 20 years.

The influence of damp air is shown in the two upper graphs between the fifth and sixth years. When both of the bars, after having been in dry air for 6 months, were placed in damp air, each of them expanded about 0.10 per cent in length due to the moisture that the colloid took up from the air.

An unexpected phenomenon is shown in the progressive expansion of all the bars when rather long periods of immersion in water followed periods of dryness. The bars still showed a fluctuation of about 0.10 per cent between the wet and dry states, but instead of fluctuating about zero they fluctuated around a mean length of +0.20 to +0.50 per cent. This progressive expansion is due to the hydration of the kernels of unchanged cement clinker. Each time the dried bars were immersed in water, some water penetrated through the shrunken shell of colloid and reached a surface of unchanged clinker. The effect of this progressive expansion on the destruction of concrete structures exposed to the weather will be referred to later.

FIG. 165.—Cement floor showing shrinkage cracks.

The volume changes have been discussed for neat cement. Sand or gravel acts as a diluent and lessens the volume changes, particularly with lean mixtures. During the first year or two, there may be sufficient internal voids to allow room for the increase in volume, but after some years even lean concrete commences to show progressive expansion if continuously exposed to the weather.

Shrinkage Cracks in Floors.—The practical effect of these volume changes may be made clearer by a few photographs of concrete structures. The cracked floor of Fig. 165 shows what happened when a top coat of rich mortar was spread over a floor slab of reinforced concrete. The builder thought that he would make the wearing coat so strong and thick that it would not crack. He therefore did not try to bond the top coat to the slab, but on the contrary separated it from the slab by a layer of tarred paper. The top coat was poured 1½ in. thick and was covered with damp sawdust for 30 days. When the sawdust was removed, the floor was hard and without a crack. In less than 30 days more, after the floor had become dry, it presented the appearance shown in Fig. 165 with large and irregular shrinkage cracks.

These cracks would have been much smaller if the concrete slab had been cleaned and the top coat poured directly on it so as

Fig. 166.—Upheaval of concrete curb due to expansion.

to obtain a good bond between the new top and the old base. The cracks might have been prevented by a large amount of steel reinforcement in the top coat. The shrinkage might have been directed into less noticeable channels by cutting the surface into squares, not over 2 ft on a side. A square of that size would probably have shrunk as a unit and pulled away from its neighbors without its own surface being cracked.

Progressive Expansion of Concrete.—The concrete curb in Fig. 166 is an illustration of progressive expansion of concrete due to alternate exposure to wet and dry conditions. This could not have happened in a dry climate like that of Arizona, but in Michigan there is enough rainfall to cause progressive expansion of concrete sidewalks and pavements. An expansion of 0.10 per cent may seem a small amount, but it is 1.2 in. on 100 ft and exerts a great pressure unless it is allowed freedom to adjust itself. The practical solution is to make an expansion joint every 100 ft or sometimes oftener. A joint with a width of ¾ in. filled with an asphaltic composition will at least delay the formation of pressure ridges for a good many years. The progressive expansion of the concrete will be shown by the mushrooming of the asphalt as it is pressed out of the joint by the expanding concrete, and then flattened out by the traffic passing over it.

The saucer-shaped slabs of Fig. 167 are an evidence of differential expansion due to moisture. When this area was paved, a

Fig. 167.—Warping and cracking of sidewalk slabs due to unequal expansion and contraction of the top and bottom portions

base of lean and rather dry concrete was tamped into place and a top coat of a rich mortar was immediately spread over it so as to get a good bond between the two layers. The parting lines between the blocks were cut in as soon as the top coat had started to set. The rich top coat contracted more than the base in dry weather, and expanded more than the base in wet weather. The lean base was thicker than the top coat but also weaker, so that the top coat buckled the base until the latter went to pieces. This picture shows each of the squares forming a shallow saucer. The pieces of the top coat were hard and strong. The base had been worked back and forth until it had disintegrated.

Influence of Freezing on Concrete.—Liquid water expands on freezing, and if concrete is frozen soon after it has set, the ice formation may crack it. Specifications prescribe that concrete shall not be poured in freezing weather unless it can be kept warm. After the concrete has hardened and the liquid water has been changed into the combined form, no expansion occurs or freezing. The bars 131E and 131G of Fig. 163 were each frozen four successive times at the sixth year and again near the seventh year, where the marks F4 and F3 appear on the curve, without any measurable expansion taking place.

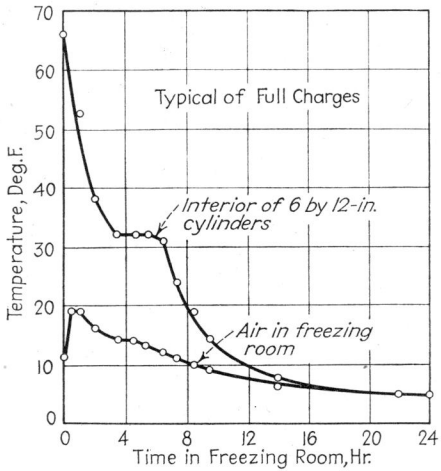

FIG. 168.—Temperature curves showing rate of freezing of cylinders of fresh concrete. [*From Schofield, Proc. A.S.T.M.*, **37**, II, 306 (1937).]

The effect of freezing concrete cylinders at various ages has been studied by Schofield[1] who reported that dry concretes (with a 2-in. slump) were uninjured if cured for 24 to 48 hr before freezing. Wet concretes required curing for a considerably longer period to avoid injury by freezing. Concrete cylinders placed in a room whose temperature quickly became +5°F reached an interior temperature of 32°F in about 3 hr, but did not fall below 32°F for almost 4 hr more, so freezing did not actually take place until about 6 hr after the cylinders were placed in the cold room as shown by Fig. 168. Cylinders of 1:2:3 concrete made with a 2-in. slump showed 50 to 60 per cent of normal

[1] *Proc. Am. Soc. Testing Materials*, **37**, II, 306, (1937).

strength at 28 days with some improvement at periods up to 4 years. Cylinders of 1:3:5 concrete made from regular cement were damaged somewhat more by the early freezing than were those of the richer 1:2:3 concrete. High-alumina cements showed no damage even when mixed with so much water that the mixture showed a 9-in. slump.

Influence of Temperature on Concrete.—Concrete expands and contracts with moderate changes of temperature at the rate of 0.0000055 in. per inch per degree Fahrenheit. This is, fortunately, about the same expansion as that of steel, and so steel

FIG. 169.—Concrete highway disrupted by expansion due to rains and hot weather. (*Courtesy Dr. W. A. Collings.*)

reinforcement may be placed in concrete without noticeable strains being produced during ordinary climatic fluctuations in temperature. The expansion of a slab 100 ft long when heated 100°F as in changing from winter to summer will amount to 0.055 ft, or 0.055 per cent. This may introduce stresses of importance into structures, but it is only one-third of the volume change produced when neat cement changes from the dry to the wet state.

The photograph of Fig. 169 shows a highway that "blew up" on a hot June day after a series of rains. In this case, the temperature and the moisture worked additively to produce expansion.

Concrete as a Fireproofing Agent.—In buildings of reinforced concrete, the outer layers of the concrete act not only to stiffen the structure but also to protect the reinforcing steel from the disastrous expansion that would take place if its temperature rose too high. Concrete in a building is usually dry and therefore rather porous and a fair thermal insulator. In case of a serious fire, the outer layers of the concrete will become dehydrated, and will absorb heat in the process as the water of hydration becomes changed to steam. The concrete will shrink and crack during this dehydration process, and if the fire is intense and maintained for a long enough time the steel will expand, bursting away the loosened concrete and causing the structure to fail. If the fire is of short duration, the concrete will be found to have spalled on the surface, but to have protected the steel. It is frequently sufficient to plaster the spots that show surface spalling to put the structural elements back into good condition.

The Danger of Free Magnesia in Portland Cement.—Mention has been made of the slowness with which overburned magnesia hydrates. In the manufacture of hydrated lime, especial care must be taken in the burning process because the hydrating process is a short one. Cases have been known where lime plaster on masonry walls broke loose from the wall because of slow expansion. In portland cement, the magnesia may go into combination with the silica, in which case it forms a feeble hydraulic cement which does not add much to the strength but which does no harm. If there is much magnesia in the cement, there is danger of some of it remaining in the free form. There is no easy way of testing cement to see if it contains free magnesia, and therefore the standard specifications limit the total amount of magnesia to 5 per cent in the belief that if the total is limited to that amount, the proportion in the free form will be so small as to be harmless.

The effect of free magnesia in cement is shown in Fig. 170 where the changes in length of a set of experimental bars of neat cement are shown. Bar 83A was made from a normal cement. 83B had 1 per cent of hard-burned magnesia added to it in the grinding mill. Bar 83C contained 2 per cent MgO, 83D had 3 per cent, and 83E had 4 per cent of hard-burned MgO added in a similar manner. The bars all showed a small and normal expansion when kept in water for 1 year. At the end of the second year, a slightly greater expansion could be noted in the bars containing 2, 3, and 4 per cent of added magnesia. At the end of 4 years, the bars with 3 and 4 per cent showed marked expansion, and at the end of 8 years the bar with 3 per cent had

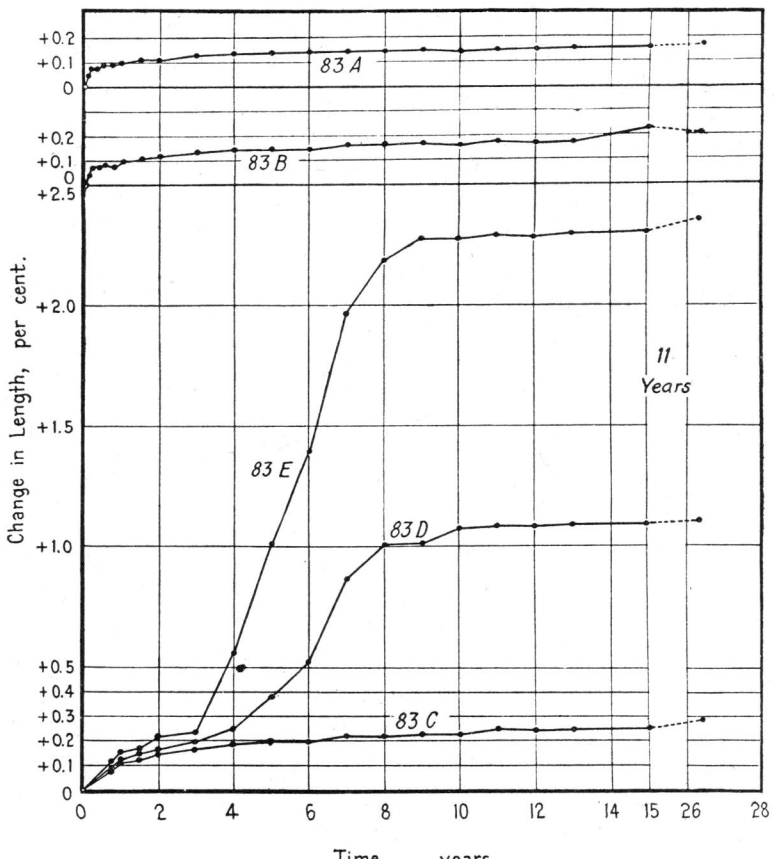

FIG. 170.—Effect of free magnesia on expansion of neat cement in water. [*From A. H. White, Proc. A.S.T.M.*, **28**, II, 398 (1928).]

elongated 1.0 per cent and that with 4 per cent had elongated 2.2 per cent.

Heat Evolved on Hydration of Portland Cement.—The heat evolved on hydration of portland cement is considerable, but it is evolved so slowly that it is not usually noticeable. The figures for the complete hydration of the normal major constituents of cement, with lime and magnesia added for comparison, are given by Lerch and Bogue as follows:[1]

	Heat of Hydration, Cal per Gram
Tricalcium silicate	120
Beta dicalcium silicate	62
Tricalcium aluminate	207
Tetracalcium aluminoferrite	100
Magnesia	203
Lime	279

The effect of this heat is not noted in ordinary concrete construction, although it is a factor in preventing concrete from freezing while it sets. If the aggregate, cement, and water are all heated before mixing, concrete may be laid in rather cold weather if it is insulated by hay or similar porous material spread on the surface, or is protected from loss of heat in other ways.

The temperature will rise considerably in the center of large blocks of concrete, and in the construction of Boulder Dam cooling coils were imbedded in the concrete to keep the temperature down. A high temperature in the center of a large block of concrete would be followed by decrease in volume and shrinkage strains as the mass cooled.

High-early-strength Cements.—The preceding paragraphs have indicated that the early strength of portland cement is due to the hydration of the two constituents $3CaO.Al_2O_3$ and $3CaO.SiO_2$. One logical way to increase the early strength is therefore to increase the lime content of the clinker. The higher the lime content, the greater the danger of free lime, and therefore the manufacture of these early-strength cements requires great care and excellent equipment. Some mills burn their clinker once, grind it, and put it through a second burning process to ensure greater uniformity of composition. Another way to increase the high early strength is to grind the cement to a finer powder.

The strength requirements as set forth in Table 61 require tensile tests to be made at the age of 1 day and 3 days. Tests at 28 days may be required at the option of the purchaser, with the

[1] Portland Cement Association Fellowship at the U. S. Bureau of Standards, *Paper* 26, 1934.

TABLE 61.—STRENGTH REQUIREMENTS FOR HIGH-EARLY-STRENGTH PORTLAND CEMENT

Age at test, days	Storage of specimens	Option No. 1 tensile strength, psi	Option No. 2 compressive strength, psi
1	1 day in moist air	275	1300
3	1 day in moist air and 2 days in water	375	3000

requirement that the 28-day test shall be higher than the 3-day test. Compressive tests may be substituted for tensile tests, and the method of making the compressive test of portland cement mortars has been adopted as a Tentative Standard of the American Society for Testing Materials.[1] The specification of the mortar to be tested states that there shall be 1 part cement to 2.77 parts graded Ottawa sand by weight and 53 per cent water by weight of cement (water-cement ratio of 0.8 per cent by volume). The mortar shall be molded into 2-in. cubes and shall remain in the molds in a moist closet for 24 hr. The cubes shall then be placed in water for further storage.

Fused Cements.—An entirely different class of silicate cements is made by fusing slags high in alumina in an electric furnace. Similar cements may be made by clinkering in a rotary kiln. These cements were first developed in France and are sometimes referred to by the French name *ciment fondu*, or fused cements.

TABLE 62.—COMPOSITION AND TENSILE STRENGTH OF A FUSED ALUMINA CEMENT

Chemical Composition
SiO_2 .... 8.50 ⎫
Fe_2O_3 .... 18.54 ⎬ 64.28
Al_2O_3 .... 37.24 ⎭
CaO 31.60
MgO 1.15
SO_3 .... 1.47
Loss on ignition 2.08

Tensile Strength
1:3 Ottawa Sand Briquets
  1 day .... 464 psi
  7 days 537
  3 mos. 591

---

[1] A.S.T.M. Tentative Standards, 1937, p. 459.

They set very quickly, attain high strength quickly, and are resistant to attack by sea water. On the other hand, they develop much heat on setting and their volume changes between the wet and dry condition are greater than with portland cement. This product cannot be sold as portland cement because it has been fused. There are no standard specifications for it in this country.

The properties and composition of one of the American cements of this type are given in Table 62. It will be noted that its strength after 1 day is distinctly higher than that specified for the high-early-strength cement after 3 days. This rapid attainment of high strength was of great value during the World War, since heavy artillery could be mounted and fired within 24 hr after the foundations for the guns were poured.

Precast Building Units.—The building unit that is most widely used is the hollow block which is frequently made with cinders as a lightweight aggregate. The mixture is made so dry that it can be tamped into a mold by an automatic machine to yield a block which is stiff and strong enough so that the mold can be stripped at once. The blocks are then set aside to harden, sometimes in a steam oven to accelerate the hardening. If these units are allowed to become dry before use, they will already have undergone their initial shrinkage. They are sometimes made in small and poorly equipped plants where the proportioning and mixing are not thoroughly and uniformly accomplished, with the result that the blocks are uneven in quality.

Reinforced-concrete roofing tile are made from plastic concrete cast in molds that remain closed until the concrete has set. These are usually made in plants that are well-equipped and produce a reliable product.

Sand-lime Brick.—Sand-lime brick are made from a dry mixture of sand and 5 to 10 per cent of hydrated lime which is dampened slightly and pressed into brick under a pressure of about 15,000 psi. The brick are cooked in superheated steam (100 to 150 lb pressure) for about 8 hr, and at this temperature some of the lime reacts with the surface of the sand particles to form a hydrated silicate which acts as a bond. When the brick are removed from the cooker and stacked in the air, the balance of the hydrated lime reacts with the carbon dioxide of the air to form calcium carbonate which increases the strength of the brick. The compressive strength of the bricks is specified in the A.S.T.M. Standards to be, as the mean of five tests, 4500 psi or over for Class A bricks, 2500 to 4500 for Class B, and 1250 to 2500 lb for Class C. These brick come into direct competition with clay brick in locations where they may be made economically.

Durability of Mortars, Stuccoes, and Concretes Exposed to the Weather.—The cements and mortars discussed in the last two chapters may be used somewhat interchangeably, and the controlling factors in deciding which to use are usually cost and durability.

The solubility of gypsum in water is so great that it is not used for permanent structures to be exposed to the weather except in rainless regions. If gypsum slabs are used in roof construction, they must be carefully protected from the weather.

Magnesium oxychloride cements hydrolyze and decompose in water and are not reliable for exterior use except in dry climates.

Lime mortars gain strength slowly and are liable to be washed away by a rain if one comes soon after they are first applied. In the older practice, it was customary to mix a small amount of hydraulic lime with a larger amount of lime putty and all of the sand the mixture would carry. Some of these old stuccoes on brick are still good after nearly 100 years of service in a trying climate. The brick on which they were applied was hard-burned, and the stucco was an ornamental rather than a protective coating. This stucco is porous and absorbs water, but the coating is thin and the water either evaporates or runs off before it freezes.

Stuccoes of portland cement and sand made from rich mixtures are strong and hard, but crack because of the large volume changes on alternate wetting and drying. These cracks permit water to penetrate and corrode wire lath if the stucco is applied over that as a base. The volume changes cause rich stucco to split off of brick, whose volume changes are small.

Concrete that is permanently wet as in deep foundations and subaqueous work should be very permanent, provided harmful chemicals are not present. Concrete that is kept continuously dry as in concrete buildings should also be permanent. Concrete exposed to changing weather conditions will not be permanent unless provision is made for taking care of the volume changes through expansion joints.

Even if expansion joints are provided to take care of the large movements, fine cracks will form on the surface. These will gradually become deeper, and will permit water to collect and freeze. The expansion due to ice formation will rapidly enlarge the cracks, and ultimately cause disintegration of the concrete.

Protective Coatings for Concrete.—The only way to ensure permanence to concrete structures exposed to the weather is to prevent water from getting to them. Top coats of bituminous material are used to protect concrete roofs and highways. Waterproofings mixed with the concrete, called "integral waterproofings," are sometimes effective and sometimes not. Paints may be used only under certain conditions. The subject is discussed more fully in Chap. XXIII.

References

MEADE, R. K.: Portland Cement, Chemical Publishing Co., Easton, Pa., 1926.

ECKEL, E. C.: Portland Cement Materials and Industry, *U. S. Geol. Survey, Bull.* 522, 1913.

BLOUNT, BERTRAM: Cement, Longmans, Green & Co., New York, 1920.

BAUER, E. E.: Plain Concrete, 2 ed., McGraw-Hill Book Company, Inc., New York, 1936.

PORTLAND CEMENT ASSOCIATION: Design and Control of Concrete Mixtures, 6th ed., 1938.

BOGUE, R. H.: A Digest of the Literature on the Constitution of Portland Cement Clinker, Portland Cement Association, Fellowship at the Bureau of Standards, *Paper* 3, 1927.

BOGUE, R. H.: A Digest of the Literature on the Nature of the Setting and Hardening Processes in Portland Cement, Portland Cement Association Fellowship at the Bureau of Standards, *Paper* 17, 1928.

WHITE, A. H.: Volume Changes of Portland Cement As Affected by Chemical Composition and Aging, *Proc. Am. Soc. Testing Materials*, **28**, II, 398 (1928)

Properties and Manufacture of Concrete Building Units, *U. S. Bur. Standards, Cir.* 304, 1926.

American Society for Testing Materials Standards, Part II, 1936.

CHAPTER XXI

FUELS AND COMBUSTION

Combustion.—Combustion is the process of rapid oxidation of a fuel through combination with the oxygen of the air. Fuels are those materials which may be readily made to combine with the oxygen of the air and which are commercially available to provide heat for industrial operations. The important fuels are all made up of the elements carbon and hydrogen in varying proportions. Sulfur is a constituent of minor importance. Oxygen in a fuel has a negative value. Heat is evolved when fuel reacts with the oxygen of the air. $C + O_2 \rightarrow CO_2 + 14{,}544$ Btu per pound carbon. Carbon dioxide is not a fuel because the carbon has already combined with the oxygen. Hydrogen is a fuel, and the equation for its combustion may be written $2H_2 + O_2 \rightarrow 2H_2O$ (liquid) $+ 60{,}810$ Btu per pound hydrogen. Water is not a fuel because the hydrogen has already combined with oxygen and given up its heat in the process of combination.

The products of complete combustion of fuels are therefore CO_2 and H_2O, with SO_3 as a minor constituent. The ash that is present in solid fuels may react to a minor extent with oxygen or with SO_3 and retain some of the reaction products in a solid form. Iron pyrites (FeS_2) will burn to Fe_2O_3 and SO_2 or SO_3, and the latter may in turn react with $CaCO_3$ to form $CaSO_4$.

The heat of combustion of solid fuels is usually expressed in British thermal units (Btu) per pound, although in many texts the values are given in calories per gram, Calories per kilogram, or British thermal units per pound mol. Gaseous fuels have their heating values reported as British thermal units per cubic foot of gas measured when saturated with water vapor at a temperature of 60°F and a barometric pressure of 30 in. of mercury. Liquid fuels are usually valued in British thermal units per U. S. gallon.

Measurement of the Heat of Combustion.—The heat of combustion of fuels is measured in a calorimeter in which a known amount of the fuel is burned. The heat of combustion of solid fuels and sometimes of liquid fuels is determined in a closed bomb that contains a weighed amount of the fuel and a large excess of oxygen under a pressure which is about 300 psi. The bomb is immersed in a vessel of water, and the rise in temperature of the water, after the coal has been burned, may be used to calculate the heating value of the fuel. The heating value of gases is usually, and that of volatile liquids is sometimes, determined in a continuous calorimeter in which a measured stream of gas is burned. The heat evolved is absorbed in a stream of water whose rise in temperature is measured.

In both types of calorimeters, the gases are cooled to substantially the initial temperature of the system and the water formed in combustion is condensed to liquid. The value obtained represents the maximum heat that may be obtained from the fuel, and is never attained in practice.

Calculation of the Heat of Combustion.—The heat of combustion of pure carbon varies somewhat with its crystalline form. Diamond gives off about 1 per cent less heat than the carbon of coke, and the figures given by various authorities vary slightly from the value of 14,544 Btu per pound. In order to calculate the heating value of a fuel, it is necessary to know the ultimate analysis, which states the percentages of each element in the fuel and the heating value of each element. Oxygen actually detracts from the heating value of a fuel, and its influence will be discussed in a separate paragraph.

It is assumed for purposes of calculation that the oxygen is all in combination with hydrogen as water and that only the surplus hydrogen is "available" for combustion with gaseous oxygen. The ratio of hydrogen to oxygen in water is as 1:8 by weight, and the available hydrogen in a fuel is said to be $H - O/8$. A coal whose percentage composition was 83 carbon, 12 oxygen, and 5 hydrogen would be recalculated to be composed of 83 carbon, $5 - 1.5 = 3.5$ available hydrogen, and $12 + 1.5 = 13.5$ combined oxygen and hydrogen which would not have any fuel value. This method of calculation is approximately accurate, but has several minor errors to which no reference can be made here. The method of direct experimental determination of heating value is always preferable.

Heating Value of Gases by Weight and Volume.—Gases are nearly always sold by the cubic foot, although sometimes the basis is a therm, a heat unit equalling 100,000 Btu. Some of the properties of gases commonly used as fuels are given in Table 63.

TABLE 63.—CONSTANTS FOR SELECTED GASES AND VAPORS*

Name	Formula	Mol. wt.	Sp. gr. at 60°F, air = 1.00	Cu ft per lb, 60° and 30"	Btu per cu ft	Btu per lb	Boiling point, °F
Hydrogen.........	H_2	2.015	0.071	187.72	323.9	60,810	−422.9
Carbon monoxide...	CO	28.000	0.967	13.51	323	4,362	−310.
Methane.........	CH_4	16.031	0.554	23.56	1016	23,955	−258.5
Ethane...........	C_2H_6	30.046	1.049	12.45	1781	22,215	−126.9
Propane..........	C_3H_8	44.062	1.562	8.36	2572	21,564	−48.1
Butane...........	C_4H_{10}	58.077	2.066	6.32	3253	21,247	+33.1
Pentane..........	C_5H_{12}	72.092	2.487	5.25	3981	20,908	+97.2
Hexane...........	C_6H_{14}	86.107	2.970	4.40	4467	20,526	+156.2
Benzene..........	C_6H_6	78.046	2.692	4.85	3740	18,150	+175.3
Methanol.........	CH_3OH	32.031	1.106	11.81	866	10,238	+148.1
Ethanol..........	C_2H_5OH	46.046	1.590	8.21	1617	13,309	+173.3
Carbon dioxide....	CO_2	44.000	1.528	8.55	.....	.....	−108.4
Water............	H_2O	18.015	0.621	21.02	.....	.....	+212.
Oxygen...........	O_2	32.00	1.105	11.82	.....	.....	−297.4
Nitrogen.........	N_2	28.016	0.967	13.5	.....	.....	−320.4

* From Gas Chemists Handbook.

Hydrogen has the highest heating value per pound, 60,810 Btu, but its specific gravity is so low, 0.071 compared with 1.00 for air, that its heating value per cubic foot is only 323.9 Btu, which is so small as to make hydrogen rather undesirable as a major constituent of gas that is to be sold for domestic and for many industrial uses. Methane (CH_4) is the chief constituent of natural gas. Its composition may be calculated from the atomic weights of carbon (12) and hydrogen (1) to be 75 per cent of carbon and 25 per cent of hydrogen. Its heating value may be calculated with approximate accuracy, but may be determined experimentally more exactly to have a heating value of 23,955 Btu per pound, which is less than 40 per cent that of hydrogen. However methane is sold by the cubic foot, and on that basis its heating value is more than three times that of hydrogen.

The law of Avogadro states, roughly, that a cubic foot contains the same number of molecules of gas, no matter what the gas, or mixture of gases may be. This law is not strictly accurate, and deviations become of importance with gases of high molecular weight, but it gives a useful approximation. Its application may be seen by the following figures extracted from Table 63.

Gas	Formula	Mol wt	Cu ft per lb	Btu per lb	Btu per cu ft
Hydrogen	H_2	2	187.7	60,810	324
Methane	CH_4	16	23.5	23,955	1016
Hexane	C_6H_{14}	86	4.4	20,526	4467

The cubic feet per pound vary inversely as the molecular weights. In any given series, the heating value per cubic foot increases with increase in molecular weight, because according to Avogadro's law, a cubic foot of hexane vapor will contain as many molecules of hexane as a cubic foot of methane does of methane.

The Influence of Oxygen on Heating Value.—The oxygen that exists in a fuel has already given up its energy of combination and is therefore inert. Its influence has sometimes been compared with that of ash in coal, but it lowers the heating value more than a given weight of ash, for the oxygen carries with it as inert matter the element with which it is already combined.

The effect of oxygen may be illustrated by the relative heating values of methane (CH_4) and methanol (methyl alcohol) (CH_3OH). For purposes of calculation, the formula for methanol may be written ($CH_2 + H_2O$), which indicates that it contains 14 parts by weight of combustible material plus 18 of water. A pound of methanol should therefore have approximately $14/32$ as high a heating value as a pound of methane. This gives a calculated value of 10,480 Btu per pound which is in fair agreement with the experimental value of 10,238 Btu. If methane and methanol are to be rated on their values per cubic foot of gas or vapor, the discrepancy is not so great since a cubic foot of CH_3OH contains just as many molecules as a cubic foot of CH_4 and the ($CH_2 + H_2O$) gives off approximately $14/16$ as much heat per cubic foot as the CH_4. This calculation gives 1 cu ft of methanol vapor a heating value of 889 Btu, and the experimental value is reported as 866.

Net Heating Value.—The method of determining heating value in the calorimeter involves cooling all of the products of combustion to room temperature and condensing all steam to liquid water. In almost all commercial combustion operations, the steam escapes out of the stack as vapor, and since the latent heat of steam is high, a correction has been proposed which would deduct 1020 Btu per pound of water per pound of fuel burned from the total heat as determined in the calorimeter. This figure represents the heat required to convert the liquid water to vapor. This lower figure is called "net heating value." Those who advocate the use of the net heating value claim that their method of computation gives a closer approach to the actual commercial value of a fuel. However the efficiency with which a fuel is used depends upon so many factors that it is usually considered better to start with the total heating value and calculate from that the efficiency which has been obtained under a given set of operating conditions.

The Process of Combustion.—Combustion evolves heat and proceeds spontaneously, once it has been started. In commercial furnaces, an excess of oxygen is usually present, and the principal products of combustion are CO_2 and H_2O together with the nitrogen that accompanied the oxygen of the air when it entered the furnace and any excess of air which may have passed through the combustion chamber unchanged. The steps in the combustion process may be quite complicated. When fuel oil is sprayed into a hot furnace, the first step is vaporization of the drops of liquid oil, the cracking of the oil vapors into simpler hydrocarbons, with hydrogen and carbon as the end products of the cracking process, and combustion of the cracked products. Fortunately in studying combustion problems, it is usually unnecessary to consider the steps of the reaction, since all calculations are based on the fuel entering and the combustion products leaving the furnace.

Sensible Heat and Chemical Energy of Gases.—Energy available for useful work may exist in gases in two forms, sensible heat and chemical, or potential, energy.

Methane, for example, has a heating value of 1016 Btu per cubic foot which can be made available only by combustion and may be said to be in the form of potential, or chemical, energy. If the methane should be heated to 200°F before it entered the furnace, it would carry an added amount of energy in a form that can be felt, and so is called "sensible heat." After complete combustion, all of the chemical energy will have been changed to sensible heat which will, in the first instance, all be found in the combustion gases. Part of this sensible heat will be absorbed in the furnace to generate steam or do other useful work, part of it will pass through the walls of the furnace and be dissipated by radiation or convection, and part of it will pass out of the stack as sensible heat in the gases.

Efficiency of Furnaces.—The efficiency of a furnace may be defined as the percentage of the total input of heat units that are utilized by the furnace. The combustion chamber is usually part of the furnace, and the efficiency is then based on the maximum heat units that are released by complete combustion of the fuel.

If the heat input is denoted by H_1 and the heat lost is denoted by H_2, then

$$\text{Efficiency} = \frac{H_1 - H_2}{H_1}$$

The term H_2 includes heat lost through incomplete combustion of the fuel, as sensible heat in the stack gases, and as radiation or convection from the hot walls of the furnace.

If the fuel is not burned completely in the combustion chamber and unburned products, as shown, for example, by smoke, pass through the furnace, the efficiency is lowered. The loss of heat in unburned products is usually low, and the greatest objection to smoke is the damage it causes to others rather than the loss that it brings to the owner of the furnace.

The greatest loss of heat comes through the sensible heat of the stack gases, and the loss increases both with the volume and temperature of the gases. The steam formed in combustion escapes as vapor instead of being condensed as in the calorimeter, and the correction for the latent heat of steam becomes of importance in a fuel such as natural gas which is high in combined hydrogen. The figures of Table 64 show the losses in the stack gases of a furnace fired with natural gas, which is for this purpose assumed to be pure methane with a heating value of 1016 Btu per cubic foot. One set of figures assumes that the gas was burned with only 10 per cent excess of air, which is a small excess. The other

TABLE 64.—Loss of Heat from Furnace with Varying Proportions of Excess Air and Varying Temperatures of Stack Gases
The fuel is natural gas, assumed to be pure methane.

Temp. of stack gases, °F	Percentage of heat lost	
	10 per cent excess air	100 per cent excess air
400	16.1	23.0
1000	29.4	43.7
2000	53.4	83.5
3000	78.2	

set of figures assumes that the gas was burned with 100 per cent excess air, which is needlessly high but is sometimes reached with careless operation. A stack gas temperature as low as 400°F may be reached in a modern steam power plant, and under the circumstances assumed, the stack loss would be 16.1 per cent with 10 per cent of excess of air, and 23.0 per cent with 100 per cent excess air. If the temperature of the gases leaving the furnace should be 1000°F, the losses would rise to 29.4 and 43.7 per cent, respectively. The losses at 2000°F would be 53.4 and 83.5 per cent and at 3000° would be 78.2 per cent if only 10 per cent excess of air was used in combustion. No figures are given for the loss with 100 per cent excess of air, because the chemical energy of methane is not sufficient to furnish the necessary sensible heat, and so a temperature of 3000°F could not be reached with that large excess of air.

The gases leaving the hearth of an open-hearth steel furnace are hotter than the melting point of steel and so are over 3000°F. The regenerators absorb some of the heat and return it to the incoming gas and air. Even with a modern regenerative system, the gases escape at about 1500°F. This may decrease the loss in the stack from 80 or 85 per cent to 60 per cent, but losses by radiation will amount to nearly 20 per cent so that the efficiency of an open-hearth furnace with its regenerators is not usually over 20 per cent.

Maximum Flame Temperatures.—The maximum flame temperature is a theoretical figure that could be obtained if all of the heat evolved in combustion were used to heat the gaseous products of combustion. It may be calculated from a knowledge of the heat units available and the weights, or volumes, and the specific heats of the gases formed in combustion. The heat brought to the combustion chamber as sensible heat in the gas and air will be added to that obtained by combustion, and so regeneration, by preheating the incoming gas and air, will help to raise the temperature of the flame.

The old hand-operated puddling furnace burned coal on a grate with a rather large excess of cold air and could not attain a temperature high enough to melt the ferrite resulting from the puddling operation. The open-hearth furnace with gaseous firing, close control of the amount of air, and regenerators can easily attain the melting point of pure iron, though using only about half as many British thermal units per ton of steel as were required to make a ton of wrought iron.

Advantages of Gaseous Fuels.—A gaseous fuel permits ready mixing of the gas with the air needed for combustion, with the result that a minimum of excess air is used, and high temperatures and high furnace efficiencies may be attained. It is only with gaseous fuels that both the air and gas may be preheated in regenerators, but not all gases can be preheated without decomposition and liberation of soot. The composition of the furnace atmosphere can be regulated, with gas firing, so that a reducing or neutral atmosphere may be maintained. This is desirable in a reheating furnace for steel sheets and in other furnaces where scaling is to be avoided. The atmosphere may be made so high in carbon monoxide that steel may be casehardened. Convenience of operation and cleanliness are other advantages of gaseous fuels.

The chief disadvantage of gaseous fuel is its cost. If it is to be manufactured from coal, the cost of manufacture must be added to the cost of the coal. The cost of distribution adds to the cost of both natural and manufactured gas. Storage of gas is expensive, because of its bulk. Public utilities serving cities feel it necessary to build large gas holders providing a reserve sufficient to supply their customers for 24 hr in case of an accident. Compression of gas into cylinders where it may be stored under high pressure is much more expensive than the construction of large holders to hold the gas at atmospheric pressure. The composition and properties of some commercial gas supplies are given in Table 67.

Advantages of Liquid Fuels.—Liquid fuels may be blown into the firebox as a spray of fine droplets which mix with air and burn in a hot firebox almost as readily and efficiently as a gas. The air may be preheated in a regenerator, but the liquid fuel may not be preheated much without decomposition and liberation of soot. Most liquid fuels can be stored in tanks at atmospheric pressure, but some of the volatile liquid fuels like butane can be stored only under higher pressure.

Fuels for Internal-combustion Engines.—The so-called explosion in an internal-combustion engine is merely rapid combustion of a compressed mixture of combustible gas or vapors with air. Gasoline, the usual motor fuel, is a mixture of petroleum hydrocarbons which may be stored as a liquid but which forms enough vapor when brought into intimate contact with air so that an explosive mixture results. Motor fuel for use in winter contains more of the highly volatile constituents, so that the mixture will be rich enough to start the engine promptly even if both the fuel and engine are cold. The cost of motor fuel of standard grade, if bought in carload lots at the refinery, is usually about 5 cents a gallon. The higher price that the motorist pays is due to the cost of distributing this volatile fuel and the taxes which are placed upon it.

Distillates that are somewhat heavier and less volatile than gasoline may be used in internal-combustion engines if an explosive mixture may be formed in the cylinder. The oil used in Diesel engines is injected into the cylinder as a liquid spray. The compression stroke heats the liquid spray and the air so that the spray changes to vapor and the mixture ignites either from contact with the hot walls or from the heat of compression. It is usually necessary to provide a small amount of a more volatile fuel for starting the engine. A gallon of Diesel engine oil contains more heat units than a gallon of gasoline because there are more pounds in a gallon of the heavier oil. The lower price of Diesel oil is due to the lower costs of distributing a fuel with low volatility and to the absence of the taxes placed on gasoline motor fuel.

Disadvantages of Solid Fuels.—No one who has ever shoveled coal into a furnace needs to be told that it is a nuisance to have to give frequent attention to the job and that it is difficult to maintain an even heat. A disadvantage which is not so apparent is the larger amount of excess air that is needed to ensure complete combustion. Some coals give off large quantities of gas and tarry products when heated, so that incomplete combustion and smoke are apt to follow the introduction of each lot of fresh fuel. Automatic stokers are made that will give fairly satisfactory results even in household furnaces, but the coal must be selected for the purpose and be crushed to definite sizes. If coal is crushed to a fine powder, it may be burned almost like a liquid fuel, but the installation for crushing the coal is expensive and available only to operators of large plants.

Conversion of Carbon to Gaseous Fuel.—If carbon combines with oxygen according to the equation $C + O_2 \rightarrow CO_2 + 14{,}544$ Btu per pound carbon, all of the possible heat has been set free. If it is made to combine with oxygen according to the reaction $2C + O_2 \rightarrow 2CO + 5844$ Btu per pound carbon, it is evident that only part of the heat has been set free and that more heat may be liberated by combustion of this CO according to the equation $2CO + O_2 = 2CO_2 + \text{heat}$.

The first law of thermodynamics, also known as the law of the conservation of energy, teaches that the amount of energy liberated in a reaction is dependant only on the initial and final states of the materials reacting in a closed system and is independant of the rate and path of the reaction. If a stick of wood burns in the fireplace in 10 min, it gives off exactly as much heat as if it took 10 hr to burn, or if it took 100 years, lying on the ground in the forest, to rot and eventually become completely oxidized and converted to the same quantity of CO_2 and H_2O that would result from rapid combustion in the fireplace.

If a pound of carbon is burned directly to CO, there will be 5844 Btu evolved as sensible heat, and the balance of the 14,544 Btu, or 8700 Btu, will remain as potential energy in the CO to be released on further combustion of the CO to CO_2. Thus, if no energy were lost through radiation or convection in the transportation process, coal could be burned to CO in one piece of equipment and the gas could be transported to a separate firebox and burned there to CO_2 with exactly the same amount of heat being available for the furnace as would have been the case had the solid coal been burned in the firebox attached to the furnace.

The illustrations of Fig. 171 depict diagrammatically a puddling furnace for making wrought iron, heated with coal burned on a grate, and an open-hearth furnace equipped with a gas producer, fired with producer gas and provided with regenerators. Each pound of carbon burned in the two furnaces has the possibility of producing the same amount of heat, but the capacity of the two units for utilizing heat is very different. In the puddling furnace, the products of combustion escape up the stack at almost the full temperature of the hearth so that the efficiency of the fuel is low. The open-hearth furnace recovers part of the heat of the combustion gases in regenerators, which, working in pairs, alternate in absorbing heat from the combustion

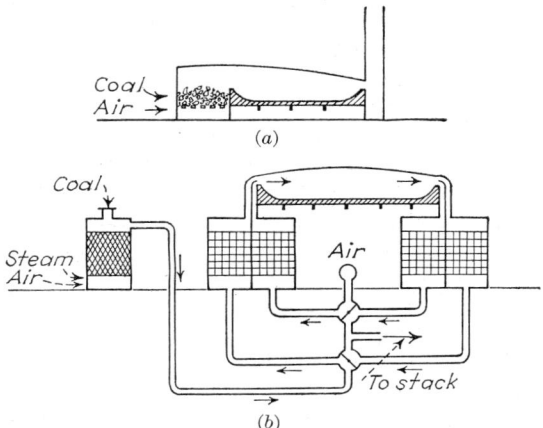

Fig. 171.—Diagrammatic cross section of (a) puddling furnace, and (b) open-hearth furnace with gas producer and regenerators.

gases and in giving it back to the incoming gas and air. The increased efficiency is due in part to the lower temperature of the gases escaping up the stack and in part to the smaller amount of excess air which is required for the complete combustion of gaseous fuels. The puddling furnace required as much as 1000 lb of coal per ton of iron, but the open-hearth furnace needs only half of that amount for a ton of steel.

Origin and Classification of Solid Fuels.—Almost all of our fuels are derived from vegetable tissues which the plant is able to synthesize from the carbon dioxide and water of the air. The transformations absorb heat, but the chlorophyll of green plants is able to transform the radiant energy received from the sun into chemical energy, liberating oxygen and thus regenerating the oxygen of the air. The first reaction may be written in a simple way as follows:

$$CO_2 + H_2O + \rightleftarrows CH_2O + O_2$$

The reaction product is formaldehyde (CH_2O), and the living plant is able to build this up into more complex compounds. Glucose ($C_6H_{12}O_6$) may be considered arithmetically to be $6(CH_2O)$, and cellulose, although a very complex molecule, has a composition that is arithmetically $C_6H_{10}O_5$. When vegetable tissues are burned to CO_2 and H_2O, the heat liberated is theoretically that which was absorbed from the sun in their formation.

Growing plants contain small amounts of nitrogen in combination as protein and other complex molecules. Sulfur is present in small amounts, and also minute quantities of other inorganic materials. When plants die and decay on the surface of the ground, a considerable part of their tissues is oxidized to CO_2 and H_2O. If however plant tissues collect under water, as in swamps where the amount of oxygen is very restricted and the process of decay is modified, H_2O, CO_2, and more complex compounds are split off of the molecule without much oxidation by the air. The formula for CO_2 shows that 32 weights of oxygen are combined with 12 of carbon, and that for water shows 16 weights of oxygen for 2 of hydrogen. Plant tissues decomposing in this manner lose much more oxygen than hydrogen and carbon, and so the modified vegetable tissues have a higher heating value. The first recognized step in the progress of vegetable tissues toward coal consists in the formation of peat, a soft black or brown mass in which small stems of plants are frequently found.

Some peat beds formed many thousand years ago were covered by soil and subjected to pressure which in turn produced moderate heat. These two agencies caused further elimination of CO_2, H_2O, and other products, some of them composed of carbon and hydrogen like methane. The net effect was to decrease the oxygen and increase the relative percentages of carbon and hydrogen with formation of coal. The older the coals and the more complete the changes, the higher their heating value became, until a maximum was reached at the point of transition from bituminous coal to anthracite. The layers of peat as they accumulated in the swamp for centuries were not uniform. Sometimes storms washed in considerable clay and silt, and the character of the vegetation changed in the course of years. When these peat deposits were covered and compressed, the stratification remained and may still be seen in the coal, as is shown in Fig. 172. The figures of Table 65 show in a generalized way steps in the conversion of wood through peat, lignite, and

Fig. 172.—Polished section of bituminous coal, approximately natural size. [*From Bur. Mines, Bull.* 344 (1931).]

bituminous coal to anthracite, often called "hard coal." The element that suffers the greatest change in this series is oxygen which decreases from 44.1 per cent in wood to 2.7 per cent in anthracite. The carbon shows a relative increase through the series, and the hydrogen decreases only slightly until anthracite is reached, when it drops rather abruptly. The net result is an increase in the percentage of carbon and available hydrogen, and

TABLE 65.—PERCENTAGE COMPOSITION OF SOLID FUEL*
Calculated to a Fuel Free from Moisture and Ash.

	Wood	Peat	Lignite	Bituminous coal Western	Bituminous coal Eastern	Anthracite
C	49.7	55.6	74.2	82.9	87.5	93.5
H	6.1	6.5	5.5	5.7	5.2	2.8
O	44.1	36.4	19.1	9.9	5.7	2.7
N	0.05	1.4	1.2	1.5	1.6	1.0
Rearranged for calculation of heating values						
C	49.7	55.6	74.2	82.9	87.5	93.5
Available H	0.6	2.0	3.1	4.5	4.5	2.4
Calculated heating value, Btu/pound	7,610	9,315	12,685	14,848	15,388	15,068

* From CLARKE, F. W., Data of Geochemistry

hence in the heating value, as vegetable tissues pass through the transitions to anthracite. Anthracite has the highest carbon content, but its percentage of available hydrogen is so low, 2.4, that its heating value is less than that of the best bituminous coal.

Proximate Analysis of Coal.—The preceding paragraph has discussed the classification of coals on the basis of their ultimate analysis. A method that is used more frequently depends on the behavior of the coal when heated to redness in a closed crucible. Under these conditions, almost all of the oxygen is driven off as CO_2, CO, and H_2O together with a small amount present in more complicated compounds such as are found in the suspensions of smoke and in tar. The available hydrogen of the coal is mainly driven off as hydrocarbons, compounds of carbon and hydrogen of which methane (CH_4) and ethylene (C_2H_4) are common examples.

The residue left in the closed crucible after the heating process is largely carbon and ash, with fractional percentages of oxygen, nitrogen, and sulfur. Many coals soften to a pasty mass at temperatures below a red heat. When the gas is evolved at higher temperatures, the pasty mass stiffens and becomes a hard porous lump called "coke." In the method of proximate analysis, a weighed amount of crushed coal is placed in a crucible with a cover which fits quite closely, and then heated in a furnace under conditions that are minutely described in the standard methods of the American Society for Testing Materials. The loss in weight during the heating process is partly moisture, which is determined separately, and partly volatile matter formed by the decomposition of the coal. The residue in the crucible, consisting of carbon and ash with very small amounts of other materials, is weighed and then completely burned to leave a residue of ash. The complete analysis consists of the four items moisture, volatile matter, fixed carbon, and ash. If, after the heating process, the fixed carbon is present in the crucible as a hard button of coke, the coal is said to be "coking" or "agglomerating." If the fixed carbon is found to be in fine particles, the coal is said to be "noncoking."

This process of decomposition of a carbon compound by heating to redness in a closed vessel was formerly called "destructive distillation," but the terms "carbonization" or "pyrolysis" are now more frequently used for the process. The processes of producing coke from coal and charcoal from wood are instances of the commercial applications of pyrolysis.

Classification of Coals According to Volatile Matter and Vein Moisture.—Classifications of coal which are widely used are based on proximate analysis. The differences between the various ranks of coal are not sharply defined, and the divisions must be made somewhat arbitrarily, so there is no complete

TABLE 66.—CLASSIFICATION OF COALS ON BASIS OF VOLATILE MATTER AND VEIN MOISTURE

The coals are calculated to an ash-free basis.

Coal	Volatile matter, per cent	Vein moisture, per cent
Anthracite	Below 5	
Semianthracite	5–10	
Semibituminous	15–22	
Bituminous, Eastern	23–35	2–4
Bituminous, mid-continental	35–45	6–17
Black lignite or subbituminous	35–45	17–20
Brown lignite	25–45	20–25

agreement on nomenclature. One of the simpler classifications is that proposed by S. W. Parr which is given in Table 66. It recognizes the importance of moisture in the coal as mined (vein moisture), as well as the percentage of volatile matter, in judging the usefulness of a fuel and placing it in its proper class. The divisions into classes by volatile matter correspond closely with those of Table 65 based on ultimate analysis.

The hard anthracite coal contains little oxygen as shown in Table 65 and less than 5 per cent of volatile matter according to Table 66. The main sources of anthracite coal in the United States are scattered areas in eastern Pennsylvania which are so small that they are inconspicuous on the map of Fig. 173. Semianthracite is the next recognized class with 5 to 10 per cent volatile matter, and then semibituminous with 15 to 22 per cent of volatile matter. These coals do not contain any appreciable amount of moisture when they are taken from the mine. The next class embraces the large group of bituminous coals. In the United States, the older group of bituminous coals is found in a long band stretching along the Appalachian Mountains through Pennsylvania, West Virginia, Virginia, Kentucky, Tennessee, and into Alabama as shown in Fig. 173. This Eastern division contains 23 to 35 per cent of volatile matter in addition to 2 to 4 per cent of vein moisture. The bituminous coals of the midcontinent area are of more recent origin and are not of such high grade. Table 65 shows that they contain almost 10 per cent of oxygen, and Table 66 states that they contain 35 to 45 per cent of volatile matter, as well as 17 to 20 per cent of moisture when mined. Lignites, which are the youngest coals, contain still more oxygen and therefore show still higher volatile matter. In addition, they may contain as much as 25 per cent of vein moisture. This vein moisture evaporates when the lignites are stored in the air, and the subsequent shrinkage in volume is so large that the lumps break down into fine pieces which cannot be burned efficiently on grates. The lignites, and the western bituminous coal are distinctly inferior to the high-grade bituminous coals and the anthracite of the Eastern district of the United States.

Ash in Coal.—The ash in coal may consist largely of clay which, like other clays, may have either a low or a high melting point. It sometimes contains iron pyrites (FeS_2) which on combustion

FIG. 173.—Map showing coal deposits of United States. (*Courtesy Keystone Coal Manual.*)

forms Fe_2O_3 (or FeO) and causes a lowering of the fusion point of the ash. In a furnace where the temperature of the fire is low, the ash in coal gives little operating trouble. As soon as the temperature in the combustion chamber rises to the point at which some of the constituents of the ash commence to fuse, a pasty mass of clinker starts to form at the hottest point in the fuel bed. This clinker prevents air from passing through the fuel bed evenly. Local cold spots and hot spots are liable to form, and the capacity of the furnace will thereby be decreased. A coal with ash of high melting point, 2600°F and above, is preferable to one with a low melting point, 2200 to 2400°F.

Petroleum.—Petroleum is a liquid composed almost entirely of hydrocarbons, a name given to compounds containing only carbon and hydrogen. Oxygen, nitrogen, and sulfur are contained only in small quantities. Crude petroleum is a mixture of a large number of complex hydrocarbons whose average composition is approximately C_nH_{2n}, indicating that there are two atoms of hydrogen to each atom of carbon. The percentage composition of crude petroleum averages 85.7 per cent carbon and 14.3 per cent hydrogen by weight, which gives a calculated heating value of 21,200 Btu per pound. Very few petroleums attain this value, but in general 1 lb of petroleum is equal in fuel value to 1½ lb of coal.

Petroleum may be burned for fuel just as it comes from the ground, but it is usually subjected to a preliminary distillation to remove the constituents such as gasoline, naphtha, and kerosene which have a lower boiling point and sell for a higher price. Sometimes the distillation is conducted carefully in a vacuum still so as to recover lubricating oils as well as the lighter fractions. More frequently the heavier portions of the oil which have the higher boiling point are heated under pressure until they become decomposed due to incipient pyrolysis, or "crack" into lighter fractions, some of which form gasoline and some of which combine to form heavier oils that have little value except for fuel. The heating value per pound does not vary greatly in the different grades, but fuel oil is sold by the gallon, and the number of pounds in a gallon differs materially, because of the differences in specific gravity of the oil. The viscosity of fuel oils also affects the price. Oils which are limpid enough to flow readily in winter weather command a higher price than those which are so stiff that they must be warmed before they can be pumped. The lighter oils are used in household oil burners, and the more viscous grades are used in industrial installations and on steamships. The American Society for Testing Materials has established a tentative specification dividing fuel oil into six classes. Number 1 is a distillate oil for use in burners requiring a volatile fuel, and the successive numbers decrease in volatility and increase in viscosity to No. 6, an oil for use in burners able to use a high-viscosity fuel.

Natural Gas.—Natural gas consists of hydrocarbons of such small molecular weight that they are gases at ordinary temperatures and pressures. The predominant constituent is methane (CH_4) with higher members of the series, ethane (C_2H_6) and propane (C_3H_8), present in smaller extent. Some of the properties of these gases are given in Table 63. Illustrations of the compositions of natural gas are given in Table 67. There is an

TABLE 67.—COMPOSITION AND PROPERTIES OF SOME COMMERCIAL GAS SUPPLIES*

Component gases	CO	H_2	CH_4	C_2H_6	Ills.	CO_2	O_2	N_2	Btu per cu. ft.	Sp. gr.
1. Producer gas	25.3	13.2	0.4			5.4	0.5	55.2	129	0.878
2. Blue gas	38.3	52.8	0.4			5.5	0.1	2.9	295	0.521
3. Coal gas	5.9	53.2	29.6		2.7	1.4	0.7	6.5	548	0.375
4. Carbureted water gas	32.6	38.2	8.0	2.2	8.6	3.4	0.5	6.5	530	0.643
5. Refinery gas	1.2	13.1	23.3	21.7	39.6	0.1	1.0		1468	0.890
6. Natural gas			78.8	14.0		0.4		6.8	1013	0.635
7. Natural gas			82.8	16.3	0.8	0.1			1145	0.650

* *Proc. Am. Gas Ass.*, 1931, p. 809.

increase in the heating value per cubic foot and in the boiling point of the liquefied gases as the molecules become more complex. Butane (C_4H_{10}) boils at 33.1°F and pentane (C_5H_{12}) at 97.2°. Natural-gas fields are closely associated with petroleum fields, and frequently both products come from a single well. Some of the gases contain so much of the higher boiling constituents that they are scrubbed to recover gasoline before being used for fuel.

448   ENGINEERING MATERIALS

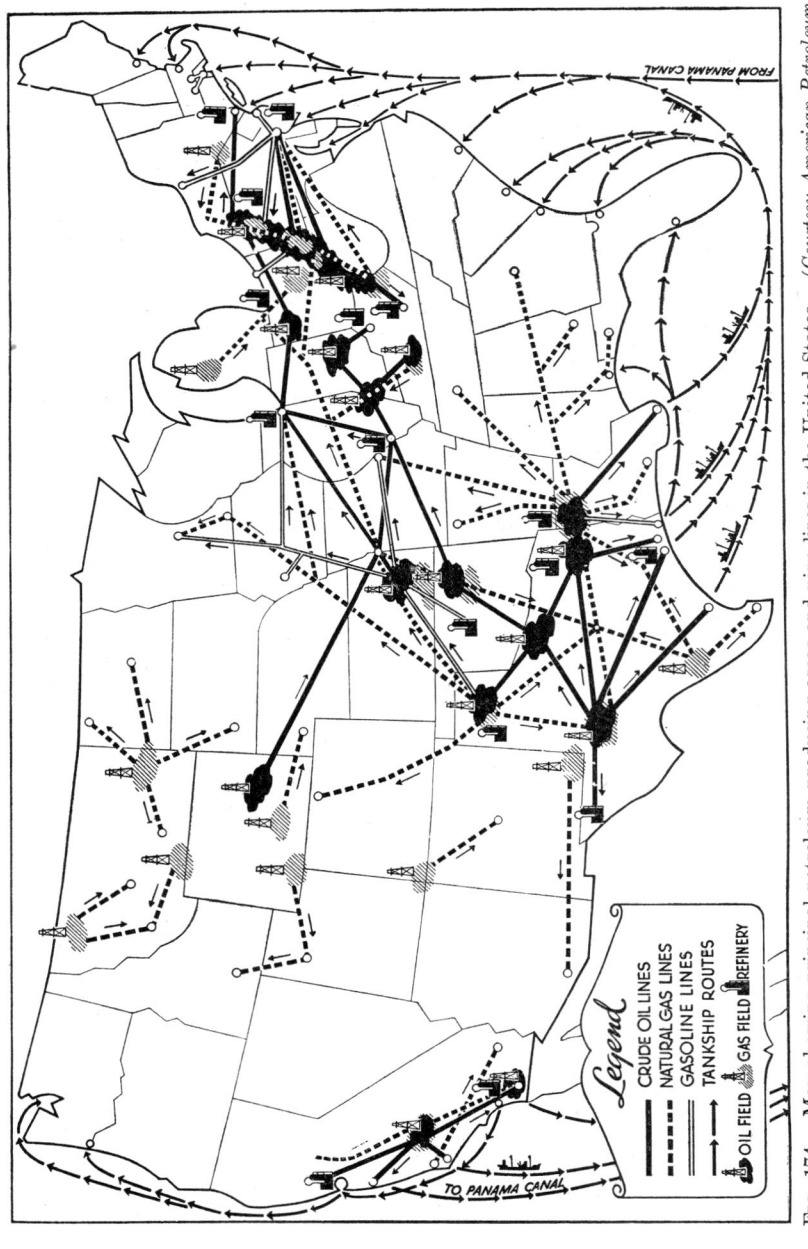

Fig. 174.—Map showing principal petroleum producing areas and pipe lines in the United States. (*Courtesy American Petroleum Institute.*)

The locations of the chief producing areas of petroleum and natural gas in the United States are shown in Fig. 174. If they are compared with the coal areas of Fig. 173, it will be seen that there is considerable similarity between the producing areas. The greatest reservoirs of petroleum and natural gas occur in California, Texas, and Oklahoma. These three states now produce over three-fourths of the crude petroleum of the United States. Petroleum and natural gas have been formed by similar process and occur together. Since they are liquid or gaseous, they can wander through porous rocks and are found only where a favorable conformation of the rock structure has kept them imprisoned. A diagrammatic section of an oil field is presented

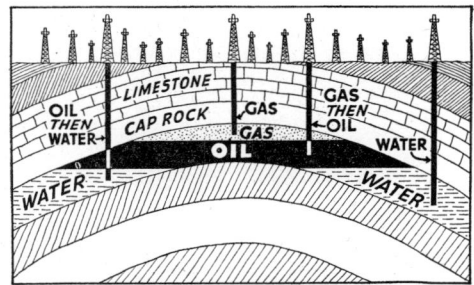

Fig. 175.—Diagrammatic cross section of an oil field. (*Courtesy American Petroleum Institute.*)

in Fig. 175. The rock formations resemble a pile of inverted saucers, and the oil and gas are contained in a stratum of porous stone, usually sandstone, which is covered by a layer of impervious caprock, usually shale. The gas will collect in the upper part of the dome, the oil will collect below the gas, and below the gas the porous stone is usually saturated with water. A well drilled near the highest part of the dome will yield gas, one on the edge will give nothing but water, and one drilled at the proper point will yield oil.

The Carbonization of Coal to Produce Gas and Coke.—All coal will decompose somewhat when subjected to destructive distillation, or pyrolysis, at temperatures above a low red heat. Bituminous coal of high grade, such as is found in Pennsylvania and West Virginia, is the type usually selected for carbonization because it yields strong coke and gas of a good quality. The behavior of bituminous coal when heated in a closed vessel has

Fig. 176.—Appearance of surface and cross section of pieces of coke made from high-grade bituminous coal. a and a', coked at 1100°F; b and b', coked at 1800°F. [*From Bur. Mines, Bull.* 344, (1931).]

been mentioned in the discussion of the proximate analysis of coal. A good coking coal melts to a pasty mass at 700 to 750°F and decomposes at somewhat higher temperatures, giving off gas and leaving behind a solid residue composed mainly of fixed carbon and ash, and known as coke. The outward appearance and the structure of a cross section of two pieces of coke is shown in Fig. 176. Carbonization is conducted usually in retorts or ovens made of fire clay or other refractory brick. The rate of heat transfer through the walls of the retort is so slow that the thickness of the mass of coal to be heated is usually not over 18 in. even when heat is being applied on both sides of the retort. One of the modern coke ovens is composed of chambers each 40 ft long, 14 ft high, and 16 in. wide at one end, expanding to 18 in. wide at the discharge end. Each chamber can hold 20 tons of crushed coal. The time required for carbonization in such an oven is 18 to 20 hr. At the end of the operation, the temperature in the center of the mass of coke is about 1800°F.

Coke finds its principal market as fuel for blast furnaces making pig iron, and the coke ovens and blast furnaces are usually located close together. In recent years, the trend has been to center the industry near the southern shores of Lake Michigan and Lake Erie and along the Detroit river where the ore coming by boat from the Lake Superior mines meets the coal coming from Pennsylvania and West Virginia to produce coke, pig iron, and steel most economically. The gas and tar produced during the coking process are rated as by-products and may be burned for fuel. If the coke ovens are located near a city, both the gas and coke are frequently sold for distribution to industries and to homes. The composition of coal gas is illustrated in Table 67 and differs from that of natural gas in its larger percentages of hydrogen and carbon monoxide. These have lower heating values per cubic foot than methane or the other hydrocarbons, and so the heating value of coke-oven gas varies from 525 to 600 Btu per cubic foot, whereas natural gas is frequently over 1000 Btu. Hydrogen and carbon monoxide both burn more rapidly than methane, and although both fuels may be used with entire satisfaction, there must be a readjustment of burners before one fuel can be substituted for the other.

Producer Gas.—When air comes in contact with glowing carbon, CO_2 is formed and heat is evolved. If this CO_2 is kept in contact with an excess of carbon at a bright red heat, the CO_2 is reduced to CO according to the equation

$$2CO_2 + C \rightleftharpoons 2CO$$

The net result of this reaction between air and carbon, as already explained, is to produce a gas that contains about 40 per cent of the energy of the carbon as sensible heat and 60 per cent as potential energy to be obtained by burning the CO. The heating value of this gas is very low because of the dilution by the nitrogen of the air and because of the low heating value of CO (323 Btu per cubic foot). The heating value of producer gas from coke is theoretically only 108 Btu per cubic foot and, if mixed with some CO_2 as it is in practice, may have a heating value as low as 100 Btu. If some steam is injected with the air, the heating value will be somewhat higher as shown in Table 67.

The blast furnace may be looked upon as a gas producer. At a point slightly above the tuyère level, the gases in the blast furnace have almost the same composition as producer gas. As they rise through the furnace, the CO takes oxygen away from the ore, and CO_2 is evolved by dissociation of the limestone so that the gases escape from the top of the furnace with 15 per cent CO_2, $25CO$, $4H_2$, and $56N_2$, and a heating value of 94 Btu per cubic foot.

Water Gas.—When steam reacts with glowing carbon, there are two reactions known as the "water-gas reactions" that may take place

$$C + H_2O \rightleftharpoons CO + H_2$$
$$C + 2H_2O \rightleftharpoons CO_2 + 2H_2$$

Both of these reactions absorb heat, but the first absorbs more and predominates at the higher temperature. The first gas consists theoretically of equal volumes of CO and H_2 and has a heating value of 323 Btu per cubic foot. The second gas consists of one volume of CO_2 and two of H_2 and has a heating value of 216 Btu per cubic foot.

Since both of these reactions absorb heat, it follows that if steam only is blown continuously into a gas producer the temperature will drop, and if the process is continued, the fuel bed in the producer will become cold.

A small amount of steam is usually blown with the air into a gas producer. The steam has a helpful effect on the hot clinkers in the fuel bed, chilling them and causing them to break up and be removed more readily. It also forms some water gas, and the absorption of heat in the water-gas reaction lessens the amount of energy appearing as sensible heat in the resulting gas. If the gas is to be burned hot as it comes from the producer, the efficiency will be 100 per cent, since both the sensible and the latent heat of the gas will be available for heating the furnace. If, however, the producer gas is made in central installation, as is usually the case in large plants, some of the sensible heat of the gas will be lost in transit to the furnace, and so it is desirable to have as much of the energy in the form of water gas as is feasible.

If pure water gas is desired, some means must be found of keeping up the temperature of the producer while steam is being injected. It is not economical to supply heat from an external source, and the usual process is to blow air and steam alternately. During the blasting period, air only is blown into the fuel bed which becomes heated to a bright yellow heat. The air is then shut off, and steam is admitted for the "run" which lasts until the fuel bed has cooled to a rather dull red heat and it is necessary to commence blasting again. The process is thus conducted in alternate steps. During the blasting process, a producer gas with a heating value of somewhat over 100 Btu per cubic foot is made, and during the run, "blue" water gas with a heating value somewhat over 300 Btu per cubic foot may be produced. Its composition is illustrated in Table 67. The economical utilization of the lower grade producer gas frequently presents a difficult problem, and even the blue water gas has such a low heating value that it is expensive to distribute it to customers.

Carbureted Water Gas.—The problem of using the producer gas advantageously has been solved in the manufacture of carbureted water gas where the producer gas produced during the blasting process is burned to provide the heat needed for the pyrolysis of petroleum to enrich the blue water gas. The equipment as shown diagrammatically in Fig. 177 consists of a gas producer A followed by two chambers B and C usually called the "carburetor" and the "superheater." They are both lined with firebrick and filled with checkerwork of firebrick to act as heat regenerators. During the blasting process, air (primary air) is admitted at D and passed up through the fuel bed, forming CO and liberating heat, and then into the carburetor as hot producer gas. A blast of secondary air is introduced at E in sufficient quantity to burn this producer gas, and the combustion gases pass down through B, up through C, and out through the open stack valve F, having given up much of their sensible heat to the checkerwork. When the apparatus is in regular operation, a blasting period of 2 or 3 min. is adequate to bring the coke bed in the producer to the operating temperature. The air supply, both primary and secondary, is then shut off, and steam instead of air is admitted at D. Liquid petroleum is injected at G and is cracked in the stream of hot water gas to form rich hydrocarbon gases. The stack valve at F is closed, and the carbureted water gas passes out at H to the condensing and purifying equipment. The period of steam admission is termed the "run," and after the run has continued for 2 or 3 min the temperature of the fuel bed has dropped to the point where it is advisable to start the blast again.

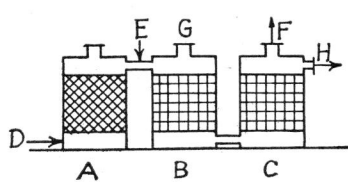

FIG. 177.—Diagrammatic cross section of water-gas set.

In this method of gas manufacture, the gas is the only saleable product, and its cost is frequently greater than that of gas from by-product coke ovens. However the process is one that can be quickly started up and so is a valuable accessory for peak loads in periods of emergency.

Combustion of Coal on Grates.—The fire bed in a simple furnace is supported on grate bars above which is a layer of ashes and clinkers a few inches thick. It is not desirable to have too thick a bed of ashes because it restricts the draft, but a thin layer is desirable since the grates are kept cooler, and there is less danger of unburned fuel dropping between the grate bars.

If the fuel contains little volatile matter, like coke or anthracite coal, whose pieces do not swell or fuse, the incoming air will rise between the lumps of fuel with little resistance, provided the particles are not too small. If the particles are too fine, unburned fuel will drop between the grate bars and the draft will be too restricted because of the resistance offered by the bed of fine particles. If the fire is hot and the layer of fuel is deep, part of the CO_2 formed in the lower layers of the fuel bed will become reduced to CO in the upper layers. There is usually an excess of air leaking around the borders of the fuel bed, and the CO may be seen to burn on top of the fuel with a flickering blue flame. A generous excess of air is almost necessary in a simple furnace of this sort, and the efficiency is therefore rather low even when selected sizes of coke or anthracite are used as fuel.

If the fuel is bituminous coal, the even process of combustion is complicated by the softening of the coal and by the gases evolved during its pyrolysis. If several inches of fresh coal are spread on top of a hot fire, the pieces next to the hot coals soften and fuse together obstructing the passage of air. The fused coal then gets hot enough for pyrolysis and commences to evolve gases and tar vapors, which are cooled by the fresh coal above them so that they do not ignite readily. In addition, the supply of air is restricted by the layer of fresh fuel, with the result that the gases do not get burned and therefore emerge from the stack as smoke. Sometimes the proportions of unburned gas and air attain those of an explosive mixture and, occasionally, an explosion results within the firebox. Under normal circumstances, enough air gets through the fuel bed so that, after a few minutes, the gases ignite without explosion, the fresh coal cokes, and after a few minutes more the fire bed resembles that when coke or anthracite is used for fuel.

In small boiler plants whose furnaces are fired by hand, as illustrated in Fig. 178, the proper procedure is to throw the fresh coal in a thin layer over only a portion of the fire bed. The hot uncovered portion of the fire bed provides prompt ignition of the gases evolved from the fresh coal. The smaller the firebox, the more care is necessary in the selection of the quality and size of the fuel to be used.

In the boiler setting of Fig. 178, the hot gases must pass to the back of the setting before entering a zigzag channel through the tubes. The combustion chamber must be sufficiently large so that combustion will be complete before the gases enter the banks of tubes, because the gases are chilled so quickly by the relatively cold metal that combustion cannot continue. The setting that is illustrated would be adapted for coke or hard coal but could not be used satisfactorily for bituminous coal unless the fireman used great care in handling his fire.

456 ENGINEERING MATERIALS

Any system of hand-firing suffers from the disadvantage that relatively large amounts of fresh coal must be added at intervals, and the fuel bed must therefore be of constantly varying thickness and, especially with bituminous coal, of constantly varying quality.

FIG. 178.—Steam boiler with hand-fired setting. (*From Steam Boiler Engineering. Heine Safety Boiler Co.*)

Automatic Stokers.—Automatic stokers are used partly to cut down labor costs. They are more important because of the added efficiency with which the fuel is burned. With automatic stokers, the attempt is made to add coal continuously and in a quantity proportioned to the demands upon the furnace. They require that the coal be crushed to sizes usually less than $\frac{1}{4}$ in. in dimension so that the coal may be carried in worm conveyors or by other mechanical devices to the fuel bed. The speed of the conveyor is governed by the change in steam pressure or the change in temperature at some remote point acting through a

FUELS AND COMBUSTION

system of electrical relays. In large installations, the air blowers are connected to the same control so that the air is provided in proportion to the amount of coal that is fed.

The three common types of automatic stoker are shown diagrammatically in Fig. 179. The side-feed and the chain-grate stokers are alike in principle in that the fresh coal is introduced in a layer under an arch of hot firebrick. The gases evolved are swept forward under the arch and meet a stream of hot air coming through the far end of the fire bed which consists mostly

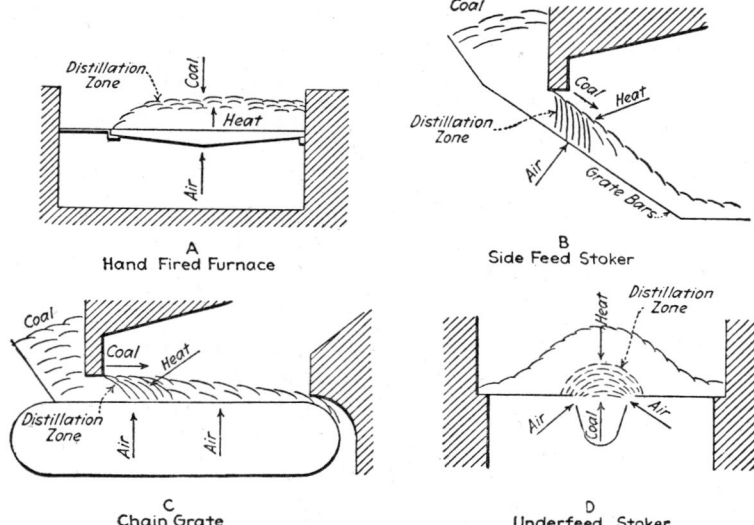

FIG. 179.—Classification of furnaces according to method of feeding coal. (*From Steam Boiler Engineering. Heine Safety Boiler Co.*)

of ashes. The hot gases and the hot air react promptly and completely so that no smoke escapes. The motion of the chain grate breaks up the coke formed, so combustion in the central portion of the fire bed proceeds freely. Some system of rocking grates is frequently provided to accomplish the same purpose with the side-feed stoker.

In the underfeed stoker illustrated in Fig. 179, the crushed coal is forced in and up into the fuel bed by a screw conveyor. If it is a bituminous coal, coking takes place at the bottom of the fire and the gases become preheated as they rise so that they burn readily and completely. The coke that is formed is supposed to be crushed by the upward pressure of the new coal being forced in, so that the fire remains open. The ashes remain on top of the fire, and, if the temperature is right, will overflow into an ash pit. Sometimes the ash forms clinkers which may be taken off with a hook. Stokers for household furnaces sometimes

Fig. 180.—Sectional view of part of modern boiler and setting using underfeed Stokers. (*Courtesy American Engineering Company.*)

operate on this principle. Unless the clinkering temperature of the ash is suitable, trouble is sometimes experienced in the removal of ashes.

A Modern Boiler and Automatic Stoker.—Underfeed stokers for large plants are provided with means for pushing the fuel bed forward and for removing ashes and clinkers as shown in the photograph of a sectional model in Fig. 180. This modern installation will produce 40,000 lb of steam per hour continuously at 450 lb pressure and a temperature of 700°F. The volume of the furnace chamber is 950 cu ft, and at normal load 50,000 Btu will be liberated per cubic foot of volume.[1]

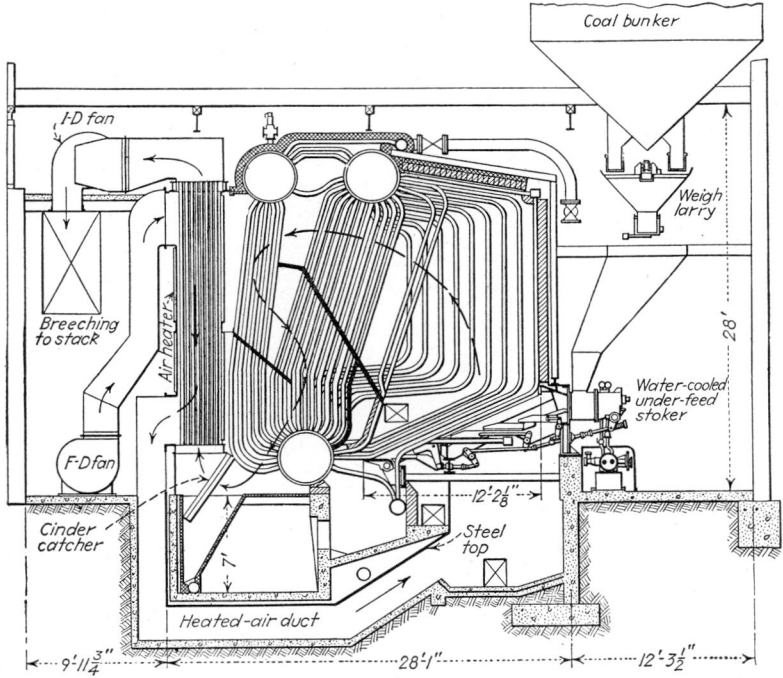

Fig. 181.—Modern steam boiler plant burning coal with underfeed stokers. Rating 40,000 lb of steam per hour continuously at 450 lb pressure. (*Courtesy American Engineering Co.*)

The furnace chamber is completely lined with tubes forming part of the boiler. A section of the complete setting of this same boiler is shown in Fig. 181. The air is blown by a fan at the left of the illustration through an air heater, which raises the temperature to 375°F, through a duct below the furnace floor and into the fire. The combustion gases pass through the tubes as indicated, out through the air heater, and to the fan that blows them up the stack. The installation has almost complete

[1] *Power Magazine*, July, 1938.

automatic controls, and the boiler and furnace efficiency is 86.5 per cent.

Burning Powdered Coal.—Powdered coal is ground to an extremely fine powder and blown into the furnace by a jet of air which burns it while it is in suspension. Bituminous coal is usually used, not only because of its cheapness but because of the gas that it gives off when heated. The particles of powdered coal are subjected to almost instantaneous pyrolysis when blown into a hot furnace. The gas burns, and the minute

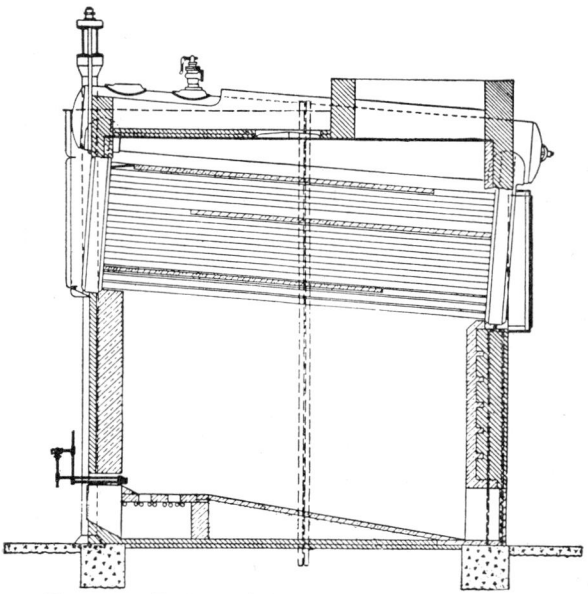

FIG. 182.—Boiler with furnace designed to burn oil.

particles of coke are heated to redness and burn rapidly. The still more minute particles of ash are usually fused in the high temperature. Some of them agglomerate, and drop to the bottom of the firebox as molten slag. Most of the particles are carried on with the combustion gases and pass out of the stack unless special recovery systems are installed. This fly ash becomes a nuisance, and many plants have been compelled to install rather expensive recovery systems. It is difficult to find a use for this fly ash after it is recovered.

Burning Fuel Oil.—A small installation for burning fuel oil is illustrated in Fig. 182. The oil is blown in a fine spray by steam or air into a large combustion chamber. Its simplicity is in marked contrast to the complications that are necessarily present when coal is burned.

Fuel Resources of the United States.—The sources of the energy, other than that of the sun, generated in the United States are set forth in Table 68 for the years 1929 and 1935. The

TABLE 68.—ANNUAL ENERGY SUPPLY OF THE UNITED STATES*
Expressed in trillions of British thermal units with energy derived from water power calculated to its British thermal units equivalent.

	Trillions of Btu		Percentage of total	
	1929	1935	1929	1935
Anthracite coal	2,008	1,489	7.9	6.6
Bituminous coal	14,017	11,373	55.1	50.1
Petroleum	6,518	6,785	25.7	29.9
Natural gas	2,062	2,231	8.1	9.8
Water power	810	798	3.2	3.6
Total energy	25,415	22,676	100.0	100.0

* FIELDNER, A. C., *Proc. Am. Soc. Testing Materials*, **37**, I, 31 (1937).

persistence of the business depression made the total about 10 per cent lower in 1935 than in the peak year of 1929. The use of petroleum and natural gas increased during the period so that together they accounted for nearly 40 per cent of the total. Coal produced nearly 57 per cent and water power less than 4 per cent of the total.

Our resources of coal are so vast that it is probable we have not yet mined 1 per cent of our total supply, although anthracite coal and some of the highest grade bituminous coals are much more nearly exhausted. The reserves of petroleum are not so well known, but the actual proven reserves are sufficient for only 12 or 15 years. New discoveries and improved methods of production have thus far brought in additional supplies as fast as the older fields have been depleted.

The position of the United States in the world fuel market is shown in Fig. 183. It produces two-thirds of the world's petroleum and nearly one-third of the world's coal. Germany produces nearly as much coal as the United States, and Great

Britain ranks third. The rapid rise of Soviet Russia in the last six years is especially noteworthy. The United States is by far

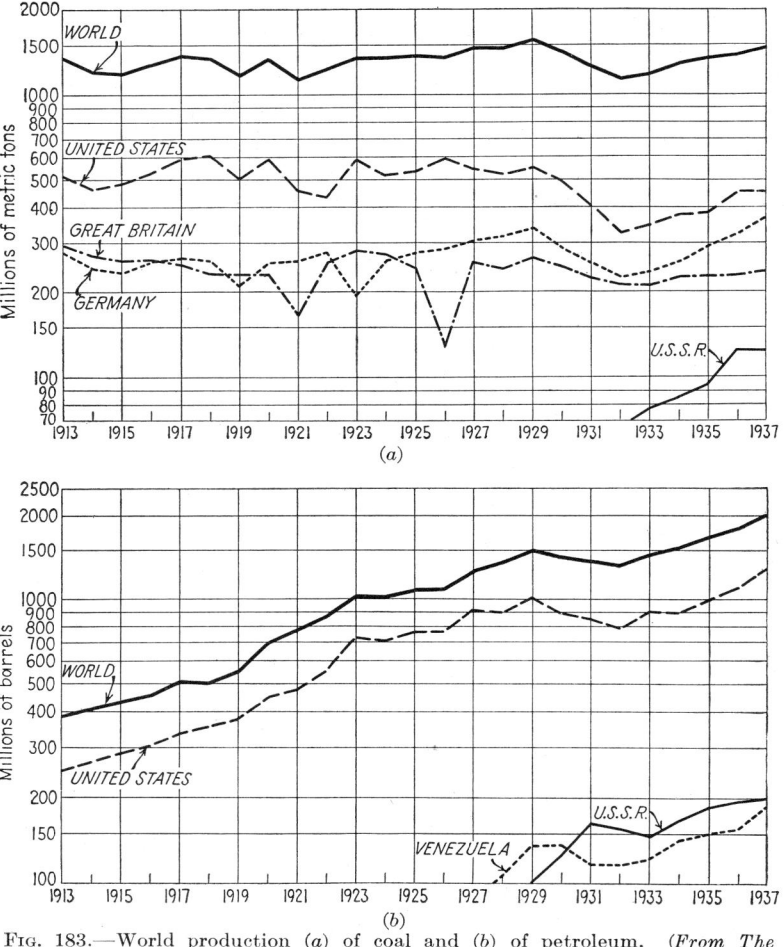

Fig. 183.—World production (a) of coal and (b) of petroleum. (*From The Mineral Industry for* 1937.)

the largest producer of petroleum in the world. Again the recent rise of Russia is worthy of special attention.

References

Bell H. S.: American Petroleum Refining, 2d ed., D. Van Nostrand Company, Inc., New York, 1930.

CROSS, ROY: Handbook of Petroleum, Asphalt and Natural Gas, Kansas City Testing Laboratory, Kansas City, Mo., 1931.
HAMOR and BACON: American Fuels, 2 vols., McGraw-Hill Book Company, Inc., New York, 1922.
HASLAM and RUSSELL: Fuels and Their Combustion, McGraw-Hill Book Company, Inc., New York, 1926.
Minerals Yearbook, 1937, U. S. Department of Interior, Bureau of Mines.
PARR, S. W.: The Analysis of Fuel, Gas, Water and Lubricants, 4th ed., McGraw-Hill Book Company, Inc., New York, 1932.
PERRY, J. H.: Chemical Engineers' Handbook, Section 21, Fuels by H. A. Curtis and others, McGraw-Hill Book Company, Inc., New York, 1934.
PORTER, H. C.: Coal Carbonization, Reinhold Publishing Corporation, New York, 1924.
PORTER, H. C.: Coal Processing—Its Progress Since 1908, Silver Anniversary Volume of American Institute of Chemical Engineers, Chap. IX, D. Van Nostrand Co., Inc., New York, 1933.

CHAPTER XXII

WATER AND ITS INDUSTRIAL UTILIZATION. SOAPS

Rain Water.—Water of perfect purity cannot be obtained even by the most elaborate technique. It always contains small quantities of dissolved gases and solids dissolved from the vessel in which it is contained. Rain becomes saturated with air as it falls, and the amounts of the common gases that it contains are shown in Table 42 of Chap. XVI. Rain also contains variable but small amounts of nitric acid formed during electrical storms and of sulfuric acid formed from the sulfur of coal during the combustion process. The total amounts, though small, are not insignificant. Experiments at the Agricultural Experiment Station at Rothamsted[1] in England showed that 17.4 lb of SO_3 and 2.4 lb of combined nitrogen were brought down on each acre of land annually by rain and snow. Rain also contains dust particles, with soot from coal smoke and particles of soil as the predominating constituents.

Water of Lakes and Rivers.—The water of lakes and rivers consists partly of the rain that has fallen directly on the surface of the water, partly of water that has been in contact only with the surface of the soil, and partly of water that has percolated through the soil and had opportunity to dissolve the soil constituents. One of the purest lake waters is that of Lake Superior whose composition is given in column A of Table 69. As this water flows through Lake Huron, Lake Erie, Lake Ontario, and into the St. Lawrence River, it collects water from various tributaries which have flowed through agricultural and industrial communities. The lakes provide such large sedimentation basins that the turbidity remains low, but the dissolved mineral matter increases as is shown in column B which gives the composition of the river at Ogdensburg, New York.

The water of Lake Superior comes from a rain shed composed largely of igneous rocks and with a sparse population, and so represents an unusually pure water. The chief mineral ion is

[1] CLARKE, F. W., Data of Geochemistry, 5th ed., pp. 49 and 55.

TABLE 69.—ANALYSES OF WATERS OF LAKES AND RIVERS IN PARTS PER MILLION*

	A	B	C
Turbidity	2	4.5	556.
Silica (SiO_2)	7.4	6.6	24.
Iron (Fe)	0.06	0.05	0.61
Calcium (Ca)	13.	31.	36.
Magnesium (Mg)	3.1	7.2	12.
Sodium and potassium (Na + K)	3.2	6.3	19.
Carbonate (CO_3)	0.0	2.9	0.0
Bicarbonate (HCO_3)	56.	116.	129.
Sulfate (SO_4)	2.1	12.	43.
Nitrate (NO_3)	0.5	0.3	1.7
Chlorine (Cl)	1.1	7.7	8.6
Total dissolved solids	60.	134.	202.

A. Lake Superior at Sault Ste. Marie.
B. St. Lawrence River at Ogdensburg, N. Y.
C. Mississippi River, Memphis, Tenn.

*From CLARKE, F. W.: The Composition of the River and Lake Waters of the United States, *U. S. Geol. Survey, Prof. Paper* 135, 1924.

calcium, and if the calcium and magnesium should be calculated as bicarbonates, it would be found that the HCO_3 ion would be almost exactly that required for this bicarbonate combination. The water of the St. Lawrence River at Ogdensburg has increased its total dissolved solids from 60 to 134 ppm, the main increases being due to the positive Ca and Mg ions and the negative HCO_3 and SO_4 ions. The increase in the Cl ion reflects additions from chemical plants working with salt brines, as well as sewage contamination.

In contrast to the water of the Great Lakes and the St. Lawrence River with its low turbidity is that of the Mississippi River at Memphis, which is given in column C of Table 69. The turbidity of the river due to suspended solids varies from **1600** ppm at flood stage to **170** when the flow of the river is at a minimum. The average is given as **556** ppm. The SO_4 ion is one-third of the bicarbonate ion instead of only one-tenth as in the St. Lawrence River. The importance of this will be considered when the subject of water for steam boilers is being discussed. The total solids in solution in the Mississippi River water averages **202** ppm.

The amount of dissolved solids carried away in solution by the rivers of the United States is estimated by F. W. Clarke[1] to be 98 tons per square mile per year. The inclusion of organic impurities would raise the amount by about 10 per cent. The amount carried away as suspended solids is much larger than that in solution.

The Action of Bacteria and Other Living Organisms in Changing the Composition of Waters Containing Organic Matter.—The upper layers of soil contain vegetable and animal residues and also tremendous numbers of microscopic single-celled vegetable organisms, of which molds and bacteria are the most numerous and important. These organisms will grow only in the presence of moisture, and are more active at summer temperatures than when kept only a few degrees above freezing. Their activity becomes very slow if ice forms, and some of the organisms are killed by freezing. The organisms also require food, but they are vigorous enough to thrive in most situations where they have access to decaying vegetable or animal tissues.

A major group of bacteria, called "aerobic," require oxygen for their growth. The energy for the life cycle is obtained from the heat evolved by the oxidation of the organic matter which is in solution or suspension, and if conditions are right, the bacteria will continue their work until all of the organic matter has been oxidized. In bacterial sand filters used in some municipal filtration plants, the raw water is allowed to filter through a layer of rather coarse sand which is 3 to 5 ft thick. The rate must be so slow that the water remains in the sand about 8 hr. A jellylike film of bacteria forms around each grain of sand in the upper portion of the filter bed and traps suspended particles until they become oxidized. Organic matter in solution will be oxidized as the water flows down through the sand, and the water will emerge from the bottom of the sand filter free of clay and other suspended solids and also free of dissolved organic matter. The carbon of the organic matter will have been converted to CO_2, the nitrogen to HNO_3, and the hydrogen to H_2O. More important, the water will also be free of bacteria which will have attached themselves to the gelatinous film around the sand grains. The main condition to be fulfilled to obtain this result is that the raw water shall move slowly and smoothly through

[1] *Ibid.*, p. 116.

WATER AND ITS INDUSTRIAL UTILIZATION. SOAPS

the sand and shall carry more oxygen than is necessary to oxidize all of the organic matter, so that the effluent will still contain dissolved oxygen. The same phenomenon of oxidation will take place less effectively in the stream itself, and so a river is said to purify itself as it flows.

If the stream is badly polluted by sewage or industrial wastes, the amount of organic matter becomes more than the dissolved oxygen can care for. The aerobic bacteria give up the struggle as the oxygen disappears and are replaced by anaerobic bacteria which thrive only in absence of air. The gaseous products of decomposition of the organic matter become predominantly hydrogen and methane, instead of carbon dioxide and water. The sulfur compounds pass off as H_2S and other compounds with bad odors, so that the process of anaerobic fermentation is objectionable. The dangerous disease germs are mostly anaerobic. This process is used in many sewage-disposal plants where the anaerobic fermentation is allowed to proceed in closed tanks. The gases evolved are conducted to the boiler house where they are burned to provide much of the steam necessary in the plant. After the anaerobic bacteria have completed their work, the liquid is filtered from the undigested sludge and saturated with air. Aerobic bacteria can then renew the work of oxidation, and the resulting effluent will be almost free from color, odor, organic matter, and dangerous bacteria. It may be discharged into streams without doing any harm.

The Solubility of $CaCO_3$, $MgCO_3$, $Ca(OH)_2$, and $Mg(OH)_2$.— The solubility of the hydroxides and carbonates of calcium and magnesium is influenced very strongly by the amount of the CO_2 dissolved in the water, and this in turn is affected by the amount of CO_2 in the air. The equations involved are

$A.$ (1) $CaO + H_2O \rightleftharpoons Ca(OH)_2$
(2) $Ca(OH)_2 + CO_2 \rightleftharpoons CaCO_3 + H_2O$
(3) $CaCO_3 + CO_2 + H_2O \rightleftharpoons Ca(HCO_3)_2$

$B.$ (1) $MgO + H_2O \rightleftharpoons Mg(OH)_2$
(2) $Mg(OH)_2 + CO_2 \rightleftharpoons MgCO_3 + H_2O$
(3) $MgCO_3 + CO_2 + H_2O \rightleftharpoons Mg(HCO_3)_2$

The heat evolved when lime and magnesia react with water is so great that the formation of the hydroxides in equations A 1 and B 1 is practically complete in presence of excess of water.

The solubility of $Ca(OH)_2$ at 20°C in water free from dissolved CO_2 is 1250 ppm of CaO, and that of $Mg(OH)_2$ is only 8.7 ppm MgO.[1] The formation of the carbonates is influenced very strongly by the amount of CO_2 in solution in the water. The concentration of CO_2 in air is about 0.04 per cent, and water saturated with air dissolves some CO_2 which in turn produces enough $Ca(HCO_3)_2$ to produce a solubility of 69 ppm calculated as $CaCO_3$. If the percentage of CO_2 in the air with which the water is saturated is artificially raised to 10 per cent, the amount of $Ca(HCO_3)_2$ in solution will increase, under equilibrium conditions, to 670 ppm of $CaCO_3$.

The solubility of $Mg(OH)_2$ in the absence of CO_2 is extraordinarily low, only 8.7 ppm. If only a small amount of CO_2 is present in the water, the hydrate becomes changed to the carbonate whose solubility is much greater. The influence of CO_2 is extraordinarily large, the solubility in water saturated with air at room temperature rising to 3970 ppm calculated as $MgCO_3$, but present largely as bicarbonates.

Temperature has some direct effect on the solubility of the carbonates of lime and magnesia, but its main effect is indirect through its influence on the amount of CO_2 that can remain in solution.

Water from Wells and Springs.—Rain water which percolates through cultivated ground dissolves organic matter which is usually oxidized by bacteria, so that after the water has reached a depth of 2 or 3 ft the organic matter has been completely oxidized and the water has increased its percentage of CO_2 and HNO_3. As the water percolates further through the soil, it continues to dissolve mineral matter. If the soil contains $CaCO_3$ and $MgCO_3$, the water will dissolve rather large amounts of these salts because of the dissolved CO_2 present. The underground water flows through gravel and other porous strata and may ultimately come to the surface from a well. The amount and kind of dissolved mineral matter will depend on the nature of the rocks with which the water has been in contact. The amount of dissolved solids will usually be larger than is the case with surface waters. The water from wells and springs should be free from organic matter and bacteria, but there is no certainty that such will be the case. Organic matter, such as that

[1] SEIDELL, Solubilities of Inorganic and Organic Compounds.

contained in sewage leaking from a cesspool or sewer several feet below the surface, may travel underground for long distances without complete oxidation and without elimination of the bacteria it contains. The water from springs and wells is not to be considered as safe for drinking unless it is proven so by frequent laboratory examinations.

The water from some wells may be entirely clear and transparent when first drawn, and become cloudy upon standing in the air. This is usually because the CO_2 formed underground by the oxidation of organic matter has brought more $CaCO_3$ into solution as bicarbonate than can remain when the water comes again into contact with the air and gives up part of its CO_2 to the air, with the result that some $CaCO_3$ must precipitate. If water in the ground has come in contact with $FeCO_3$, a soluble ferrous bicarbonate will be formed which in contact with the air will be oxidized to ferric hydroxide, giving a brown deposit.

Hard and Soft Water.—Water that contains little dissolved solids has traditionally been considered "soft," and that which contains much dissolved solids, especially lime and magnesium salts, has been called "hard." The origin of these terms is probably due to the behavior of the water with soap, since it is hard to make a lather if the water contains much calcium and magnesium ions.

Fat Acid and Soap.—Ordinary soap consists of the sodium salt of a fat acid, and a fat acid gets its name from the fact that it is produced by the hydrolysis of a fat. The fats, whether of animal or vegetable origin, are compounds (esters) of glycerin and a fat acid. The fat acids are all organic compounds composed of carbon, hydrogen, and oxygen which have combined to form a series of related compounds. The commonest series, that of the saturated acids, starts with formic acid (HCOOH) as its simplest member. In organic chemistry, the carboxyl group —COOH is always the sign of an acid. This radical is linked to hydrogen, or to a hydrocarbon radical of which methyl (CH_3) is the simplest. The next member in the series above formic acid is therefore CH_3COOH which is acetic acid and is well known because it is the predominant acid in vinegar. The next member of the series would contain the ethyl radical ($CH_3.CH_2$) and would have the formula $CH_3.CH_2.COOH$. These lower members of the series are freely soluble in water, but the solubility becomes less as the complexity of the molecule increases, until when stearic acid [$CH_3(CH_2)_{16}COOH$] is reached the solubility is very slight.

Alcohols and Glycerin.—Glycerin is an alcohol. Just as the formula for an acid group is —COOH, so the formula for an alcohol group is —OH. In inorganic chemistry, the OH group signifies a base, and NaOH represents sodium hydroxide. In organic chemistry when the OH group is linked to a hydrocarbon radical, the product is called an "alcohol." The simplest alcohol is methyl alcohol (CH_3OH) which in modern chemistry is called methanol to show that it is the alcohol formed from methane (CH_4). The next member of the series is ethyl alcohol, or ethanol (CH_3CH_2OH), and higher members, propanol and butanol, are formed by replacing one hydrogen of propane or butane by the hydroxyl group. These alcohols do not hydrolize to any material extent when dissolved in water and so do not yield alkaline solutions as NaOH does. The alcohols may, however, act as bases to combine with an organic acid to form a compound which is not called a salt, but an ester.

In inorganic chemistry, we may have a hydroxide like $Al(OH)_3$, and similarly in organic chemistry, more than one hydrogen of a hydrocarbon may be replaced by a hydroxyl group. If three hydrogens of propane (C_3H_8) are replaced by hydroxyls, glycerin [$C_3H_5(OH)_3$] is formed. This alcohol is a constituent of all of the fats, both of animal and vegetable origin.

Fats and their Hydrolysis.—Almost all fats are esters of glycerin and one of the complex fat acids. Stearin, which is the largest constituent of mutton and beef fat, is the ester of glycerin and stearic acid. It is quite insoluble in water but is slowly hydrolyzed according to the equation

$$C_3H_5[CH_3(CH_2)_{16}COO]_3 + 3HOH \rightleftharpoons C_3H_5(OH)_3 +$$
Stearin   Water   Glycerin
$$3CH_3(CH_2)_{16}COOH$$
Stearic acid

The reaction is reversible, and stearin may be synthesized by the combination of glycerin and stearic acid. The illustration refers to stearin, but all of the fats may be similarly hydrolyzed into glycerin and various fat acids. The fats are such complex molecules that their solubility is slight and hydrolysis is slow. It is accelerated by an excess of water and an elevated temperature.

In earlier days, tallow was used to lubricate the cylinders of steam engines because no petroleum oil had sufficient viscosity for the purpose. The tallow hydrolyzed and yielded a fat acid, itself quite insoluble, but sufficiently soluble in condensed steam to act as an acid and corrode the cylinders. Modern cylinder oils are made from petroleum with the addition sometimes of insoluble soaps rather than fats.

Soaps.—Common soap consists of the sodium salts of a mixture of fat acids, with some water, and sometimes materials of foreign origin added for a specific purpose. It is made by boiling fat with a solution of NaOH and the equation, again using stearin as an illustration, may be written

$$\underset{\text{Stearin}}{C_3H_5[CH_3(CH_2)_{16}COO]_3} + \underset{\text{Caustic soda}}{3NaOH} \rightleftharpoons \underset{\text{Glycerin}}{C_3H_5(OH_3)} +$$
$$\underset{\text{Sodium stearate}}{3CH_3(CH_2)_{16}COONa}$$

Sodium stearate is a major constituent of most laundry soaps which are to be used with hot water. Its solubility is too small to make an effective soap for cold water, and so toilet soaps are usually made from fats whose acids are of somewhat lower molecular weight and whose solubility is greater. The effectiveness of soap as a cleansing agent is due to its ability to lower the surface tension of water and cause foaming and emulsification of particles of dirt which may be on the skin or on fabrics. Potassium and ammonium soaps are occasionally used instead of sodium soap where greater solubility is desired.

Insoluble Soaps.—The usual soaps are composed of the salts of the monovalent metals, sodium, potassium, or ammonium. If a soap is made with divalent metals such as calcium and magnesium, there are two molecules of fat acid associated with each atom of the base, and the resultant more complex soap molecule is so much less soluble than the usual soap that it is valueless as a cleansing agent and is usually termed "insoluble." The soaps of the trivalent metals like aluminum and ferric iron are still less soluble. These insoluble soaps are stable and water repellent, and find some use in waterproofings for concrete and also as ingredients to be emulsified with heavy petroleum lubricating oils to form cup and sponge greases to be used as lubricants for heavy machinery.

Soaps in Hard Water.—When a soluble soap dissolves in hard water, the calcium, magnesium, aluminum, and other di- and tri-valent ions in solution unite with the fat acids of the soap to precipitate the insoluble soap. The equation may be illustrated

$$2Na\ soap + CaSO_4 \rightleftharpoons Ca\ soap + Na_2SO_4$$

The equation is written as a reversible reaction, but actually the solubility of the calcium soap is so small that there is very little reversibility. Therefore when soap is dissolved in hard water, it immediately reacts with the ions of calcium, magnesium, iron, and other polyvalent metals and is itself precipitated as the insoluble soap. These insoluble soaps form a greasy emulsion which tends to collect as a sticky ring around the edges of a wash bowl or bath tub. When clothes are washed in hard water, the insoluble soaps stick to the fabrics, and especially if iron is present, cause brown stains that prevent a pure white color on linen. Since soap does not become effective in a hard water until all of the calcium, magnesium, and iron ions have been precipitated as insoluble soaps, it is evident that hard water wastes soap, in addition to its other objectionable features.

Methods of Reporting Water Analyses for Industrial Purposes.—Water analyses are made with varying degrees of completeness depending on the particular use to which a water is to be put. Some industries are deeply concerned with color, others with sewage contamination and bacterial content, and others with the acidity or alkalinity of the water. Most industrial analyses are, however, primarily concerned with the suitability of the water for boiler feed water, either without treatment or more usually after chemical treatment.

Waters often contain suspended solids which are usually filtered off and reported separately. In some cases, the amount of dissolved gases is of importance, and when they are to be determined, the sample of water must be collected and stored very expertly to avoid changes in the gas content before analysis. The salts that are present in the filtered water are in solution and, for the most part, are ionized. The simplest and most accurate expression of the analysis is to report the ions. The modern method is to report these in parts by weight per million parts of water (ppm). The older way was to report them in grains per gallon. One grain per U. S. gallon at 62°F is equivalent to 17.14 ppm. The British gallon is 1.2 the size of the U. S. gallon, and in reading British literature allowance should be made for that difference.

The operator of a steam boiler is interested, not so much in knowing the composition of the water entering the boiler, as in the way the salts will behave when the water becomes concentrated by evaporation with ultimate separation of scale-forming materials. Many analysts attempt to combine the ions into salts to indicate how they will separate on concentration. Not all analysts follow the same rules for making these combinations, but the methods are in rough agreement.

The difference in the two methods of reporting an analysis is shown in Table 70. The figures in the ionic analysis seem to have very little in common with those reported as hypothetical combinations, but they actually represent the same water. The analyst obtained the results given in the ionic analysis and then calculated the hypothetical combinations. Both agree in the amount of suspended solids, which were removed by filtration prior to the analysis. Both of them also report the same amount of free carbon dioxide, the CO_2 which is in excess of that present as the bicarbonate ion. They also agree in the amount of total solids by evaporation, which are obtained by actually evaporating the water gently to dryness at a final temperature not over 212°F. These total solids by evaporation are less than the sum of the ions reported in the analysis, because in the process of evaporation the $Ca(HCO_3)_2$ breaks down to

$$CaCO_3 + CO_2 + H_2O.$$

For each CO_3 remaining in the solid residue, one molecule of CO_2 and one of H_2O have disappeared with the steam. The volatile and organic matter is determined by heating the dried residue gently in an open dish until it reaches a red heat. The organic matter is burned off, and the water of crystallization associated with the calcium sulfate is expelled in this process. The silica and the iron oxide and alumina are the same in the two reports since they are not assumed to enter into combination on evaporation.

474 ENGINEERING MATERIALS

TABLE 70.—COMPOSITION OF WATER BEFORE AND AFTER SOFTENING WITH LIME AND SODA*

Ionic analyses in parts per million

Substance	Raw water	Treated lime soda
Calcium (Ca)	167.0	5.0
Magnesium (Mg)	28.0	0.7
Sodium (Na)	76.8	112.8
Silica (SiO_2)	26.0	11.6
Iron oxide (R_2O_3)	3.4	5.2
Bicarbonate (HCO_3)	532.0	9.1
Carbonate (CO_3)	.....	32.8
Sulfate (SO_4)	213.0	157.5
Chloride (Cl)	29.6	24.5
Volatile and organic	26.0	5.0
Total solids	830.0	358.0
Suspended matter	30.0	None
Carbon dioxide (CO_2)	231.0	
Hardness as $CaCO_3$	532.5	15.5

Hypothetical combinations for water

Substance	Raw Parts per million	Raw Grains per gal	Treated, lime soda Parts per million	Treated, lime soda Grains per gal
Calcium carbonate	321	18.75	12	0.70
Calcium sulfate	131	7.63		
Magnesium carbonate	97	5.66	2	0.12
Silica	26	1.52	12	0.70
Iron oxide	3	0.17	5	0.29
Sodium carbonate	...	.....	49	2.86
Sodium sulfate	178	10.38	233	13.58
Sodium chloride	48	2.80	40	2.33
Volatile and organic	26	1.52	5	0.29
Total solids	830	48.42	358	20.87
Suspended matter	30	1.75	None	None
Carbon dioxide	231	13.45		

* From COCHRANE Corporation *Bull.* 689, p. 15 (1934).

The most important combinations in the hypothetical report are those of the calcium and magnesium ions with the carbonate and sulfate ions. On the basis of this report, a boiler evaporating 1,000,000 lb of untreated water in 24 hr (approximately 1200 boiler horsepower) would separate daily within the boiler 131 lb $CaSO_4$, 321 $CaCO_3$, 97 $MgCO_3$, 26 SiO_2, and 3 Fe_2O_3. The concentration of NaCl and Na_2SO_4 would not have become high enough to form a saturated solution and would never be permitted to become higher than a few thousand parts per million because part of the water would be blown off to prevent too great an accumulation of these soluble salts. The blowoff (or blowdown) would also have carried out of the boiler much of the suspended $CaCO_3$ and $MgCO_3$, and probably part of the $CaSO_4$. The table shows however quite clearly that the water would give trouble with scale formation. The table of ionic analyses gives the same information but not in a form that is so readily available.

Sedimentation, Coagulation, and Aeration.—In Chap. XVII, when discussing clay, it was stated that only particles with a diameter of less than 0.002 mm were entitled to be classified as clay. These fine particles will not settle in 24 hr unless they are coagulated by chemical treatment. If the water is made slightly acid (pH about 5.5), the particles become flocculated. The chemicals used to produce this flocculation are usually salts of iron and aluminum which become hydrolyzed to give the required acidity while simultaneously forming a gelatinous precipitate of the hydroxides of iron and aluminum which entangles the fine particles of clay and makes the sediment settle more rapidly, and filter more readily.

Aeration is sometimes a separate operation and is sometimes combined with coagulation. A well water that contains $Fe(HCO_3)_2$ and perhaps also a small amount of H_2S will have the H_2S and part of the dissolved CO_2 removed by intimate contact with air. The removal of the CO_2 and the oxidizing action of the air will cause the iron to be precipitated as the ferric hydroxide which will aid in coagulating clay or other suspended matter so that it will be more readily removed by sedimentation or filtration.

Temporary and Permanent Hardness.—The two agents that cause the greatest trouble because of hardness are $Ca(HCO_3)_2$

and $CaSO_4$. When water is boiled, part of the CO_2 is boiled off from the bicarbonate and $CaCO_3$ is formed. The equation is written

$$Ca(HCO_3)_2 \rightarrow CaCO_3 + CO_2 + H_2O$$

The reaction is written as going only to the right because the CO_2 is driven off with the steam and hence disappears from the reaction. The solubility of $CaCO_3$ is very small, as has been already stated. When a water containing much bicarbonate of calcium (or magnesium) is boiled, most of the $CaCO_3$ (and $MgCO_3$) is precipitated and the water becomes much softer. This bicarbonate hardness which is removable by boiling is called "temporary" hardness. The solubility of $CaSO_4$ is not much less in hot water than in cold water as will be discussed in the paragraph on boiler scale, and therefore sulfate hardness is called "permanent" hardness. These terms are not used much in modern discussions of water softening.

Boiler Scale.—A steam boiler is a closed vessel in which water is boiled to provide steam which is taken away from the boiler for other purposes. The gases that are dissolved in the water are driven off with the steam, but the nonvolatile materials such as dissolved salts and suspended solids remain in the boiler and increase in amount as the water is evaporated. When the solution in the boiler becomes saturated for a given salt, then the saturated salt commences to separate as a solid. In the operation of a boiler, it is customary occasionally to blow out part of the water with its suspended solids and then bring the volume back to normal with fresh water. If the precipitated solids remain in suspension, this method of blowing down is effective. In many cases however, the deposits adhere to the surface of the boiler and form a scale.

A very thick scale in the tube of a water heater is shown in Fig. 184. An illustration of a boiler tube completely choked by scale which had become loosened and fallen down is shown in Fig. 185.

If the interior surface of the metal of a boiler is clean, the heat is conducted through the metal and then away from the metal by the boiling water as fast as it can be supplied by the flames on the outside of the boiler so that, even when a boiler is being forced to its limit, the temperature of the steel plates and tubes of

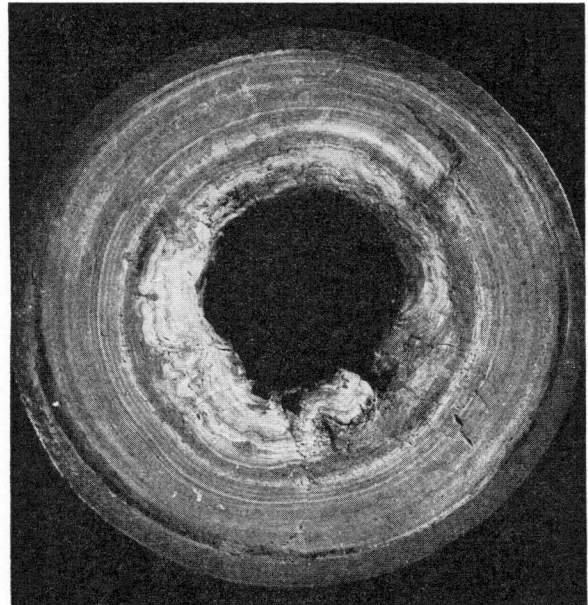

FIG. 184.—Feedwater pipe almost completely closed by scale.

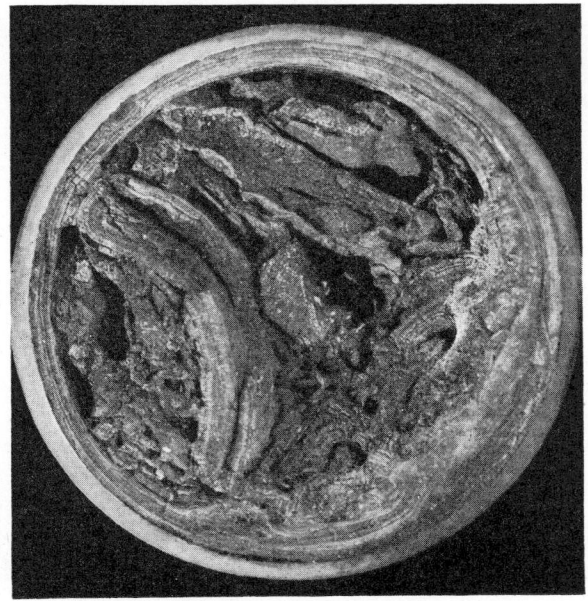

FIG. 185.—Boiler tube completely blocked by deposits and fragments of scale.

the boiler is very little higher than that of the water on the inside. If however the steel plates and tubes become covered on the

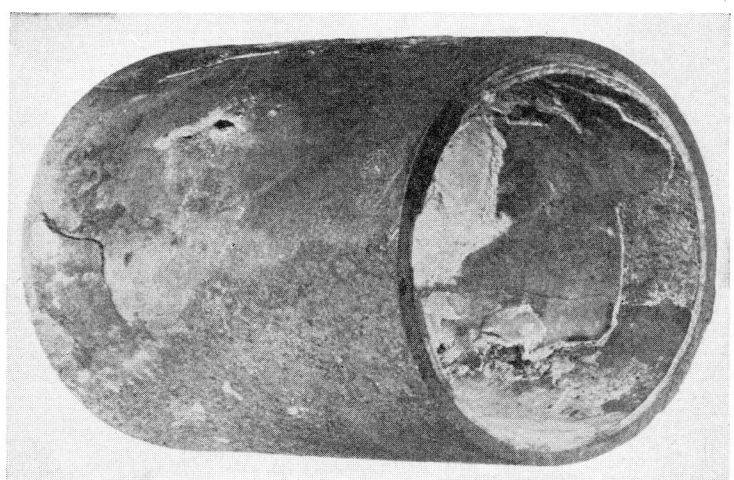

Fig. 186.—Boiler tube showing thin deposit of scale and small blowout.

Fig. 187.—Boiler tube ruptured in service.

inside with a layer of scale whose heat conductivity is poor, then the metal will become considerably hotter than the temperature of the boiling water, and the metal may become so hot that it will become oxidized and so thin that the wall may bulge, with a small blowout resulting as is shown in Fig. 186, or a bad blowout as shown in Fig. 187. There is some loss of efficiency of the boiler due to scale formation, but the most serious disadvantage of scale is the danger to the boiler due to overheating of the metal.

Calcium Sulfate Scale.—The most frequent type of hard scale formed in boilers is due to calcium sulfate. The changes that gypsum ($CaSO_4.2H_2O$) undergoes when heated in dry air and when brought in contact with water at room temperatures have been discussed under the heading of gypsum plasters in Chap. XIX. It was stated there that at room temperatures (20°C or 68°F) the solubility of $CaSO_4.\frac{1}{2}H_2O$ was about 9000 ppm of $CaSO_4$, and that of $CaSO_4.2H_2O$ was about 2000 ppm of $CaSO_4$. The stable phase was therefore $CaSO_4.2H_2O$, and plaster of Paris ($CaSO_4.\frac{1}{2}H_2O$) reacted with water to form the crystalline compound $CaSO_4.2H_2O$. The curves of Fig. 188 show solubilities under equilibrium conditions at higher temperatures. The solubility of the hemihydrate or half-hydrate ($CaSO_4.\frac{1}{2}H_2O$) is shown to decrease very rapidly, whereas that of gypsum ($CaSO_4.2H_2O$) decreases less rapidly so that the solubility of the two becomes identical at approximately 100°C. At higher temperatures, gypsum becomes incapable of existence.

The curves of Fig. 188 show that anhydrite ($CaSO_4$) has a still lower solubility than the hemihydrate and that it therefore should be the stable phase. Anhydrite however shows a reluctance to crystallize at temperatures below 284°F (140°C), but at higher temperatures it becomes the form of $CaSO_4$ which is precipitated as boiler scale. These three curves for the solubilities of $CaSO_4$ are all unusual in that their solubilities decrease with rising temperatures, whereas most salts become more soluble with rising temperature. This type of curve is sometimes called an "inverted solubility curve" or a "solubility curve with negative slope." It is the negative slope of the solubility curve that is the most important factor in causing calcium sulfate to form such a dense scale. Figure 189 shows the mechanism of the formation of calcium sulfate scale in an experimental cell. Photograph *A* taken at a magnification of 75 diameters shows a bubble of steam forming on the hot metal surface from a solution saturated with $CaSO_4$. Photograph *B* taken 2 min later shows that, as the bubble grew, a minute ring of fine crystals formed at the edge of the dry surface within the bubble where the water had all evaporated. When the bubble of steam broke away from the hot metal, the surface became wet again, but the crystals could not redissolve because the solution was saturated for its

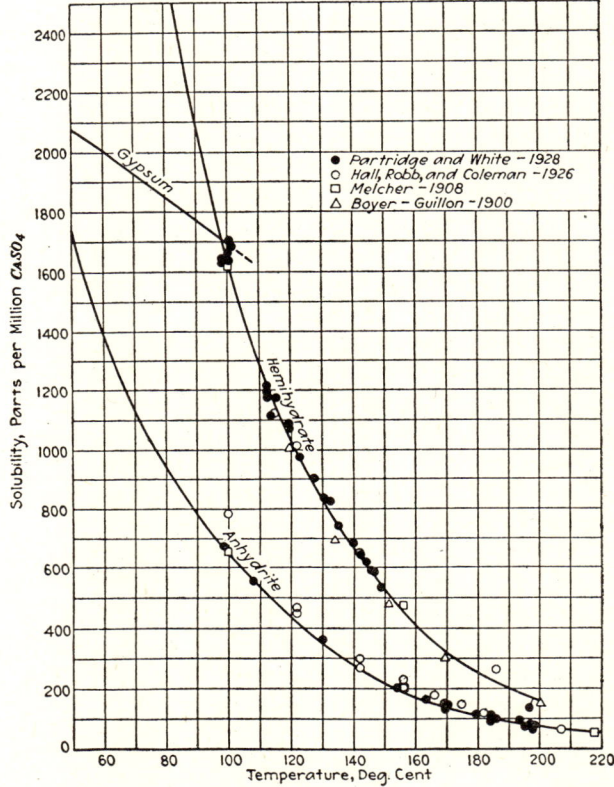

Fig. 188.—Solubilities of calcium sulfate in water at various temperatures. [From E. P. Partridge and A. H. White. *Trans. A.S.M.E.*, **51**, 383 (1929).]

temperature, and the crystals in contact with the heating surface were a fraction of a degree hotter than the solution and therefore had a lower solubility. Successive bubbles forming and breaking resulted in the formation of interlocking rings which finally built up a layer of hard scale. The experimental data of Fig. 188 extend only to a little above 200°C (398°F) which corresponds to a gage pressure of about 250 psi. There is every reason to

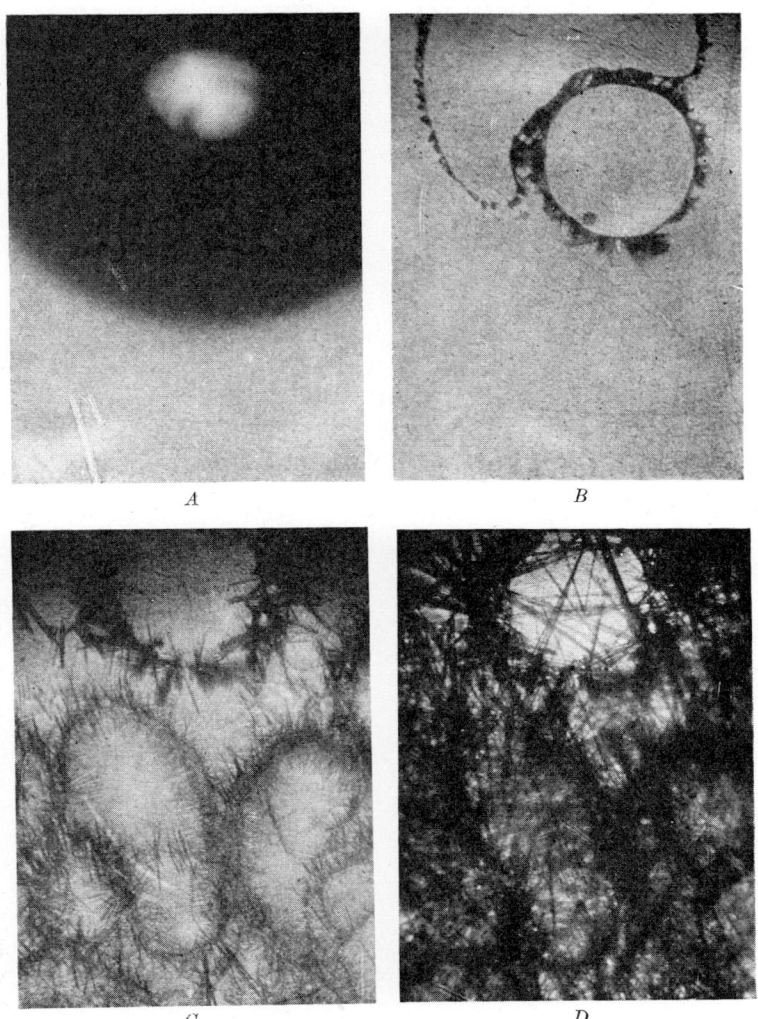

Fig. 189.—Deposition of calcium sulfate scale crystals by bubble evolution at evaporative surface. ×75. *A*, bubble attached to surface; *B*, ring of crystals left by bubble (2 min later than *A*); *C*, other rings left by bubbles (6 min later than *A*); *D*, growth of crystals (34 min later than *A*). [*From E. P. Partridge and A. H. White. Ind. and Eng. Chem.* **21**, 834 (1929.).]

believe that the same relations continue at higher temperatures and pressures.

The most dangerous conditions exist in the front rows of tubes of boilers in large power plants that are exposed directly to the radiant heat from the intense fire. The evaporation is extremely rapid, and even a thin film of scale will cause the temperature of the metal to rise dangerously.

The Formation of $CaCO_3$ Scale.—When water containing $Ca(HCO_3)_2$ is boiled, and the CO_2 is driven off, $CaCO_3$ is left behind in suspension in the water. Calcium carbonate is not formed in direct contact with the hot metal as is $CaSO_4$ scale, and therefore does not form an adherent scale but a loose sludge which may be blown out of the boiler with the blowoff water, provided it does not accumulate in places where the circulation is poor and become cemented by other materials. The hot-water supply of many households is provided in winter from a coil placed in the firebox of the furnace. If the water contains much $Ca(HCO_3)_2$, it will deposit $CaCO_3$ at the inlet of the boiler where the water first becomes hot. This will form a soft scale, but it may ultimately choke the inlet almost or quite completely. The coil will then become overheated and oxidized until it burns out.

The Formation of $Ca(OH)_2$, $Mg(OH)_2$ and Silicate Scale.—Both $CaCO_3$ and $MgCO_3$ will hydrolyze in a steam boiler according to the equations

$$CaCO_3 + H_2O \rightleftharpoons Ca(OH)_2 + CO_2$$
$$MgCO_3 + H_2O \rightleftharpoons Mg(OH)_2 + CO_2$$

These equations reading from right to left are those which represent the hardening of lime mortar at room temperature. Under boiler conditions, the CO_2 is removed with steam and the $Ca(OH)_2$ or $Mg(OH)_2$ may build up to a saturated solution with scale formation resulting. Calcium silicate is an ingredient of some scales, and under conditions of excessive local evaporation, hard scales consisting mainly of sodium aluminum silicate may be formed.

Theory of Softening Water by the Lime-soda Process.—The least soluble of the cheaper salts of calcium is the carbonate, and the lime-soda system of softening water converts all other salts of calcium into the carbonate and removes the sludge by sedimentation or filtration. Magnesium salts are likewise removed as the carbonates, sometimes as the hydroxides. The equations for the removal of the calcium salts are written as follows:

$$Ca(HCO_3)_2 + Ca(OH)_2 \rightleftharpoons 2CaCO_3 + 2H_2O$$
$$CO_2 + Ca(OH)_2 \rightleftharpoons CaCO_3 + H_2O$$
$$CaSO_4 + Na_2CO_3 \rightleftharpoons CaCO_3 + Na_2SO_4$$

If the water to be softened contains CO_2 in addition to the amount required to form the bicarbonate, sufficient lime must be added to combine with it as well as the bicarbonate CO_2. The lime for water softening should be high in CaO, or $Ca(OH)_2$ if hydrated lime is purchased. $Mg(OH)_2$ has a lower solubility than $CaCO_3$ and so is a useless constituent for this purpose.

The cheapest chemical to convert $CaSO_4$ and other stable salts of calcium to the carbonate is Na_2CO_3, which is bought under the trade name of soda ash. The relative amounts of lime and soda ash to be added to the water must be determined after chemical analysis. One mol of $Ca(OH)_2$ must be added for each mol of free CO_2 and $Ca(HCO_3)_2$, and one mol of Na_2CO_3 must be added for each mol of $CaSO_4$ (and other fixed calcium salt) in order to secure the maximum precipitation of $CaCO_3$ and the minimum amount of calcium ions remaining in solution.

Equations for the reaction of salts of magnesium may be written in a similar way to those for calcium. If an excess of $Ca(OH)_2$ should be added, the magnesium salts could be converted to the least soluble form $Mg(OH)_2$, but an excess of the hydrated lime is undesirable, and so it is not usually used.

Softening by the Cold Lime-soda Process.—It is well known that all chemical reactions are accelerated by an increase in temperature. If a municipal water supply is to be softened, the temperature of the raw water in winter may be only a few degrees above freezing. Under these conditions, the water-softening reactions may not be complete in 24 hr, whereas at temperatures just below the boiling point they may go to substantial completion in 10 min. In softening water supplies for cities, care must be taken to avoid an excess of lime and soda ash, and water containing some calcium and magnesium salt is usually considered to have a better taste, and so municipal supplies are rarely softened as completely as those intended for boiler feed waters. The softened water from municipal plants might, especially in winter, still contain some $Ca(OH)_2$ which has not yet entered into reaction. This might react while in the mains, or after it is drawn by the consumer, with the formation of a sediment of $CaCO_3$ in the water. To avoid this delayed precipitation, the water is frequently treated with CO_2 as the last step before it leaves the softening plant, with the result that any $CaCO_3$ that forms is converted into the soluble $Ca(HCO_3)_2$.

Railroads use the cold process for water softening in plants set up to provide softened water for locomotives. Although the water is ultimately to be heated, the cost of keeping the water hot in the softening plant and in the tanks in the tender of the locomotive make it more economical to install a larger softener which will give time for reaction even in cold weather.

Softening Water by the Hot Lime-soda Process.—If water containing bicarbonate hardness is heated to boiling, some of the dissolved CO_2 and other gases are driven off, with resultant diminution in the amount of lime required for the softening process. It is not ordinarily feasible to find a use for the steam evolved at atmospheric pressure in the preliminary boiling process, and the main reason for heating the water before addition of the chemicals is to increase the rate of reaction so that the capacity of the reaction chamber may be much less than would be the case if the cold process were used. A modern plant for continuous softening by the hot process is illustrated in Fig. 190. The description of this equipment will start with the chemical tank in the lower left-hand corner. The chemicals to be added are hydrated lime and soda ash, and as may be shown by chemical equations, it is immaterial whether they are added to the raw water separately or together. It is more convenient to add them together, and at convenient intervals weighed amounts of hydrated lime, soda ash, and water are added to the mixing tank. The creamy mixture is kept in suspension by a circulating pump which draws part of the mixture from the bottom of the tank and pumps it to the chemical proportioner from which it flows back to the chemical tank. If no water is being drawn from the softener, the chemical mixture is simply pumped round and round and no part of it is withdrawn.

The level of the water in the central tank is kept constant by a float which actuates the valve on the raw water line at the upper

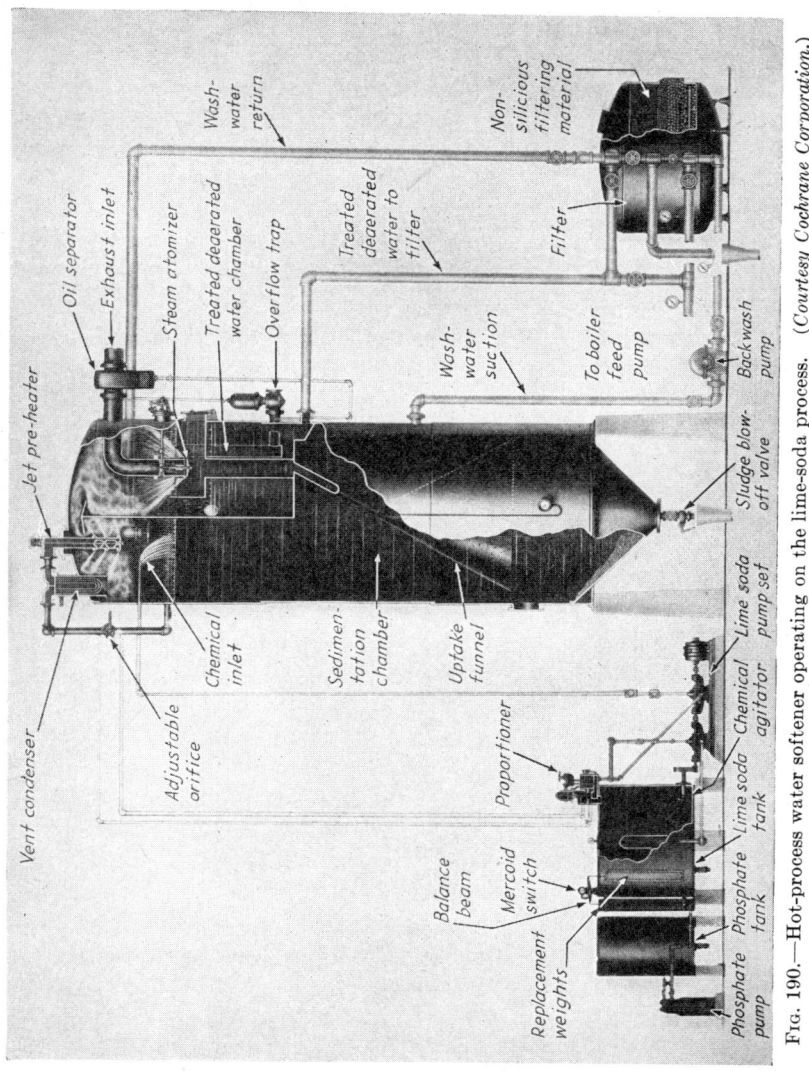

Fig. 190.—Hot-process water softener operating on the lime-soda process. (*Courtesy Cochrane Corporation.*)

left of the picture. When softened water is drawn off, this valve is opened and the raw water starts to flow into the softener. A difference in pressure is set up on the two sides of the orifice set in the raw water line, and this difference is transmitted to the chemical proportioner where it actuates a throttle valve diverting a proportionate part of the chemicals to the chemical feed pump, which forces this proportionate part of the mixture to the top of the treating tank where it mixes with the hot raw water. The raw water entering the top of the treating tank is sprayed into a chamber containing exhaust or other low-pressure steam and is thus heated. A part of the cold water is diverted to a vent condenser, which permits the gases released from solution to leave the softener but prevents any escape of steam. The stream of hot water meets the stream of chemicals as it flows into the top of the reaction chamber. Reaction takes place as the water flows down the sedimentation tank. Toward the bottom of the sedimentation tank, the water encounters an inverted cone. The sludge slides off of the cone to the bottom of the tank from which it is withdrawn occasionally. The softened water flows up the inside of the inverted cone into a chamber where it is heated to a higher temperature by the incoming steam and is thus deaerated more completely. The hot deaerated water passes out to a filter which removes solids still in suspension. This filter is not filled with sand because of the danger of dissolving silica in the somewhat alkaline water. Anthracite coal, carefully washed and sized, or other inert materials are used for the filter bed. When the filter accumulates a layer of precipitate, it is washed by drawing some of the softened water from the sedimentation tank and pumping it from the bottom to the top of the filter bed. The softened water and suspended sediment are pumped back to the treating tank where the sedimentation process is repeated.

A separate tank for the introduction of phosphate solution is shown at the left of Fig. 190. The value of phosphates in water treatment is discussed in a later paragraph.

The change in composition of a very hard water on treatment with the hot lime-soda process is shown in Table 70. The raw water was treated with a slight excess of soda, so that the treated water showed 49 ppm of Na_2CO_3. The excess of alkali permitted more complete precipitation of the lime and magnesia than would have been possible if the water was to have been used for a municipal supply. The treatment removed all of the suspended solids and reduced the total Ca ions from 167.0 to 5.0 ppm and the Mg ions from 28.0 to 0.7 ppm. The sodium ions increased because of the Na_2CO_3 added. The chlorine and sulfate ions should not have been affected by the treatment, except as small amounts of these ions may have been introduced with the chemicals. Actually, the water was diluted about 20 per cent by the steam condensed in the heating section of the softener so that these ions were diminished to about that extent.

The Zeolite Process of Water Softening.—The class of zeolites includes a number of minerals that are complex silicates of calcium, aluminum, and sodium. Similar compounds are made synthetically. The sodium and calcium atoms in these zeolites are readily interchangeable, and though the solubility of the mineral as a whole is very slight, there will be a rather free interchange of ions from the water with the atoms on the surface of the mineral grains. Equations for the removal of calcium ions from the water may be written as follows:

$$2Na \text{ zeolite} + CaSO_4 \rightleftharpoons Ca \text{ zeolite} + Na_2SO_4$$
$$2Na \text{ zeolite} + Ca(HCO_3)_2 \rightleftharpoons Ca \text{ zeolite} + 2NaHCO_3$$

After some time, the sodium atoms on the surface of the grains will be so largely replaced by calcium that the reaction will become slow and incomplete. The zeolite may then be regenerated by flooding it with a rather strong solution of NaCl (which is the cheapest source of sodium ions), when the reaction may be written

$$Ca \text{ zeolite} + 2NaCl \rightleftharpoons 2Na \text{ zeolite} + CaCl_2$$

This second reaction is merely the reverse of the first reaction with the substitution of NaCl for Na_2SO_4 or $NaHCO_3$. The concentrated solution of the sodium chloride is used to facilitate the reaction according to the law of mass action. The cross section of a zeolite softener is shown in Fig. 191. It consists of a steel shell in the bottom of which is a layer of coarse gravel acting as a support for the zeolite which looks like coarse sand. The method of operation may be followed readily from the descriptive labels of the figure.

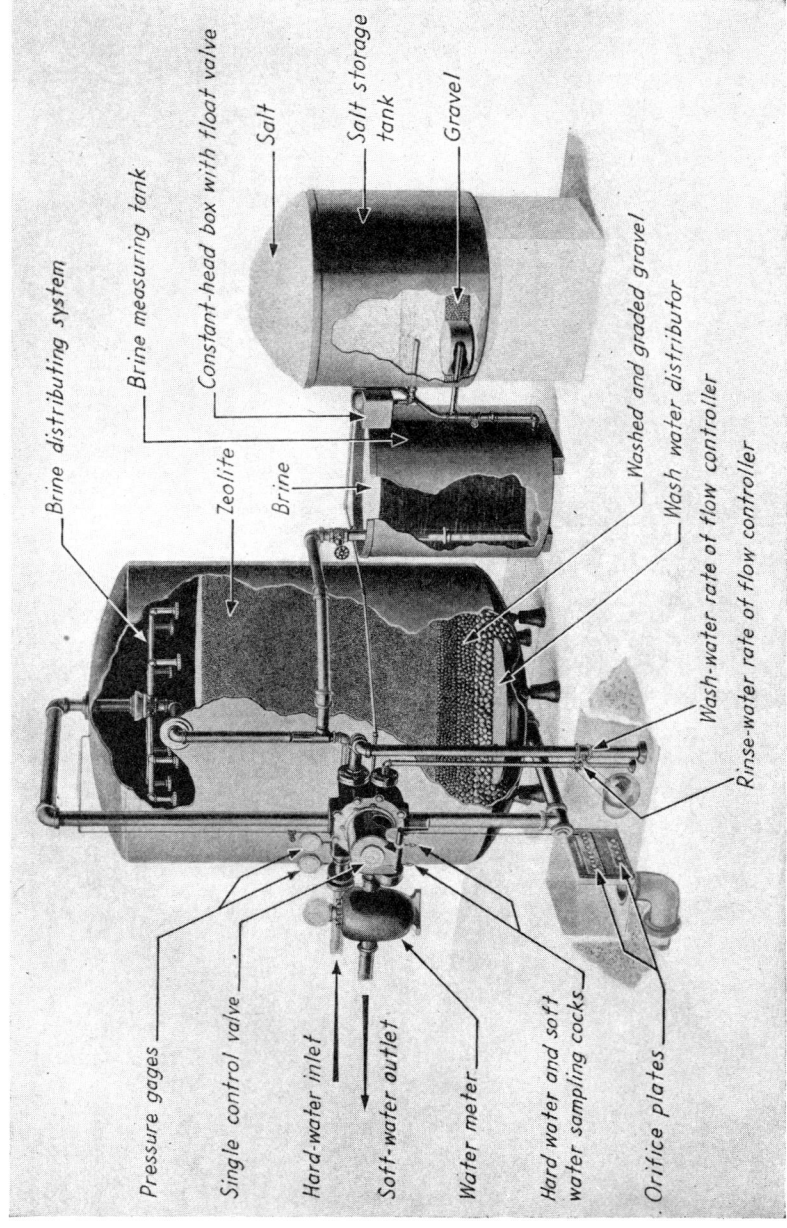

Fig. 191.—Water softener operating on the zeolite process. (*Courtesy Permutit Company.*)

The zeolite process may be used in large power plants, but is especially adapted to homes, hospitals, and other small units that do not maintain an engineering staff. The lime-soda process requires careful and frequent chemical control. The zeolite process will work with only occasional attention without any serious harm resulting. The average householder lets his zeolite plant run along until there is complaint that the water is too hard, when he goes down cellar, by-passes the softener, adds salt to regenerate the zeolite and, after a few hours of contact, washes out the brine and puts the softener back into service. Some of the household plants are made to operate quite automatically.

The analyses of Table 71 show how a water already comparatively soft is rendered still softer by zeolite softening. The combined Ca and Mg ions are reduced to 1.0 ppm after softening, whereas after the lime-soda softening illustrated in Table 71, the combined Ca and Mg ions amounted to 5.7 ppm. The anions have gone through the zeolite bed unchanged, and so the HCO_3 ion increases the alkalinity. This is shown in the lower columns of Table 71 by the rise in pH value from 7.6 in the raw water to 8.4 in the softened water.

Carbonaceous Zeolites for Removing Metallic Ions from Solution.—The usual silicate zeolite exchanges Na ions for those of Ca and Mg but does not reduce the total number of ions in solution. It has been discovered rather recently that charcoal and coke, after chemical-activating treatments, gain the power of absorbing the ions not only of Ca and Mg but also of Na. When the carbon has taken up so many ions that it has become inactive, it may be regenerated by treatment with acid in the same way that zeolite of the silicate type may be regenerated with salt.

If the abbreviation H_2Z is used for this carbonaceous zeolite, the equations may be written

$$CaSO_4 + H_2Z \rightleftharpoons CaZ + H_2SO_4$$
$$2NaHCO_3 + H_2Z \rightleftharpoons Na_2Z + H_2CO_3$$

It is apparent that the H_2CO_3 will be removed by boiling but that the H_2SO_4 will give the water a permanent acidity.

If a portion of the raw water is passed through a silicate zeolite, the $Ca(HCO_3)_2$ of that portion of the water will be con-

TABLE 71.—CHANGES IN COMPOSITION OF WATER AFTER ZEOLITE TREATMENT AND SUBSEQUENT ACIDIFICATION*
Quantities in parts per million unless otherwise stated.

Cations	Raw water	After zeolite	After acid feed and deaeration
Silica................................	3.0	5.1	5.1
Iron oxide and alumina...............	2.0	0.7	0.7
Calcium.............................	26.4	0.8	0.8
Magnesium..........................	6.4	0.2	0.2
Sodium.............................	3.8	45.0	45.0
Anions			
Sulfate.............................	20.1	20.1	54.0
Chloride............................	5.9	5.9	5.9
Bicarbonate........................	87.0	87.0	27.5
Carbonate..........................	0.0	0.0	9.0
Total dissolved solids...............	154.6	164.8	148.2
Hardness as CaCO₃ (gravimetric)......	92.25	2.74	2.74

Acid feed—35 parts of 100 per cent H_2SO_4 per million parts of water treated.

	Raw water	After zeolite	After acid feed	After deaerator	In boiler	Steam
Temperature, °F...........	40.0	40.0	40.0	215.0	365.0	365.0
Pressure, lb. ga...........	45.0	7.5	......	......	155.0	
pH value.................	7.6	8.6	6.4	8.5	......	5.4
CO₂ (free)................	1.8	......	18.1	0.0	0.0	25.0
O₂ cc per liter............	6.03	6.03	6.03	.016	......	.044
NaHCO₃..................	0.0	120.0	60.5	38.0		
Na₂CO₃..................	0.0	0.0	0.0	14.2	174.0	
Na₂SO₄..................	0.0	30.0	81.0	81.0	1500.0	
NaOH....................	0.0	0.0	0.0	0.0	360.0	
Total alkalinity as Na₂CO₃..	......	......	......	......	650.0	
$\frac{Na_2SO_4}{\text{Total alk. as } Na_2CO_3}$					2.3	

* From WHITE, WALKER, PARTRIDGE, and COLLINS, Zeolite Water Treatment in a Large Central Heating Plant, *Am. Water Works Assn.*, **18**, 241 (1927).

verted to $NaHCO_3$. This alkaline water from the silicate zeolite may be used to neutralize the water from the carbonaceous zeolite to give a water which, after boiling off the CO_2, becomes neutral and contains much less total solids than were carried by the original water.

Changes in Boiler Waters during Boiler Operation —When the boiler feed water enters the boiler, it is heated to its boiling point under the pressure prevailing in the boiler and then starts to boil. The dissolved gases pass off with the steam, and the salts in solution become more concentrated. If the water has not been softened adequately, scale may form, and under other conditions foaming may result. There will be dissociation and hydrolysis of the carbonates as illustrated by the following equations:

$$Ca(HCO_3)_2 \rightleftharpoons CaCO_3 + CO_2 + H_2O$$
$$CaCO_3 + H_2O \rightleftharpoons Ca(OH)_2 + CO_2$$
$$2NaHCO_3 \rightleftharpoons Na_2CO_3 + H_2O + CO_2$$
$$Na_2CO_3 + H_2O \rightleftharpoons 2NaOH + CO_2$$

The alkalinity of the water will therefore increase during the boiling process. Ultimately the concentration of soluble salts will rise so high that it must be decreased. A valve in the bottom of the boiler is opened, and sediment and a portion of the water is blown out. In large plants, there is usually a continuous blowdown through a heat exchanger, so that the heat of the water blown out is used to preheat some of the feed water. The harmful effects of alkalinity in boiler water are discussed in the following paragraph.

Caustic Embrittlement or Hydrogen Embrittlement of Boiler Steel.—With operation of boilers at high pressures and high steaming rates and with softened water, disturbing failures of the metal were occasionally encountered. Cracks were sometimes formed extending from one rivet hole to another as shown in Fig. 192. Laboratory investigations showed that this type of crack could be produced artificially only in boiler plate which was highly stressed and exposed to solutions which were rather strongly alkaline. It was shown that possibilities for such concentrations existed in the small cracks under rivet heads. The theory is not clearly defined, but the prevention seems to lie in the deposition of a thin protective coating on the surface of the steel plate.

One of the first remedies to find wide acceptance was based on the protective action of Na_2SO_4. The American Society of Mechanical Engineers has indicated that if the ratio of the weight of sodium sulfate to the total alkalinity expressed as sodium carbonate is kept up to certain limits, dependent on the operating pressure of the boiler, caustic embrittlement will be avoided. The suggested ratios are given in Table 72. Still more recent

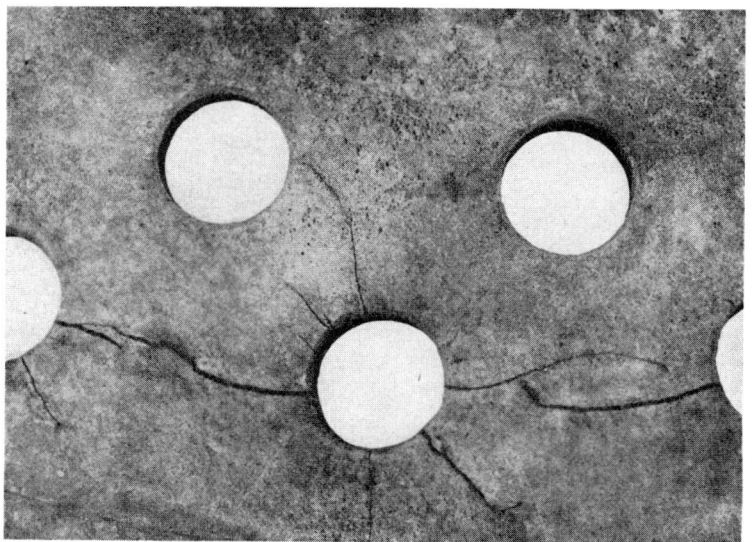

Fig. 192.—Cracks in boiler plate caused by caustic embrittlement. The apparent distortion of the holes is due to drilling out the rivets while dismantling the drum. Magnification $\frac{3}{4} \times$. (*Courtesy Babcock and Wilcox Co.*)

experiments have indicated that the sulfate-carbonate ratio is not infallible, but it still stands as the only official statement of a preventive measure.

TABLE 72.—RATIOS OF SULFATE TO CARBONATE RECOMMENDED FOR INHIBITION OF CAUSTIC EMBRITTLEMENT*

For Pressures	Parts of Sulfate Present (as Sodium Sulfate) per Part of Total Alkalinity (as Sodium Carbonate)
Up to 150 lb	1
150–250 lb	2
Over 250 lb	3

* Suggested Rules for Care of Power Boilers, A.S.M.E. Boiler Construction Code, p. 81 (1935).

Acid Treatment of Boiler Feed Water.—In the lime-soda process of water softening, almost all of HCO_3 ions are precipitated as $CaCO_3$. In the zeolite process, all of the HCO_3 ions go through to the finished water and in the boiler become CO_3 or OH ions. In Table 71, the water softened by the zeolite process is stated to contain 120.0 ppm $NaHCO_3$ but only 30 ppm Na_2SO_4. The 120 ppm $NaHCO_3$ would on boiling yield 74.4 ppm Na_2CO_3 which, according to the A.S.M.E. code for boilers operating at 150 to 250 lb pressure, should be accompanied by at least 147 ppm Na_2SO_4 instead of the 30 ppm actually present. One remedy would be to add Na_2SO_4, but this would increase the total salts in solution and therefore the amount of water to be blown off. Another method would be to decrease the amount of $NaHCO_3$, and this was done in the plant from which the data were taken, by additions of a mixture of sulfuric and phosphoric acids, the latter acid being added because of the greater protection against corrosion which it afforded. After the addition of the acid,[*] the pH of the water changed from 8.4 to 5.8. When this acid water was heated to boiling in the deaerator, the CO_2 and other dissolved gases were boiled off and the pH went back to the alkaline side (8.8). When this water went into the boiler and reached the concentration designated for the blowdown, it contained 1600 ppm Na_2SO_4, 225 ppm Na_2HPO_4, 225 ppm Na_2CO_3, and 70 ppm $NaOH$. The protection against caustic embrittlement was therefore considered to be ample, and no trouble has been experienced in the operation of the boiler.

Phosphates as Water-softening Agents.—The solubility of calcium phosphate $[Ca_3(PO_4)_2]$ is less than that of $CaCO_3$, and the phosphates are now used widely instead of soda ash. The most common of the phosphates is trisodium phosphate (Na_3PO_4). This is sold under proprietary names as a water softener for household use. A small amount of it added to the water in the laundry tub, or in the bath prior to the addition of soap, precipitates the calcium and magnesium salts and so permits soap to become immediately effective. An objection to this salt is its alkalinity, and Na_2HPO_4 is sometimes used in its place.

Sodium metaphosphate in the glassy modification, sodium hexametaphosphate $[(NaPO_3)_6]$ and to a lesser extent sodium pyrophosphate ($Na_4P_2O_7$) have the advantage over the orthophosphate in that they form soluble salts of lime and magnesia

[*] *Am. Waterworks Assn.*, **18**, 242 (1927).

and so soften the water without producing a precipitate. These salts likewise come on the market under trade names for household use. They ultimately hydrolyze to the orthophosphate, the equation for the metaphosphate being

$$NaPO_3 + H_2O \rightleftharpoons NaH_2PO_4$$

This is one of the acid phosphates and so introduces less alkalinity per unit of phosphoric acid than the trisodium phosphate does. Phosphoric acid introduces no alkalinity.

Extraordinarily small amounts of the glassy sodium metaphosphate are sufficient to prevent precipitation when a water containing calcium carbonate is used cold or heated to a temperature not above the boiling point. Only 1 or 2 ppm of the metaphosphate has been found sufficient to prevent the formation of scale and also even to remove deposits of old scale in industrial and municipal water-softening plants and in the condensers of power plants. The addition of this minute amount of metaphosphate is sometimes known as the "threshold treatment."

Barium Salts as Water Softeners.—When it is necessary to use a water high in sulfates as a boiler feed water, it may pay to use $BaCO_3$ as a softening agent in spite of its expense and its poisonous properties. The reaction

$$CaSO_4 + BaCO_3 \rightleftharpoons BaSO_4 + CaCO_3$$

shows that the products are $BaSO_4$ and $CaCO_3$, both of which are very insoluble, and precipitate out, thus reducing the SO_4 as well as the CO_3 ions.

Foaming and Priming.—When a boiler is steaming rapidly, some particles of liquid water are torn from the boiling surface and carried off with the steam. Baffles are placed in the upper steam drum and the offtake pipe of the boiler to separate this entrained water, but under some circumstances foam forms, or the boiler "primes," which means that larger masses of water are carried over. The presence of liquid water in the steam is objectionable because the solids in suspension or solution may deposit crusts on the turbine blades. Foaming and priming are associated phenomena. Their appearance is favored by a high concentration of dissolved salts, by oil films, and by the presence of finely divided solids of the type that float on the surface of the water.

Internal Treatment of Boiler Waters.—It is evident that if hard water is introduced into a steam boiler the $Ca(HCO_3)_2$ will be broken down to $CaCO_3$ but the $CaSO_4$ will not be changed chemically. If Na_2CO_3 is introduced into the boiler, the $CaSO_4$ will be decomposed to form $CaCO_3$ just as it would be in an external softening plant. It is preferable to carry out these reactions in a separate plant and remove the sludge before the water is introduced in the boiler. Proprietary compounds recommended for injection into the boiler frequently contain Na_2CO_3 or Na_3PO_4 and also various types of organic matter. Colloidal materials introduced into the boilers may or may not act to collect the suspended precipitates and facilitate their removal. Boiler compounds should be used only after an analysis has been made of the water and the operating conditions have been studied by a competent engineer. Patent medicines are just as dangerous for boilers as they are for human beings.

References

BUSWELL, A. M.: The Chemistry of Water and Sewage Treatment, Reinhold Publishing Corporation, New York, 1928.

CLARKE, F. W.: The Data of Geochemistry, *U. S. Geol. Survey, Bull.* 770, 1924.

COLLINS, W. D.: Relations between Quality of Water and Industrial Development in the United States, *U. S. Geol. Survey, Water-supply Paper* 559, 1926.

COLLINS, LAMAR, and LOHR: The Industrial Utility of Public Water Supplies in the United States, *U. S. Dept. Interior, Geol. Water-supply Paper* 658, 1934.

FOLWELL, A. P.: Sewerage, 11th ed., John Wiley & Sons, Inc., New York, 1936.

HARDENBERGH, W. A.: Water Supply and Purification, International Textbook Company, Scranton, Pa., 1938.

HARDENBERGH, W. A.: Sewerage and Sewerage Treatment, 1st ed., International Textbook Company, Scranton, Pa., 1936.

PARTRIDGE and WHITE: The Formation and Thermal Effects of Calcium Sulfate Boiler Scale, *Trans. Am. Soc. Mech. Eng.*, **51**, FSP-51-49, 383 (1929).

PARTRIDGE and SCHROEDER: The Embrittlement of Boiler Steel, *Metals and Alloys*, **6**, 145, 187, 253, 311, and 355 (1935).

POWELL, S. T.: Boiler Feed Water Purification, McGraw-Hill Book Company, Inc., New York, 1927.

POWELL, S. T.: Purification of Water for Sanitary and Industrial Uses, Silver Anniversary Volume of American Institute of Chemical Engineers, Chap. XXII, D. Van Nostrand Co., Inc., New York, 1933.

Ryan, W. J.: Water Treatment and Purification, McGraw-Hill Book Company, Inc., New York, 1937.
Tolman, C. F.: Ground Water, McGraw-Hill Book Company, Inc., New York, 1937.
Waterman, E. L.: Elements of Water Supply Engineering, John Wiley & Sons, Inc., New York, 1934.
Weston, R. S.: Stream Pollution and Waste Disposal, Silver Anniversary Volume of American Institute of Chemical Engineers, Chap. XXIII, D. Van Nostrand Co., Inc., New York, 1933.

CHAPTER XXIII

ORGANIC PRESERVATIVE MATERIALS AND PROTECTIVE COATINGS

The three most important engineering materials that are liable to disintegration are wood, steel, and concrete. The metallic coatings used to protect steel have been mentioned in Chap. XVI. The nonmetallic protective materials are almost all organic compounds, composed principally of carbon, hydrogen, and oxygen, with nitrogen and sulfur occurring less frequently. The properties of these compounds depend upon the way the atoms are linked together, and a full knowledge of their behavior involves much complicated chemistry. The treatment in this chapter must necessarily be very elementary.

Decay of Wood.—The main enemies of wood are bacteria, molds, fungi, and insects which feed upon some of the materials in the wood. It will not decay under conditions that do not permit these living organisms to grow. Wood does not decay in dry air, nor does it decay when immersed deeply in water, because bacteria and molds do not grow under these conditions. Wooden piles driven into mud or water decay for only a short distance below the surface of the water. Bridge piers and important buildings are built upon wooden piles cut off far enough below the surface so that the tops will always be kept wet. Such piles will last for hundreds of years. Fence posts rot most rapidly a few inches above the ground and a few inches below the ground. The timbers used in framing a house are protected from the weather and are attacked only in damp climates, especially the tropics, where the wood absorbs enough moisture so that the termite ants can eat it. The shingles on a house become weathered where they are exposed to the sun, but become rotten only where one shingle overlapping the other permits moisture to remain for rather long period of time. Wooden floors in a cellar decay through what is called "dry rot" as a result of the action of a fungus which finds that wood in a damp cellar contains enough moisture to permit its use as food.

Protection of Wood by Impregnation with Poisonous Materials. Zinc chloride is a water-soluble salt which is poisonous to bacteria and fungi. It may be used where the wood is not exposed to circulating water. The most common preservative for such materials as telephone poles and railroad ties is creosote oil, obtained by the distillation of coal tar. It is a cheap material containing complex phenols, which are poisonous to the organisms, and also hydrocarbons, which tend to keep out the water. Telephone poles are impregnated by stacking them vertically in a tank of creosote oil of the required depth. The creosoted portion should extend at least 2 ft above the ground after the pole is in place, since the ground moisture will be drawn up almost that far by capillary action.

Observations on telephone poles of chestnut wood[1] on the line between Warren, Pennsylvania, and Buffalo, New York, showed that two-thirds of the poles that had been immersed in creosote, either as green or seasoned poles, were still rated in good condition after 24 years service, whereas of the untreated seasoned poles none were rated as in good condition, 84 per cent were decaying and 13 per cent had been removed because of decay. The creosote oil imparts a brown stain and a disagreeable odor which restricts its use to outdoor structures.

The crossties used on railroad tracks must be protected very thoroughly since the steel spikes penetrate to the center of the tie and permit water to enter, and so the creosote must also penetrate to the center. The ties are impregnated by placing them in steel tanks which can be closed tightly. The creosote oil is sometimes pumped in under pressure, and is sometimes forced in by vacuum formed by blowing steam through the tank containing the ties until the air has been driven out from the pores, then closing the tank and permitting the steam to condense. The creosote oil is then admitted to the tank and sucked into the wood by the partial vacuum.

Protective Coatings for Wood.—Protective coatings occasionally contain poisonous materials, but in most cases the coatings prevent decay by keeping the moisture content of the wood so low that the destructive organisms do not grow. The most common protective coatings are paint and varnish, and they

---

[1] WIRKA, R. M., *Elec. World*, July 22, 1933.

will be discussed after a brief statement of the chemical reactions involved in the drying and disintegration of paint films.

Linseed Oil.—Linseed oil has been used for hundreds of years and is still the most important constituent of paint. It is pressed from the seed of the flax plant as a limpid light-yellow oil. Chemically, linseed oil consists of a mixture of fats, which were defined in the preceding chapter as esters of glycerin and a fat acid. The illustration in the last chapter was stearin, and linseed oil, like stearin, may be made into soap or hydrolyzed by water into its component fat acids and glycerin.

The fat acid of stearin is stearic acid, whose formula has already been given as $CH_3.(CH_2)_{16}.COOH$. Both stearin and stearic acid are saturated compounds and change very slowly on exposure to air. Linseed oil contains unsaturated acids which react readily with oxygen so that the limpid oil on exposure to air becomes a tough and elastic film. Before this process of "drying" linseed oil can be understood, there must be some further explanation of the structure of organic compounds.

Saturated and Unsaturated Compounds.—The simplest hydrocarbon is methane (CH_4), whose formula is sometimes written more in detail as

$$H-\overset{\overset{\displaystyle H}{|}}{\underset{\underset{\displaystyle H}{|}}{C}}-H$$

showing that each hydrogen is attached directly to the carbon by a single linkage. It is more frequently written

$$\overset{H}{\underset{H}{HCH}}$$

without expressing the linkages, it being understood that all the unions are through single linkages unless there is a definite indication of some other type. Methanol (CH_3OH) may in a similar way be written

$$\overset{H}{\underset{H}{HCOH}}$$

and acetic acid (CH_3COOH) as

$$\underset{H\ OH}{\overset{H}{HC.C=O}}.$$

These examples are all illustrations of saturated compounds, as shown by the fact that the carbon atoms are all linked to each other by a single bond. In the case of acetic acid, there is a double bond linking the carbon with oxygen, but oxygen is divalent and therefore needs two bonds.

The next hydrocarbon above methane in the saturated series is ethane (C_2H_6 or $CH_3.CH_3$) which may also be written

$$\begin{array}{c} H\ \ H \\ |\ \ \ | \\ H-C-C-H \\ |\ \ \ | \\ H\ \ H \end{array}$$

and is a saturated hydrocarbon. There is another hydrocarbon, ethylene, which, like ethane, contains two carbon atoms but only four hydrogen atoms so that its formula is C_2H_4, which may also be written $CH_2\!=\!CH_2$, or $\begin{array}{c} H\ \ H \\ C\!=\!C \\ H\ \ H \end{array}$. This is an unsaturated hydrocarbon as is shown by the double bonds between the two carbon atoms. Still another hydrocarbon with two carbon atoms is acetylene (C_2H_2, $CH\equiv CH$, or $\begin{array}{c} H\ \ H \\ C\equiv C \end{array}$). This triple linkage between the two carbons indicates unsaturation to a greater degree than in C_2H_4.

Unsaturated compounds are unstable. They may be made to unite with oxygen or with hydrogen or with each other under proper conditions. Thus, C_2H_2 may by addition of hydrogen be converted to C_2H_6, the saturated compound ethane. If unsaturated compounds are forced to unite with each other, a process known as "polymerization," the molecules frequently form long chains and the products may be of great industrial importance. A derivative of butadiene ($CH_2\!=\!CH\!-\!CH\!=\!CH_2$) may be polymerized to give rubber, and another derivative of this hydrocarbon may be polymerized to give Duprene, a valuable synthetic material similar to rubber in many of its properties but superior to rubber for some purposes.

The Drying of Linseed Oil.—Linseed oil is a mixture of fats, all of them glycerides, or esters of glycerin with various fat acids. Almost all of these fat acids have 18 carbon atoms and differ from each other in the number of hydrogen atoms, a difference that is reflected in the number of double linkages. The glyceride stearin, which is present to only a small extent in linseed oil, is a saturated fat and the others are all unsaturated in varying degrees. The formulas for some of the fat acids are presented in Table 73. Oleic acid contains two less hydrogen atoms than

ORGANIC PRESERVATIVE MATERIALS

TABLE 73.—ILLUSTRATIONS OF SATURATED AND UNSATURATED FAT ACIDS

Name	Condensed formula	Structural formula	Name of fat formed from this fat acid
Stearic	$C_{18}H_{36}O_2$	$CH_3(CH_2)_{16}COOH$	Stearin
Oleic	$C_{18}H_{34}O_2$	$CH_3(CH_2)_7CH=CH(CH_2)_7COOH$	Olein
Linoleic	$C_{18}H_{32}O_2$	$CH_3(CH_2)_4CH=CH\ CH_2CH=CH(CH_2)_7COOH$	Linolein
Linolenic	$C_{18}H_{30}O_2$	$CH_3CH_2CH=CH\ CH_2CH=CHCH_2CH=CH(CH_2)_7COOH$	Linolenin

stearic and one double bond showing an unsaturated linkage. Linoleic acid contains two double bonds, and linolenic acid contains three double bonds. The fat olein is present to a rather small extent, and the chief constituents of linseed oil are the highly unsaturated fats linolein and linolenin.

The unsaturated linkages in these fats may be saturated by adding hydrogen in the presence of catalysts, which will convert linolenin by successive steps into stearin. This is done commercially in the process of hydrogenation by which hard cooking fats like Crisco are made from cottonseed oil. Linseed oil is not usually subjected to hydrogenation, because it is more valuable in its native condition as a paint oil. When linseed oil is exposed to the air, it absorbs oxygen in the unsaturated linkages. A molecule of oxygen O_2 probably enters into the unsaturated linkage to form a peroxide as illustrated below.

$$\text{Unsaturated linkage} \quad \begin{array}{cccc} H & H & H & H \\ -C & -C & =C & -C- \\ H & & & H \end{array}$$

$$\text{Peroxide} \quad \begin{array}{cccc} H & H & H & H \\ -C & -C & -C & -C- \\ H & O & -O & H \end{array}$$

This peroxide may later break down to the oxide

$$\text{Oxide} \quad \begin{array}{cccc} H & H & H & H \\ -C & -C & -C & -C- \\ H & & & H \\ & & O & \end{array}$$

and may later break completely, giving off CO_2 and H_2O.

The absorption of oxygen causes a skin to form on the surface of the oil. If the oil is spread in a thin film on a plate of glass or a sheet of steel, it changes to a tough, elastic skin. This process has been known for hundreds of years, and the change was thought to be due to the drying of the oil. It is a process of oxidation and not one of drying, but the name persists, and linseed oil and some others carrying a high percentage of unsaturated fats are known commercially as "drying oils."

The process of oxidation takes place on the surface, and the film formed does not permit oxygen to diffuse through it at all rapidly. Those who have examined a can of paint that has been opened and then allowed to stand exposed to the air know that a thick wrinkled skin forms on the surface, which protects the balance of the contents against oxidation for many weeks. If a film of oil is to dry properly, it must be very thin. Since the lower side of the film is bonded to the surface on which it is applied, the film cannot contract as it did on the liquid surface of the paint in the can, and the film will often be porous or contain fine shrinkage cracks. A second coat of oil or paint applied after the first coat has dried will likewise dry, and a third coat will add to the total thickness of the film. It is not desirable that a paint for exterior use on wood be entirely impermeable, since moisture originating within the house must have an opportunity to escape through a "breathing film."

Catalysts Promoting Oxidation. Driers.—The oxidation of linseed oil may be hastened by the incorporation of catalysts which are known as "driers." They usually consist of the soaps of lead, manganese, and sometimes cobalt. These soaps are soluble in turpentine and petroleum naphtha and may be bought under the name of "liquid driers." It will be noted that each of the metals lead, manganese, and cobalt is capable of existing in at least two states of oxidation. The theory is that the metal of the drier takes up oxygen from the air to assume its higher state of oxidation, and then passes the oxygen over to the unsaturated linkage of the oil, the metal reverting in the process to the lower form of oxidation which puts it in condition to renew the cycle.

Paint.—Paint consists of a suspension of a pigment in a vehicle consisting of a drying oil containing a drier and a thinner in solution. The drying oil is usually linseed oil, and the amount and type of the drier is determined by the use to which the paint is to be put. The thinner is a volatile compound, usually turpentine or petroleum naphtha, added to thin the paint to the desired viscosity. It evaporates rapidly, and the paint film stiffens as it disappears. A paint that is to be applied with a brush should have a different viscosity from one that is to be sprayed or into which an article is to be dipped.

The pigment is usually thought of as imparting color, but it has a much more important function in reinforcing the paint film. A film of dried linseed oil is elastic but soft. Particles of pigment reinforce the film and make it harder and more resistant to abrasion. When the oil film dries, contraction takes place and shrinkage cracks form. The particles of pigment tend to lessen these cracks just as the sand and gravel in concrete minimize shrinkage cracks. All paint pigments are ground very finely, and some of the particles are of almost colloidal dimensions, but their reinforcing action will be greater if there is graded fineness within the very fine ranges. In the manufacture of paint, the pigment and a portion of the oil must be ground together thoroughly in mills, so that the particles of the pigment will be completely wetted and dispersed in the oil. Paints are sometimes shipped in this condition of paste, which may be thinned quite readily with more oil because each particle of pigment has been already wetted with the oil.

White House Paints for Exterior Work.—Almost all light-colored paints are made by adding tinting colors to a white paint. The most important pigments for exterior use are white lead, white zinc, and titanium oxide. The white lead, which has been made for hundreds of years, is still made by corroding metallic lead with carbon dioxide in the presence of dilute acetic acid. The product is a basic carbonate. In rather recent years, a basic sulfate has been introduced which is also sold under the name of "white lead." Both forms are characterized by extreme fineness of division, good reflection of light, and good hiding power. White zinc is usually zinc oxide made by burning the vapor of zinc. Its particle size is extremely small. Zinc sulfide is also used, and a precipitated mixture of zinc sulfide on an inert base such as barium sulfate finds wide use under the name "lithopone." Titanium oxide has been introduced more recently and has probably the greatest brightness and hiding power of any of the pigments.

There are other pigments used in a minor amount called "inerts" or "extenders." They consist of crystalline minerals such as silica, talc, asbestine, mica, and barium sulfate which are finely ground, but still are much coarser than white lead or white zinc. The coarser particles reinforce the paint film and prevent cracking of the film on aging.

An old formula for repainting outside woodwork calls for 100 lb white lead, 2 gal linseed oil, 2 gal turpentine, and 1 pt of drier. This will make 7 gal of paint which should cover about 4200 sq ft with one coat. Three coats of paint are usually used on new work, an interval of several days being allowed between coats to permit the preceding coat to dry thoroughly. Each coat has, after drying, a thickness of 0.001 to 0.002 in.

House paints for outside use were formerly made exclusively from white lead and linseed oil. White lead favors the formation of a rather soft oil film which disintegrates at the surface and "chalks," leaving the paint below it in good condition. White zinc on the other hand forms a harder film which tends to "flake" or spring completely off of the wood in spots leaving the bare board showing. Modern practice favors a mixture of pigments for outside work, with the larger proportion white lead and a minor amount of white zinc and titanium oxide.

The effectiveness of various paints and varnishes in resisting damp air is shown in Table 74 embodying data gathered by the Forest Products Laboratory. Linseed oil alone is surprisingly ineffective, one coat receiving a rating of only 3 and three coats 21. The incorporation of white lead raised these ratings to 19 for one coat and 73 for three coats. When lead and zinc were both incorporated, the corresponding values became 33 and 74.

An exterior paint fails, in part, because of the increasing brittleness of the film as it gets older. No paint film is entirely waterproof, and the wood expands and contracts with changes in moisture, causing cracks to form in the embrittled film. Oxidation also takes place in the outer layers of the film, especially where it is exposed to sunlight, with the linseed oil ultimately becoming oxidized to carbon dioxide and water.

If ordinary paint is exposed continuously to water as on the bottom of a boat, the oil will hydrolyze and the film will lose its

TABLE 74.—EFFECTIVENESS OF ONE, TWO, AND THREE COATS OF DIFFERENT PAINTS, MEASURED AGAINST EXPOSURE TO DAMP AIR FOR ONE WEEK*

Description of paint	Effectiveness rating in per cent for—		
	1 coat	2 coats	3 coats
Paste aluminum in Bakelite varnish	75	92	94
2 lb dry aluminum in 1 gal Bakelite varnish	34	88	95
1 lb dry aluminum in 1 gal Bakelite varnish	12	77	90
2 lb dry aluminum in 1 gal ester-gum varnish	6	61	90
Aluminum in white-lead linseed-oil paint	9	58	72
White-lead linseed-oil paint	19	63	73
Lead and zinc linseed-oil paint	33	71	74
Titanox and zinc linseed-oil paint	24	65	70
Lithopone and zinc linseed-oil paint	32	73	75
Indian-red linseed-oil paint	23	53	56
Red-lead linseed-oil paint	19	56	67
Asbestine in linseed oil	7	37	55
White lead in Bakelite paint oil	65	86	91
White lead in 75-gal ester-gum varnish	3	62	83
Bakelite varnish	12	49	73
75-gal ester-gum varnish	5	14	35
Linseed oil	3	5	21

* BROWNE, F. L.: *Paint, Oil and Chem. Rev.*, Sept. 7, 1933.

toughness. Copper or mercuric oxide are sometimes incorporated in marine paints to poison algae and barnacles that tend to grow on the bottoms of boats.

White House Paints for Interior Work.—House paints for interior work are not exposed to the ultraviolet rays of the sun, and the wood on which they are applied is not subject to volume changes like the boards on the outside of houses. Interior paint does not therefore need to be as elastic as that for exterior use. It should, however, be hard and very white, and therefore zinc and titanium pigments and especially lithopone which is a complex zinc sulfide-barium sulfate pigment are used extensively.

Oil Varnishes.—It has been known for hundreds of years that some hard resins could be melted when heated and then dissolved in hot linseed oil. Longer cooking polymerized or bodied the oil, and the clear solution, after cooling somewhat, was thinned with turpentine to form a transparent varnish. Varnish of this type is similar to a paint in that it contains linseed oil, a thinner, and usually a drier. The pigment has, however, been replaced by a resin that is either in true solution or colloidal suspension, and the linseed oil has been polymerized by heat so that its properties have been changed materially from those of the paint oil. The film that is formed is more elastic and resists water better than a paint film does.

Varnish Resins.—The type of resin with which most of us are familiar is that which is present in the knots of a freshly sawed board from one of the coniferous trees. This fresh resin is a sticky material with an aromatic odor. An extensive industry in the Southern states involves tapping the pine trees and collecting the thick sticky oleoresin. This thick material is put in a copper still and distilled in an atmosphere of steam. Turpentine goes off as vapor with the steam and is condensed. The residue in the still is run out while still molten and hardens to form the ordinary rosin of commerce. This is too soft and "tacky" to make good varnish but may be improved by chemical treatment. The resins that the older varnish makers used came from the tropics as lumps of hard semitransparent material. Some of them had been in the ground so long that the types of trees which formed them had disappeared from the earth, and insects that had been trapped in the fresh resin likewise belonged to a past era. These "fossil" resins or "gums" gave harder and more brilliant films than the ordinary rosin. They came on the market under a variety of trade names with "kauri" and "copal" as common terms. When these gums became scarce and high priced, the ordinary rosin was modified chemically to improve its properties. Recently, entirely new types of synthetic resins with superior properties have been introduced. Some description of these will be given in the next chapter.

Boiled or Polymerized Varnish Oils.—If linseed or other drying oil is slowly heated to a temperature of 500°F, the oil commences to bubble as it gets hot, owing in part to small amounts of water being driven off as steam, and in larger part to the destructive distillation of minute particles of vegetable tissues present in the oil. These reactions give the appearance of boiling. This process has been practiced by varnish makers for hundreds of years, and the product is still known by the name of "boiled oil," which they gave to it. The oil becomes more viscous the longer the heating is continued, because of polymerization. In case air is permitted to pass over or is blown through the oil, a more rapid thickening occurs because oxidation takes place as well as polymerization. The boiled oil used by varnish makers is usually heated as described above, but that used in paints is frequently only heated to 150°F with added driers and with some air blown through the oil to accelerate the oxidation.

Old-style Varnishes.—About 100 to 125 lb of the varnish resin was placed in a large copper kettle and heated to a temperature of 550 to 650°F. It lost 10 to 25 per cent of its weight and became liquid during the process. Hot boiled oil was added to the molten resin, and the heating was continued for several hours until the mixture was completely homogeneous. It will be understood that not only was the resin becoming dissolved in the oil, but also the oil was polymerizing during the cooking process so that the time and temperature of cooking were very important. When the mixture had cooked enough, it was cooled somewhat, and then thinned with turpentine or petroleum naphtha, the proper amount of drier being added towards the end of the thinning process.

The properties of the finished varnish were influenced strongly by the amount of oil added. A furniture varnish should be hard and glossy and should not get sticky when rubbed with a fine abrasive to smooth the surface for subsequent coats of varnish. Such a varnish was made with a minimum amount of linseed oil (6 to 10 gal per 100 pounds of resin). On the other hand, varnishes for outside exposure, and especially "spar" varnishes for use on ships, carried a great deal of oil (25 to 30 gal per 100 lb of resin) and were called "long-oil varnishes." The type of resin, the kind of drying oil, and the method of cooking all caused variations in the properties of the varnish so that a single manufacturer of varnish might have many hundred formulas.

Enamels.—When a pigment is ground in varnish or in a viscous-bodied oil instead of unheated linseed oil, the resultant film is harder and more glossy than a paint film. Such products, termed "enamels," have been much used for steel beds, and other furniture where the original color of the surface was to be changed. Sometimes the drying of the varnish was accelerated by gentle heat, but the natural resins used in these enamels would not stand the temperatures used for baking japans, nor those used for the varnishes containing the modern synthetic resins.

Spirit Varnishes. Shellac.—Shellac occurs in the crude state as a scale exuded by the lac insect on the twigs of trees growing, especially, in China. It dissolves in alcohol to form a colloidal solution which hardens rapidly through solution of the volatile solvent. If an oil varnish is applied to an untreated board, it will soak in and be lost. If the board has first been given a coat of shellac, the particles of shellac will have filled the surface pores, and the oil varnish will remain on the surface and give a lustrous film. Other resins may also be used in spirit varnishes, but shellac is the most important. Spirit varnishes become hard as soon as the solvent has evaporated, and a coating of an oil varnish may be applied over shellac in an hour after the shellac was applied to the board.

Protection of Steel Against Corrosion.—The causes of the corrosion of steel and its protection by metallic coatings have been discussed in Chap. XVI. Bacteria and other living organisms do not play an important role with steel as they do with wood. The three factors simultaneously present in almost all cases where steel is corroded are oxygen, moisture, and slight acidity.

The function of a paint or varnish on steel is to retard the penetration of moisture and to lessen the rate at which oxygen and acid gases like CO_2 and SO_2 diffuse to the steel. No paint or varnish is absolutely nonporous, so that access of corrosive materials can only be retarded and not prevented. Some pigments exert a greater protective action then others, and it is of first importance that the protective coating be applied to a surface that is clean and dry.

Cleaning Steel.—It was stated in the chapter on Corrosion that spots of rust or scale accelerated corrosion through the formation of concentration cells. If paint is applied over rust spots, it will not stop the rusting, because enough oxygen and moisture will diffuse through the paint film to continue the corrosion. Steel sheets and shapes that have been hot-rolled are cleaned from mill scale by a bath of hot acid, sometimes aided by electrolytic action. The acid and loosened scale are removed by a jet of hot water, followed sometimes by a bath of hydrated lime which after drying leaves a loose coating of hydrated lime or calcium carbonate, which tends to prevent corrosion during the interval before paint is applied.

Sheets that are cold-rolled or are pressed cold, like those forming automobile bodies, are freed from scale before the final forming operations and are then coated with grease to facilitate the slipping of the metal of the dies. This grease may be removed by petroleum solvents or by a shower of hot alkaline cleansing solution. This solution usually contains sodium carbonate, trisodium phosphate, or caustic soda. The cleaned metal is finally treated with a solution containing phosphoric acid which forms an adherent film of complex phosphates of iron, protecting the surface from rust and giving a surface to which paint will adhere better than it will to the smooth steel. When an old structure like a steel bridge is to be repainted, the surface should be cleaned with wire brushes or preferably a sand blast, which grinds off the old paint and any rust to leave clean metal. Steel should never be painted while it is wet, because the film of moisture will prevent the adherence of the paint to the steel.

Paints for Steel.—Paints for steel have as a basis linseed oil or other drying oil, a pigment, a thinner, and a drier just like those for wood. A paint for outside woodwork made with a white-lead pigment is a good paint for steel, although other pigments are considered better. Pigments to be avoided are those which may carry acids. Some iron oxide pigments are made by roasting ferric sulfate and contain some residual acid, but some iron oxide pigments are inert and are used in large quantities in painting steel freight cars. Some carbon blacks likewise stimulate corrosion, but others are safe. The most widely used pigments for steel paint are all oxidizing and all happen to be bright orange or red in color. The pigment most commonly used is red lead, whose formula is given as Pb_3O_4, although in practice it consists of a mixture of oxides of lead. Perhaps even better but more expensive are the chromates of lead and zinc. It is possible that these pigments inhibit corrosion by forming a thin protective film of oxide of iron on the steel.

Specifications for structural steel usually require that the fabricating mill shall clean the steel and give it two coats of red lead and linseed oil. After the steel has been erected, the new rivets must be painted, and so the whole of the structure is repainted. This last coat does not need to be red lead, and a different color is frequently adopted to facilitate inspection. When a structure like a bridge begins to show the red color of the undercoats, it is a sign that the outside layer is gone and that it is time to repaint. If the undercoats are in good condition, it will not be necessary to remove them by sand blasting.

Aluminum as a Pigment.—When metallic aluminum is powdered in a stamping mill, it forms very small and thin flakes. When these particles are incorporated in boiled linseed oil or a varnish, they tend to rise to the surface and arrange themselves as overlapping scales, which afford a high degree of protection to the surface on which the coating is applied. The microscopic structure of such a film is shown in Fig. 193. The data of

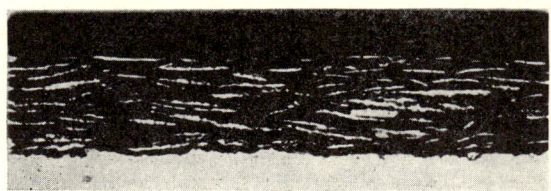

FIG. 193.—Microscopic structure of section of aluminum paint film. ×500. Two coats of paint made with aluminum paste pigment and a Bakelite resin base varnish were applied on a piece of aluminum. The white area below the paint film is the metal which was painted. The surface of the paint film is indicated by the top line of aluminum flakes. (*From J. D. Edwards, Aluminum Research Laboratories.*)

Table 74 show that a 75-gal ester-gum varnish has an effectiveness rating against moisture of 5 for one coat, 14 for two, and 35 for three coats. The incorporation of 2 lb of dry aluminum into 1 gal of the ester-gum varnish raises its effectiveness rating to 6 for one coat, 61 for two, and 90 for three coats. These figures are somewhat better than those given in the same table for white lead in this same type of varnish.

Aluminum has a good reflective power, and aluminum paint is extensively used on oil tanks and other structures exposed to the sun where the temperature should be kept as low as is feasible.

Baking Japans.—Although most asphalts are soft and sticky, there are some that are hard and may be used in place of the usual varnish resins. These hard asphalts are melted, cooked with one of the drying oils, and thinned to make an asphalt varnish. The glossy black coating used 20 years ago on the steel fenders of automobiles was obtained by dipping them in this asphalt varnish and then passing them through a baking oven at a temperature of 400 to 500°F. The thinner evaporated quickly, the asphalt melted, and the drying oil oxidized while the fender was passing through the oven so that after it emerged from the oven and had cooled it was covered with a hard, glossy surface which gave good protection. This type of coating was only possible with asphalts, because the old varnish resins would not stand the heat of the baking oven. The introduction of synthetic resins has, in recent years, permitted a baked finish to be produced in colors.

Lacquers.—A lacquer consists mainly of cellulose nitrate, sometimes called "collodion" or simply "soluble cotton." In the process of manufacture, purified cotton or wood pulp is treated with concentrated nitric and sulfuric acids under controlled conditions to form a nitrate which is then purified carefully. The thick liquid that is bought in tubes at drugstores for the protection of cuts and abrasions on the skin is a solution of cellulose nitrate. The solvents are sometimes alcohol and ether, but in the industrial lacquers they are complicated mixtures which are carefully formulated. The cellulose nitrate itself gave too brittle a film, and so nonvolatile "plasticizers" had to be added. Pigments were mixed with the thick solution, and the finished lacquer was sprayed onto the prepared steel surface. The solvent evaporated rapidly, and the film became hard as soon as the solvent was gone. Lacquer does not adhere well to steel, and so one or more primer coats of varnish were necessary before the lacquer was applied. Several coats of lacquer were necessary with a sanding process between each coat.

Finishing Automobile Bodies.—In the days when automobiles had wooden bodies, the wood was coated with paint and then with varnish. Ten coats were sometimes applied, with hand rubbing following the application of several of the coats. It required about a month to finish a body, and acres of floor space were required for the storage of the bodies set aside to dry. About 1920, improvements were made in the formulation of lacquers which permitted them to supplant the older varnishes.

More recently, some of the synthetic resins have been incorporated into enamels which dry to a smooth coat while baking at about 250°F. These finishes dry so rapidly that a body may be competely finished in 2 hr instead of the month that was required 20 years ago. The modern finishes are not only cheaper but much superior to the old product. They will be discussed somewhat in the next chapter.

The Disintegration of Concrete.—The disintegration of concrete which has been properly mixed, placed, and hardened is due mainly to changes in volume caused by differences in content of moisture, with formation of ice as a factor of great influence in the final stages of disintegration. The effect of temperature is minor compared with the effect of moisture. The effect of chemicals is of importance in a rather small number of cases. Structures of well-made concrete may be considered to be permanent so long as they are continuously wet or continuously dry. Concrete that is exposed alternately to dry and moist conditions is very likely to go to pieces for the reasons outlined in Chap. XX.

The best method of protecting concrete from disintegration is to prevent large fluctuations in its water content. Concrete that is constantly damp, as in deep foundations, needs no protection unless in contact with corrosive waters. Concrete that is continually dry, as in reinforced concrete buildings, needs no protection.

Asphalt Coatings for Concrete.—Asphalt is a viscous black hydrocarbon which is inert chemically and is found in nature, and may also be manufactured from petroleum. Pitch obtained by the distillation of coal tar has similar properties. The softening point and viscosity of these materials are always adjusted by mixing different grades of asphalt and incorporating solvents. Both asphalt and pitch shrink and get more brittle in cold weather, and tend to soften in hot weather. A coating of asphalt may crack in winter, and the cracks may heal themselves in summer. Although asphalts do not absorb oxygen like linseed oil, they do slowly oxidize and become more brittle.

Asphalt on Concrete Pavements.—Hot asphalt, sometimes thinned by a volatile solvent, is frequently sprinkled on old concrete pavements as a coat about $\frac{1}{8}$ in. in thickness. It flows into large cracks and covers fine cracks. A layer of coarse sand or fine gravel is thrown on the film of asphalt while it is still soft, and traffic may then be allowed to proceed as usual.

The pressure of the tires forces the sand and gravel into the asphalt and stiffens the coat. After a few days of traffic, the excess gravel may be swept off. A coating of this sort, renewed every year or two, will prevent the expansion and contraction of the concrete due to seasonal moisture and will make the life of the pavement a long one. The asphalt is sometimes made an important part of the new pavement instead of being merely a surface coating of an old one. A concrete base is covered with a mixture of prepared asphalt, sand, and fine gravel applied hot and rolled into place with heavy pressure. This sheet asphalt may be 2 in. thick and protects the concrete base very effectually. It will crack in winter and will need minor repairs every spring.

Asphalt Membrane Coatings for Roofs and Cellar Walls.—A concrete foundation is usually watertight when it is new. After the building has been completed and the cellar has dried out, shrinkage cracks form. A coating of asphalt paint is sometimes applied on the outside of the wall before the dirt is filled back, but this coating is not thick enough or elastic enough to bridge cracks.

Concrete roofs also crack as they dry out and require thorough waterproofing. The membrane method as applied to roofs and cellar walls uses sheets of felt that have been previously saturated with asphalt or pitch by their manufacturer. The concrete roof is swabbed with hot asphalt and is at once covered with overlapping sheets of the felt. More asphalt is swabbed on this, and a second and then often a third layer of the asphalt and felt is applied. More asphalt is swabbed on the top, and gravel is then spread over the whole surface to provide a top coat resistant to cuts and scuffing of feet. The concrete acts merely as the physical support for the membrane consisting of three coats of felt and four of asphalt. This membrane is elastic enough to bridge any shrinkage crack which may appear in the roof.

Oil Paints on Concrete and Plastered Walls.—It will be recalled that linseed oil and other drying oils are esters of glycerin and various fats acids and that they are saponified by alkalies like caustic soda. Hydrated lime is also an alkali and can saponify linseed oil slowly. A wall that has been recently plastered with lime plaster will contain calcium hydroxide. Reference to Chap. XX will show that calcium hydroxide is one of the products formed during the hydration of portland cement. If paint is applied to a surface of concrete, or a wall that has been stuccoed with lime mortar, and which is exposed to the weather, enough hydrated lime may be present at the wall surface to saponify the paint. The soap does not possess the elasticity of the oil film, and so the paint peels off. If paint is applied to an interior wall that is quite dry, no saponification may be noted. Sometimes three walls of a room show paint in good condition, whereas the fourth wall, whose outer surface is exposed to the weather, will have permitted enough moisture to penetrate to allow saponification of the paint. After a plastered wall has been exposed to the air for about a year, the hydrated lime will all have changed to the carbonate and it may be painted safely. Concrete ceilings and floors in heated buildings may also be painted after a year. Cellar floors, walls, and outside concrete work will cause saponification of paint for several years.

Some of the modern products using synthetic resins which are described in the next chapter are not subject to saponification and may be applied directly to concrete even when it is quite fresh.

Soaps as Integral Waterproofing for Concrete.—Soaps do not possess sufficient elasticity to be used as paints. They may, however, be added to the concrete mixer and thus incorporated as a fine suspension in the concrete. If a solution of sodium soap is used, it will react with the hydrated lime set free as the cement sets to form a suspension of fine particles of the calcium soap, with caustic soda as a by-product. Ammonium soap is better, in that the ammonium hydroxide formed is volatile. Suspensions of calcium and aluminum soaps are added in small amounts—less than 1 lb of the soap to 100 lb of cement—and are effective in interrupting the passage of water by capillary action because of their water-repellent action. It is well known that water will rise in a clean capillary tube but not in one whose capillary is greasy. Insoluble soaps will not be effective in preventing the passage of water through concrete which has large pores, nor which contains large cracks. Asphalt may be dispersed in the concrete to give a similar effect, but soaps have the advantage over asphalt in that they are colorless. If a soap should be incorporated in the concrete used for a cellar wall or floor, it would be an effective waterproofing provided no cracks formed.

Cement containing integral waterproofing must be kept damp for at least 28 days before it is permitted to dry out. Ordinary concrete will become damp when it comes in contact with water and will resume the hardening process. Waterproofed concrete will not absorb moisture readily after it has once become dried, and so must be permitted to gain as much strength as is needed before it loses its initial moisture.

References

HUNT and GARRATT: Wood Preservation, 1st ed., McGraw-Hill Book Company, Inc., New York, 1938.

ABRAHAM, HERBERT: Asphalts and Allied Substances, 4th ed., D. Van Nostrand Company, Inc., New York, 1938.

SABIN, A. H.: Technology of Paint and Varnish, 2d ed., John Wiley & Sons, Inc., New York, 1917.

TOCH, M.: The Chemistry and Technology of Paints, 3d ed., D. Van Nostrand Company, Inc., New York, 1925.

HOLTON, E. C.: Paints, Varnishes and Lacquers Show Many Advances, Silver Anniversary Volume American Institute of Chemical Engineers, Chap. XIV, D. Van Nostrand Company, Inc., New York, 1933.

GARDNER, H. A.: Paint Researches and Their Practical Application, Judd and Detweiler, Washington, D. C., 1917.

GARDNER, H. A.: Paint Technology and Tests, McGraw-Hill Book Company, Inc., New York, 1911.

Symposium on Paint and Paint Materials, American Society for Testing Materials, Philadelphia, 1935.

WHITE and BATEMAN: Soaps as Integral Waterproofings for Concrete, *Proc. Am. Concrete Inst.*, **22**, 535 (1926).

Symposium on Correlation between Accelerated Laboratory Tests and Service Tests on Protective and Decorative Coatings, American Society for Testing Materials, Philadelphia, 1937.

Symposium on the Outdoor Weathering of Metals and Metallic Coatings, American Society for Testing Materials, Philadelphia, 1934.

WILSON, S. P.: Pyroxylin Enamels and Lacquers, 2d ed., D. Van Nostrand Company, Inc., New York, 1927.

BROWN and CRAWFORD: A Survey of Nitrocellulose Lacquer, Reinhold Publishing Corporation, New York, 1928.

ZIMMER and CAMERON: Nitrocellulose Ester Lacquer, D. Van Nostrand Company, Inc., New York, 1934.

CHAPTER XXIV

PLASTICS AND RELATED PRODUCTS

Properties of Plastics.—A material that is in the plastic state deforms when a small stress is applied, and continues to deform as long as the same stress is applied. An elastic material deforms slightly with a small stress, but stiffens and does not deform further, even if the small stress continues to act upon it for an indefinite time. Wet clay and soft putty are instances of plastic substances, and steel and glass at room temperatures are instances of elastic substances. Steel and glass are elastic at room temperatures, but if they are heated to a bright red heat, they both become plastic. The materials that have become of great importance in recent years and are called "plastics" are not plastic at the temperature at which they are used. They are plastic during the molding stage, which takes place at temperatures up to 400°F, but are fairly elastic at room temperatures. The use of the word plastics is therefore purely conventional because, strictly speaking, glass and a modern plastic like cellulose acetate behave alike, except that glass must be heated to a much higher temperature before it becomes plastic.

The materials to which we usually give the name of plastics are all organic chemicals, made up of carbon, hydrogen, oxygen, and nitrogen, with sulfur, chlorine, and other elements sometimes playing important roles. Metals and minerals are conspicuous by their absence except as they may be incorporated mechanically as inert aggregates. Some of these plastics, like asphalt and shellac, are natural products which have been known for hundreds of years. Some of them, like hard rubber and celluloid, start with materials occurring in nature. The chemist found means of modifying these substances nearly a century ago to form valuable products, and further knowledge has improved their quality. Most of the plastics are synthetic products unknown in nature, and developed by man within the last generation.

TABLE 75.—IMPORTANT CHARACTERISTICS AND FIELDS OF USE OF PLASTICS*

Plastic	Principal characteristics determining fields of use	Important and typical uses
A. Sheeting used as such		
Pyroxylin	Toughness, transparency, colorability	Safety glass interlayer, heel covering, advertising novelties
Cellulose acetate	Toughness, transparency, colorability, nonflammability	Safety glass interlayer, lamp shades, transparent containers, playing cards
Ethyl cellulose	Toughness, transparency, colorability, nonflammability	(Uses not yet established)
Polymethyl methacrylate	Rigidity, superior clearness and colorability	Panes, screens, illuminating accessories, decorative articles
Polyvinyl acetals	Toughness, clearness	Safety glass interlayer
Phenol-formaldehyde, laminated	Rigidity, resistance to heat, water, solvents and chemical influences, durability, strength, electrical properties	Architectural paneling, table tops, counters, bars, gear wheels, electrical equipment
Urea-formaldehyde, laminated	Rigidity, colorability, translucency	Architectural paneling, illuminating accessories
B. Sheets, rods, tubes and other primary shapes from which articles are fabricated by machining		
Pyroxylin	Toughness, colorability, ease of machining	Combs and other toiletware, fountain pens
Polymethylmethacrylate	Rigidity, superior clearness and colorability, ease of machining	Costume jewelry, buttons, ornaments, umbrella handles, illuminating accessories
Phenol-formaldehyde, cast	Rigidity, clearness, color ability, ease of machining, resistance to solvents and chemicals	Costume jewelry, handles, buttons, hardware
Casein	Low cost, ease of machining, colorability, ease of staining and polishing	Buttons, buckles, game pieces, novelties
C. Sheets, rods, tubes from which articles are fabricated by die pressing, swaging, blowing		
Pyroxylin	Toughness, colorability, ease of fabrication	Toothbrush handles, dice, typewriter keys, boxes, toys, novelties
D. Molding compounds		
Cellulose acetate	Toughness, colorability, ease of molding by compression or injection	Automobile hardware, pens and pencils, costume jewelry and ornaments
Ethyl cellulose	Toughness, colorability, compatibility with modifiers	(Uses not yet established)
Polymethyl methacrylate	Superior clearness and colorability, water resistance, permanence of dimensions	Containers, ornaments, costume jewelry, hardware, illuminating accessories, lenses
Shellac (filled)	Low cost, ease of molding	Sound records, insulation
Phenol-formaldehyde: Filled	Low cost, ease of molding, resistance to heat, solvents and chemicals	Electrical insulating parts, distributor heads, radio tube bases, telephone hand set, housings, containers, closures, ash trays
Unfilled	Same as for filled, and availability in transparent colors	(Uses not yet established)
Urea-formaldehyde (filled)	Resistance to heat, translucency, colorability	Housings, containers, illuminating accessories, tableware, kitchenware
Phenol-furfural (filled)	Similar to those of phenol-formaldehyde	Similar to those of phenol-formaldehyde
Polyvinyl esters	Ease of molding, colorability	Sound records, surfacing of metal panels
Polystyrene	Electrical properties, suitability for injection molding, moisture resistance	Small electrical insulating parts
Cold-molded	Low cost, adaptability to cheap process of molding, heat-resistance	Electrical accessories

* From RANDOLPH, A. F., A.S.T.M. Symposium on Plastics, p. 2, 1938.

General Properties and Uses of Plastics.—Plastics have a lower density than any metal, those which have organic fillers incorporated having a density of 1.1 to 1.5 and those with large amounts of inorganic filler a density rising to 2.0. Comparison may be made with magnesium whose density is 1.738. The coefficients of thermal expansion of the plastics are high compared with the metals, and allowance must be made for shrinkage in designing the molds. The plastics have low thermal conductivity, and this makes them desirable for objects that are to be grasped by the hand when they are much above or below body temperature. Almost all plastics are good electrical insulators.

The important characteristics and fields of use of many plastics are given in Table 75.

Thermoplastic and Heat-hardening Resins.—A thermoplastic material is one that softens when heated and hardens when cooled, and retains this property for an indefinite number of cycles. Asphalt and shellac belong in this class, as well as many of the newer synthetic materials.

A thermo-setting or heat-hardening resin is one that softens when heated for the first time, but undergoes a chemical change while in the hot state, so that it changes to a substance that will no longer soften when reheated to its previous softening temperature or even a much higher temperature. Some of these hardened resins can be heated without softening to a temperature at which they become charred.

Bituminous Plastics.—The use of bituminous materials as protective coverings for concrete roofs and roadways has been discussed in the previous chapter. The most important molded asphaltic products are the boxes that contain the storage batteries of the automobile. They are made from asphalts of a suitable softening point which are mixed hot with diatomaceous earth and asbestos and then molded, becoming hard and strong on cooling. Cold-molded bituminous plastics are made from asbestos fibers wetted with a solution of asphalt in a volatile solvent like benzene. The solvent is allowed to evaporate until the proper consistency is reached, and then the material is pressed into shape. The solvent is driven off by gentle heat which also softens the asphaltic mixture. Asphalt is the cheapest of the plastics. Its use is restricted by the color, the rather low strength, and the low softening point. It is thermoplastic, and may be repeatedly softened by heat and hardened by cooling.

Shellac.—The use of shellac varnish as a priming coat for wood before the application of an oil varnish has been discussed in the previous chapter. The shellac resin itself is thermoplastic and softens enough at 150°F to be molded readily. It has been used as the material from which phonograph disks were pressed almost from the beginning of that industry. Grinding wheels were made from granular abrasives bonded with shellac, but the low softening point and low tensile strength of the shellac were

FIG. 194.—High-speed abrasive wheel bonded with a phenolic resin. (*Courtesy Bakelite Corporation.*)

serious disadvantages, and grinding wheels are now bonded with synthetic resins. The grinding wheel illustrated in Fig. 194 with its high speed and heavy duty could never have been made with anything but a synthetic resin as a bonding agent. Paper coated with shellac, and mica flakes impregnated with shellac and pressed into sheets were much used as electrical insulating materials, but have been largely replaced by synthetic resins.

Casein Plastics.—When milk becomes sour, the curd that separates is largely casein. A product that is quite similar may be separated from the meal of the soya bean after the oil has been extracted. Casein is a protein, a complex structure containing amino (NH_2) groups which are capable of reacting with formaldehyde somewhat as urea [$CO(NH_2)_2$] can. The plastic takes dyes readily and is produced in rods or sheets which can be turned or machined easily and which can be pressed into simple shapes. Casein plastics find their principal use in buttons, buckles, and other ornamental articles, for which their attractive appearance, bright colors, and workability make them especially adapted.

Phenolic Resins.—In 1909, Dr. L. H. Baekeland announced the successful manufacture of a synthetic heat-hardening resin which he named Bakelite. One raw material was phenol (C_6H_5OH), a derivative of benzene (C_6H_6) and a material known to the layman because of its use as a germicide in the fields of medicine and sanitary science. The second raw material was formaldehyde (CH_2O), derived from methanol, a gas with an acrid odor appearing in commerce as a 40 per cent solution containing some methanol. These two materials will combine if heated together in the presence of proper catalysts and will continue to form larger complexes, the longer the heating and the higher the temperature. The chemistry of the process is complicated and will not be discussed here. Both of the raw materials are quite soluble in water. As the reaction proceeds, a liquid product is formed, which has slight solubility in water. Further reaction produces a resin, solid at room temperatures but softening at somewhat higher temperatures. Still further heating, under pressure to prevent the formation of gas bubbles, causes the formation of a hard and strong resin which does not fuse even if it is heated so hot that it commences to char. The products form a continuous series from the oily liquid to the hard, infusible solid so that many different grades of commercial products are possible. Other aldehydes, especially furfurol, and modified phenols have come into use.

The commercial resin is, in general, an intermediate product which is solid when cold but softens when hot. It comes on the market as a powder with which mineral matters and fibers may be incorporated. Fabrics and paper may be dipped in a still softer product, heated somewhat, and then pressed hot into laminated sheets.

The molding of a simple ash tray is illustrated in the several pictures of Fig. 195. The proper weight of the molding powder

PLASTICS AND RELATED PRODUCTS 521

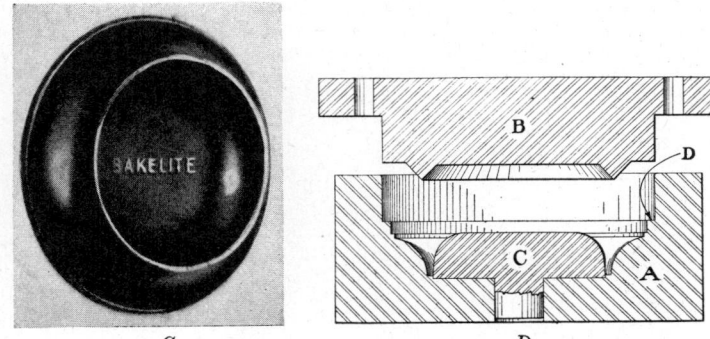

Fig. 195.—Steps in the molding of an ash tray. (*Courtesy Bakelite Corporation.*)

is compressed cold into a tablet which can be seen in the hand of the operator who is inserting it in the press. The two parts of the die are also shown in cross section at D. The molds of the press are heated to temperatures of 270 to 375°F, and after the press is closed, the molding compound is subjected to pressures from 1000 to 8000 psi. The powder first softens and is forced by the pressure into intimate contact with all parts of the mold. The temperature and pressure are maintained for 2 to 5 min, after which the press is opened and the hot moldings, now permanently hard as shown at B, are removed. The finished ash tray is shown at C. The phenolic resin without filler has a tensile strength of 6000 to 9000 psi and may be used continuously at 250°F. It has very low water absorption and is resistant to many chemicals. The introduction of a wood flour filler or a mineral filler like asbestos may raise the tensile strength to 10,000 lb and the temperature for safe continuous operation to 350°F for a filler of wood flour, and 450°F for mineral fillers. Laminated fabrics are discussed in a separate paragraph.

Urea Resins.—Urea is an amino compound [$CO(NH_2)_2$] synthesized by heating NH_3 and CO_2 under pressure. It is a crystalline compound which dissolves in and reacts with an aqueous solution of formaldehyde (CH_2O), when heated with catalysts, to form a thick liquid and later a clear, transparent, and colorless resin, whose specific gravity is about half that of glass. Products molded from the pure resin tend to crack in the dry air prevailing in American homes in the winter, but the incorporation of fillers reduces this tendency. The filled products may have the color of ivory or almost any brilliant color since dyes will unite with the resin. It is largely used for drinking glasses, dishes, and ornamental boxes for the toilet table, where lightness of weight, relative toughness, and possibility of varied color make it especially desirable. The molding process is similar to Bakelite, but lower temperatures and longer curing times are usually employed.

Pyroxylin Plastics. Celluloid.—Cellulose in the form of purified cotton or wood pulp may be nitrated through reaction with concentrated nitric and sulfuric acids to form esters of cellulose and nitric acid. The highly nitrated product is manufactured into smokeless powder for military and sporting purposes. Material not so highly nitrated can be dissolved in solvents which, on evaporation, leave a transparent film. Such films were used 75 years ago but were unsatisfactory in many ways. John W. Hyatt and his brother Isaiah discovered in 1869 that if camphor was incorporated with a special grade of cellulose nitrate (pyroxylin) in a closed mixer, then only a little volatile solvent was needed to bring the mass to a doughlike consistency. The solvent was expelled by slow drying, and the camphor remained in the product as a plasticizer. This product, called "celluloid," became plastic under moderate heat but was tough at ordinary temperatures. It was, and is, much used for such items as combs, fountain pens, and toilet articles. It can be formed by pressing hot or by machining and can be made colorless and transparent, or in light and bright colors. It was also the material used in the early manufacture of laminated safety glass, but it discolored on exposure to the ultraviolet rays of the sunlight and lost its adherence to the glass as it aged, so that it is now seldom used for this purpose.

Modern pyroxylin plastics are molded at temperatures of 185 to 250°F and under pressures of 2000 to 5000 psi. The product may not be used for continuous service much above 140°F since it is thermoplastic and commences to soften at 25 to 50° above that temperature. It must be protected from high temperatures because it decomposes with evolution of poisonous fumes of oxides of nitrogen, and burns fiercely if it catches fire. Its tensile strength at room temperature is 5000 to 10,000 psi, and its elongation varies from 10 to 40 per cent.

Cellulose Acetate.—The preceding paragraph dealt with the nitric acid esters of cellulose and mentioned as disadvantages the danger of decomposition by heat and the discoloration and brittleness caused by sunlight. There are many other acids that form esters with cellulose, but acetic acid gives the most usable commercial product. It may be dissolved in various organic solvents and extruded as a thick liquid through a small opening to form a thread which, after the evaporation of the solvent, is used in the manufacture of a superior grade of rayon. The liquid may also be flowed out as a sheet to produce a transparent film for wrapping packages. The material that remains after the evaporation of the solvent is fundamentally the same as that used for molding. The sheet that is used in safety glass is pressed between glass plates previously coated with a cement, at a temperature of 210 to 320°F and at a pressure of 500 to 5000 psi. This sheet has a tensile strength of 6000 to 11,000 psi and an elongation 20 to 55 per cent at room temperature. It is superior to pyroxylin in that it does not discolor on exposure to light, but it does become brittle at low temperatures and so loses some of its protective value in cold winter weather. Some cellulose acetate products soften at 140°F, and even with fillers, the softening temperature does not rise much above 260°F.

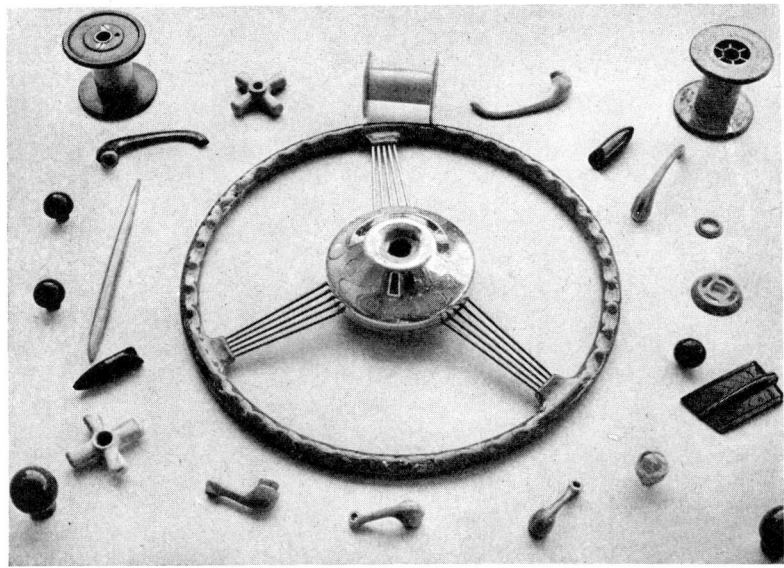

Fig. 196.—Illustrations of articles molded from cellulose acetate. (*Courtesy Thermoplastics, Inc.*)

It may be produced as transparent or as brilliantly colored products.

Various articles molded from cellulose acetate are shown in Fig. 196. The rim of the steering wheel has a core of a solid steel ring, around which the plastic has flowed so as to make a continuous coating.

Ethyl Cellulose.—Cellulose may be made to combine with an alcohol to form an ether, and that formed with ethyl alcohol has made considerable commercial progress. Its properties are somewhat similar to cellulose acetate.

Methyl Methacrylates.—Acrylic acid is a synthetic material whose formula is $CH_2=CHCOOH$. The modification that has found the greatest industrial use is the ester of this acid with methanol. The double bond in the formula indicates the possibility of polymerization, and this may be produced in varying degrees. The resins are thermoplastic, only slightly affected by aging, and have extraordinary transparency, the light transmission being between 90 and 92 per cent. The internal reflection from a highly polished surface is so perfect that it permits light to be "piped" through a polished curved rod to emerge where a frosted surface or a plane surface at right angles to the beam is encountered. The transparency, light weight, and ease of molding has made this material valuable for curved windows and other transparent parts of airplanes. It has been introduced so recently that its field of usefulness has not yet been defined.

Elastic Rubber and Hard Rubber.—Natural rubber is present as an emulsion in the milky juice or latex of various trees and plants. It may be made synthetically by polymerization of the hydrocarbon isoprene.

$$CH_2=C.CH_3.CH=CH_2$$

It is cheaper to obtain rubber from trees than it is to synthesize it, and so very little synthetic rubber is made. There are however synthetic products manufactured on a large scale that are somewhat similar to rubber but superior for certain purposes, and so find a market in spite of the higher price. Purified raw rubber becomes sticky in hot weather and brittle in cold weather. Its valuable properties become apparent after incorporation of 1 to 3 per cent sulfur and catalysts, and heating in closed molds heated by steam under about 40 lb pressure. This process, called "vulcanization" and invented by Charles Goodyear in 1839, forms the basis of all later developments in the rubber industry.

The highly elastic inner tubes and the less elastic but tough and resistant outer cases of tires for automobiles contain accelerators to hasten the reactions between the rubber and the sulfur, and antioxidants to lessen the deterioration on exposure to the air. The tires also contain mineral matter like carbon black and zinc oxide in an extremely fine state of subdivision which act as reinforcing agents somewhat as the pigment in paint and the aggregate in reinforced concrete. The tire consists of layers of cords and fabric impregnated with the proper materials, and the whole tire is assembled before it is vulcanized in a hot mold under pressure. A rubber tire is therefore a molded product, like a plastic, but its elastic properties at room temperature put it outside of the class commercially called plastics.

If about 30 per cent sulfur is incorporated into the raw rubber and the temperature of vulcanization is raised and the time increased, hard rubber is obtained. Hard rubber may be molded at pressures of 285 to 350°F under pressures of 1200 to 1800 psi. Its tensile strength is 4000 to 10,000 psi and its elongation 8 to 15 per cent. It commences to soften at temperatures of 150 to 190°F. Goodyear developed hard rubber almost as soon as he did the elastic variety, and for over 50 years it was almost the only material of the type that was available. The telephone receivers of the usual household sets were made of hard rubber until a few years ago. The newer models are molded from a phenolic resin.

Modified Rubbers.—The formula for isoprene with its two unsaturated linkages indicates the possibility of formation of polymers and isomers from rubber by heat without the use of sulfur as a vulcanizing agent. Modified rubbers prepared by various chemical processes may be molded readily at 260 to 300°F under pressures of 1200 to 1400 psi. The finished product softens at 165 to 200°F and is quite resistant to strong acids and alkalies.

Duprene.—The formula isoprene, the simple unit from which native rubber is built by nature, has been given as $CH_2=C.CH_3.-CH=CH_2$. The du Pont Company developed a product called Duprene based upon the polymerization of a related product $CH_2=C.Cl.CH=CH_2$. This product is more expensive than natural rubber but finds uses because of its special advantages. It is especially inert to the attack of hydrocarbons such as gasoline and lubricating oil and is used as a lining material for the hose through which these materials are pumped.

Thiokol.—The hydrocarbon ethylene (C_2H_4 or $CH_2=CH_2$) is available in large amounts as a constituent of the gases formed in carbonizing coal and in cracking petroleum. If it is treated with chlorine and then with a water solution of a sodium polysulfide (Na_2S_4), a plastic rubberlike material is formed, which comes on the market under the name Thiokol. This product can be compounded with sulfur and other materials and vulcanized. The vulcanized material can then be powdered and molded at 300°F into gaskets, sheets, and printing plates which are not swollen by oils nor subject to oxidation. It has a disagreeable odor which limits its uses.

Vinyl Resins.—Vinyl chloride (CH_2=$CHCl$) and vinyl acetate (CH_2=$CHOOCCH_3$) may both be polymerized to yield products varying from soft and readily soluble materials to harder but still fusible and thermoplastic resins. In making cartons for holding ice cream, or oil, the flat fiber board made from paper pulp is coated with a solution of the resin and the solvent evaporated. The container is then formed and the seam sealed by a short application of heat. In making putty for wood, the resin and solvent are mixed with wood flour to produce a plastic mass that has practically no shrinkage on drying and, after drying, may be sawed or planed like wood.

If the acetates are hydrolyzed to alcohols and condensed with formaldehyde or other aldehydes, polyvinyl acetals are formed. These resins form a desirable bonding film for safety glass since they do not become brittle in cold weather. They are affected so slightly by moisture that it is unnecessary to seal the edges of the glass plates as must be done when other plastic sheets are used. These resins may be molded at 250 to 300°F and at pressures of 1500 to 2500 psi. They soften at 130 to 160°F.

Polystyrene Resins.—Styrene is a colorless liquid hydrocarbon having the formula C_6H_5CH=CH. It polymerizes rather readily into a transparent white resin. It has a low water-absorption value and an extremely low power factor which has made it especially valuable to manufacturers of radio and television sets. It is a thermoplastic resin and may be molded at 220 to 275°F under a pressure of 1000 to 5000 psi. Its tensile strength is 5500 to 8500 psi, and the elongation is about 1.0 per cent. Its softening point is 190 to 250°F.

Methods of Shaping Plastics.—The plastics may be divided into groups according to the method used to fabricate articles from them.[1]

[1] RANDOLPH, A. F., American Society for Testing Materials, Symposium on Plastics, p. 2, 1938.

1. Molding compounds which consist of separate particles that can be welded or fused together by heat and pressure to form a continuous mass having the shape of the mold cavity.

2. Die-pressing compounds which do not form homogeneous masses through welding of separate particles but are furnished in the form of sheets or blanks that can be shaped by heat and pressure.

3. Plastics which are shaped by machining and not by molding.

The molding compounds consisting of an intimate mechanical mixture of a resin together with fillers, dyes, and any other materials are frequently preformed without heat into pills or tablets of the correct weight to make the article being molded. The pressman places one tablet in each mold and closes his press, which is already hot. The resin softens and flows into the crevices of the mold and around any metallic inserts that may have been placed in the mold. In case a heat-hardening resin is being used, the articles may be removed from the press while they are still hot since they are permanently hard.

In injection molding, a thermoplastic material is softened in a heated cylinder and a measured portion of the soft and flowable mass is forced through a nozzle into a die which is cold or only slightly warm. The mold is filled almost instantly, and being at a temperature below the softening point of the plastic, absorbs heat rapidly, causing the article to cool and harden quickly so that it can be ejected from the mold within a few seconds after its formation. The steering wheel illustrated in Fig. 196 was produced by an injection process.

Cast Phenolic Resins.—If the reaction between phenol and formaldehyde is allowed to take place under carefully controlled conditions, a thick syrupy liquid results which is almost ready to form a gel. This liquid may be poured into lead molds and heated in closed ovens for 4 to 12 days until the resin reaches the proper hardness, when the finished casting is ready for removal from the mold.

Cold-molded Resins.—The cold-molding process uses as its basic materials a large proportion of asbestos mixed with a solution of asphalt or resin, with the addition frequently of a drying oil. The plastic mass coming from the mixer must be quite stiff or must be made stiffer by evaporation of the solvent. Just as in the manufacture of dry-pressed brick the clay had to feel barely damp as it went into the press, so in this process there must be so much asbestos, 80 per cent, and so little of the viscous liquid that the material may be molded under pressures as high as 25,000 psi to give a dense and strong product, which is usually finished by heating up to 200°F to eliminate the last of the solvent, melt the resin, and oxidize the drying oil. The great value of these products lies in their resistance to heat. It is stated that some of them can be used continuously at temperatures up to 1300°F, but if that is the case, the organic binder

FIG. 197.—Gears made of laminated phenolic resin. (*Courtesy Bakelite Corporation.*)

must have been burned away, and left only the compressed asbestos. The improvements in the phenolic resins have made the cold-molded resins less important than formerly.

Laminated Products.—It has been mentioned that the phenolic resins, during their manufacturing process, pass from the state of a thick liquid to a solid which fuses quite readily, but which at higher temperatures become hard and completely infusible. Paper, canvas, and thin strips of wood may be impregnated with the liquid and the impregnated sheets united by heat and pressure into a mass that is tougher and more elastic than other

530 ENGINEERING MATERIALS

forms of the resin. It finds an important use in gears where quietness of operation is important. A group of laminated gears is illustrated in Fig. 197.

The cellular structure of wood makes it a strong and light structural material when it is dry. It absorbs water readily, and swells and warps. Plywood is made by cementing together thin sheets of wood, with the grain of the various layers running at different angles to limit warping as much as possible. The

Fig. 198.—Comparative water resistance of laminated wood panels. The three samples at the left were bonded with glue and those at the right with phenolic resin. (*Courtesy Haskelite Manufacturing Corporation.*)

older animal and vegetable glues were themselves affected by water, but the use of synthetic resins in a cement applied like a varnish and cured under pressure has resulted in products of increased strength and lightness, which are almost completely impervious to water.

The illustration of Fig. 198 shows the results of alternate wetting and drying on plywood panels bonded with three different cementing agents. The three panels at the left, bonded with glue, separated as shown after a single cycle of soaking in water for 16 hr and drying in air at 150°F for 8 hr. The next three panels are bonded with a type of adhesive sometimes called "water resistant." The plies commenced to separate as shown in the picture after three cycles of wetting and drying. The three panels on the right were bonded with a phenol-formaldehyde cement. The photograph shows no separation of these plies although the panels had been subjected to 16 cycles of the alternate wet and dry treatment.

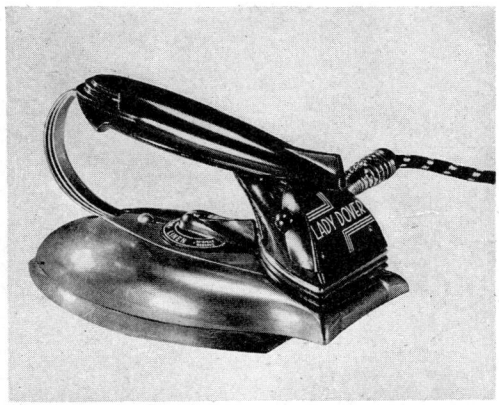

Fig. 199.—Phenolic resin improves domestic flat iron and ignition coil case for automobile. (*Courtesy Bakelite Corporation.*)

Plastics for the Electrical Industry.—All of the plastics mentioned in this chapter are insulators when dry. A small amount of absorbed water will decrease the insulating value markedly, and a small water absorption is advisable. Paper, cloth, and asbestos fabrics must be rendered waterproof to be effective. The waterproofing agent should also be resistant to heat. Resins of the phenolic type are used both in the form of varnish on fabrics and as molding resins. The pure phenolic resin absorbs only 0.1 to 0.2 per cent of water in 24 hr, the laminated fabric somewhat more because of the incomplete waterproofing of the fibers. The resin has a high breakdown voltage and does not soften even when heated until it chars.

Fig. 200.—Armature of large electrical generator with coils impregnated with phenolic resin. (*Courtesy Bakelite Corporation.*)

The ignition coil case and the flatiron of Fig. 199 indicate the usefulness of these products in the automobile industry and in the household. The windings of the large armature shown in Fig. 200 have been impregnated with phenolic varnish to insulate and waterproof them.

The newer styrene resins are even better than phenolic resins for some purposes, their water absorption being practically zero and their breakdown voltage being higher. The styrene resins however soften at 190 to 250°F.

Laminated or Safety Glass.—In the usual method of making laminated glass, two panes of plate glass about $\frac{1}{6}$ in. thick are cemented together by a layer of a plastic about 0.025 in. in thickness. The plates of glass are coated with a cement, the plastic sheet is placed between them, and the three parts are compacted by passing through heated rolls. Thus assembly is further compacted by a longer application of heat and pressure. The edges must be sealed, with some types of plastics, to prevent moisture from entering. The plastic layer was formerly of the celluloid type, but because of its discoloration in the sunlight and tendency to form bubbles it has been abandoned. Cellulose acetate does not have the disadvantages of discoloration but becomes brittle in cold weather. Quite recently, a vinyl acetate resin has been introduced which possesses superior properties.

Synthetic Resins and Modern Varnishes.—The natural varnish resins were of uneven quality, acidic in nature, and high in price. The acid nature could be removed by forming a glycerin ester known in the trade as "ester gum" which was an improvement. Linseed oil was replaced by heat-treated tung (china wood) oil. These modifications gave better varnishes without changing the essential nature of the product. The introduction of quick-drying lacquers made the old varnishes obsolete as finishes for motor cars. The demand was for a synthetic resin that should be itself rather elastic and should be soluble in oil. The phenolic resins were modified so as to be soluble in hot oil, and resins of new types were developed. One of the most successful of the varnish resins is made from glycerin and phthalic acid and, in various modifications, is sold under the trade name of Glyptol or Alkyd. This resin is mildly heat reactive and may be plasticized with a rather small amount of tung oil. An outline of a formula for a varnish to dry in 4 hr at room temperature calls for heating 200 parts of tung oil, incorporating 100 parts of a modified phenolic resin, then adding 50 parts of bodied linseed oil and the proper driers, and then 275 parts of thinner. A white refrigerator enamel may be made by grinding white pigments and a phthalic resin, containing a small amount of semidrying oil, in a ball mill containing solvents.

Steel coated with this enamel may be baked for 2 hr at 250°F to yield a white, lustrous, and resistant finish.

Modern Finishes for Motor Cars.—Until 1920, motor cars were made with wooden bodies finished with many coats of paint and varnish, each coat being allowed to dry before the application of the following coat, and many of the coats being sanded and rubbed to ensure a smooth and even surface. At this same time, the fenders were being finished quickly with a black asphaltic baking japan. This black japan could not be applied to the wooden body because the wood could not be heated to the temperature necessary to melt the japan. By 1925, the nitrocellulose lacquers had been developed. These dried to a hard film as soon as the volatile solvent had evaporated. The lacquer films were quite brittle and did not adhere well to the bare metal. Two or three priming and surfacing coats, consisting of heavily pigmented varnishes, were first applied, each coat being hardened by gentle heat. The surface was smoothed with sandpaper and water, and the first coat of lacquer was sprayed on. This was rubbed and followed by other coats. A disadvantage of lacquer was its viscosity, which required large amounts of thinners, resulting in a correspondingly dilute solution. The low percentage of solids made each coat thin, and several coats had to be applied and polished to get the necessary thickness.

The development of the alkyd resins permitted thicker coats to be sprayed and hardened by gentle heat. The primer coat must be somewhat more elastic than the surface coat. It is possible by using enamels of this type to start with the cleaned steel body and complete the surface coating in less than 2 hr.

References

BELL, LESLIE M. T.: The Making and Molding of Plastics, Reinhold Publishing Corporation, New York, 1936.

BURK, THOMPSON, WERTH, and WILLIAMS: Polymerization, Reinhold Publishing Corporation, New York, 1937.

DAVIS and BLAKE: Chemistry and Technology of Rubber, Reinhold Publishing Corporation, New York, 1937.

KLINE, GORDON M.: Organic Plastics, Government Printing Office, Washington, D. C., 1936.

LEWENZ, H. J.: Processes and Machinery in the Plastics Industry, Pitman Publishing Corporation, New York, 1938.

MANSPERGER and PEPPER: Plastics—Problems and Processes, International Text Book Company, Scranton, Pa., 1938.

MORRELL, BARRY, BRITTON, and LANGTON: Synthetic Resins and Allied Plastics, Oxford University Press, New York, 1937.
RAHM, L. F.: Plastic Molding, McGraw-Hill Book Company, Inc., New York, 1933.
ROWELL, H. W.: The Technology of Plastics, Reinhold Publishing Corporation, New York, 1936.
Symposium on Plastics, American Society for Testing Materials, Philadelphia, 1938.
WEITH and MORY: Modern Plastics—A New-old Industry, Am. Inst. Chem. Eng., Silver Anniversry Volume, Chap. XV, 1933.

INDEX

A

Ac points, 31
Acidity, measurement, 290
Adobe brick, 333
Age-hardening, low-carbon steel, 53
  duralumin, 268
Aggregate, graded size, 325
Air furnace, 154
Alclad sheet, 270
Alloys, definition, 12
Aluminum, as an addition to steel, 120
  corrosion, 270
  metallurgy, 257
  properties, 259
  in steel for nitriding, 261
  world's production, 256
  wrought alloys, 236
Aluminum alloys, for casting, 264
  copper, 245, 262
  die casting, 270
  duralumin, 268
  magnesium, 264
  manganese, 263
  iron, 261
  silicon, 261
  zinc, 263
Annealing steel, 56
Antimony-lead alloys, 279
Ar points defined, 31
Armco iron, 40
Ash as a slagging agent, 345
Asphalt as a plastic, 518
Atomic structure, 2
Austenite, changes on cooling, 50
  defined, 35
Automobile bodies finishing, 511, 534

B

Babbitt metal, 286
Basalt, 317

Bearing metals, 252, 285
  Babbitt, 286
  bronzes, 288
  microscopic structure, 285
  white, 286
Bessemer process, in copper smelting, 226
  for steel manufacture, 101, 105
Blast furnace, for iron manufacture, operating data, 85
  reactions, 81
  for nonferrous metals, 225
Boiler scale, 477, 482
Boiler water, 492
  (*See also* Water)
Boilers, caustic embrittlement in, 491
Brass, alpha, 238
  annealing, 241
  beta, 243
  cast, 242, 252
  cold work, 241
  leaded, 252
  machinability, 244
  uses, 244
Brick, burning, changes in properties, 354
  effect of organic matter, 355
  at high temperatures, 334
  influence of methods, 353
  kilns, 350, 352
  from deaerated clay, 331
  durability when exposed to weather, 354
  face brick, 356
  fire clay, 346, 360
  forming, 329
  lime pops, 355
  preparation of clay, 329
  repressed, 356
  salmon, 356
  sand lime, 426

Brick, shrinkage on heating, 334
  sun dried, 333
  thermal conductivity, 364
  water absorption and compressive strength, 353
Bronze, aluminum, 245, 250
  bearing, 288
  manganese, 247
  phosphor, 250
  silicon, 250
  tin, 245
  welding rods, 284
Btu defined, 429
Building stones, durability, 322
  (See also Rocks)
Busheling furnace, 93

C

Calcium carbonate, boiler scale, 482
  solubility in water, 467
Calcium sulfate, boiler scale, 481
  solubility in water, 480
Carbide of iron, 33
Carbon, solid solution in alpha iron, 40
Carborundum, 364
Carburizing compounds, 141
Casehardening steel, 140
Casein plastics, 519
Cast gears, 209
Cast iron, annealing, 170
  chilled, 169
  chromium in, 197
  classification, 168
  foundry, 161
  graphite in, 161, 165, 167
  gray, 160
  high strength, 169
  malleable (see Castings)
  manganese in, 164
  nickel in, 193
  phosphorus in, 164
  physical properties, 167
  pig irons used, 164
  silicon in, 161
  sulfur in, 164
  temperature of pouring, 170

Cast iron, volume changes on cooling, 166
  welding, 171
  wheels for freight cars, 170
  white, 160
Castings, centrifugal, 159
  cooling phenonema, 149
  design of patterns, 152
  die, 158
  flow of metal, 152
  finishing, 154
  malleable, 161
    carbon content, 173
    chemical composition, 174
    manufacture, 172
    microscopic structure, 177
    properties, 174
    rate of malleabilization, 175
    short cycle, 178
  melting furnaces, 154
  melting nonferrous alloys, 156
  metal molds, 157
  patterns, 151
  sand molds and cores, 150
  shrinkage, 153
  steel, 157
  stresses in solidification, 153
Caustic embrittlement prevention, 492
Celluloid, 522
Cement, fused alumina, 425
  hydraulic lime, 389
  Keene's, 384
  magnesium oxychloride, 385
  masonry, 392
  natural, 389, 391
  portland, burning, 396
    chemical composition, 394
    colloidal properties, 412
    fineness of grinding, 401
    gypsum as retarder, 400
    heat evolved on hydration, 423
    high early strength, 424
    hydration, 398
    magnesia in, 422
    mineral constituents, 395
    soundness, 401
    standard specifications, 404

INDEX

Cement, portland, testing, 402
    time of set, 400
    volume changes, 414
    water-cement ratio, 408
  pozzuolanic, 388
  Roman, 390
  silicate types, 388
  slag, 389
Cementite, 33
Centrifugal castings, 159
  for automobile gears, 210
Chrome alloy steels, 203, 205
Chrome-magnet steels, 199
Chromium, active and passive states, 310
  in alloy steels, 195
  in cast iron, 197
Ciment fondu, 425
Clay, burning, 334, 347, 349, 354, 359
  casting hollow articles, 332
  chemical composition, 358
  colloidal nature, 327
  deaeration, 331
  drying, 333
  fineness of particles, 319
  formation from rocks, 319
  forming clay wares, 329
  glass formation in burning, 336
  harmful constituents, 355
  organic matter in, 355
  plasticity, 327
  preparation, 329
  properties, 320
  strength of dried, 328
  vitrefying temperature, 336, 358
Clay ware, glazed, 357
  physical properties, 359
  sanitary ware, 357
  terra cotta, 357
  (*See also* Clay)
Coal, ash, 444
  carbonization, 449
  classification of, 442
  combustion, 454, 456
  fields of the United States, 445
  formation of, 440
  powdered as fuel, 460

Coal, proximate analysis, 442
  world production, 462
Coke, 449, 450
Cold work, removed by annealing, 24
Cold-rolled steel, 146
Cold-shortness in steel, 124
Combustion, of coal on grates, 454
  defined, 429
  heat of, available hydrogen, 430
    calculation, 430
    measurement, 429
  maximum flame temperature, 436
  process of, 433
Concrete, aggregates, 406
  asphalt as protective coating, 512
  designing mixtures, 407
  disintegration, 418, 422, 512
  durability, 427
  expansion, 416
  for exposure to weather, 410
  fireproofing properties, 422
  freezing, 420
  hardening, 412, 424
  increase of strength, 410
  integral waterproofings, 514
  oil paints, 513
  precast units, 426
  progressive expansion, 416, 418
  protective coatings, 428
  shrinkage cracks, 417
  slump test, 409
  soaps as waterproofing agents, 471
  volume changes, 414, 421
  water-cement ratio, 408
Constantan, 236
Cooling curve, pure metal, 10
Copper, electrolytic refining, 226
  equilibrium diagram, of copper-aluminum alloys, 246
  of copper-tin alloys, 246
  of copper-zinc alloys, 238
  extraction from ore, 225
  machinability, 244
  in magnesium oxychloride cements, 386
  properties, 227
  in steel, retarding corrosion, 304

Copper, uses, 227
  world production, 229
Copper alloys, aluminum, 245
  in brass, 238
  nickel, 13, 235
  in steels, 183
  tin, 245
  zinc, 238
Core binders, 151
Corrosion, concentration cells, 295
  of copper alloys, 302
  copper-bearing steel, 304
  due to lack of homogeneity, 300
  effect of acid and alkali on zinc coatings, 309
  effect of strains, 302, 303
  electrolytic, 298
  fatigue, 302
  galvanic, 298
  intergranular, 305
  of iron, in air, 293
    due to local defects, 296
    functions of oxygen, 291
    in water solutions, 294
  of lead in concrete, 309
  nickel-copper alloys, 304
  pitting, 301
  protective coatings, chromium, 306, 310
    galvanizing, 306
    inorganic salts, 308
    nickel, 306
    organic chemical compounds, 312
    phosphates, 308
    tin, 307
    zinc, 306
  protective films, 297
  relative resistance of metals, 299
  stainless steel, 305
  of steel at high temperatures, 311
  two metal, 298
  of zinc, 309
Crankshafts cast for automobiles, 213
Creep in steel, 215
Cristobalite, 337
Crucible steel, 97

Crystals, structure, 6
Cupola furnace, 154

D

Decay of wood, 497
Dezincification of copper alloys, 302
Diatomaceous earth, 364
Die castings, 158
Dolomite, 363
Dowmetal, 274
Duralumin, 268
  age-hardening, 268

E

Earth, composition of, 313
Elastic limit defined, 27
Elastic material defined, 23
Electric furnaces in steel manufacture, 108
Electrolytic refining of copper, 226
Elements, physical constants table, 7
Elongation measurement, 28
Embrittlement of steel in boilers, 491
Enamels, varnish, 341
  vitreous, 341
Equilibrium, illustrated, 3
Equilibrium diagram, alumina silica, 346
  aluminum copper, 262
  aluminum magnesium, 264, 272
  construction, 14
  copper aluminum, 246
  copper tin, 246
  copper zinc, 238
  iron carbon, 34
  lead antimony, 279
  lead tin, 282
  lime silica, 342
  limited solubility, 16
  solid solution in all proportions, 12
Eutectic, definition, 18
Eutectoid, definition, 39

INDEX

F

Fat acids, 469
Fatigue failures in steel, 208
Fats, 470
Ferrite-cementite diagram, 35, 36
    mechanical properties, 48
Fire clay, 346
Fire-clay brick, 360, 365
Fire-clay mortar, 361
Forces, atomic, 2
Forging steel, 134, 136
Foundry sands, 150, 326
Fuel (*see* Coal; Petroleum)
Fuels, gaseous, advantages, 436, 439
    from carbon, 438
    for internal combustion engines, 437
  liquid, advantages, 437
  resources of United States, 461
  solid, 437, 439
Furnaces, burning coal, 456, 460
  burning fuel oil, 460
  efficiency, 434, 435
  maximum flame temperature, 435
  precautions in heating and cooling, 365
  regenerative, 439
Fusible alloys, 288

G

Ganister, 363
Gas, from carbonization of coal, 449
  producer gas from coal, 451
  water-gas formation, 452
Gas fuel, advantages, 436
Gases, heating values, 430
Gears, automobile, centrifugal castings, 211
German silver, 237
Glass, composition, 339
  fiber, 344
  laminated, 527
  tank furnace, 340
Glazes, 341, 357
Grain refinement, steel, 56
Grains, definition, 6

Granite, properties, 317
Graphite, in cast iron, 165, 167
  stable phase, 34
Gravel, 325
Gray-iron castings, physical properties, 167
Gypsum, calcination, 380
  calcined, 383
  half hydrate, 379
  Keene's cement, 384
  plaster, 379, 383
  plasters, retarders, 382
  tile, 384
  wallboards, 383

H

Hardness, methods of testing, 29
Heating value, constants for selected gases, 431
  of gases, by weight and volume, 430
  influence of oxygen, 432
  net, 433
Heats of formation, metallic oxides, 73
High-speed steels, 221
Hydrated lime, 375
Hydraulic limes, 389
Hydrogen in fuels, 430
Hypereutectoid, definition, 40
Hypoeutectoid, definition, 39

I

Ingotism, 33
Intercrystalline material, 8
Invar, 191
Iron, allotropic forms, 32
  alpha, 32
  beta, 32
  changes on heating, 32
  cooling curve, 11
  in copper alloys, 247
  corrosion (*see* Corrosion)
  delta, 32
  gamma, 32
  pure, 31, 33, 34

Iron manufacture, blast furnace, 77, 79, 85
  Catalan forge, 77
  primitive methods, 74
Iron ore, composition, 71
Iron-carbon diagram, 35, 37, 46

K

Kaolinite, formed by weathering, 318
Keene's cement, 384
Kilns for brick, 350, 352

L

Lead, metallurgy, 276
  -antimony alloys, 279
  properties, 277
  poisonous nature, 279
  -tin alloys, 17, 21, 282
  world's production, 276
Lead alloys, bearing metals, 285
  fusible alloys, 288
  solders, 283
  type metal, 285
Lead-antimony alloys, 279
Lead-tin alloys, 17, 21, 282
Ledeburite, defined, 36
Lime, hydrated, 373, 375
  hydraulic, 389
  kilns, 368
  mortar, 376, 378
  over-burning temperatures, 372
  putty, 373
  slaking, 373
  standard specifications, 372
Lime-soda process for water softening, 483
Limestone, burning, 367
  chemical composition, 371
  properties, 322
Liquid fuels, advantages, 437

M

Magnesite, 363
Magnesium, metallurgy, 270
  oxychloride cement, 385

Magnesium, properties, 271
Magnesium alloys, aluminum, 264 273
  Dowmetal, 274
  manganese, 273
Magnesium carbonate, solubility in water, 467
Magnet steels (*see* Chromium)
Magnetic iron-nickel alloys, 192
Magnetic properties of metals, 29
Malleable castings, 171, 174, 178
Manganese, in alloy steels, 184
  in cast iron, 164
  in copper alloys, 247
  in steel, 123
Marble, properties, 322
Martensite, defined, 51
Metals, as electrical conductors, 29
  temperature and properties of, 2
Molds, metal, 157
  sand, 151
Molybdenum in alloy steels, 202
Monel metal, 236
Mortar, aggregates, 406
  cement, free magnesia in, 422
  uses, 407
  durability on exposure to weather, 427
  for fire-clay brick, 361
  lime, 376
Mullite refractories, 362
Muntz metal, 243

N

Natural gas, composition, 447
  fields of the United States, 448
Nickel, in cast iron, 193
  depressing critical range of steel, 188
  metallurgy of, 230
  promoting graphite formation, 188
  properties, 230
Nickel alloys, with copper, 13, 235
  German silver, 237
  with iron, 187

INDEX

Nickel alloys, with low coefficient of expansion, 191
  magnetic, 192
  nickel silver, 237
  nickel-chrome steel, 203
  in steel, 187
Nitriding steel, 143
Nitrogen, in steel, 124
Normalizing steel, 56

O

Open-hearth furnace, 90
Open-hearth process for steel manufacture, 106
Oxides dissolved in steel, 124
Oxygen as a cause of corrosion, 291

P

Paint, 499
  driers, 502
  (*See also* Protective coatings)
Patterns for castings, 151
Pearlite, lamellar, 40
  mechanical properties, 48
  spheroidized, 40
Permalloy, 192
Petroleum, fields of the United States, 448
  properties, 446
  world production, 462
pH system, 290
Phases defined, 3
Phosphates in water softening, 493
Phosphorus, in cast iron, 164
  in copper alloys, 247
  in steel, 124
Physical constants, table of elements, 7
Physical testing methods, 25
Plaster, decomposing oil paints, 513
  gypsum, 379
    hardening, 381
    rate of setting, 382
  lime, 377
Plastics, bakelite, 520
  bituminous, 518

Plastics, casein, 519
  celluloid, 522
  cellulose acetate, 523
  classification, 517
  cold-molded resins, 528
  definition, 23
  in electrical industry, 517, 527, 532
  ethyl cellulose, 524
  general properties, 516
  general uses, 517
  heat-hardening, 518
  laminated, 529
  methyl methacrylate, 525
  molding, 521
  phenolic resins, 520
  polystrene, 527
  rubber, hard, 525
    synthetic, 526
  shaping, 527
  shellac, 519
  thermoplastic group, 518
  thiokol, 526
  urea resins, 522
  varnishes, 533
  vinyl resins, 527
Portland cement, 392
  (*See also* Cement)
Pozzuolanic cements, 388
Proportional limit defined, 27
Protective coatings, aluminum as a pigment, 510
  asphalt on concrete, 512
  baking japans, 510
  boiled oil, 506
  driers, 502
  drying of linseed oil, 500
  effectiveness of various types, 505
  enamels, 507
  lacquers, 511
  linseed oil, 499
  membrane coatings for roofs, 513
  metals, 305
  oil paints on concrete, 513
  organic chemical compounds, 312
  paint, 499, 502, 509
    for steel, 509
  shellac, 508

Protective coatings, soaps for concrete, 514
  synthetic resins, 533
  for wood, 498
  varnish, 506
Protective films, see Corrosion
psi, defined, 28
Puddling furnace, 91
Pure metal, behavior on heating and cooling, 10
Pyrometric cones, 349

Q

Quartz, 337
Quick lime, 372

R

Recrystallization following cold work, 25
Reduction of area defined, 28
Refractories, alumina brick, 362, 364
  basic, 363
  chrome brick, 364
  fire clay, 360
  lime-silica equilibrium diagram, 342
  mullite, 362
  neutral, 364
  selection, 364
  silica brick, 363, 365
Resins (see Plastics; Varnish)
Reverberatory furnace, 90
Riveted joints, 145
Rocks, basalt, 317
  chemical composition, 314
  clay as bonding agent, 325
  crushed stone, 325
  dolomite, 320
  durability of building stones, 322
  foundry sands, 326
  graded size, 325
  granites, 317
  igneous, chemical composition, 315
    common minerals, 316

Rocks, limestone, 320, 322
  magnesite, 320
  metamorphic, 321
  products of weathering, 318
  for roads, 317, 325
  sand and gravel, 325
  sandstones, 323
  selective sedimentation, 321
  shale and slate, 324
  traprock, 317
  weathering, 318
  wool, 344
Rubber, 525
Rusting (see Corrosion)

S

Sand, 325
Sand molds, 150
Sand-lime brick, 426
Sandstone properties, 323
Sanitary ware, 357
Screw stock, automatic steel, 123
Season cracking, 302
Segregation in steel, 113
Semisteel, 169
Sewage disposal, 467
Shale, 324
Shellac (see Plastics; Protective coatings)
Silica, vitreous, 337
Silica brick, 363
Silicon, in alloy steels, 183
  in aluminum alloys, 261
  in cast iron, 161, 168
  in copper alloys, 247
  in steel, 122
Slags, acidic and basic constituents, 343
  composition, 342
  corrosive action, 345
  lime-alumina-silica eutectics, 343
  utilization, 344
  wool, 344
Slaking lime, 373
Slate, 324
Slipbands, formation and removal, 24

INDEX

Soap, as cleansing agent, 471
  in hard water, 472
  insoluble, 471
  as integral waterproofing, 514
  soluble, 469
  as waterproofing agent in concrete, 471
Soil constituents, classification, 319
Solders, 282, 284
  brass, 284
  lead-tin alloys, 22
  silver, 284
Solid solution, properties and structure, 15
Sorbite, defined, 51
Specifications standards, 124
Spring steel, 209
Stainless steels, 200
Steel, age-hardening, 53, 132
  alloying constituents, chrome nickel, 203
    chromium, 194
      in magnet steels, 199
      in stainless steels, 200
    classification, 182
    cobalt, 222
    copper, 183
    manganese, 184
    molybdenum, 202
    nickel, 187
    silicon, 182
    tungsten, 202
    vanadium, 201
  annealing, 57
  austenitic manganese, 185
    nickel, 188
  automatic screw stock, 123
  blister, 96
  blow holes in ingots, 117
  blue brittleness, 54
  brittleness at blue heat, 127
  burned, 134
  casehardening, 140
  castings, 157, 213
    centrifugal, 209, 211
  caustic embrittlement in boilers, 491

Steel, cement, 96
  cleaning before protective coatings, 297, 508
  coating with tin, 307
  cold-rolling, 146
  colors at various temperatures, 63
  corrosion, influenced by distribution of carbides, 301
    at high temperatures, 311
  critical range, as defined by A.S.T.M., 56
    volume changes, 55
  creep, 215
  crucible, 97
  crystal growth in ingots, 119
  cutlery steels, 201
  deep hardening, 218
  deformation in punching, 146
  deoxidation, 104
  drawing the temper, 63
  electric furnace process, 108
  for electrical machinery, 183
  endurance limit, 206
  fatigue failures, 206
  flow lines due to forging, 136
  galvanizing, 306
  gases dissolved in, 112
  grain refinement, 56
  grain size, affecting physical properties, 68
  hardening and tempering, 61
  hardness, correlated with microscopic structure, 52
    throughout cross section, 139
    effect of carbon, 49
  heat-treating diagram, 59
  heat-treatment, carburized steel, 142
    cyaniding, 142
    after machining, 137
    nitriding, 143
    quenching, 138
  inclusions, 112
  manufacture, acid processes, 100, 106
    basic processes, 100, 106
    Bessemer process, 101
    control of grain size, 120

Steel, manufacture, cooling rails, 128
   deoxidation, 104
   dissolved gases, 112
   electric furnace process, 108
   general principles, 100
   historical development, 99
   phosphorus removal, 100
   pipes in ingots, 115
   recarburization, 104
   rolling-mill operation, 122
   scrap used, 111
   sheets and strips, 128
   statistics of production, 110
   sulfur removal, 107, 109
   tubing, 129
 machining, 137
 manganese in, 123
 microscopic structure, affected by cold work, 132
   correlated with hardness, 52
   of 1015 steel, 42
   of 1040 steel, 44
   of 1.10 carbon, 45
   of overheated, 135
 nickel for structural purposes, 188
 nitrogen in, 124
 normalizing, 57, 59
 oxidation rate at high temperatures, 311
 oxides in solution, 124
 patenting, 60
 phosphorus in, 124
 process annealing, 59
 properties, cold-work effect, 131
   at elevated temperatures, 127
   influence of grain size, 68
   seamless tubing, 130
   1045 steel, 65
   1080 steel, 68
   2340 steel, 190
   5140 steel, 198
   3140 steel, 204
 protective coatings (see Protective coatings)
 quenching, 138
   cracks, 140
   media, 62
   rails, 125, 128

Steel, recrystallization, 33
 red-shortness in, 123
 reheating for forging, 134
 rimmed steel, 118
 riveted joints, 145
 scrap, importance in steel manufacture, 111
 segregation in ingots, 113
 selective crystallization, 113
 shallow hardening, 218
 shatter cracks, 126
 silicon in, 122
 slow deformation at high temperatures, 215
 S.A.E. nomenclature, 65
 spheroidizing pearlite, 61
 spiral rolling, effect, 129
 spring, 209
 stainless, chrome-nickel, 205
   corrosion resistance, 305
   18 and 8, 205
 stress-strain diagrams, 131
 structural, 125
 sulfur in, 123
 temper colors and temperature, 63
 tempering, 63, 139
 tensile strength, effect of carbon, 49
 tool, 217
   classification, 220
   low alloy, 219
   high cobalt, 222
   high speed, 221
   for hot work, 221
   tungsten carbide, 223
 toughness, 218
 U.S. production, 87
 volume changes in critical range, 53
 welding, 144
Stellite, 222
Stokers, automatic, 457
Stress-strain diagrams, 27
 for hot- and cold-worked steel, 131
Stucco, durability on exposure to weather, 427
Sulfur, in cast iron, 164
 in steel, 114, 123

INDEX

T

Temperature, effect on properties of materials, 2
Tempering steel, 139
Tensile test, illustration of method, 27
Terra cotta, 357
Tile, clay, 357
  gypsum, 384
Tin, alloys with copper, 245
  with lead, 281
  metallurgy of, 233
  plate on steel, 307
  properties, 234
  world's production, 234
Tool steels, classification, 217, 220
  high speed, 221
Traprock, 317
Tridymite, 337
Troostite, defined, 51
Tungsten in alloy steels, 202
Tungsten-carbide tools, 223
Type metal, 284

U

Ultimate strength, 28

V

Vanadium in alloy steels, 201, 205
Varnish (see Protective coatings)
Varnishes, modern, 533
Vitrification of clay products, 336

W

Water, aeration, 475
  anaerobic bacteria, 467
  changes during boiler operation, 491
  coagulation, 475
  hard, 469
  hardness, permanent, 475
    temporary, 473, 475
Water, ionic analysis, 473
  lakes and rivers, 464
  purification by bacteria, 466
  rain, 464
  salts in solution, 474
  sand filters, 466
  scale formation, 476
  soft, 469
  solubility of carbonates, 467
  from wells and springs, 468
Water gas, 452, 453
Water softening, acid treatment, 493
  barium salts, 494
  carbonaceous zeolites, 489
  lime-soda process, 482, 484
  phosphates, 493
  zeolite process, 487
Welding rods, bronze, 284
Welding steel, 144
White cast iron, 46
Wrought iron, Aston process, 93
  composition, 96
  manufacture, 90
  properties, 94
Wood, decay, 497
  laminated, 530
  preservation, protective coatings, 502, 505
    by impregnation, 498
Wood's metal, 288

Y

Yield point, 27
Yield strength, 27

Z

Zeolite process for water softening, 487
Zeolites, carbonaceous for removing metallic ions, 489
Zinc, alloy die castings, 253
  alloys with copper, 238
  metallurgy of, 231
  properties, 233
  world's production, 232

rbon Steels	Silicon add Resilience to Steel
10 — % Carbon	(springs)
↓ % Mang.	Nickel toughens, corrosive proof
95	Porous — Bronze — C.I
free cutting steels	*pearlite* ◯ eutectoid
12 .06 – .16	
15	
↓	
3/5	
kle Steels	
3 15 → Mang % Ni	
3 30	
↓	
15	
kle Chrome Steels	
1 15 → C, Ni, Ch	
ickel Moly	
4 30	
↓	
4 B 20	
rome Steel	
20	
00 Ch General Class	
tooless	
0,000	
om Va	
000	
Va	
000	
in Ch	
000	
AE SYSTEM	